ACOUSTICS

BY

Alexander Wood, M.A., D.Sc.

Late Fellow and Tutor of Emmanuel College
Cambridge

DOVER PUBLICATIONS, INC.

New York

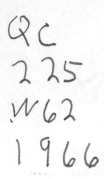
This Dover edition, first published in 1966, is an unabridged and unaltered republication of the second (1960) edition of the work originally published by Blackie and Son, Limited, in 1940.

This edition is published by special arrangement with Blackie and Son, Limited, 5 Fitzhardinge Street, Portman Square, London W 1.

Library of Congress Catalog Card Number: 66-29155

Manufactured in the United States of America
Dover Publications, Inc.
180 Varick Street
New York, N.Y. 10014

PREFACE

This book makes no claim to originality. Acknowledgments on a subsequent page and in the text indicate the many sources to which I am indebted, and there may be others, although I hope few, inadvertently omitted. The book has been written primarily for the interest of writing it, and I trust that some of my own interest may have communicated itself to the printed page.

An attempt has been made to preserve interesting historical material and to hold theory and practice as close together as possible. Detailed references are given throughout, in the hope that they may be useful to students who wish to read more widely.

I have had much help from Dr. G. E. Pringle, who has been responsible for Chapter XVI, has made many valuable suggestions and has read the proofs. I am also indebted to my former secretary, Miss Wright, for her careful and accurate work on the typescript and for preparation of the material for the illustrations. Finally, I am grateful to the household of the peaceful farm on a Norfolk river where, on annual visits, most of the book was written.

A.W.

EMMANUEL COLLEGE,
CAMBRIDGE

PUBLISHER'S NOTE

This masterly text-book is now reprinted in its original form, having been first published in 1940. Although there have been major developments since then in the electrical techniques of sound reproduction, these are mainly the province of the electrical engineer. It was felt that a revision by another hand to cover the needs of both engineers and physicists would serve no useful purpose.

MARCH, 1960

ACKNOWLEDGMENTS

The author desires to express with thanks his indebtedness for kind permission to use copyright illustration material for the following sources:

Bagenal and A. Wood, *Planning for Good Acoustics* (Methuen & Co., Ltd.). Figs. 19.3, 19.4, 19.6, 19.7, 19.8, 19.12.

Barton, E. H., *Textbook of Sound* (Macmillan & Co., Ltd.). Figs. 7.2, 12.2.

Bergmann, *Ultrasonics* (G. Bell & Sons, Ltd.). Figs. 9.10, 10.22, 10.23.

Bragg, W. H., *The World of Sound* (G. Bell & Sons, Ltd.). Fig. 3.9.

Crandall, I. B., *Vibrating Systems and Sound* (D. Van Nostrand Co., Inc., New York). Figs. 4.5, 4.6, 16.6, 16.7, 16.8.

Davis and Kaye, *Acoustics of Buildings* (G. Bell & Sons, Ltd.). Fig. 1.35.

Fletcher, *Speech and Hearing* (D. Van Nostrand Co., Inc., New York). Figs. 13.10, 13.11, 13.14, 13.19, 13.21, 17.1, 17.2, 17.11, 17.16, 19.16.

Greenlees, *Amplification and Distribution of Sound* (Chapman & Hall, Ltd.). Figs. 18.9, 18.15, 18.17, 18.18, 18.19, 18.21, 18.25.

Havelock, T. H., *Propagation of Disturbances in Dispersive Media* (Cambridge University Press). Fig. 16.12.

Hughes and Du Bridge, *Photo-electric Phenomena* (McGraw-Hill Book Co., Inc., New York). Fig. 18.24.

Miller, D. C., *The Science of Musical Sounds* (Macmillan Co., New York). Figs. 13.7, 13.8, 13.12, 13.13.

Miller, D. C., *Sound Waves, their Shape and Speed* (Macmillan Co., New York). Figs. 1.32, 1.33, 10.11, 13.4.

Olson and Massa, *Applied Acoustics* (Blakiston, Philadelphia). Figs. 17.7, 17.8, 17.13, 18.26.

Ortmann, *Physical Basis of Piano Touch and Tone* (Kegan, Paul). Fig. 14.14.

Pender-McIlwain, *Electrical Engineers' Handbook, Communication-Electronics* (John Wiley & Sons, Inc., New York). Figs. 18.22, 18.23.

Rawdon-Smith, *Theories of Sensation* (Cambridge University Press). Fig. 17.17.

Richardson, E. G., *Textbook of Sound* (Edward Arnold & Co.). Figs. 12.1, 15.3.

Sabine, P. E., *Acoustics and Architecture* (McGraw-Hill Book Co., Inc., New York). Figs. 19.5, 19.9.

Stevens and Davis, *Hearing* (John Wiley & Sons, Inc., New York). Figs. 17.5, 17.6, 17.10, 17.12, 17.14, 17.18.

Trendelenburg, *Akustik* (Springer, Berlin). Figs. 18.12, 18.13, 18.14.

Whitaker, *Physics in Sound Recording*. Figs. 18.20, 18.29.

White, W. H., *Physics* (Clay & Sons). Fig. 10.3.

Wilkinson and Gray, *The Mechanism of the Cochlea* (Macmillan & Co., Ltd.). Fig. 17.3.

Wood, A. B., *Textbook of Sound* (G. Bell & Sons, Ltd.). Figs. 3.10, 5.4, 13.1, 18.7, 18.8.

Wood, R. W., *Physical Optics* (Macmillan Co., New York). Fig. 1.30.

Annalen der Physik. Fig. 11.1.

Annales de l'Institut de Physique du Globe. Fig. 7.6.

Bell System Technical Journal. Figs. 18.1, 18.2.

Canadian Journal of Research. Fig. 8.30.

Helvetica Physica Acta. Fig. 10.18.

Journal of the Acoustical Society of America. Figs. 5.1, 5.2, 13.5, 13.6, 17.9, 18.16, 18.27, 18.28, 19.10, 19.11.

Journal of the Institution of Electrical Engineers. Figs. 18.6, 19.13, 19.14, 19.15.

Nature. Figs. 15.10, 19.18.

Philosophical Magazine. Figs. 3.6, 3.7, 3.8, 10.14, 15.1, 19.20, 19.21.

Philosophical Transactions of the Royal Society. Figs. 11.5, 11.6.

Physical Review. Figs. 4.3, 8.7, 10.2, 10.13, 11.9, 11.10, 11.11, 18.10.

Physikalische Zeitschrift. Figs. 10.16, 10.17, 10.20, 10.21.

Proceedings and *Transactions of the Royal Society of Canada.* Fig. 11.2.

Proceedings of the American Academy of Arts and Sciences. Figs. 9.9, 9.11, 12.4, 17.14.

Proceedings of the American Philosophical Society. Figs. 8.18, 8.19, 8.20, 8.21.

Proceedings of the Physical Society. Figs. 8.29, 11.3, 12.3, 15.5, 15.6, 15.7, 19.21.

Proceedings of the Royal Institution. Fig. 17.15.

Proceedings of the Royal Society. Figs. 10.4, 10.5, 10.6, 10.7, 10.8, 11.4, 11.7, 15.11.

Proceedings of the Royal Society of Edinburgh. Fig. 7.5.

Reports on Progress in Physics. Figs. 5.3, 10.19.

Review of Scientific Instruments. Figs. 10.9, 10.10.

Revue générale de l'Electricité. Fig. 18.5.

Science Progress. Figs. 8.14, 8.15.

Zeitschrift für Geophysik. Fig. 7.7.

CONTENTS

CHAPTER I

WAVE MOTION

CHAPTER II

ANALYTICAL DISCUSSION OF WAVE MOTION

vii

CHAPTER III

FORCED VIBRATION

CHAPTER IV

RESONATORS, FILTERS, AND HORNS

CHAPTER V

DISSIPATION OF ENERGY OF SOUND WAVES

CHAPTER VI

REFLECTION OF SOUND WAVES

CHAPTER VII

REFRACTION OF SOUND WAVES

CHAPTER VIII

SUPERPOSITION OR INTERFERENCE

CHAPTER IX

DIFFRACTION

CHAPTER X

MEASUREMENT OF THE VELOCITY OF SOUND

CHAPTER XI

INTENSITY OF SOUND

CHAPTER XII

PITCH AND FREQUENCY

CHAPTER XIII

ANALYSIS OF SOUNDS

CHAPTER XIV

VIBRATIONS OF STRINGS

CHAPTER XV

ORGAN PIPES

CHAPTER XVI

RODS, MEMBRANES, AND PLATES

CHAPTER XVII

THE EAR AND HEARING

CHAPTER XVIII

RECORDING AND REPRODUCTION OF SOUND

CHAPTER XIX

ACOUSTICS OF BUILDINGS

CHAPTER I

Wave Motion

1. Nature of Wave Motion.

The concept of wave motion is one of the most important in modern physics. We use it to elucidate and relate to one another not only the phenomena of sound but also those of light, wireless, X-rays and γ-radiation. What does the term "wave" in its most general sense mean? We talk of waves on the sea, of waves caused by the wind on a field of standing barley, of a heat wave which is on its way from America, or a wave of crime spreading through the country. Have these uses of the word "wave" anything in common?

In general, two requirements are implied: (1) a condition which is propagated, and (2) a medium through which the condition is propagated. In some cases the insistence on a medium arises from a desire to picture to ourselves hidden processes, which are familiar in other connexions, and in terms of which the observed facts of propagation can be described. Thus, free space has properties which allow the propagation of electromagnetic waves; we sometimes express this by saying that electromagnetic waves are "propagated in the ether", but when the relevant equations have been derived the behaviour of the waves can be deduced without reference to the properties of any material medium.

Waves are classified according to the nature of the forces concerned in them. Sound waves are a special kind of elastic wave; these occur in media which have two properties, inertia and elasticity. If an element of the medium is displaced it must be subject to a restoring force tending to annul the displacement, and if the medium is to be capable of transmitting a train of waves it must possess inertia, so that when it is restored to its undisplaced position, the momentum which it has acquired may carry it through that position to a displacement opposite to the original one. If the waves are of constant type, i.e. if the various characteristics of a particular wave are unchanged during its propagation, then we can describe the propagation by assuming that all the particles or elements of the medium execute identical orbits in the same time, each element being a little later than its neighbour nearer the source and a little earlier than its neighbour

1

more remote from the source. In other words, the phase of the vibration varies continuously along the line of propagation. If the wave involves visible displacement the impression produced on an observer is that of a definite shape imposed on the medium and travelling with a definite velocity.

2. Types of Wave.

The orbits of the elements of the medium may vary enormously, giving different types of waves. The orbits may be linear and executed in the line of propagation. This is the case for sound waves in a fluid, for compressional waves along a spring, and, approximately, for "long" water waves in shallow water. Waves of this type are said to be *longitudinal*. On the other hand, the orbits, still linear, may be executed at right angles to the direction of propagation. This is the case for trans-

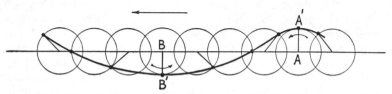

Fig. 1.1.—Wave travelling from right to left, due to particles describing circular orbits anticlockwise, e.g. wave on the surface of water

verse waves along a stretched string. Waves of this type are said to be *transverse*. The orbits, however, need not be linear. In the case of waves on the surface of deep water the orbits are vertical circles about the undisplaced position. Thus, A, B (fig. 1.1) are undisplaced positions of water particles. A', B' are displaced positions at the instant when A is at the crest and B at the trough of a wave moving from right to left. The figure explains the fact, familiar to swimmers, that water at the crest of a wave is always moving forward, whereas that at the trough of a wave is always moving backward. Here the plane of the circle is parallel to the direction of propagation. In the case of torsional waves along a rod the orbits are again circular (or circular arcs), but now the planes of the circles are perpendicular to the direction of propagation of the waves.

3. Displacement Curves.

The form of a wave may be shown graphically by means of a displacement curve. This is a graph in which distance along the line of propagation is measured along the x-axis and the corresponding displacement along the y-axis. It enables the state of displacement along the line of propagation to be seen at a glance. For transverse waves the curve shows the actual displacements, but for longitudinal waves, where the displacements are in the line of propagation, we have to apply a convention. It is usual to represent forward displacements by upward ordinates and backward displacements by downward ordinates. Thus if the curve shown in fig. 1.2 applies say to the transverse waves along a stretched string, OABCDE may represent the undisplaced position of the string, while OA'BC'DE' may represent the string as it transmits the waves at the instant chosen. The portion of the string from O to B is displaced upwards, from B to D, downwards, and so on. On the other hand, if the string is transmitting longitudinal waves (evoked by rubbing the string with resined cloth), or if OE represents a line of propagation of sound waves in air, then, interpreting the diagram in terms of our convention, we see that the portions of the medium normally lying between O and B are displaced forwards,

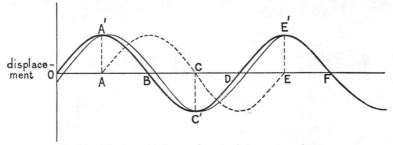

Fig. 1.2.—Displacement diagram for a simple harmonic or sine wave

those between B and D backwards, those between D and F forwards, and so on. The displacement curve in fig. 1.2 is a sine curve, corresponding to simple harmonic waves (p. 53). It is worth noticing that since each element of the medium describes the same vibration and these vibrations show a continuous change of phase as we pass from O to D, the simultaneous displacements of successive elements are represented by the same curve as that which represents the successive displacements of any one element. Therefore if we regard OF as a time axis our displacement curve shows the successive displacements of any particular element of the medium.

Continuing to apply our curve to waves in air, we see that since the layers from A to B are displaced forwards and those from B to C backwards, B must represent a compression. Similar reasoning shows that D represents a rarefaction. Since the curve at A' and C' is parallel to the x-axis it follows that layers in the neighbourhood of A and C are displaced by the same amount. These are therefore places of normal density, and if we draw a curve to represent the variation of pressure along the line of propagation it will take the form shown by the dotted line, the pressure being in excess at B, in defect at D, and normal at A and C.

If the waves are moving from left to right we can represent the position at an instant later than the one originally chosen, by the thin line. The difference of the ordinates of the two curves at any point represents the change in displacement and is therefore proportional to the velocity. Obviously the velocity at A and C is zero. Between A and C the velocity is a forward one, greatest at B; between C and E the velocity is a backward one, greatest at D. We thus see that all the elements in compression are moving forwards, the layer in maximum compression having the maximum velocity, and all the elements in rarefaction backwards, the layer in maximum rarefaction

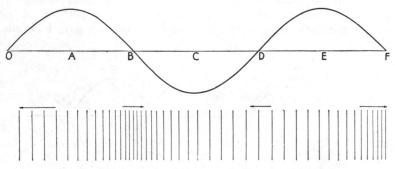

Fig. 1.3.—Relation between displacement, density and particle velocity

again having the maximum velocity. Layers at normal density are at rest. The distribution of particle velocity and density for a progressive air wave is shown in fig. 1.3.

4. Wave-Front and Ray.

The wave-front may be defined as the continuous locus of the points in the medium which are in the same phase of their vibration. If the waves are emitted by a point source immersed in the medium the wave-fronts are obviously concentric spheres. If the source is very distant the radii of the spheres are very great and the wave-fronts become practically plane. After reflection or refraction the wave-fronts may assume different forms, but plane and spherical waves are the only ones we are much concerned with in the subject of sound.

The ray is the path of an element of the wave-front. In the case of unobstructed sound waves the ray is always normal to the wave-front. If we use the analogy of a line of men on the march—like the waves on the surface of water, a good illustration of a wave in two dimensions—then the line of men represents the wave-front and the path of each individual man, which is ordinarily at right angles to the line, is a corresponding ray. Thus for plane waves the rays are parallel lines normal to the wave-fronts, while for spherical waves they are radii of the corresponding spheres.

5. Huygens' Principle.

Huygens (1629–1695) stated a principle, applicable to all waves, which gives a simple method, although only an approximate one, of treating many of the phenomena of wave motion. The principle states that in a medium traversed by waves each point on a wave-front at any instant may be treated as the source of secondary wavelets. The subsequent position of the wave-front is obtained by constructing the envelope of the secondary wavelets due to point sources distributed over the initial position of the wave-front. Plainly we can use this principle to obtain the ordinary cases of propagation of waves. If we take a plane wave in any given position and apply the principle to find its position t seconds later, then about each point in the plane we describe a sphere of radius ct, where c is the velocity of the disturbance in the medium. The envelope of these spheres—i.e. the surface that touches them all—is another plane parallel to the first at perpendicular distance ct from it.

Two limitations have to be applied:

(1) We must assume the secondary wavelets to be effective only where they touch their envelope, otherwise the disturbance would be distributed through the intervening parts of the medium instead of being concentrated in the new wave-front.

(2) We must assume that there is no propagation backwards, otherwise we should be led to expect a second wave-front moving backwards and at a distance ct to the rear of the original position of the wave-front.

The physical reasons for these restrictions will become clear later.

6. The Inverse Square Law.

Waves carry both momentum and energy, so that if there is no dissipation of energy in the waves and they are spherical waves diverging from a point, it follows that the energy crossing any unit of area at right angles to the direction of propagation must vary inversely as the square of the distance of the area from the source. In the case of light waves this gives us the well-known relation that the intensity of illumination of a surface is inversely proportional to the square of its distance from the source of light. Since the energy is as a rule proportional to the square of the amplitude, the amplitude is inversely proportional to the first power of the distance from the source.

7. Impact of Waves on an Obstacle.

Here we have to distinguish two cases:

(1) *Dimensions of the obstacle large compared with the wave-length.*— In this case we get a reflected wave moving back from the obstacle, a shadow behind the obstacle, and a certain amount of diffraction or

bending round the edges of the obstacle. A small island in the ocean has calm water in its lee, although the waves may be seen spreading round both ends. The same is true of an artificial breakwater, and here the diffraction round the end is quite obvious. A perfect circular disc of the size of a threepenny-piece is a large obstacle for light waves, and if light from a pinhole is allowed to fall on a disc of this size it produces a circular shadow but with a bright spot in the centre, showing that diffraction has occurred.

The curvature of the reflected waves will in general be different from that of the incident waves. A convex surface will increase convexity, a concave surface will diminish convexity, and a plane surface will leave the curvature unaltered. The reflection of a plane

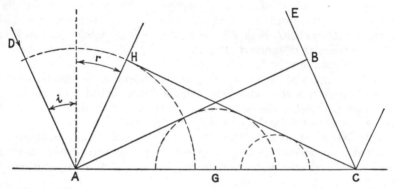

Fig. 1.4.—Huygens' construction for reflection of a plane wave AB at a plane surface AC

wave from a plane surface can be deduced at once by applying Huygens' principle.

If AB in fig. 1.4 represents a plane wave incident on a plane surface AC, then the end B will continue to travel along the normal to the wave-front (the ray) EB, until it meets the surface at C. Meanwhile the secondary wavelet which started from A will have travelled a distance AH equal to CB. The reflected wave will be the envelope of a series of hemispheres representing the secondary wavelets generated as the wave reaches various points on the surface. The reflected wave-front is represented by the line HC, which makes the same angle with AC as the incident wave AB does. The incident and reflected waves are thus equally inclined to the reflecting surface and the rays are therefore equally inclined to the normal to the surface, i.e. angle i = angle r.

If the incident wave is spherical we can draw the position AEB (fig. 1.5) which it would have occupied if the reflecting surface CD had not been there. To find the reflected portion of this wave we draw

any ray ORT. The distance RT is the distance that the secondary
wavelet will have gone after the primary wave struck the surface
at R and before its edges reached the position CA and DB. Accordingly, with centre R and radius RT we describe a hemisphere. If we
do this for a number of rays we get a sufficient number of hemispheres
to define the position of their envelope, which is found to be CFD,
having the same curvature as AEB but in the opposite direction, i.e.
the reflected wave appears to diverge from a point I on the normal
to the surface and as far behind the surface as the original source O
is in front. In optical language, I is the image of O, and as the waves

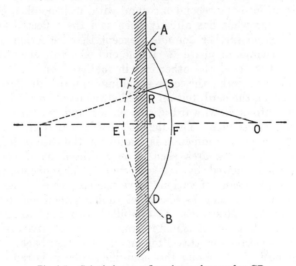

Fig. 1.5.—Spherical wave reflected at a plane surface CD

only *appear* to diverge from it and have never actually passed through
it, it is a " virtual " image. If the construction is applied to the case
of a concave reflecting surface and a wave diverging from a point
distant from the surface by not less than half the radius of curvature
of the surface, it is found that the reflected wave is convergent and
therefore gives rise to a real image.

(2) *Dimensions of the obstacle small compared with the wave-
length.*—In this case the phenomenon is very different. No true reflection takes place. If we watch waves impinging on the supports
of a pier we see no sign of a " shadow " behind the pier. The waves
seem to divide, pass and join again behind, giving no reflected waves
and no sheltered water in the rear. Shadows are cast only by obstacles
which are large in proportion to the length of the wave. Careful
observation in the case of small obstacles, however, will often reveal

the fact that the obstacle has become the source of a new set of waves spreading out in every direction. This is the phenomenon of *scattering*, which is very important in the case of light waves and gives rise to the blue of the sky, and, in the case of water holding fine particles in suspension, to the blue colour of many mountain lakes. (The latter must not be confused with the reflection of the blue sky.)

8. Impact of Waves on the Surface separating two Media in which they travel with different Speeds.

Here two sets of waves are in general produced: one, the reflected set, travels back again in the original medium; the other, the refracted set, travels on into the second medium, with, in general, a change of direction. After what has already been said the reflected system of waves requires no further comment except that reflection may take place " with change of phase ". If one end of a rubber cord is fixed to a wall, and we hold the other end in the hand and then give the hand an upward jerk, the corresponding upward displacement is propagated along the cord, but on reaching the fixed end it is suddenly transformed into a downward displacement and returns along the cord to the hand as such. The displacement and particle velocity are reversed. A similar phenomenon is familiar in the case of light waves and explains the black area seen in very thin films of transparent substances when viewed by reflected light. The phenomenon can be illustrated by means of various wave models. One of the simplest is that in which two lengths of rubber tubing joined end to end are suspended by vertical strings. One is filled with sand to increase its linear density. A wave transmitted from either end gives rise to two waves at the junction, one travelling on and the other back. When the original impulse is sent along the sand-filled tube it is reflected with the direction of displacement unchanged, but when sent along the empty tube it is reflected with the direction of displacement *reversed*. We shall find later that a pulse travelling up an organ pipe is reflected with the direction of displacement reversed if the end of the pipe is closed. If the end of the pipe is open the wave is reflected with the direction of displacement unchanged.

The refracted system of waves can be illustrated using the analogy of a line of men (CA in fig. 1.6) on the march and approaching a boundary line (AB) between grassland and ploughed land. If (*a*) each part of the line is to be kept straight and (*b*) each man must always march at right angles to the line, then since the velocity on ploughed land is less than it is on grass, the line must swing round, taking the position HF, and travelling on with the wave-front parallel to this new direction. The path of an individual man—i.e. a ray—is refracted as DAH.

We can obviously use the same diagram for Huygens' construction. If AC is the incident wave-front, v_1 the velocity of the wave in the first medium, and v_2 the velocity of the wave in the second medium, then the element C takes a time to reach F given by CF/v_1. In this time the secondary wavelet starting from A travels a distance $AH = v_2 \times CF/v_1$. With A as centre and $v_2 \times CF/v_1$ as radius we accordingly describe a sphere. The plane, perpendicular to the plane of the paper, which touches this sphere and passes through F will be the refracted wave.

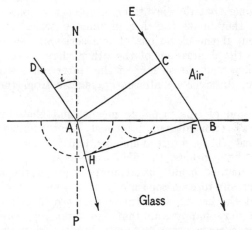

Fig. 1.6.—Refraction of a plane wave AC at a plane surface AB

This is, of course, the method of derivation of Snell's law for wave motion generally. From fig. 1.6 we have

$$\sin i = \sin DAN = \sin CAB = \frac{CF}{AF},$$

$$\sin r = \sin PAH = \sin HFA = \frac{AH}{AF},$$

$$\therefore \ \frac{\sin i}{\sin r} = \frac{CF}{AH} = \frac{v_1}{v_2}$$

$$\text{or} \ \sin i = \mu \sin r,$$

$$\text{where} \ \mu = \frac{v_1}{v_2}.$$

9. Interference or Superposition.

Interference or superposition is a very important phenomenon. It was first referred to by Thomas Young (1773–1829) in a letter written from Emmanuel College, Cambridge, in 1799. Writing again on the same subject in 1804 he describes * the phenomenon in terms of water waves: " Suppose a number of equal waves of water to move upon the surface of a stagnant lake, with a certain constant velocity, and to enter a narrow channel leading out of the lake. Suppose then another similar cause to have excited another equal series of waves, which arrive at the same channel, with the same velocity and at the same time with the first. Neither series of waves will destroy the other, but their effects will be combined; if they enter the channel in such a manner that the elevations of one series coincide with those of the other, they must together produce a series of greater joint elevations; but if the elevations of one series are so situated as to correspond to the depressions of the other, they must exactly fill up those depressions and the surface of the water must remain smooth; at least I can discover no alternative either from theory or from experiment."

The extension of this principle means that the same portion of a medium may transmit simultaneously any number of different series of waves. These proceed independently, each undisturbed by the presence of the others, the displacement of the medium at any point at any instant being the algebraic sum of the displacements due at that instant to each separate wave system. It will be obvious from this that the use of the term *interference* to denote the phenomenon is not very happy and that the term *superposition* is more suitable. The former term has undoubtedly arisen from the concentration of attention on the points where the sum of the displacements is always zero and where, therefore, the medium is always at rest owing to the fact that it is transmitting simultaneously two or more sets of waves. It can easily be seen that if we have two sources vibrating in the same period and in the same phase the state of vibration will be the same at all points of the medium for which the difference of the distances from the two sources is the same. Thus if A and B are the two sources and P any point, then all points for which AP — BP has the same value will be in the same state of vibration. Now

$$AP - BP = \text{constant}$$

gives a rectangular hyperbola as the locus of P. Thus the loci of maximum and minimum vibration are a series of rectangular hyperbolas with A and B as foci, if we consider the problem as a two-dimensional one. If we extend our consideration to three dimensions, the loci are hyperboloids of revolution obtained by rotating the curves about the line AB as axis. The interference fringes which we ordinarily observe in the case of light are the intersections of these surfaces of interference

---

* Reply to the Edinburgh Reviewers.

with the screen on which the fringes are examined or the plane on which the observing microscope is focused.

In the case of light waves we cannot deal with single sources. A pinhole or slit includes a large number of such sources. Interference cannot be observed when two independently illuminated pinholes or slits are used, since, on the wave theory, each point source on the one produces interference with each point source on the other and confusion results. The two sources are said not to be " coherent ". If, however, one pinhole or slit only is used and the light is taken by two paths to the point at which the interference is to be observed, then each point source produces its own interference effect at the point of observation, and if the sources are not too large fringes will be visible, although some confusion may appear. The confusion sets a limit to the size of source admissible. In the case of sound waves, however, individual sources may be used; two such sources will be coherent even if independent, and will give rise to interference effects.

10. Diffraction.

Diffraction is the name given to the departure from rectilinear propagation shown by light under certain conditions. If the truth of Huygens' principle is assumed, the difficulty is not to account for these departures but to account for the law of rectilinear propagation.

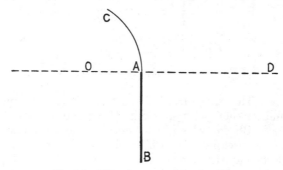

Fig. 1.7.—Diffraction at a straight edge AB

This law of propagation obviously holds closely in the case of light, and if it breaks down manifestly in the case of sound, how can both sound and light be explained in terms of wave propagation? It was this line of argument which considerably delayed the acceptance of the wave theory of light after the wave theory of sound had been established.

If we take first the case of the shadow thrown by the edge of an obstacle it is clear that if O (fig. 1.7) represents a source of waves and CA an instantaneous position of a wave-front originating at O, then the region between AD and AB which lies inside the "geometrical shadow" must receive waves from points on AC, by Huygens' principle.

The case of the divergence from a slit is still more interesting. Let AB (fig. 1.8) represent a slit on which plane waves are incident from the left. Let C be the mid-point of the slit. Then AB may be regarded as the instantaneous position of a wave-front and each point on it may be regarded as the source of a set of secondary waves. With centre B and radius λ, the wave-length of the disturbance, describe the arc of a circle and from A draw AD to touch this arc. Join BD. Then in the direction BD the waves from B start a wave-length behind those from A, while those from C start half a wave-length behind

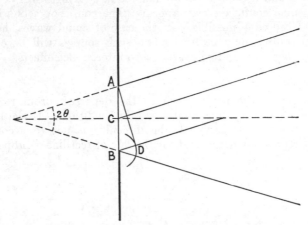

Fig. 1.8.—Divergence of waves from a slit

those from A. The waves from C and from A are thus mutually destructive, and for each point source in AC we can find a corresponding point source in CB for which this holds; so no wave motion is propagated in the direction BD which makes with the normal to the slit an angle θ such that $\sin\theta = \lambda/e$, where e is the width of the slit. A more rigorous discussion of the phenomenon shows that some wave motion is propagated in directions more oblique than this, but the proportion is very small, so that broadly speaking all the energy propagated lies within a wedge whose edge lies parallel to the slit and whose semi-angle is $\sin^{-1}\lambda/e$.

We see, then, that for a given wave-length the narrower the slit, the wider the divergence, and for a given width of slit the longer the wave-length, the wider the divergence. If $e = \lambda$, then $\theta = \pi/2$ and the waves spread from the slit in all directions. For $e < \lambda$ there is no real value for θ and we still get a spread in all directions.

We can also see from elementary considerations that the shadow

of a circular disc presents an interesting case. If we place a source
of waves on the axis of the disc we can consider the effect of the waves
at a point on the axis on the opposite side of the disc. If we suppose
Huygens' point sources to be distributed round the edge of the disc
the secondary waves from these all arrive at any point on the axis
of the disc at the same time and therefore in the same phase. It follows
that at the centre of the geometrical shadow there must be considerable
disturbance. This is manifested in the bright spot at the centre of the
shadow of a circular obstacle, the existence of which was demonstrated
by Fresnel (1788–1827) and Arago (1786–1853).

11. Wave Models.

Many of the phenomena associated with wave propagation become
much more intelligible when we study the behaviour of suitable models.
The fundamental distinction between the motion of the wave and the
motion of the medium may be made clear by the use of the model in
fig. 1.9 (p. 14). If the handle seen on the right of the figure is turned,
each of the balls at the top performs an up-and-down motion. These
motions are not simultaneous, but each ball is at a stage of its motion
just a little earlier than its neighbour on one side and a little later than
its neighbour on the other side. The result of a continuous turning
of the handle is that waves appear to pass along the top of the model
horizontally, whereas each ball is clearly seen to be moving up and
down in a vertical path. The distance which a ball moves from its
mean or average position is called the *amplitude*, and it is obvious
that all the balls have the same amplitude. The number of complete
vibrations executed in one second is called the *frequency*, and the
distance between any two consecutive balls in the same stage of vibration is called the *wave-length*. Thus in the case of the waves illustrated
by the model or in the case of water waves, the wave-length is the
distance from crest to crest or from trough to trough.

A very important relation exists between the frequency, the wave-
length, and the velocity, which may easily be deduced from the model
and is true for all kinds of wave motion. If we fix our attention on a
ball which is at the highest point of its vibration and therefore coincides
with the crest of the wave, and watch it while it performs a complete
vibration, we shall find that it now coincides in position with the
crest of the next wave, the crest of the first wave having moved
through one wave-length. If we call the frequency f, then in one second
the ball will have described f complete vibrations and the original
crest will be f wave-lengths away. It will thus have travelled a distance
$f\lambda$, where λ is the wave-length; but since this is the distance travelled
in one second, it is the velocity of the wave c, so that we have

$$c = f\lambda.$$

If we now turn to the model shown in fig. 1.10 we can illustrate some further properties of wave motion. It consists of a row of wooden laths so connected that if one is disturbed it transmits its motion to the next, and so on. It comes nearer to an actual wave than the model previously used, since the displacement is conveyed from lath to lath instead of being communicated separately to each as in the case

Fig. 1.9.—Wave model

of the balls. If the end lath is displaced, a wave of displacement travels from end to end of the model. If the lath at the other end is fixed, the wave does not stop, but is reflected from it and even if the end lath is left free, reflection still takes place. This illustrates the reflection of a wave, which, for elastic waves, takes place not only at a rigid boundary but at any boundary which separates two media in which the wave travels with different speeds. Thus a sound may be reflected not only from a wall or cliff but from a fog bank, the fog serving to make visible two regions of air in which the conditions of temperature and moisture are different, and in which, therefore, sound waves travel with different speeds. In the case of a wall, however, the reflection is almost complete, whereas in the case of a fog bank a considerable proportion of the energy passes on into the fog and only a fraction is reflected. A similar instance in the case of light waves is the reflection of sunlight from a glass window. When the sun is low the reflection is easily seen by observers at a considerable distance from the window, while people inside the room receive the light which has been transmitted and are hardly conscious that the brightness of the sunshine has been impaired at all.

Let us now produce simultaneous displacements of the laths at the two ends of the model. Two waves immediately start towards

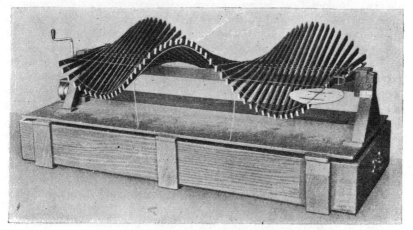

Fig. 1.10.—Vinycomb wave model

the centre, meet, pass, and continue their journey unchanged. At the point where they meet we get the superposition already referred to. They do not interfere with one another, but the displacement of any lath is the algebraic sum of the displacements due to each wave separately. Thus if both waves are produced by upward displacements, then where they meet the laths will have a double upward displacement; but if one wave carries an upward displacement and the other an equal and opposite downward displacement, then where they meet the laths will be undisplaced but the progress of the waves will not be arrested.

The principle of superposition has important practical results. In its application to sound waves it means that the air in a room is capable of carrying many waves at once, so that during an orchestral performance, for instance, the waves produced by the violins do not destroy the waves produced by the wind instruments, and we can listen to either at will. In the case of light it means that 500 people in a room can be looking at 500 different things, and the waves from each object will find their way to the corresponding eye without being affected by the other sets of waves.

Another aspect of the phenomenon can also be illustrated by this model. If we apply a continuous vibration to the end lath and fix the lath at the farther end, waves are transmitted along the model and reflected from the farther end. These two sets of waves become superposed so that some laths remain permanently at rest, while midway between these we have laths in maximum motion.

The way in which this so-called *stationary vibration* arises may perhaps be made clearer by referring to the diagram in fig. 1.11. Let the two broken lines represent two equal sets of waves moving in opposite directions, and at the instant shown on the top line having their crests and troughs coincident. The continuous line shows the resultant displacement of the medium. Subsequent positions of the waves and the resultant displacement of the medium at successive intervals of a quarter period are shown in the three lines below. It will be noticed that at the points A, E, G the displacement is always zero, either because the displacement due to each wave is zero or because the displacements due to the two waves are equal and opposite. At C and F, on the other hand, the displacement is first a double displacement upwards, then zero, then a double displacement downwards, then zero again, and finally a double displacement upwards. At B and D the motion is similar but the amplitude is less. The points of zero motion are known as *nodes*, and the points of maximum motion as *antinodes*.

So far we have been considering models which illustrate transverse waves, that is to say, waves in which the motion of the particles of the medium is at right angles to the motion of the waves. There is another type of wave, however, the type to which sound waves really belong, in which the motion of the particles of the medium is a to-and-fro vibration in the direction in which the wave is travelling. This type may be very simply illustrated by means of a long spiral of copper wire, each turn of which is suspended by two threads from a wooden frame, so that the spring hangs horizontally. If the diameter of the spiral and the thickness of the wire are suitably chosen, then when one end of the spring is struck with the hand, a slow wave of compression travels to the farther end of the spring. This wave is produced by a to-and-fro vibration of the turns of the spring. If the other end of the spring is either free or fixed the wave will be reflected. If similar waves are started simultaneously from opposite ends, then as in the case of the previous model they pass through one another and continue their journey unchanged.

With this model also we can illustrate stationary waves by apply-ing a to-and-fro motion to one end of the spring while the other is held fixed. By careful timing of the vibration the spring can be made

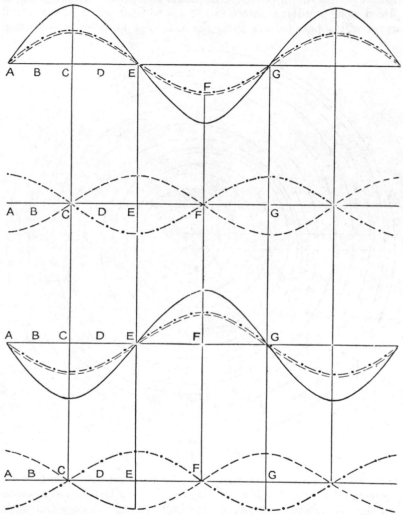

Fig. 1.11.—Stationary wave due to two unequal sets of waves travelling in opposite directions

to break up into a well-marked series of nodes and antinodes, the coils at the antinodes moving to and fro between two adjacent nodes.

As the longitudinal type of vibration is the one with which we have to deal in sound waves, it may be worth while to give one further illustration of it in a way which enables us to study the motion in detail. Fig. 1.12 illustrates the arrangement known as Crova's disc. Circles with radii increasing by a uniform amount are drawn with the equidistant points shown on the small circle as centres. If now a slit is placed along a radius as shown by the dotted lines and the disc rotated, waves will appear to pass along the slit. For purposes of projection

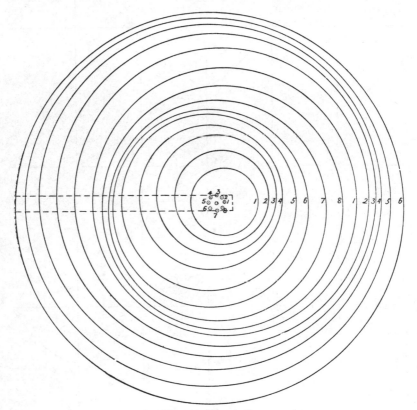

Fig. 1.12.—Crova's disc

the circles are drawn on glass and the arrangement placed in the projection lantern. The lines crossing the slit may be taken to represent invisible boundaries between layers of air through which sound waves are being propagated. Where the distance between the lines is small the air will be compressed; where it is rather large it will be rarefied. If we fix our attention on any particular layer, say the layer which is most compressed, and move the model slowly, we shall see that the compressed layer is moving forward in the direction of the wave and gradually expanding. Its forward motion becomes slower and ceases altogether when its density becomes normal (i.e. at its average width). As it becomes rarefied it moves backwards with increasing velocity, until when it has its greatest width (corresponding to greatest rarefaction) it is moving backwards with its greatest speed. Still moving backwards, but with gradually diminishing speed, it becomes less rarefied, until when its density is normal it is again at rest. It now begins to move forward, its density gradually increasing, until it comes to the point at which its density and forward motion are again a maximum, which is the point from which we started.

12. Long Water Waves in a Canal.

The fundamental properties of wave motion may be illustrated by considering long water waves in a canal. The restriction imposed is that the vertical motion of the water may be neglected. A wave of this kind may be supposed to originate in the sudden stoppage of water flowing through the canal with velocity v. This will result in a rise of water against the barrier as the velocity of the water is reduced to zero, and the change of level between the water now at rest and the water still in motion will be propagated as a disturbance of the

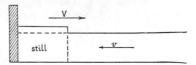

Fig. 1.13.—Formation of long water wave moving from left to right by arrest of water flowing from right to left

type in question with a velocity V which is quite distinct from that of the water. This wave of arrest is shown in fig. 1.13.

The same type of wave may be produced with the water originally at rest by a movement of the barrier from left to right for a limited time with velocity v. The water in front of it rises in level and acquires the same velocity v. A wave of starting will travel with velocity V.

Fig. 1.14.—Formation of long water wave by the starting of a limited portion into motion

When the barrier stops the water level in front of it falls to the original level and the water there resumes its state of rest. A wave has been generated which will continue to move away with velocity V, the water just in front rising in level and acquiring velocity v while the water behind loses its velocity and resumes its undisturbed level (fig. 1.14).

If after being moved forward for a limited time the barrier is moved back with a velocity v for an equal limited time the water in contact with it will acquire a backward velocity and will fall in level. We shall now have a complete wave being propagated from left to right as shown in fig. 1.15. Note that in the elevation the velocity of the water is in the same direction as that of the wave, whereas in the depression it is opposite to that of the wave.

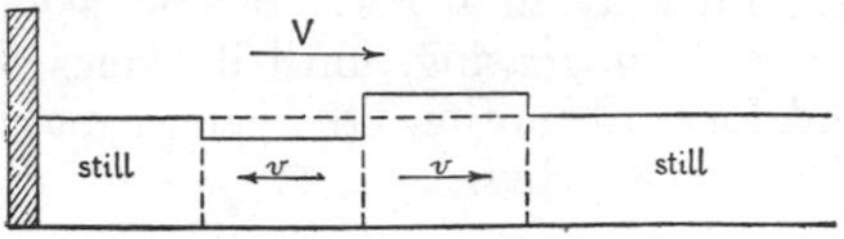

Fig. 1.15.—Formation of complete wave

In an actual case we should not have sudden changes of velocity and the corners of the wave would be rounded, but the essential mechanism of the wave is illustrated in the case we have taken. It enables us to distinguish clearly between v, the temporary velocity of the water (the " particle velocity ") and V, the velocity of the wave. It also shows us that the energy of a wave is made up of a distortional phase (the change in level) which is potential and a velocity phase which is kinetic. It can be shown that the energy is equally distributed between these phases, and this, we shall find later, is a general property of wave motion.

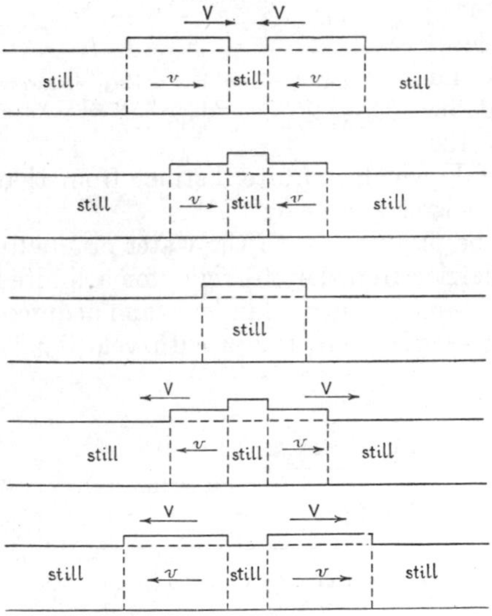

The long water wave is actually an important factor in the disposal of floodwater. A sudden accession of water due to heavy local rainfall may cause a local rise in level. This change in level is propagated as a long wave, and at points downstream a measurable rise in level may be noted long before the actual flood water carrying solid matter in suspension makes its appearance.

Fig. 1.16.—Superposition of two waves of elevation

Let us next consider how these waves may be used to illustrate superposition. First let us consider two waves of elevation approaching one another as in fig. 1.16. Where they overlap their elevations will be added together and, the velocity of the water being opposite in the two waves, the resultant velocity will be the difference. If the waves are equal we shall get a double elevation with no velocity. Presently we get the two elevations completely overlapping as shown.

At both ends of the elevated portion the water level begins to drop, the water acquires a velocity v directed away from the elevated portion in each case, and the two waves move off in opposite directions. The result is exactly the same as if the two waves had passed through one another without interference. An exactly similar argument applies to two waves of depression.

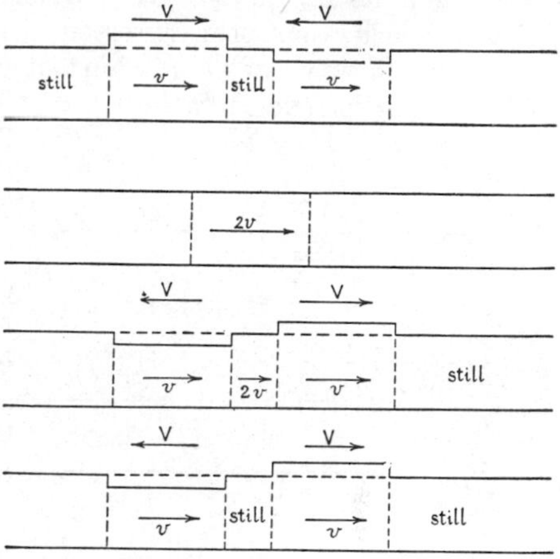

If one of the waves is an elevation and one a depression the successive changes are shown in fig. 1.17. Here at the instant of exact overlapping the water has double velocity and normal level, and again the final result is the same

Fig. 1.17.—Superposition of a wave of depression and a wave of elevation

as if each wave had passed through the other unchanged. It is worth noting that the wave which is all potential energy in fig. 1.16 and the wave which is all kinetic energy in fig. 1.17 in each case resolves itself into two waves travelling in opposite directions with energy partly potential and partly kinetic.

Some interesting points are brought out if we consider the reflection of the wave from a boundary. Suppose first that the boundary is rigid. The water begins by piling itself up to double height in front of the boundary, losing its velocity, and a wave of stopping moves back from the boundary to meet the wave of starting which is still approaching it (fig. 1.18). We next have a still portion of water in front of the boundary, half the length of the wave and of double elevation. From the plane separat-

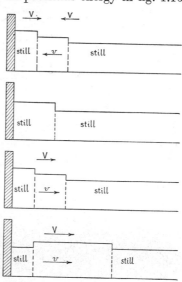

Fig. 1.18.—Reflection of water wave from a rigid boundary

ing this mass of water from that at normal level two waves of starting move in opposite directions, and finally a reflected wave

in which the elevation is the same as that in the incident wave
but which consists of water moving in the opposite direction, travels
away from the boundary. The distortion remains the same but the
particle velocity has been reversed. An exactly similar result is obtained with a wave of depression; it is reflected as a depression but
with the particle velocity reversed. The reflection can be analysed
if we imagine a wave starting
from the boundary at the instant that the incident wave
reaches it and being superposed
on the incident wave. Since
the water in front of the
boundary must be permanently
at rest, the velocity of the
water in the reflected wave
must be opposite to that in the
incident wave, and as the wave
is travelling in the opposite
direction it must be an elevation. If we imagine the reflected wave to pass through
the boundary from left to right
and the incident wave to pass
through the boundary from
right to left and superpose the
two we get the succession of
forms shown in fig. 1.18.

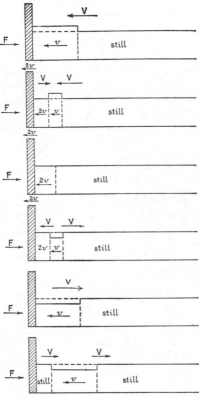

Fig. 1.19.—Reflection from a free boundary

An illustration of an im-
portant set of conditions for a
reflecting boundary may be
obtained if we consider the end
to be closed by a gate devoid
of inertia, free to move and
held in position only by a
balancing force F. When the
wave reaches the gate the latter
will be set in motion with velocity $2v$; v due to the momentum of the
water and v due to the unbalanced pressure caused by the elevation
of the water (fig. 1.19). The water in front of the gate will acquire this
same velocity. Next we have the entire energy of the wave in the
kinetic form—half the length of water now having a doubled velocity.
We can see this also by noticing that when the wave first reaches the
gate, part of the water is moving with velocity $2v$ whereas part is still
moving with velocity v. The surface separating these parts travels
back to meet the wave of arrest which is the rear boundary of the

incident wave. The two meet halfway. The gate continues to move with velocity $2v$, but from the boundary between the still and moving water we have a surface, moving to the right with velocity V, at which the water level drops and the water acquires velocity v, and a surface, moving to the left with velocity V, at which the water level drops and the velocity changes from $2v$ to v. When this latter surface reaches the gate the momentum of the water and the diminished pressure on the gate due to the lower level will balance one another and the gate will cease to move, the water filling itself up to its original level and coming to rest. The gate remains permanently displaced.

It will be noticed that this time the elevation in the incident wave becomes a depression in the reflected wave and the velocity in the incident wave is the same in direction as the velocity in the reflected wave. The distortional phase is reversed and the velocity phase is unchanged. This is exactly analogous to the reflection at the open end of an organ pipe.

Like reflection at a rigid boundary, this case might have been discussed by supposing a reflected wave to start on the left of the boundary as the incident wave meets it. Since the gate cannot withstand any difference of pressure on its two sides, the reflected wave must have a depression which when superposed on the elevation will give equilibrium level. For a depression travelling to the right, however, the velocity in the wave must be from right to left, so that the wave to be superposed on the incident wave (i.e. the reflected wave) must be a wave of depression with the particle velocity in the same direction as in the incident wave.

13. The Ripple Tank.

The properties of wave motion may be admirably illustrated by means of water ripples, and a ripple tank is an indispensable part of the equipment of every lecturer on the subject. Ripples on the surface of water travel fairly slowly and are easily followed by the eye.

For demonstration purposes the tank is usually fitted with a glass bottom, through which light may be projected vertically and then reflected horizontally on to a screen, giving a shadow of the ripples.

Huygens' principle may be illustrated by taking a straight stick with a series of nails driven into it at equal distances apart. If the stick is held with the nail heads just immersed in the water and lifted so that they break the surface simultaneously, then the point where each nail head breaks away from the surface becomes the centre of a circular system of ripples. These systems combine to give straight ripples parallel to the length of the stick.

The phenomena of reflection, refraction and diffraction can all be illustrated quite simply by groups of waves, plane waves being generated by displacement of a straight piece of wood and circular waves by touching the surface of the water with a finger or by removing the finger.

Reflection of plane waves from a plane surface may be illustrated by using a straight piece of wood to generate the waves and another similar piece to act as reflector. It will be noticed that the incident and reflected waves are equally inclined to the reflecting surface. Still using the plane surface as a reflector, we can generate circular ripples and note how they are reflected with the curvature reversed, so that they appear to come from a point behind the reflecting surface which is the virtual image of the source. If a strip of sheet zinc is bent into a circular arc it may be used as a concave mirror; when presented to a series of straight ripples it will converge them to a point, clearly shown, which is the principal focus. If this point is touched by the finger, circular ripples will start and after reflection emerge from the mirror as straight ripples. If the circular ripples are started from a point farther from the reflecting surface they will be rendered convergent by the mirror and will give a real image; if they are started from a point nearer to the reflecting surface they will be divergent and after reflection will appear to come from a virtual image behind the reflector. If the convex side of the reflector is used, the reflected waves are always divergent and the image always virtual.

The phenomena of refraction may be illustrated by taking advantage of the fact that the speed of ripples is less in shallow water than in deep water. If we immerse a plate of glass so that it is just below the surface of the water and allow straight ripples produced as before to impinge on its edge at an angle, then the line of each ripple will appear broken and the refraction will be clearly seen. The change of curvature of spherical waves on passing into another medium can be illustrated by using circular ripples. The focusing effect of a lens as for light waves may be illustrated by laying a lens on the bottom of the tank and just covering it with water. Ripples passing over it move most rapidly at its edges and least rapidly at the centre. Straight ripples thus become converging circular ripples.

The important phenomena of diffraction may be illustrated by examining the effect on straight ripples of apertures and obstacles of different sizes. Using two pieces of wood placed end to end with a small space between, we find that the ripple spreads out on the other side as a circular ripple with the aperture as centre. There is no noticeable " shadow ". On the other hand, if we place the pieces of wood farther apart, there is some spreading of the ripples into the geometrical shadow but the wave continues in the main as a plane wave. On placing a small obstacle—comparable with the wave-length—in the path of straight ripples the ripples are practically unaffected. There is no sensible shadow. If the obstacle is large, we get some spreading round the ends, but quite a marked shadow.

14. The Ripple Tank with Intermittent Illumination.

All these phenomena with ripples may be more easily demonstrated by projection if we use intermittent illumination. One prong of a large tuning-fork of low frequency (say 30) carries a light framework to which are attached two wires dipping into the water in the tank. The fork is electrically maintained and is used to drive a phonic wheel. The early forms of this wheel were due to Rayleigh * and to La Cour. A soft iron wheel with teeth revolves between the poles of an electromagnet. This electromagnet is excited by a current interrupted by the fork. If the soft iron wheel is rotating at such a speed that every time the electromagnet is excited a pair of teeth is exactly opposite the poles, then the speed of the wheel is unaffected by the electromagnet. If the rotation of the wheel tends to slow down, then a pair of teeth will just fail to reach the correct position at the instant of excitation of the magnet and the magnet will therefore exert a forward pull on the wheel, tending to accelerate its rotation. The converse will happen if the wheel is moving a little too fast. Thus the wheel tends to settle down to a steady speed controlled by the fork. The principle is similar to that used in the synchronous clocks now on the market, which are excited by the alternating current of the mains supply.

If the period of the fork is T and there are n teeth on the wheel, then the period of the wheel is nT. If the wheel carries a cardboard disc perforated with n holes through which the light used for projecting the ripple pattern passes, the pattern will be illuminated at intervals T, which is the period of the fork and therefore the interval of time during which one ripple exactly succeeds another.

A much more efficient form of phonic wheel devised by A. B. Wood and J. M. Ford † is shown in fig. 1.20 (p. 26). The rotor, mounted on ball bearings, is made from a bar of soft iron with ten slots machined longitudinally. The stator consists of a soft iron cylinder and two soft iron discs each with ten teeth corresponding to the ten bars of the rotor. The exciting coil, connected through the fork contacts, is a single former-wound coil which lies within the iron shell of the stator and completely surrounds the rotor.

If one dipping wire only is used on the frame attached to the prong of the fork, circular ripples are obtained. If the two wires are used together, two simultaneous sets of circular ripples are produced. If a thin strip of wood is fastened across the two wires with its edge just dipping into the surface, plane waves are obtained.

Instead of a dipping wire attached to the prong of a tuning-fork, R. W. Pohl has used a metal rod at the end of a lever moved by an

---

* *Nature*, Vol. 18, p. 111 (1878).   † *Journ. Sci. Inst.*, Vol. 1, p. 160 (1924).

eccentric. Figs. 1.21–1.26 are from photographic positives of ripples so obtained.*

The phenomena of superposition may also be illustrated. In this case the intermittent illumination is no advantage—rather the reverse. The stroboscopic illumination renders the ripple pattern steady; but the interference pattern is steady in any case. It is therefore better distinguished when the ripples are moving. If the two dipping wires are used, then we shall see on the surface of the water the characteristic hyperbolic lines (p. 10) with the points of contact of the wires as foci.

From *Sound*, Wood (Bell & Sons, Ltd.)

Fig. 1.20.—Phonic motor parts

If one dipping wire is used, and a plane reflector, we shall get interference between the direct and reflected systems. In effect we may treat this as interference of the waves from the real source with waves from its virtual image. The system of interference fringes is the same as before, although of course only half the system is obtained.

For lecture demonstration purposes there is something to be said for dispensing with the phonic wheel. If the disc which interrupts the illumination is rotated by a separate electric motor the speed of the motor may be adjusted until the ripples are almost stationary. If it is then slowed up very slightly—by lightly touching the driving band, for instance—the ripples will move slowly in the proper direction and their changes of form may be followed in detail.

---

* R. W. Pohl, *Physical Principles of Mechanics and Acoustics* (Blackie & Son, Ltd., 1932).

Fig. 1.21.—Diffraction through wide slit

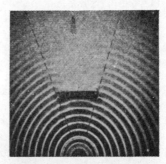

Fig. 1.22.—Diffraction past large obstacle

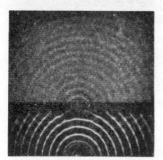

Fig. 1.23.—Diffraction through narrow slit

Fig. 1.24.—Diffraction past small obstacle

Fig. 1.25.—Reflection

Fig. 1.26.—Convergence by water lens

15. The Ripple Tank and the Acoustics of Buildings.

The ripple tank has been used for the illustration of acoustical phenomena by Davis,* and, in particular, for the study of problems in architectural acoustics at the National Physical Laboratory.

A model of the section of the building to be tested is made in wood of sufficient thickness to project above the surface of the water. Ripples are then started at a point corresponding to the position of a speaker, by a " dipper " maintained electromagnetically. The progress of the direct and reflected ripples can be followed as they spread through the space enclosed by the model.

16. The Bird-call and the Sensitive Flame.

The properties of wave motion so far discussed may be illustrated by using a generator of sound waves of very short wave-length and an instrument for detecting them. As a source we may use the bird-call

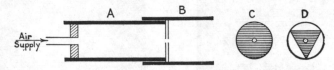

Fig. 1.27.—Rayleigh bird-call

described by Rayleigh (1842–1919). It consists of a brass tube A (fig. 1.27) about 1 in. in diameter, closed at one end by a piece of copper foil C perforated centrally by a hole about 2 mm. in diameter. Into the other end of the tube is fitted a supply pipe which can be attached to a cylinder of compressed air. Fitting tightly over this tube is another brass tube B in which is inserted a triangular piece of copper foil D, also perforated centrally with a hole about 2 mm. in diameter. This tube is then slipped on to A until the two perforated sheets of copper foil are very close together. The pitch of the note given by the arrangement can be adjusted by slightly altering the position of B and by modifying the pressure of the air introduced through the supply pipe. The arrangement can easily be made to give a note above the limit of audibility.

The use of the bird-call has certain disadvantages. It is very susceptible to changes of the blowing pressure of the air, which give rise to sudden and disconcerting changes of pitch and therefore of wave-length. A source which can be much more rigorously controlled is the valve-operated telephone used by S. R. Humby.† This

*Proc. Phys. Soc., Vol. 38, p. 239 (1925–6).   † Proc. Phys. Soc., Vol. 39, p. 435 (1927).

apparatus consists of a telephone receiver placed in the plate circuit of a three-electrode vacuum tube producing oscillatory currents of the desired frequency. The circuit can be tuned by a variable capacity and the intensity can be controlled by means of a resistance box used to shunt the telephone earpiece. The inductance has 1500 turns of wire wound as a coil of mean diameter about 3 in. The condenser has a maximum capacity of about 0·01 microfarad and the high-tension battery gives about 60 volts. This arrangement gives frequencies of 4000 to 16,000 cycles per second.

To detect the waves given by this source it is convenient to use a sensitive flame. It is a well-known fact that if a water tap is turned on slowly the resulting jet is smooth and falls in what looks like an unbroken column. If the pressure is increased a point is reached where the jet breaks up and the water splashes out irregularly. This is due to the fact that when a fluid passes through a tube there is a critical value of the velocity at which the motion ceases to be streamline motion, the fluid breaks up into eddies and the flow becomes irregular. A similar phenomenon was familiar to users of the old batswing gas burner. The phenomenon was used by Thomas Young for the detection of sounds. He drove air, impregnated with smoke, through fine nozzles at velocities just below the critical value and found that the disturbance of the air surrounding the jet caused by high-pitched sounds breaks up the streamline motion of the issuing air. When the source of the sounds is removed the jet resumes its smooth motion.

The phenomenon becomes still more striking when a jet of gas is used and ignited to show its form. If the pressure of the gas is slowly increased from a small value it forms a smooth steady flame of gradually increasing height, but soon a value of the pressure is reached for which turbulent motion sets in. The flame now " roars " and becomes very much shorter. In some cases it forks and shows two tongues. The nozzle is made by drawing down thick-walled glass tubing. Several nozzles may have to be made before a suitable one is obtained. The flame is extremely sensitive to the rattling of keys and the jingling of coins. In favourable cases it is also sensitive to the tick of a watch and if a suitable poem is recited to it, it will pick out all the sibilants and respond only to these. This sensitive flame was accidentally discovered by Leconte * and was subsequently investigated by Tyndall.† He extended his experiments to unlit gas jets made visible with smoke, and concluded that the effect of the sounds was to precipitate a breakdown into vortex motion which was already imminent if not incipient. Rayleigh ‡ made further investigations and showed that when a sensitive flame is used to explore stationary waves it responds at the displacement antinodes and not at the pressure antinodes, being in

---

* *Phil. Mag.*, Vol. 15, p. 235 (1858).   † *Sound*, p. 250 (Longmans, 1895).
‡ *Theory of Sound*, Vol. 2, p. 402 (Macmillan, 1896).

this respect different from the ear. He found further that the use of stopcocks in the supply pipe tends to diminish sensitiveness by producing premature flaring.

A detailed study of the sensitive flame has been made by Jordan and McClung.* They used tapered metal nozzles fitted into rubber tubes, the diameter at the entrance end being 0·08 in. and at the nipple 0·044 in. They were able to obtain flames stable under a pressure giving a height of flame of 30 in. They emphasize the importance of a perfectly circular orifice. Any failure to secure this condition results in the flame breaking down before the condition of great sensitiveness is reached. Smoothness, particularly at the orifice, is also essential and any obstruction or tap near the nozzle may greatly diminish the sensitiveness.

The jets used by Humby were of glass, the diameter of the tubing used being about 1 cm. and the diameter of the orifice about 0·1 cm. At the pressure of the ordinary gas supply (about 10 cm. of water) these jets were found to be sensitive to the note of the telephone with a frequency of 11,000, corresponding to a wavelength of about 3 cm.

A further study by G. B. Brown † confirms Rayleigh's view that the effect of stopcocks is bad and traces their influence to the inevitable hissing as the gas passes the constriction. It is for this reason that the use of gas cylinders is so often ineffective. The adverse effect can be eliminated by packing the supply pipe loosely with cotton-wool near the jet. Brown also confirms Rayleigh's earlier observation that jets may show a marked asymmetry, being sensitive to sounds whose sources lie in one vertical plane through the jet and comparatively insensitive to sounds whose sources lie in a vertical plane at right angles to this. The experiments were extended to jets of air impregnated with tobacco smoke; these jets were found to be (a) more sensitive to draughts, (b) sensitive at lower pressures, (c) sensitive to notes of lower pitch. The orifice was a slit and the jet was photographed stroboscopically. At a certain height above the orifice the column of smoke is found to develop a wavy appearance, the displacement in the waves being parallel to the direction of propagation of the sound. These waves increase in amplitude with distance from the orifice and the jet breaks up at a certain point into a confused conical mass. In some cases portions of the jet, half a wavelength long, seem to break off and proceed alternately up the two arms from the point where the jet forks.

In a later paper ‡ Brown extends his work very much and makes it clear that the disturbance of the jet or flame by sound is different in character from the turbulence produced by increasing the jet velocity and is always accompanied by some vortex development. This vortex development is well shown in fig. 1.28. For all the photographs the disturbing tone has a frequency $f = 126$ c./sec. In the upper half of the plate the velocity of the jet at the orifice varies from 380 cm./sec. to 100 cm./sec. In the lower half of the plate the velocity of the jet is maintained at 150 cm./sec. and the amplitude of the sound is varied.

Clearly the stream of issuing gas has the form of a wedge of very small angle up to a certain height, after which an excrescence appears alternately on the two sides. These excrescences become well-formed vortices which proceed up the jet.

If u is the velocity of the vortices, U the velocity of the air in the jet, f the frequency of the sound, λ the distance between successive vortices on the same side, then

$$u = f\lambda.$$

* *Proc. Roy. Soc. Canada*, Vol. 18, p. 197 (1924).

† *Phil. Mag.*, Vol. 13, p. 161 (1932).   ‡ *Proc. Phys. Soc.*, Vol. 47, p. 703 (1935).

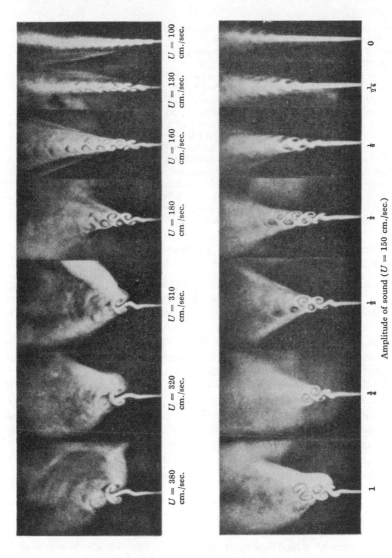

Amplitude of sound ($U = 150$ cm./sec.)

Fig. 1.28.—Smoke vortices, natural size, $f = 126$ c./sec.

From the photographs Brown measured the angular velocity of the leading filament of the vortices and found that if this is denoted by ω we have

$$\omega = \pi f,$$

the vortex performing half a revolution in one period of the wave. If this relationship holds for burning coal-gas jets, which are in some cases sensitive to frequencies as high as 20,000, the corresponding angular velocity must be as great as 10,000 revolutions per sec.

It is here that Brown looks for the explanation of a very remarkable experimental result. It was found that if a number of jets were sensitive over the same range of frequencies then the same particular frequencies gave maximum or minimum disturbance of the jet, no matter what the shape or size of the orifice, the velocity of the stream, the amplitude of the sound, or the nature of the reservoir or tubing supplying the jet with gas. Thus the most marked disturbance always occurred for the frequencies 5850, 4600, 3300 and 2400 and the least for frequencies 12,250, 10,850, 5300, 3600–3500, 2800 and 2200. Even with a hydrogen flame the frequencies for maxima and minima were in accordance with this series. As the angular velocity in the vortices seems to be the only property which is linked to the frequency of the disturbing source and to nothing else, Brown concludes that some rates of angular rotation of the vortices are more favourable to vortex development than others.

17. Illustration of the Properties of Wave Motion by Experiments with very short Sound Waves.

Equipped with a source of these short waves and a sensitive flame we can illustrate most of the properties of wave motion.

(*a*) Reflection from a plane surface can be shown by putting a screen between the source and the flame and using a drawing-board as a reflector to direct the waves round the edge of the screen on to the flame. It will be found that the board has to be fairly accurately orientated before the effect is obtained.

(*b*) Reflection from a concave surface can be shown by using two fairly large concave spherical mirrors and putting source and sensitive flame at their respective foci. When the mirrors are properly directed the roaring of the flame is very pronounced, but quite a small displacement of either mirror will render the flame quiescent again.

(*c*) Refraction is not easy to illustrate. Experiments have been described by Tyndall (1820–1893) and others in which carbon dioxide was enclosed in a lenticular bag of thin rubber or in a soap bubble, but all such experiments are vitiated by the action of the membrane which encloses the gas.

(*d*) Superposition due to two sources can readily be obtained by an arrangement which is due to Rayleigh. The whistle is fitted with an end-piece with two apertures. When the whistle is blown the two apertures act as two sources in the same phase, and when the whistle is swung round the whole set of interference surfaces is moved bodily and their passage over the flame is very obvious.

(*e*) Superposition due to direct and reflected waves from a plane surface may be demonstrated in two ways. We may direct the source towards the flame and hold a drawing-board horizontally below the line joining them. If the height of the board is altered, or if it is tilted, the interference surfaces are shifted and the flame alternately roars and is quiescent. This arrangement corresponds to Lloyd's single-mirror fringes for light. On the other hand, we can place the board vertically so as to reflect the waves back towards the source. In this case stationary vibration is set up between the source and the board. If the flame is moved between the board and the source it will flare at the antinodes and remain quiet at the nodes. The defect of this method is that the movement of the flame causes flaring and the nodes are difficult to locate. This difficulty may be overcome by leaving the flame in position and moving the board backwards or forwards. This has the effect of drawing the whole system of nodes and antinodes past the flame, which responds accordingly. If successive positions of the board for which a node occurs at the flame are noted, the distance between the nodes is half a wave-length for the sound. By moving the board through ten such positions and measuring the whole displacement we can obtain a fairly accurate measurement of the half wave-length, and dividing half the velocity of sound by this gives us the frequency of the note, in accordance with the relation

$$\frac{c/2}{\lambda/2} = \frac{c}{\lambda} = f.$$

In this way the frequency of an inaudible sound may be determined, the method being fundamentally the same as measurement of the velocity of sound by setting up stationary vibration in a tube with a tuning-fork of known frequency and measuring the wave-length (see p. 253).

(f) Diffraction through an aperture of varying width can be shown by fitting to the whistle a horn of elliptical section. The whistle is directed towards the flame with the major axis of the ellipse horizontal and is then swung round until it just fails to affect the flame. If the horn is then twisted about its own axis until the minor axis of the ellipse is horizontal, the flame is again affected and will remain so while the whistle is swung still farther from the direct line. Thus the spread is greater in the plane of the minor axis than in the plane of the major axis, showing that the narrower the aperture the greater the spread.

(g) Diffraction round a circular obstacle can also be shown by placing the source not too far from the flame and pointing towards it. If a circular disc is now inserted between the two and carefully centred, the flame will flare, whereas if the disc is not correctly centred the flame will be quiescent. This is the acoustic analogue of the famous experiment by Arago and Fresnel in which it was shown that when the shadow of a small circular object is thrown on a screen by a brightly illuminated pinhole there is a bright spot at the centre of the circular shadow.

This experiment may be made more striking by suspending the disc so that it can swing in its own plane at right angles to the line joining source and detector. If the disc is correctly centred in its equilibrium position and set swinging the flame will be seen to respond each time the disc passes through this position, and to become quiescent when the disc is at either end of its swing. An impressive extension of this experiment — the zone plate — is described later in connexion with the more complete discussion of diffraction (p. 232).

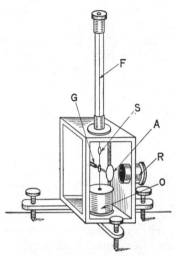

Fig. 1.29.—Sound radiometer

Further illustrations of the properties of wave motion using short sound waves can be carried out with a high-pitched whistle as source and an acoustic radiometer as detector. The apparatus is briefly described by R. W. Pohl.* The whistle emits waves for which λ is about 1·5 cm. and is placed at the focus of a parabolic mirror. The radiometer is shown in fig. 1.29. It consists of a metal plate A fixed to the arm of a sensitive torsion balance and counterpoised by a weight G. S is a mirror attached to the axis of the radiometer and the suspension F is a bronze filament. O is a damping arrangement. The waves are focused on A through the side tube R by reflection from a concave mirror. As will be seen later (p. 218), Pohl has made some very accurate measurements with this apparatus.

18. Visual Observation and Photography of Sound Waves.

Some of the phenomena of wave motion can be directly observed in the case of air waves by making the waves visible. In order to do this two difficulties have to be overcome: the high velocity of the waves and their transparency. To overcome the first difficulty nothing is needed except a very short exposure, and this is obtained by using the illumination due to an electric spark. The second difficulty is overcome by using the variation of the refractive index of air with density.

* *Physical Principles of Mechanics and Acoustics*, pp. 285–6.

Two experimental methods have been developed. The first of these was originally used by Töpler * for examining lenses in order to detect defects and was adapted by E. Mach † for the photography of the air waves due to a bullet in flight. The method was improved by L. Mach and will be understood by reference to fig. 1.30, which illustrates the apparatus with further improvements by R. W. Wood ‡ for the study of the air waves generated by the crack of an electric spark and subsequently reflected or refracted by various devices.

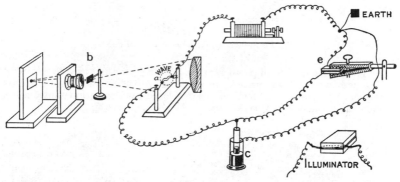

Fig. 1.30

An electric spark at *e* acts as illuminant and is focused sharply at *b* on the edge of a screen by a lens of large diameter. The spark gap at *aa* is in the same circuit and acts as the source of sound, the crack of the spark sending out a pressure wave. A capacity *c* in parallel with the illuminating spark delays it a fraction of a second relative to the sound spark, so that the wave has moved out towards the edge of the lens before it is illuminated. If the lens is perfect and there is no sound wave, light from all points on the lens will go to form the image of the spark on the edge of the screen, and the field of the telescope, which is focused on the lens, will be entirely dark. If any irregularities exist in the lens these will cause abnormal deviations of the rays passing through the corresponding points and these rays will pass below the edge of the screen, showing the irregularities as bright spots. This was the purpose of Töpler's original experiment; for lens testing the source of light may be an illuminated pinhole and no spark-gaps are necessary.

When the method is used for the study of sound waves a high-grade lens must be selected, showing no irregularities. Rays coming through the lens at various points will all go to form the image of the illuminating spark on the lower edge of the screen and the field of the telescope will be dark. If, however, a sound wave has started from the spark in front of the lens and been illuminated, while still in the field, by a spark passing in the gap behind the lens, then the rays passing through the shell of air forming the sound pulse will be abnormally deviated and the trace of the shell on a plane at right angles to the axis of the apparatus will appear in the telescope as a bright line on a dark ground.

* *Ann. d. Physik*, Vol. 131, p. 33 (1867).
† *Sitzungsber. d. Akad. d. Wissenschaft zu Wien*, Vol. 98, p. 1333 (1889).
‡ *Phil. Mag.*, Vol. 48, p. 218 (1899); Vol. 50, p. 148 (1900).

The method has also been applied by Payman, Robinson, and Shepherd * to a study of the velocity and form of an explosion wave emerging from the mouth of a tube.

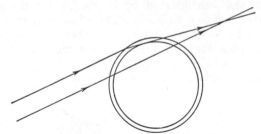

Fig. 1.31.—Refraction through a spherical shell

An alternative method of photographing the waves was first used by Dvořák.† In this method no lens was used for focusing and a shadow was thrown directly on the screen or plate. The method was developed by Boys ‡ and subsequently by Foley and Souder,§ by Quayle ‖ and by Davis and Kaye.¶ This method has

Fig. 1.32.—Photograph of a rifle bullet moving with a velocity of 2700 ft. per second.
Time of exposure less than 1/2,000,000 second

* *Safety of Mines Research Board*, Papers No. 18 and 29 (1926).
† *Ann. d. Physik*, Vol. 9, p. 502 (1880).   ‡ *Nature*, Vol. 47, pp. 415, 440 (1893).
§ *Phys. Rev.*, Vol. 35, p. 374 (1912).
‖ *Journ. Frankl. Inst.*, Vol. 193, p. 627 (1922); *Scientific Papers of the Bureau of Standards*, No. 508, Vol. 20, p. 237 (1925).   ¶ *Journ. Sci. Inst.*, Vol. 3, p. 393 (1926).

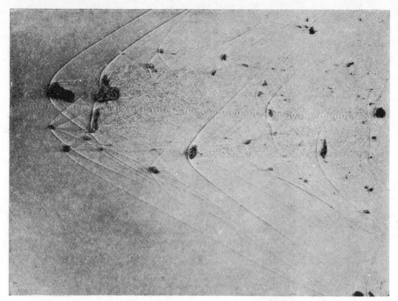

Fig. 1.33.—Splinters of wood due to a bullet with flattened nose fired through a board of maple wood

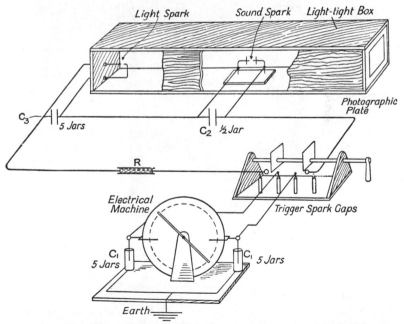

Fig. 1.34.—Apparatus for photographing sound waves, used at the National Physical Laboratory for studying the reflection in the small-scale model of the section of a building

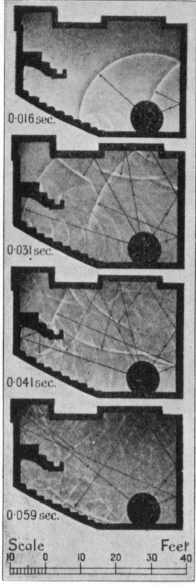

Fig. 1.35.—Sequence of sound pulse photographs in a small-scale model of the
longitudinal section of the Royal Institution Lecture Theatre

considerable advantages over the other.   All optical parts are dispensed with,
so high-grade optical apparatus is not required.   The size of the sound wave is
limited only by the size of the photographic plate and not by the diameter of

the lens or mirror. No light is cut off by a screen as in the Töpler method. The principle is shown in fig. 1.31 (p. 36). If this represents a spherical shell of compressed air illuminated by a source of light, rays penetrating into the interior of the shell will be affected very little. Rays which are nearly tangents from the source to the wave, however, will not penetrate into the interior and will be deviated as if by a prism of large angle on which they were incident with a large angle of incidence. Thus the shadow will closely represent a meridian section of the sound wave at right angles to the path of the light from the source.

A very full account of the various methods is given by Cranz *, with many beautiful photographs. A summary is also given by D. C. Miller †, from whose book fig. 1.32 (p. 36) is taken.

Fig. 1.32 shows two well-marked wave-fronts. These waves are analogous to the V-shaped ripple system caused by drawing the finger across the surface of water. It can easily be seen that if v is the velocity of the finger and c the velocity of the ripples, then the ripple started by the finger when at A has travelled to B while the finger has travelled from A to D. In fact DB is the envelope of the Huygens wavelets started on the surface of the water by the finger in its passage to D. It follows that $c/v = AB/AD = \sin\theta$, where 2θ is the angle of the V.

Obviously, if $v < c$, $\sin\theta$ has no real value and the Huygens wavelets have no envelope.

In the case of the bullet the wave-fronts are of course conical but appear only if the velocity of the bullet exceeds the velocity of sound. The sine of the semi-vertical angle of the cone gives the ratio of the velocity of sound and the velocity of the bullet. Fig. 1.33 (p. 37) shows the variation of the angle of the wave with the speed of the projectile.

The apparatus used at the National Physical Laboratory for testing the acoustics of a model of an auditorium is shown in fig. 1.34 (p. 37) and a series of photographs in fig. 1.35. In these latter photographs reflected rays corresponding to the wave-fronts are shown.

---

* *Lehrbuch der Ballistik*, Vol. 3 (Springer, Berlin, 1927).
† *Sound Waves, Their Shape and Speed* (Macmillan Co., New York, 1938).

CHAPTER II

Analytical Discussion of Wave Motion

1. Periodic Vibrations.

The movement of a point is said to be periodic when at equal intervals of time, measured from any instant, it is always to be found in the same condition, i.e. having the same displacement, the same velocity and the same acceleration. The interval of time in which the cycle of values is repeated is the *period*. The reciprocal of this, i.e. the number of cycles completed in unit time, is the *frequency*. The maximum displacement from the undisturbed position is the *amplitude*. The *phase* is a quantity which defines the stage of the vibration at a given instant.

2. Simple Harmonic Motion.

The most important type of periodic vibration is that known as *simple harmonic motion*. It is the type given approximately by the bob of a simple pendulum executing oscillations of small amplitude. It is given by all types of elastic displacement, i.e. by all systems which, when displaced, are acted on by a force directed to their undisplaced position and proportional to their distance from that position. Another very important fact is that any periodic vibration, however complicated, may be analysed into a series of these simple harmonic motions and built up by compounding such a series (p. 337).

We may study this type of vibration from two different starting-points.

(1) We may define simple harmonic motion as the projection of the motion of a point, describing a circle with uniform speed, on a straight line in the plane of the circle. We can then deduce its properties from the known properties of circular motion. Thus if, for convenience, we take the diameter of the circle in fig. 2.1 as our straight line, and if the point P describes the circle with uniform speed v, then the point N will move with simple harmonic motion.

If a is the radius of the circle, then obviously a is the amplitude of the motion of N, and its period is $2\pi a/v$, or, if ω is the uniform angular velocity of P, $2\pi/\omega$.

If x denotes the displacement ON, then

$$x = ON = OP \cos XOP = a \cos \theta,$$

where θ is the angle between OP and the x-axis.

The velocity of N is

$$\frac{dx}{dt} = -a \sin \theta \frac{d\theta}{dt} = -\omega a \sin \theta,$$

a result which can be obtained at once by resolving along the x-axis the velocity of P (ωa along TP).

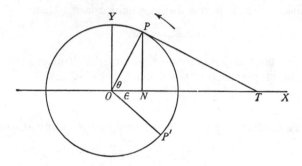

Fig. 2.1.—Simple harmonic motion

The acceleration of N is

$$\frac{d^2x}{dt^2} = -\omega a \cos \theta \frac{d\theta}{dt} = -\omega^2 a \cos \theta = -\omega^2 x.$$

Thus the acceleration is always opposite in direction to the displacement and proportional to it, and the motion is represented by the equation

$$\frac{d^2x}{dt^2} + \omega^2 x = 0. \quad \ldots \ldots \quad (2.1)$$

It is obvious that the acceleration could also have been obtained directly by resolving along the x-axis the acceleration of P ($\omega^2 a$ along PO).

The period of the motion of N is of course the same as the period of the motion of P. If then we call the period $T(=2\pi/\omega)$, and if for dx/dt we write $\dot{x}$, and for d^2x/dt^2, $\ddot{x}$, we have

$$\omega^2 = -\frac{\ddot{x}}{x} = \text{acceleration at unit displacement;}$$

the negative sign is a reminder that the acceleration is opposite in direction to the displacement. Hence

$$T = \frac{2\pi}{\sqrt{(\text{Acceleration at unit displacement})}}. \qquad . \quad (2.2)$$

Since this equation does not contain a, it follows that the period of the motion is independent of the amplitude—the result which Galileo (1564–1642) obtained experimentally for the pendulum when he timed the swings of the great lamp in the Cathedral at Pisa by the beats of his pulse.

Also, if the particle has mass m and the force which urges it to its mean position when it is at a displacement x is F_x, then

$$F_x = m\ddot{x}.$$

Since the acceleration is proportional to the displacement the force must also be proportional to the displacement, so that

$$F_x = -f_1 x,$$

where f_1 is a constant equal to the restoring force at unit displacement. Hence

$$m\ddot{x} + f_1 x = 0;$$

$$\therefore\ T = \frac{2\pi}{\sqrt{(f_1/m)}} = 2\pi\sqrt{\frac{m}{f_1}}.$$

We thus have the period given by

$$T = 2\pi\sqrt{\left(\frac{\text{Mass}}{\text{Restoring force at unit displacement}}\right)}.$$

We are now in a position to interpret the angle θ in a way which makes clear how general the equation for the displacement is. Let the particle which at the instant t is at P be in the position P′ when the time is zero, i.e. at the instant $t = 0$. The angle P′OP is then ωt, and if we denote the angle P′OX by ϵ we have

$$\theta = \omega t - \epsilon,$$
$$x = a \cos(\omega t - \epsilon);$$

ϵ is called the epoch of the motion.

(2) We may also define simple harmonic motion as the motion in a straight line of a point whose acceleration is always directed towards a fixed point in that straight line and proportional to the displacement from that point.

This at once gives us the equation

$$\ddot{x} + \omega^2 x = 0,$$

where ω^2 is a constant.

This is a linear differential equation of the second order—linear because x and its derivatives occur in the first power only, second order because the second order derivative is the highest that occurs in the equation. Many equations of this type may be solved by putting $x = e^{mt}$ and finding values of m for which the equation is satisfied. Thus if

$$x = e^{mt},$$

we have $\qquad\qquad \dot{x} = me^{mt}, \; \ddot{x} = m^2 e^{mt}.$

Substituting in the differential equation we have

$$m^2 e^{mt} + \omega^2 e^{mt} = 0,$$
$$e^{mt}(m^2 + \omega^2) = 0,$$
$$\therefore \quad m^2 + \omega^2 = 0.$$

This equation is called the *auxiliary equation*. From it we finally have

$$m = \pm i\omega,$$

where $\qquad\qquad i = \sqrt{-1}.$

The differential equation is therefore satisfied by

$$x = e^{i\omega t} \quad \text{and} \quad x = e^{-i\omega t}.$$

These are *particular integrals*, each of which satisfies the original equation. If we write x_1, x_2 respectively for these two solutions, then any linear combination of them, $A_1 x_1 + A_2 x_2$,

     (1) is a solution of the original equation,

     (2) contains two arbitrary constants.

It is therefore a complete solution of the equation. (A_1 and A_2 may be complex.)

Then we have

$$x = A_1 e^{i\omega t} + A_2 e^{-i\omega t}$$
$$= A_1(\cos \omega t + i \sin \omega t) + A_2(\cos \omega t - i \sin \omega t)$$
$$= (A_1 + A_2) \cos \omega t + i(A_1 - A_2) \sin \omega t,$$

i.e. $\qquad\qquad x = A \cos \omega t + B \sin \omega t, \quad \ldots \ldots \ldots \ldots$ (2.3)

where $\qquad A = A_1 + A_2, \; B = i(A_1 - A_2).$

Thus x may be made real by choosing A_1 and A_2 suitably.

Alternatively, we may simply regard A and B as new arbitrary constants and choose real values for them. They may be expressed in terms of the initial conditions, i.e. the displacement and velocity when $t = 0$.

Thus, from (2.3),

$$x = A \cos \omega t + B \sin \omega t,$$
$$\dot{x} = -A\omega \sin \omega t + B\omega \cos \omega t.$$

If when $t = 0$ the displacement is x_0 and the velocity $\dot{x}_0$, then

$$x_0 = A, \ \dot{x}_0 = B\omega,$$

so that

$$x = x_0 \cos \omega t + \frac{\dot{x}_0}{\omega} \sin \omega t.$$

If when $t = 0$ the displacement is a and the velocity is zero, then

$$a = A, \ 0 = B,$$
$$\therefore \ x = a \cos \omega t.$$

If when $t = 0$ the displacement is zero and the velocity is $\dot{x}_0$, then

$$A = 0, \ B = \dot{x}_0/\omega, \text{ and } x = \frac{\dot{x}_0}{\omega} \sin \omega t.$$

Here $\dot{x}_0/\omega$ is the maximum value of the displacement, i.e. the amplitude a,

$$\therefore \ x = a \sin \omega t.$$

We can throw the solution of the differential equation into another form by putting

$$A = a \cos \epsilon, \ B = a \sin \epsilon.$$

We now have two arbitrary constants such that if we take the positive value of the square root,

$$a = \sqrt{(A^2 + B^2)},$$

$$\sin \epsilon = \frac{B}{\sqrt{(A^2 + B^2)}},$$

$$\cos \epsilon = \frac{A}{\sqrt{(A^2 + B^2)}},$$

$$\epsilon = \tan^{-1} \frac{B}{A},$$

and the equation becomes

$$x = a \cos (\omega t - \epsilon),$$

in which a and ϵ are new arbitrary constants.

Here it is obvious that a is the maximum value of x, i.e. the amplitude; and that ω is a quantity such that when t changes by $2\pi/\omega$ the value of x recurs.

Since
$$\dot{x} = -\omega a \sin(\omega t - \epsilon),$$

the value of $\dot{x}$ also recurs, and $2\pi/\omega$ is therefore the period of the motion.

The figure from which we originally started provides us with geometrical interpretations of all these quantities.

The quantities themselves may, as before, be determined from the initial conditions. If we take the same initial conditions as in the last case ($x_0 = 0$, $\dot{x} = \dot{x}_0$ when $t = 0$), we have

$$0 = a \cos(-\epsilon) = a \cos\epsilon$$

$$\therefore \quad \epsilon = \pi/2.$$

Further,
$$\dot{x}_0 = -\omega a \sin(-\epsilon) = \omega a \sin\epsilon = \omega a,$$

$$\therefore \quad x = a \cos(\omega t - \epsilon)$$

$$= \frac{\dot{x}_0}{\omega} \sin\omega t, \text{ as before.}$$

(3) There is a third way of treating the solution of the equation. As we are interested in real solutions only, we can use $Ae^{i\omega t}$ as a solution on the understanding that the real part only is meant. Then since A is generally complex it contains two arbitrary constants, which may be taken either as the real and imaginary parts or the modulus and argument (R and $-\epsilon$, say). That is,

$$Ae^{i\omega t} = Re^{i(\omega t - \epsilon)},$$

and the real part is just $R\cos(\omega t - \epsilon)$, in which R is the amplitude of the motion and ϵ the epoch.

Further,
$$\frac{d}{dt}(Ae^{i\omega t}) = i\omega Ae^{i\omega t}$$

$$= i\omega Re^{i(\omega t - \epsilon)}.$$

The real part is now $-\omega R \sin(\omega t - \epsilon)$. Thus the use of the complex form may be extended to the derivative, and for many purposes it is sufficient to use the form $Re^{i\omega t}$ without actually taking the real part.

3. Energy of Simple Harmonic Vibrations.

Let the mass of a body executing simple harmonic motion be m and the acceleration at displacement x be $\ddot{x}$, where

$$\ddot{x} = -\omega^2 x.$$

The force required to maintain displacement x is $m\omega^2 x$.
The work done in the small displacement dx is $m\omega^2 x \,.\, dx$. Hence

V, the potential energy at displacement $x = \displaystyle\int_0^x m\omega^2 x \,.\, dx = \tfrac{1}{2}m\omega^2 x^2.$

That is, the potential energy is proportional to the square of the displacement.

The velocity at displacement x is $\dot{x} = -a\omega \sin(\omega t - \epsilon)$

$$= -a\omega\sqrt{1 - \cos^2(\omega t - \epsilon)}.$$

T, the kinetic energy $= \tfrac{1}{2}m\dot{x}^2$

$$= \tfrac{1}{2}m\omega^2 a^2 \sin^2(\omega t - \epsilon)$$
$$= \tfrac{1}{2}m\omega^2(a^2 - a^2 \cos^2 \overline{\omega t - \epsilon})$$
$$= \tfrac{1}{2}m\omega^2(a^2 - x^2).$$

Hence the total energy

$$= \tfrac{1}{2}m\omega^2 x^2 + \tfrac{1}{2}m\omega^2(a^2 - x^2)$$
$$= \tfrac{1}{2}m\omega^2 a^2,$$

and this is obviously

(1) the value of the potential energy at maximum displacement $(x = a)$, and
(2) the value of the kinetic energy at zero displacement $(x = 0)$.

Using the fact that there is no dissipative force at work and that the energy is therefore constant, we can derive the differential equation. In this case we cannot assume that

$$\dot{x} = a\omega \cos(\omega t - \epsilon).$$

We have, however,

$$V + T = \text{constant.}$$
$$\therefore \tfrac{1}{2}m\omega^2 x^2 + \tfrac{1}{2}m\dot{x}^2 = \text{const.}$$
$$\therefore \omega^2 x^2 + \dot{x}^2 = \text{const.}$$

Differentiating with respect to t, we have

$$\omega^2 . 2x . \dot{x} + 2\dot{x}\ddot{x} = 0,$$
$$\therefore \ \ddot{x} + \omega^2 x = 0$$

as before.

4. Transverse Vibrations of a Light Loaded String.

Let M be the mass at the centre of the string, l the length of the string, P the tension of the string. We assume the displacement of the mass to be so small that no change of tension results and ACB $\doteqdot$ AOB $= l$ (fig. 2.2).

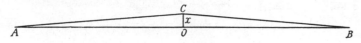

Fig. 2.2.—Transverse vibrations of string

Then the force in direction of displacement

$$= -2P \cos \text{ACO}$$
$$\doteqdot -2P . \frac{x}{l/2}$$
$$\doteqdot -\frac{4P . x}{l}.$$

That is, the motion is simple harmonic:

$$M\ddot{x} = -4\frac{P}{l} . x,$$

so that
$$T = 2\pi\sqrt{\frac{Ml}{4P}} = \pi\sqrt{\frac{Ml}{P}}. \quad \ldots \ldots \quad (2.4)$$

5. Resisted Simple Harmonic Motion.

All actual vibrating systems are subject to a resisting force which causes decay of amplitude or " damping ". If disturbed and left to themselves they oscillate for a time and finally come to rest, the energy given to them by the initial displacement being used up in doing work against the resisting force. We shall have a fair approximation to the common case if we assume the resisting force to be proportional to the velocity. If we take its magnitude as $2r$ per unit mass per unit velocity, our equation for the oscillation becomes

$$\ddot{x} + 2r\dot{x} + \omega^2 x = 0. \quad \ldots \ldots \quad (2.5)$$

In order to find the auxiliary equation we put $x = e^{mt}$.

Then $\qquad\qquad\qquad \dot{x} = me^{mt}, \ \ddot{x} = m^2 e^{mt},$

and substitution in the differential equation gives

$$m^2 e^{mt} + 2rm e^{mt} + \omega^2 e^{mt} = 0,$$

whence $\qquad\qquad\qquad m^2 + 2rm + \omega^2 = 0$

and $\qquad\qquad\qquad m = -r \pm \sqrt{r^2 - \omega^2}.$

The solution thus depends on whether r is greater or less than ω. For $r > \omega$ the roots of the auxiliary equation are both real and the solution has the form

$$x = A_1 e^{(-r + \sqrt{r^2 - \omega^2})t} + A_2 e^{(-r - \sqrt{r^2 - \omega^2})t}$$
$$= e^{-rt}(A_1 e^{\sqrt{r^2 - \omega^2}\,t} + A_2 e^{-\sqrt{r^2 - \omega^2}\,t}). \quad \cdots \quad (2.6)$$

This case is not of much interest in acoustics. When displaced the system returns to rest asymptotically and is aperiodic. When $r = \omega$, the system is said to be *critically damped*.

If $r < \omega$ the roots of the auxiliary equation are imaginary and we may write

$$x = e^{-rt}(A_1 e^{i\sqrt{\omega^2 - r^2}\,t} + A_2 e^{-i\sqrt{\omega^2 - r^2}\,t}) \quad \cdots \quad (2.7)$$

which may (as before, cf. 2.3, p. 43) be put into the form

$$x = e^{-rt}(A \cos qt + B \sin qt), \quad \cdots \cdots \quad (2.8)$$

where $\qquad\qquad\qquad q = \sqrt{(\omega^2 - r^2)},$

or $\qquad\qquad\qquad x = a e^{-rt} \cos(qt - \epsilon). \quad \cdots \cdots \cdots \quad (2.9)$

This equation obviously represents an oscillation of diminishing amplitude and of frequency $\sqrt{\omega^2 - r^2}/2\pi$.

If ω^2 is large compared with r^2, which is the usual case in sound, then the frequency is approximately $\omega/2\pi$ and is not affected by the damping.

The displacement diagram (x plotted against t) is such (fig. 2.3) that it lies entirely between the curves $x = +a e^{-rt}$ and $x = -a e^{-rt}$.

If t is measured from the instant of zero displacement,

$$\epsilon = \pi/2, \text{ and } x = a e^{-rt} \sin qt.$$

Successive amplitudes are the various values of this expression for which $\dot{x} = 0$.

But $\qquad\qquad\qquad \dot{x} = a e^{-rt}(-r \sin qt + q \cos qt),$

$$\therefore \ \dot{x} = 0 \text{ when } \tan qt = q/r,$$

i.e. $\qquad\qquad\qquad t = \frac{1}{q}\left(\tan^{-1}\frac{q}{r} + n\pi\right).$

These values of t are separated by an interval π/q.
Also, at the instant of turning

$$\sin qt = \pm \frac{q}{\sqrt{(q^2 + r^2)}},$$

which is constant.

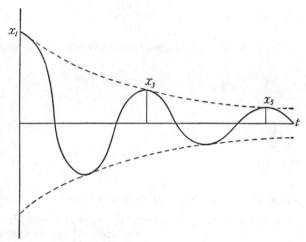

Fig. 2.3.—Damped Oscillations (t measured from instant of maximum displacement)

Let $$\tan^{-1}\frac{q}{r} = h.$$

Then for the successive amplitudes we have

t	x
$\dfrac{h}{q}$	$+\ ae^{-rh/q} \times \dfrac{q}{\sqrt{(q^2 + r^2)}}.$
$\dfrac{h+\pi}{q}$	$-\ ae^{-r(h+\pi)/q} \times \dfrac{q}{\sqrt{(q^2 + r^2)}}.$
$\dfrac{h+2\pi}{q}$	$+\ ae^{-r(h+2\pi)/q} \times \dfrac{q}{\sqrt{(q^2 + r^2)}}$
	&c.

Hence if x_{n+1}/x_n is the numerical value of the ratio of successive maximum displacements on opposite sides,

$$\frac{x_{n+1}}{x_n} = e^{-r\pi/q} = e^{-rT/2} = \text{constant},$$

where T is the period $\frac{2\pi}{q}$.

Hence
$$-\log\frac{x_{n+1}}{x_n} = \frac{rT}{2},$$

and this quantity is called the *logarithmic decrement* of the motion (δ). That is,

$$\delta = \frac{rT}{2}$$

$$= \frac{\pi r}{q} = \frac{\pi r}{\sqrt{(\omega^2 - r^2)}}. \quad \cdot \quad \cdot \quad \cdot \quad \cdot \quad (2.10)$$

It follows that
$$r = \frac{\omega\delta}{\sqrt{(\pi^2 + \delta^2)}}.$$

6. Propagation of a Plane Wave of Constant Type.

If we take any line in a medium as the axis of x and let any condition (displacement, velocity, density, &c.) of successive elements

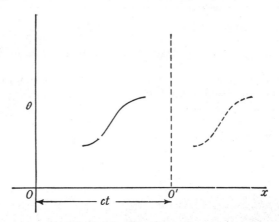

Fig. 2.4.—Wave propagation

normally situated along this line be given at any instant by $\theta = f(x)$, then this curve is the curve for the elements of the medium at time t, as in fig. 2.4. If the distribution of the condition is being propagated unchanged to the right, i.e. if a plane wave is travelling along the x-axis in a positive direction, the values of the condition will be given by $\theta = f(x)$ if we measure x from an origin travelling with the waves. If the waves have a velocity c and we measure x from a fixed origin, then at any time t' the values are given by

$$\theta = f[x - c(t' - t)].$$

If we make our measurements from the position of the origin when $t = 0$, then at any instant t

$$\theta = f(x - ct).$$

The value of θ is determined when the value of the argument in the brackets is given. We see that θ remains the same when t changes by t' and x by x', provided that

$$ct' = x',$$

i.e. Velocity of wave $c = \dfrac{x'}{t'}$.

The same may be seen to be true of the equation

$$\theta = f(ct - x), \quad \ldots \ldots \quad (2.11)$$

which must also represent a wave travelling in a positive direction with velocity c.

In an exactly similar way we may show that the equation

$$\theta = f(ct + x) \quad \ldots \ldots \quad (2.12)$$

represents a wave travelling in a negative direction with velocity c, since the value of θ can only remain the same if x diminishes while t increases.

The functions may have any form and we can choose the form to represent any type of wave.

If we represent $(ct - x)$ by z,

and $\dfrac{df(z)}{dz}$ by $f'(z)$,

then $\dfrac{\partial \theta}{\partial x} = \dfrac{d\theta}{dz} \cdot \dfrac{\partial z}{\partial x}$

$$= -f'(z) = -f'(ct - x).$$

Similarly, $\dfrac{\partial \theta}{\partial t} = \dfrac{d\theta}{dz} \cdot \dfrac{\partial z}{\partial t} = cf'(z) = cf'(ct - x).$

$$\therefore \dfrac{\partial \theta}{\partial t} = -c \dfrac{\partial \theta}{\partial x}.$$

If θ measures the displacement in a wave, then $\partial\theta/\partial t$ is the particle velocity $= \dot{\theta}$, say, and $\partial\theta/\partial x$ is the slope of the displacement curve $= \theta'$, say.

Then
$$\dot{\theta} = -c\theta'.$$

If we had started with the wave travelling in a negative direction we should have had

$$\dot{\theta} = +c\theta'.$$

That is, in general,
$$\dot{\theta} = \pm c\theta'.$$

Further, if we put $\dfrac{d^2f(z)}{dz^2} = f''(z)$ we have

$$\frac{\partial^2\theta}{\partial x^2} = \frac{\partial}{\partial x}\left(\frac{\partial\theta}{\partial x}\right) = \frac{\partial}{\partial x}(-f'(z)) = -\frac{\partial}{\partial z}f'(z)\cdot\frac{\partial z}{\partial x}$$

$$= +f''(z)$$

$$= f''(ct - x).$$

Similarly,

$$\frac{\partial^2\theta}{\partial t^2} = \frac{\partial}{\partial t}(cf'(z)) = c\frac{\partial f'(z)}{\partial z}\cdot\frac{\partial z}{\partial t} = c^2f''(z)$$

$$= c^2f''(ct - x).$$

That is, if
$$\theta = f(ct - x),$$

$$\frac{\partial^2\theta}{\partial t^2} = c^2\frac{\partial^2\theta}{\partial x^2}, \quad \ldots \ldots \quad (2.13)$$

i.e. $\theta = f(ct - x)$ is a solution of the differential equation (2.13).

In an exactly similar way, by starting with

$$\theta = f(ct + x)$$

we should have arrived at the same differential equation. The general solution of the differential equation may be expressed as the sum of the two particular solutions, and we have

$$\theta = f_1(ct - x) + f_2(ct + x) \quad \ldots \ldots \quad (2.14)$$

(where f_1 and f_2 are different arbitrary functions) as the general solution of the equation

$$\frac{\partial^2\theta}{\partial t^2} = c^2\frac{\partial^2\theta}{\partial x^2}.$$

That is, the equation represents two waves, not necessarily similar, travelling in opposite directions with velocity

$$c = \sqrt{\frac{\partial^2\theta/\partial t^2}{\partial^2\theta/\partial x^2}}. \quad \cdots \cdots \quad (2.15)$$

It is obvious that we are here dealing with plane waves in three dimensions. At any given instant t the value of θ depends only on x, so that the wave is travelling along the x-axis and the plane of the wave-front is parallel to the plane $x = 0$.

In general in three dimensions the equation

$$\theta = f(lx + my + nz - ct)$$

represents a plane wave, since θ is the same for a given value of t provided that $lx + my + nz$ is constant, i.e. at all points in the plane whose normal has the direction cosines l, m, n. Distances measured along this normal through the origin take the place of x in the simple formula, and one formula can be obtained from the other by a simple rotation of the axes.

7. Uniform Train of Simple Harmonic Waves.

Obviously we can represent a train of waves moving in a positive direction by giving to the function $f(ct - x)$ the special form

$$a \sin\frac{2\pi}{\lambda}(ct - x).$$

The equation

$$\theta = a \sin\frac{2\pi}{\lambda}(ct - x) = a \sin\left[\frac{2\pi ct}{\lambda} - \frac{2\pi x}{\lambda}\right]$$

then represents waves propagated from left to right.

Let us consider what kind of motion the equation represents.

If we consider the medium *at a given instant*, θ will assume a definite value depending on the instant chosen. We note that it changes with x according to a sine relation and that values of θ repeat themselves periodically at distances λ apart, since every time x increases by λ the quantity in the bracket changes by 2π and the sine has the same value. Let $\theta = \xi$, the displacement due to the wave. The displacements of successive elements of the medium are thus represented at any instant by a sine curve, the cycle of values being repeated in successive lengths λ and the maximum displacements being given by $\xi = a$.

Further, if instead of considering a definite instant of time we fix our attention on a particular point in space and consider how the displacement varies (which is equivalent to giving x a definite value and letting t vary) we see that ξ goes through a series of values lying on a sine curve and repeats its values every time $2\pi ct/\lambda$ increases by 2π. If T is the increment of t which increases the quantity by 2π, then

$$\frac{2\pi c(t+T)}{\lambda} = \frac{2\pi ct}{\lambda} + 2\pi.$$

$$\therefore \frac{2\pi cT}{\lambda} = 2\pi,$$

or $$T = \frac{\lambda}{c}. \qquad \ldots \ldots \ldots \quad (2.16)$$

Each element of the medium describes a simple harmonic vibration of period T and amplitude a.

Since $\lambda = cT$, the equation can be put in other forms:

$$\xi = a \sin \frac{2\pi}{\lambda}(ct - x)$$

$$= a \sin 2\pi \left(\frac{ct}{\lambda} - \frac{x}{\lambda} \right)$$

$$= a \sin 2\pi \left(\frac{t}{T} - \frac{x}{\lambda} \right). \qquad \ldots \ldots \quad (2.17)$$

Again, $$\xi = a \sin \frac{2\pi}{T} \left(t - \frac{xT}{\lambda} \right)$$

$$= a \sin \frac{2\pi}{T} \left(t - \frac{x}{c} \right). \qquad \ldots \ldots \quad (2.18)$$

If $f = 1/T$, i.e. the number of vibrations per second (the frequency), equation (2.16) gives

$$c = f\lambda. \qquad \ldots \ldots \ldots \quad (2.19)$$

It may be convenient to define here some of the most important quantities used in the study of wave motion.

The *amplitude* (a) is primarily the maximum value of the displacement, although it may also be used to indicate the maximum excess or defect of any periodic quantity from its mean value. Thus we have the pressure amplitude, velocity amplitude, &c., in connexion with sound waves.

The *phase* is the stage reached in the cycle of values of displacement, velocity, &c. If t is the time which has elapsed from the beginning of the cycle, $2\pi t/T$ gives the phase. Since $T = 2\pi/\omega$ (p. 41), the phase is also given by ωt.

The phase is also the argument of the cos or sin function, and is thus a function of position and of time. The loci of constant phase are the wave-fronts at any instant.

The *wave-length* (λ) is the distance between successive points in the medium at which the disturbance is in the same phase.

The *wave-number* (N) is the number of waves per unit length, that is, $N\lambda = 1$.

The *period* (T) is the time occupied by one complete cycle.

The *frequency* (f) is the number of cycles completed per second, that is, $fT = 1$.

The constant $2\pi/\lambda$ is useful and is frequently denoted by k. It is equal to the phase change per unit length and is known as the *wave-length constant*.

The quantity $2\pi/T$ is also useful and is denoted by ω. It is known as the *pulsatance* and is equal to $2\pi f$.

If c is the velocity of the wave motion, then we have

$$c = f\lambda, \quad \omega = kc,$$
$$\xi = a\sin k(ct - x)$$
$$= a\sin\omega\!\left(t - \frac{x}{c}\right)$$
$$= a\sin(\omega t - kx). \quad \ldots \ldots \quad (2.20)$$

8. The General Wave Equation and the Velocity of Plane Longitudinal Waves in a Fluid.

Consider a cylindrical volume of the fluid of unit area of cross-section, with its axis in the direction of propagation of the waves. Suppose that the conditions are uniform at each instant across any plane perpendicular to the axis of the cylinder.

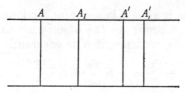

Fig. 2.5.—Longitudinal wave propagation

Take two such planes A and A_1 (fig. 2.5) and let their initial distance apart be δx. Let A' and A_1' be the disturbed positions of the fluid originally at A and A_1. If the displacement of A' is ξ, then the displacement of A_1' will be $\xi + \frac{\partial \xi}{\partial x}\delta x$. The distance apart of the planes has therefore been increased, as a result of their displacement, by

$\frac{\partial \xi}{\partial x} \delta x$. The volume of the enclosed fluid is fractionally increased by $\partial \xi / \partial x$, the " dilatation ".

If we denote by s the condensation, i.e. the increase of density at A' per unit initial density, then remembering that the product of density and volume is constant we have

$$\rho_0 \delta x = \text{mass} = \rho(\delta x + \delta \xi),$$

or
$$(1 + s)\left(1 + \frac{\partial \xi}{\partial x}\right) = 1;$$

if s is small,
$$s = -\frac{\partial \xi}{\partial x}.$$

If p is the increment of pressure required to produce the condensation s and if K is the bulk modulus of elasticity of the fluid, then

$$p = -K \frac{\partial \xi}{\partial x} = Ks.$$

The equation of motion can now be derived. The mass of the displaced element is $\rho_0 \delta x$ and its acceleration $\partial^2 \xi / \partial t^2$. The excess pressure over the normal pressure which is effective at A' is p. At A$_1$' the corresponding quantity is $p + \frac{\partial p}{\partial x} \delta x$, where p, though effective at the displaced co-ordinates, is considered as a function of the undisplaced. The resultant force acting on the cylindrical element of the medium confined between the planes A' and A$_1$' is $-\frac{\partial p}{\partial x}\delta x$. It follows that

$$\rho_0 \frac{\partial^2 \xi}{\partial t^2} = -\frac{\partial p}{\partial x}. \qquad \ldots \ldots \quad (2.21)$$

This equation as it stands is accurate, and we proceed to an approximation which depends on the assumption of a constant value for K. Since $p = Ks$, we have, if K is constant,

$$-\frac{\partial p}{\partial x} = -K \frac{\partial s}{\partial x} = K \frac{\partial^2 \xi}{\partial x^2}.$$

Hence
$$\rho_0 \frac{\partial^2 \xi}{\partial t^2} = K \frac{\partial^2 \xi}{\partial x^2},$$

or
$$\frac{\partial^2 \xi}{\partial t^2} = \frac{K}{\rho_0} \frac{\partial^2 \xi}{\partial x^2}, \qquad \ldots \ldots \ldots \quad (2.22)$$

and this has the general form of the wave equation if $c^2 = K/\rho_0$. The velocity of propagation of the waves is therefore $\sqrt{(K/\rho_0)}$.

A similar equation, involving the particle velocity v at x, instead of the displacement ξ, may be derived as follows (v and s are now to be thought of as localized quantities and strictly do not refer always to the same particles at successive instants). We then have:

(a) Equation of Continuity.

If we consider the flow through an element in time δt we have

Mass entering element across $A = \rho v \, \delta t$.

Mass leaving element across $A_1 = \left[\rho v + \dfrac{\partial}{\partial x}(\rho v)\, \delta x \right] \delta t$.

$\therefore$ Increase in mass of fluid in the element $= -\dfrac{\partial}{\partial x}(\rho v)\, \delta x \, \delta t$.

But increase in mass of fluid $= \delta x \dfrac{\partial \rho}{\partial t} \cdot \delta t$.

Since these are equal we have

$$\frac{\partial \rho}{\partial t} + \frac{\partial}{\partial x}(\rho v) = 0. \quad \ldots \ldots \text{(2.23)}$$

Putting $\qquad\qquad \rho = \rho_0(1 + s)$

and neglecting sv in comparison with v, we have

$$\frac{\partial}{\partial t}[\rho_0(1 + s)] + \frac{\partial}{\partial x}(\rho_0 v) = 0.$$

Hence $\qquad\qquad \dfrac{\partial s}{\partial t} + \dfrac{\partial v}{\partial x} = 0$

and $\qquad\qquad \dfrac{\partial^2 s}{\partial x \partial t} + \dfrac{\partial^2 v}{\partial x^2} = 0. \quad \ldots \ldots \text{(2.24)}$

(b) Dynamical Equation.

Resultant force on the element

$$= p - \left(p + \frac{\partial p}{\partial x}\, \delta x \right)$$

$$= -\frac{\partial p}{\partial x}\, \delta x.$$

Rate of change of momentum (cf. equation 2.29, p. 59)

$$= \rho \, \delta x \left(\frac{\partial v}{\partial t} + v \frac{\partial v}{\partial x} \right)$$

$$\fallingdotseq \rho \frac{\partial v}{\partial t}\, \delta x \quad \text{if} \quad v \ll c.$$

Equating these expressions, we have

$$\frac{\partial p}{\partial x} + \rho \frac{\partial v}{\partial t} = 0. \quad \ldots \ldots \quad (2.25)$$

Substituting Ks for p and differentiating with respect to t we obtain

$$K \frac{\partial^2 s}{\partial x \partial t} + \rho \frac{\partial^2 v}{\partial t^2} = 0. \quad \ldots \ldots \quad (2.26)$$

Comparing this equation with the equation of continuity (2.24), we obtain

$$\frac{\partial^2 v}{\partial t^2} = \frac{K}{\rho} \frac{\partial^2 v}{\partial x^2}. \quad \ldots \ldots \quad (2.27)$$

9. Properties of Plane Waves of Sound.

We can similarly derive a series of equations of the general form

$$\frac{\partial^2 \theta}{\partial t^2} = c^2 \frac{\partial^2 \theta}{\partial x^2},$$

where $\theta = \xi,\ v,\ s,\ \rho,$ or p.

The solution of the equation (cf. 2.14, p. 52) may be written in the form

$$\theta = A f(ct - x) + B F(ct + x)$$

which, as we have seen, represents two wave trains, each of arbitrary form, proceeding in opposite directions with the same velocity c.

Considering only one of these waves we have

$$\theta = A f(ct - x),$$

$$\frac{\partial \theta}{\partial t} = A c f'(ct - x),$$

$$\frac{\partial \theta}{\partial x} = -A f'(ct - x).$$

$$\therefore \frac{\partial \theta}{\partial t} = -c \frac{\partial \theta}{\partial x}.$$

If we take for instance $\theta = \xi$, $v/s = +c$. Similarly for a negatively travelling wave $v/s = -c$, or in general $v/s = \pm c$.

10. Propagation of Sound in Three Dimensions.

Select a small element of volume and let the velocity components be expressed as functions u, v, w, of x, y, z, and time t.

The resultant force acting on the chosen element parallel to the x-axis is $-(\partial p/\partial x)\,\delta x\,\delta y\,\delta z$.

The mass acceleration is $(du/dt)\rho\,\delta x\,\delta y\,\delta z$.

$$\therefore \frac{du}{dt} = -\frac{1}{\rho}\frac{\partial p}{\partial x}, \quad \ldots \ldots \quad (2.28)$$

with similar equations for the other directions.

In this equation du/dt denotes the total derivative of the velocity u in consequence of the lapse of time and also of the change of position of the fluid element, that is,

$$\frac{du}{dt} = \frac{\partial u}{\partial t} + u\frac{\partial u}{\partial x} + v\frac{\partial u}{\partial y} + w\frac{\partial u}{\partial z}. \quad \ldots \quad (2.29)$$

Terms other than the first are negligible if the particle velocity is small compared with the wave velocity c. Equation (2.28) is a result of thinking of u, v, w, as components of a localized vector, and such equations are usually called Eulerian equations. An alternative type of equation associated with the name of Lagrange is that already used in section 8, p. 56, for plane waves, the acceleration appearing simply as $\ddot{\xi}$.

The type of motion here considered is described as " irrotational " and for such motion it is possible to choose a function ϕ of the co-ordinates such that

$$u = -\frac{\partial\phi}{\partial x}, \; v = -\frac{\partial\phi}{\partial y}, \; w = -\frac{\partial\phi}{\partial z}; \quad \ldots \quad (2.30)$$

ϕ is Lagrange's " velocity-potential ".

In such a case equation (2.28) admits of immediate integration, for, taking (2.29) into account, we have

$$-\frac{1}{\rho}\frac{\partial p}{\partial x} = \frac{du}{dt} = -\frac{\partial^2\phi}{\partial t\partial x} + u\frac{\partial u}{\partial x} + v\frac{\partial u}{\partial y} + w\frac{\partial u}{\partial z},$$

with similar equations in y and z, so if ρ is expressed as a function of p we have

$$-\int\frac{dp}{\rho} = -\frac{\partial\phi}{\partial t} + \tfrac{1}{2}(u^2 + v^2 + w^2) - F(t) \quad . \quad (2.31)$$

or

$$\int\frac{dp}{\rho} + \tfrac{1}{2}q^2 - \phi = F(t), \quad \ldots \ldots \quad (2.32)$$

where $F(t)$ is a function of time which, for the moment arbitrary, can be made to vanish by a suitable choice of ϕ. This equation leads readily to the hydrodynamical theorem of Daniel Bernoulli (1700–1782) for steady motion, and was also used by Rayleigh to calculate the acoustic radiation pressure due to a standing wave (see section 7, p. 154).

If the square of the particle velocity q is neglected in the above expression and ρ treated as a constant, then to this degree of approximation

$$\phi = \frac{p}{\rho_0}.$$

But

$$p = Ks,$$

so

$$\phi = c^2 s. \quad \ldots \ldots \ldots \quad (2.33)$$

The equation of continuity as already found for one dimension can easily be extended to three and takes the form

$$\frac{\partial s}{\partial t} + \frac{\partial u}{\partial x} + \frac{\partial v}{\partial y} + \frac{\partial w}{\partial z} = 0,$$

or

$$\frac{\partial s}{\partial t} = \frac{\partial^2 \phi}{\partial x^2} + \frac{\partial^2 \phi}{\partial y^2} + \frac{\partial^2 \phi}{\partial z^2} = \nabla^2 \phi. \quad \ldots \quad (2.34)$$

Comparing this with (2.33), we have

$$\ddot{\phi} - c^2 \nabla^2 \phi = 0. \quad \ldots \ldots \quad (2.35)$$

This is the general form of the equation of wave propagation in three dimensions, with wave velocity c.

If we assume that the waves are spherical and isotropic the motion at any point is along the radius. Taking the radius to be the x-axis we have

$$\dot{\eta} = \dot{\zeta} = 0, \quad u = -\frac{\partial \phi}{\partial r},$$

and, from (2.33),

$$s = +\frac{1}{c^2}\frac{\partial \phi}{\partial t}.$$

Using the relation

$$r^2 = x^2 + y^2 + z^2,$$

we have

$$2r\frac{\partial r}{\partial x} = 2x.$$

$$\therefore \frac{\partial r}{\partial x} = \frac{x}{r}.$$

Hence

$$\frac{\partial \phi}{\partial x} = \frac{\partial \phi}{\partial r}\frac{\partial r}{\partial x} = \frac{x}{r}\frac{\partial \phi}{\partial r},$$

$$\frac{\partial^2 \phi}{\partial x^2} = \frac{1}{r}\frac{\partial \phi}{\partial r} - \frac{x}{r^2}\frac{\partial \phi}{\partial r}\frac{\partial r}{\partial x} + \frac{x}{r}\frac{\partial^2 \phi}{\partial r^2}\frac{\partial r}{\partial x}$$

$$= \frac{\partial^2 \phi}{\partial r^2}\frac{x^2}{r^2} + \frac{\partial \phi}{\partial r}\left(\frac{1}{r} - \frac{x^2}{r^3}\right)$$

$$= \frac{\partial^2 \phi}{\partial r^2}\frac{x^2}{r^2} + \frac{\partial \phi}{\partial r}\frac{y^2 + z^2}{r^3},$$

with similar expressions for $\dfrac{\partial^2 \phi}{\partial y^2}$ and $\dfrac{\partial^2 \phi}{\partial z^2}$.

With these expressions (2.35) gives

$$\frac{\partial^2 \phi}{\partial t^2} = c^2\left(\frac{\partial^2 \phi}{\partial x^2} + \frac{\partial^2 \phi}{\partial y^2} + \frac{\partial^2 \phi}{\partial z^2}\right)$$

$$= c^2\left(\frac{\partial^2 \phi}{\partial r^2} + \frac{2}{r}\frac{\partial \phi}{\partial r}\right)$$

or

$$\frac{\partial^2}{\partial t^2}(r\phi) = c^2\frac{\partial^2}{\partial r^2}(r\phi). \quad \ldots \ldots \quad (2.36)$$

This transformation from cartesian co-ordinates to polar co-ordinates can be deduced at once if we remember that

$$\nabla^2 \phi = \frac{1}{r^2}\frac{\partial}{\partial r}\left(r^2\frac{\partial \phi}{\partial r}\right)$$

$$= \frac{2}{r}\frac{\partial \phi}{\partial r} + \frac{\partial^2 \phi}{\partial r^2}$$

$$= \frac{1}{r}\frac{\partial^2}{\partial r^2}(r\phi).$$

The complete integral of this may be written in the form

$$\phi = \frac{1}{r}\left[F(ct + r) + f(ct - r)\right]. \quad \ldots \quad (2.37)$$

where F and f are arbitrary functions depending only on $(ct + r)$ and $(ct - r)$.

The function F is such that if t increases by δt and r diminishes by $c\delta t$ its value is unchanged. It must therefore represent a converging wave. Similarly f represents a diverging wave.

Confining our attention to the diverging wave, we have

$$u = \dot{\xi} = -\frac{\partial \phi}{\partial r} = \frac{1}{r^2}f(ct - r) + \frac{1}{r}f'(ct - r), \quad . \quad (2.38)$$

$$s = \frac{1}{c^2}\frac{\partial \phi}{\partial t} = \frac{1}{cr}f'(ct - r). \quad . \quad . \quad . \quad (2.39)$$

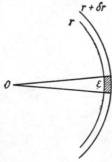

Fig. 2.6.—Diverging waves

These formulæ may be deduced directly by considering the propagation of spherical waves from a point source.

Let O be a source of wave motion in a fluid, say a small pulsating sphere. Consider two concentric spheres with centres at O and radii of r and $r + \delta r$ respectively, and a small area ϵ (fig. 2.6), traced out on the surface of the inner sphere. If radii are drawn to meet the perimeter of this area and produced to cut the second sphere they will define an element on its surface which will have an area

$$\epsilon' = \epsilon\frac{(r + \delta r)^2}{r^2} = \epsilon\left(1 + \frac{2\delta r}{r}\right) \doteqdot \epsilon.$$

Now if we consider the portion of the medium bounded by the cone and the two spheres the force acting over its outer face is

$$-\epsilon\left[P_0 + Ks + \frac{\partial}{\partial r}(P_0 + Ks)\delta r\right],$$

where P_0 is the undisturbed static pressure, s the condensation, and K the appropriate volume elasticity. That is, the force is

$$-\epsilon\left(P_0 + Ks + K\frac{\partial s}{\partial r}\delta r\right).$$

Similarly, the force over the inner face is

$$\epsilon(P_0 + Ks).$$

Hence the resultant force is $-\epsilon K\dfrac{\partial s}{\partial r}\delta r$. The mass of fluid is $\rho\epsilon\,\delta r$;

$$\therefore \; \rho\epsilon\,\delta r \cdot \frac{\partial^2 \xi}{\partial t^2} = -\epsilon K\frac{\partial s}{\partial r}\delta r,$$

where ξ is the radial displacement;

hence

$$\frac{\partial^2 \xi}{\partial t^2} = -\frac{K}{\rho}\frac{\partial s}{\partial r}. \quad . \quad . \quad . \quad . \quad (2.40)$$

In order to find s we may note that the initial volume of the air enclosed between the two complete spheres of radii r and $r + \delta r$ is $4\pi r^2 \, \delta r$.

The volume after displacement of the inner sphere by ξ and the outer by $\xi + \delta \xi$ becomes

$$4\pi(r + \xi)^2\Big(\delta r + \frac{\partial \xi}{\partial r}\delta r\Big).$$

$\therefore$ Change of volume $= 4\pi r^2 \delta r \Big(\dfrac{\partial \xi}{\partial r} + \dfrac{2\xi}{r}\Big).$

Hence
$$s = -\frac{dV}{V} = -\Big(\frac{\partial \xi}{\partial r} + \frac{2\xi}{r}\Big). \quad \ldots \ldots \quad (2.41)$$

Putting $c^2 = K/\rho$ and substituting for s in (2.40), we have

$$\frac{\partial^2 \xi}{\partial t^2} = c^2 \frac{\partial}{\partial r}\Big(\frac{\partial \xi}{\partial r} + \frac{2\xi}{r}\Big). \quad \ldots \ldots \quad (2.42)$$

If r is very large, $2\xi/r$ becomes negligible and the equation reduces to

$$\frac{\partial^2 \xi}{\partial t^2} = c^2 \frac{\partial^2 \xi}{\partial r^2},$$

which we recognize as the equation for plane waves with velocity c.

Where r is not very large,

$$\frac{\partial^2 \xi}{\partial t^2} = c^2\Big(\frac{\partial^2 \xi}{\partial r^2} + \frac{2}{r}\cdot\frac{\partial \xi}{\partial r} - \frac{2\xi}{r^2}\Big). \quad \ldots \ldots \quad (2.43)$$

The general solution of this equation is

$$\xi = \frac{1}{r}F_1{}'(ct - r) + \frac{1}{r^2}F_1(ct - r)$$

$$+ \frac{1}{r}F_2{}'(ct + r) - \frac{1}{r^2}F_2(ct + r), \quad . \quad (2.44)$$

where F_1 and F_2 stand for arbitrary functions.

Obviously the first pair of terms of the right-hand member of the equation represent a diverging wave and the second pair of terms a converging wave.

Confining our attention for the moment to the diverging waves, we have

$$\xi = \frac{1}{r}F_1{}'(ct - r) + \frac{1}{r^2}F_1(ct - r).$$

Hence $\qquad \dot{\xi} = u = \frac{c}{r} F_1''(ct - r) + \frac{c}{r^2} F_1'(ct - r),$

$$s = -\left(\frac{\partial \xi}{\partial r} + \frac{2\xi}{r}\right) = \frac{1}{r} F_1''(ct - r).$$

These expressions for $\dot{\xi}$ and s are identical with those deduced by the velocity-potential method if we put

$$cF_1'(ct - r) = f(ct - r) = r\phi.$$

We then have, as in (2.38), p. 62,

$$u = \frac{1}{r^2} f(ct - r) + \frac{1}{r} f'(ct - r) = -\frac{\partial \phi}{\partial r}, \quad . \quad . \quad (2.45)$$

and, as in (2.39),

$$s = \frac{1}{cr} f'(ct - r) = \frac{1}{c^2} \frac{\partial \phi}{\partial t}. \quad . \quad . \quad . \quad (2.46)$$

Ignoring the converging wave, suppose the disturbance at time $t = 0$ to be confined between two spheres of radii r_1 and r_2. Then all values of the function $F(ct - r)$ and its derivatives are zero outside the limits fixed by r_1 and r_2. At any time t and for any radius r', the quantity $F(ct - r')$ and its derivatives vanish unless $ct - r'$ lies between the same limits, $-r_1$ and $-r_2$, as before. The movement is therefore confined between two spheres of radii r_1' and r_2' such that

$$ct - r_1' = -r_1, \quad ct - r_2' = -r_2,$$

that is, $\qquad\qquad r_1' = ct + r_1, \quad r_2' = ct + r_2,$

and $\qquad\qquad r_2' - r_1' = r_2 - r_1.$

Hence the limits of the wave move with velocity c. In this sense the velocity of plane waves and spherical waves is the same.

The difference in propagation appears if we compare the conditions fulfilled in plane wave propagation with those obtaining for spherical waves. For plane waves:

(1) $u/s = \pm c.$

(2) The disturbances move without change and so that each element of the medium exactly reproduces the movement of any other previously reached by the wave.

For spherical waves these conditions no longer hold:

(1) $\qquad \dfrac{u}{s} = c\left[1 + \dfrac{1}{r}\dfrac{f(ct - r)}{f'(ct - r)}\right]$, from (2.45) and (2.46).

Therefore the ratio u/s attains the value c only when r is large, and for diminishing values of r it increases without limit.

(2) So far as s is concerned its propagation follows the laws for plane waves. It travels with velocity c and is only subject to variation with the factor r.

The case of u is entirely different:

$$u - \frac{1}{r^2} f(ct - r) + \frac{1}{r} f'(ct - r),$$

and the two terms differ by a factor $1/r$, so that near the source

$$u = \frac{1}{r^2} f(ct - r),$$

whereas in regions remote from the source

$$u = \frac{1}{r} f'(ct - r).$$

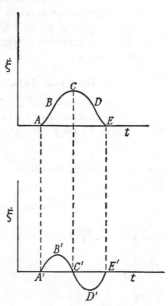

Fig. 2.7.—Variation of $\dot{\xi}$ with distance

Apart from the factors $1/r$, $1/r^2$, these two expressions are related so that the second is the first differential of the first with respect to $ct - r$. The disturbance must therefore be modified in quite a profound way, depending on the nature of the function $f(ct - r)$.

Let the displacement curve for a point near the origin be given by ABCDE (fig. 2.7), the curve giving u against time. The displacement curve at a distant point will have the form A'B'C'D'E', where $AE = A'E'$. That is, a disturbance giving velocities all in the same direction is transformed into one having velocities successively in each direction.

It can be shown that the area between the curve A'B'C'D'E' and the axis is zero.

If we consider a limited wave and a point in the medium where v and s only differ from zero between the times t_1 and t_2, then since

$$u = \frac{1}{r^2} f(ct - r) + \frac{1}{r} f'(ct - r),$$

$$s = \frac{1}{cr} f'(ct - r),$$

it follows that $f(ct - r)$ and $f'(ct - r)$ differ from zero only between these limits of time.

Since the integral $\int_{t_1}^{t_2} f'(ct - r)dt = 0$, we have

$$\int_{t_1}^{t_2} s\, dt = 0,$$

and for large values of r $\int_{t_1}^{t_2} u\, dt = 0.$

It follows that the mean value of s at any point is zero. Therefore, the disturbance must be half compression and half condensation—no other distribution is possible.

Also at great distances u has a zero mean value, a limitation which does not apply to plane waves. At great distances from the source there is no permanent displacement as a result of a limited spherical disturbance.

11. Simple Harmonic Spherical Waves.

Let us suppose that waves are being generated by the pulsation of a very small sphere of radius r_0; for any point on the surface of this sphere we may assume

$$\xi = a \sin \omega t.$$

As the equation to the waves let us take the divergent wave from (2.44), namely,

$$\xi = \frac{1}{r^2} F_1(ct - r) + \frac{1}{r} F_1{}'(ct - r)$$

and put $F_1(ct - r) = A \sin(\omega t - kr),$

where $k = \dfrac{2\pi}{\lambda}.$

Then $F_1{}'(ct - r) = Ak \cos(\omega t - kr).$

$$\therefore \xi = \frac{A}{r^2} \sin(\omega t - kr) + \frac{kA}{r} \cos(\omega t - kr). \quad (2.47)$$

If r is very small the second term is negligible. Putting $r = r_0$, where r_0 is small compared with λ, we have

$$\xi = \frac{A}{r_0{}^2} \sin \omega t.$$

$$\therefore A = a r_0{}^2.$$

$$\therefore \xi = \frac{a r_0{}^2}{r^2} \sin(\omega t - kr) + \frac{k a r_0{}^2}{r} \cos(\omega t - kr). \quad (2.48)$$

If the particle velocity is u, then

$$u = \dot{\xi} = \omega a r_0^2 \left[\frac{1}{r^2} \cos(\omega t - kr) - \frac{k}{r} \sin(\omega t - kr) \right], \quad (2.49)$$

and $\quad s = -\left(\frac{\partial \xi}{\partial r} + \frac{2\xi}{r} \right)$ from (2.41), p. 63,

$$= -\frac{k^2 a r_0^2}{r} \sin(\omega t - kr). \quad \ldots \quad (2.50)$$

Put $\qquad \dfrac{a r_0^2}{r^2} = B \cos h$

and $\qquad \dfrac{k a r_0^2}{r} = B \sin h.$

Then $\qquad B^2 = \dfrac{a^2 r_0^4}{r^4} + \dfrac{k^2 a^2 r_0^4}{r^2},$

$$\tan h = kr,$$

and $\qquad \xi = B \sin(\omega t - kr + h). \quad \ldots \quad (2.51)$

If r is small compared with $\lambda/2\pi$, then $k^2 r^2$ is small.

Writing $\qquad B^2 = \left(\dfrac{a r_0^2}{r^2} \right)^2 (1 + k^2 r^2),$

we have $\qquad B \doteqdot \dfrac{a r_0^2}{r^2} \left(1 + \dfrac{k^2 r^2}{2} \right) \doteqdot \dfrac{a r_0^2}{r^2},$

and $\qquad \tan h \doteqdot 0,$

$$\therefore \ h \doteqdot 0.$$

$$\therefore \ \xi = \dfrac{a r_0^2}{r^2} \sin(\omega t - kr).$$

The phase is calculable as for plane waves and the amplitude varies inversely as the square of the distance. This might suggest that the inverse square law for energy does not hold.

In the case of plane waves the transfer of energy is such that the whole energy distributed over a plane perpendicular to the direction of propagation may be regarded as carried forward bodily with the velocity of the wave and distributed over the same area of another plane more remote from the source. In the case of a vibrating body, however, only a fraction of its energy at any instant is being communicated to the air. All that we can immediately say about spherical harmonic waves is that the energy being propagated must obey the inverse square law if there is to be no accumulation, i.e. the energy passing through a sphere of radius r in any time must be independent of r.

In order to introduce a volume of gas δv at a point in the medium where the pressure is p an amount of work is required given by $p\delta v$. It follows that the energy transmitted across a sphere of radius r in time δt is

$$\delta W = p \,.\, 4\pi r^2 \, u \, \delta t.$$

But
$$p = P_0 + Ks,$$

where P_0 is the undisturbed pressure, s the condensation, and K the volume elasticity (p. 56);

$$\therefore \;\; \delta W = 4\pi r^2 (P_0 + Ks) \, u \, \delta t.$$

During one complete period the energy transmitted is given by

$$W = 4\pi r^2 \int_t^{t+T} (P_0 + Ks) \, u \, dt$$

$$= 4\pi r^2 K \int_t^{t+T} su \, dt,$$

since
$$\int_t^{t+T} u \, dt = 0.$$

But from (2.49) and (2.50) we have

$$u = \dot{\xi} = \omega a r_0^2 \left[\frac{1}{r^2} \cos(\omega t - kr) - \frac{k}{r} \sin(\omega t - kr) \right], \quad (2.52)$$

and
$$s = -\frac{k^2 a r_0^2}{r} \sin(\omega t - kr);$$

$$\therefore \; W = 4\pi r^2 K \left\{ \frac{k^3 \omega a^2 r_0^4}{2r^2} \int_t^{t+T} [1 - \cos 2(\omega t - kr)]dt \right.$$

$$\left. - \frac{k^2 \omega a^2 r_0^4}{2r^3} \int_t^{t+T} \sin 2(\omega t - kr)dt \right\}$$

$$= \frac{32\pi^5 K a^2 r_0^4}{\lambda^3}. \quad \cdot \quad \cdot \quad \cdot \quad \cdot \quad \cdot \quad \cdot \quad \cdot \quad \cdot \quad \cdot \quad \cdot \quad (2.53)$$

This is independent of r, and therefore the energy propagated per period is the same across all spheres described about the source, and the inverse square law for the propagation of energy holds. The result may be seen to be a consequence of the fact that the term containing $1/r^2$ in the expression for v shows a difference of phase of $\pi/2$ with s and so is eliminated in the expression for W. For a single pulse the integral $\int s u \, dt$ is the sum of two terms, and the term in $1/r^3$ vanishes, provided that the limits of the integration include the boundaries of the pulse. Hence in this case also * the total energy transmitted is independent of r.

Thus the source may be regarded as surrounded by an atmosphere in energetic vibration, only a fraction of this energy being transmitted to the more distant layers of air—a fraction which diminishes as the ratio of the wave-length to the dimensions of the source increases. This result was arrived at by Stokes † from a more general discussion. It explains the feeble communication of energy to the air from a vibrating string or tuning-fork.

It is also verified by an experiment due to Leslie ‡. Leslie placed a bell under the receiver of an air pump and exhausted the receiver until the bell was just audible. Hydrogen was now admitted to the receiver and the sound became entirely inaudible.

Putting $\lambda = cT$ and $K = \gamma P_0$ in the expression for the energy transmitted across any sphere per period, we have

$$W = \frac{4\pi^2\omega^3 P_0 \gamma a^2 r_0{}^4}{c^3}.$$

For the same source the numerator varies little for different gases. For hydrogen, however, c^3 is about 55 times as great as for air, so that at the same pressure and for the same source the propagation of energy is very much less in hydrogen than in air and is considerably less in hydrogen at normal pressure than in air at $1/20$ of this pressure.

This discussion applies of course to a continuous train of waves. The single wave is also treated by Gouy in the paper referred to.

If r is large compared with $1/k$, then kr is large and we may put

$$B^2 = \frac{k^2 a^2 r_0{}^4}{r^2}\left(1 + \frac{1}{k^2 r^2}\right).$$

Then
$$B \doteqdot \frac{kar_0{}^2}{r}\left(1 + \frac{1}{2k^2 r^2}\right)$$

$$\doteqdot \frac{kar_0{}^2}{r},$$

$$\tan h = kr \to \infty,$$

$$\therefore h = \pi/2.$$

Hence
$$\xi = \frac{kar_0{}^2}{r}\sin[\omega t - k(r - \lambda/4)]. \quad . \quad . \quad . \quad (2.54)$$

---

* Gouy, *Ann. de Chimie et de Physique*, Ser. VI, Vol. 24 (1891).
† *Phil. Trans.*, Vol. 158, p. 447 (1868).
‡ Rayleigh, *Theory of Sound*, Vol. 2, § 324.

Here we have a wave in which

(1) The amplitude depends on k and therefore on λ.
(2) The amplitude varies inversely as r.
(3) The phase is $\frac{1}{4}$ period in advance of that calculated as for plane waves.

If we put ρ for the radius of the sphere for which

$$u = \dot{\xi} = 0,$$

then, from (2.52), $\dfrac{ar_0^2}{\rho^2} \cos(\omega t - k\rho) - \dfrac{kar_0^2}{\rho} \sin(\omega t - k\rho) = 0.$

$$\therefore \cot(\omega t - k\rho) = k\rho.$$

$$\therefore \operatorname{cosec}^2(\omega t - k\rho)\left(\omega - k\frac{d\rho}{dt}\right) = -k\frac{d\rho}{dt},$$

$$(1 + k^2\rho^2)\left(c - \frac{d\rho}{dt}\right) = -\frac{d\rho}{dt},$$

or
$$\frac{d\rho}{dt} = c\left(1 + \frac{1}{k^2\rho^2}\right). \qquad (2.55)$$

Now $d\rho/dt$ is the rate of propagation of the wave-front for which $u = 0$.

Therefore $d\rho/dt$ is always greater than c and only approaches c as a limit when ρ is large compared with λ.

If $\dfrac{\lambda}{\rho} = 100$, $\dfrac{1}{k^2\rho^2} = \left(\dfrac{\lambda}{2\pi\rho}\right)^2 = \dfrac{10,000}{40} = 250$, approximately.

If $\dfrac{\lambda}{\rho} = 1$, then $\left(\dfrac{\lambda}{2\pi\rho}\right)^2 = \dfrac{1}{40}$, approximately.

12. Waves of Finite Amplitude.

It may be noted that the bulk modulus K is constant only for infinitesimal volume changes;

$$K = -v\frac{dp}{dv}, \text{ where } v \text{ is the volume.}$$

Let
$$A = v\rho, \text{ where } A \text{ is a constant.}$$

$$\therefore 0 = v\frac{d\rho}{dp} + \rho\frac{dv}{dp}.$$

$$\therefore K = -v\frac{dp}{dv} = \rho\frac{dp}{d\rho}.$$

$$\therefore c = \sqrt{\frac{dp}{d\rho}}. \qquad \cdots \cdots \cdots \quad (2.56)$$

Now as the changes in volume are adiabatic we have

$$p = A'\rho^\gamma, \text{ where } A' \text{ is a constant,}$$

$$\therefore \frac{dp}{d\rho} = \gamma A'\rho^{\gamma-1}, \text{ and increases with } \rho \text{ (fig. 2.8)}.$$

The velocity in all parts of a wave, then, can be considered constant only so long as the density changes are very small. It follows from this that

(a) intense waves will have an abnormally high velocity;

(b) the velocity will vary for different parts of the wave, being greater for the compression than for the rarefaction. Thus if the density changes are large the waves cannot be propagated without change of form.

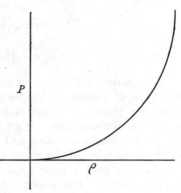

Fig. 2.8

In order to reach some appreciation of the magnitude of the effect we may start with the dynamical relation

$$\rho_0 \, \delta x \, \frac{\partial^2 \xi}{\partial t^2} = -\frac{\partial p}{\partial x} \, \delta x,$$

or

$$\frac{\partial^2 \xi}{\partial t^2} = -\frac{1}{\rho_0} \frac{\partial p}{\partial x}.$$

But

$$\frac{p}{P_0} = \left(\frac{\rho}{\rho_0}\right)^\gamma, \text{ where } P_0 \text{ is the undisturbed pressure,}$$

and

$$\frac{\rho}{\rho_0} = \frac{v_0}{v} = \left(1 + \frac{\partial \xi}{\partial x}\right)^{-1}.$$

$$\therefore p = P_0\left(1 + \frac{\partial \xi}{\partial x}\right)^{-\gamma}.$$

$$\therefore \frac{\partial p}{\partial x} = -\gamma P_0\left(1 + \frac{\partial \xi}{\partial x}\right)^{-(\gamma+1)} \frac{\partial^2 \xi}{\partial x^2}.$$

$$\therefore \frac{\partial^2 \xi}{\partial t^2} = \frac{\gamma P_0}{\rho_0}\left(1 + \frac{\partial \xi}{\partial x}\right)^{-(\gamma+1)} \frac{\partial^2 \xi}{\partial x^2}. \quad \cdots \quad (2.57)$$

This corresponds to plane waves travelling with velocity c given by

$$c^2 = \frac{\gamma P_0}{\rho_0} \left(1 + \frac{\partial \xi}{\partial x} \right)^{-(\gamma+1)} \quad . \quad . \quad . \quad . \quad (2.58)$$

If $\partial \xi / \partial x$ is small,

$$c^2 = \frac{\gamma P_0}{\rho_0} = c_0{}^2.$$

If $\partial \xi / \partial x$ is not small,

$$c = c_0 \left(1 + \frac{\partial \xi}{\partial x} \right)^{-(\gamma+1)/2}$$

$$= c_0 (1 + s)^{(\gamma+1)/2} \quad . \quad . \quad . \quad . \quad . \quad (2.59)$$

This involves different velocities in different parts of the wave. The type of the wave changes as it advances, the pressure gradient becoming steeper in front and more gradual behind. This would lead to an infinite pressure gradient at the wave-front, after which the wave must break down and re-form. The process is held in check by the divergence of the waves and by dissipation.

There is here a close analogy with water waves approaching a shelving beach. The velocity of the wave varies with the depth of the water. This is also true of the parts of the wave, and in shallow water the differences in depth between crest and trough are so considerable as to cause rapid changes in the form of the waves. The crests overtake the troughs and fall into them, after which the wave is reorganized and goes on, perhaps to repeat the process.

It ought to be borne in mind that an amplitude which is finite (in the sense with which we are now concerned) for one wave-length may be treated as infinitesimal for another and longer wave-length. It is the condensation that matters.

Now if $\qquad \xi = a \sin (\omega t - kx)$,

$$\frac{\partial \xi}{\partial x} = -ka \cos (\omega t - kx).$$

Let $\hat{s}$ be the maximum value of s.

Then $\qquad \hat{s} = \left(-\frac{\partial \xi}{\partial x} \right)_{\text{max.}} = ka = \frac{2\pi a}{\lambda} = \frac{2\pi af}{c}.$

We can obtain some idea of the abnormally high velocity in a compression if we take the figures for the minimum audible intensity of a sound wave of frequency 2000 and for the maximum audible intensity.

For the minimum audible intensity the amplitude is about 2×10^{-9} cm.

$$\therefore \hat{s} = \frac{2\pi fa}{c} = \frac{8\pi \times 10^{-6}}{33,000} \doteqdot 8 \times 10^{-10}.$$

For the maximum audible intensity the amplitude is about 4×10^{-3} cm.

$$\therefore \hat{s} = \frac{16\pi}{33,000} \doteqdot 1 \cdot 5 \times 10^{-3}.$$

It is obvious that in the first case the effect on the velocity will be negligible, but in the second case we shall have

$$c = c_0(1 + \hat{s})^{\frac{\gamma+1}{2}},$$

$$= c_0(1 \cdot 0015)^{1 \cdot 2}, \quad \text{since } \gamma = 1 \cdot 4,$$

$$= c_0(1 \cdot 0018).$$

In this case the velocity is increased by about 2 parts in 1000.

It is obvious that as $\hat{s}$ includes the product $f \cdot a$ we can form no judgment of the amplitude which is permissible for a wave of constant type unless we take the frequency into account. What is permissible for a wave of frequency 100 would cause rapid change of type in a wave of frequency 100,000.

13. Plane Longitudinal Waves in an Infinite Solid.

The propagation of these waves is not of much practical importance, except in connexion with earthquakes. If we consider a cylindrical element of material with its axis perpendicular to the wave-front, we shall see that the problem of longitudinal wave propagation is the same as that of the extension and contraction of a rod to the sides of which stresses are applied in order to keep its area of cross-section constant. Let q' be the appropriate modulus of elasticity. Then when the extension of the bar per unit length is e and the longitudinal stress per unit area of cross-section is X we have $q' = X/e$.

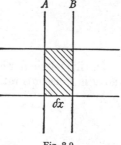

Fig. 2.9

Consider the case of a cylindrical volume of material whose axis is perpendicular to the wave-front. Let the area of cross-section of the cylinder be A and the density of the material ρ. Just as in the case of transmission of waves in a fluid, the change in length per unit length at any point is $\partial\xi/\partial x$, where ξ is the displacement in the direction of propagation. Consider the volume of material lying between two planes A, B, separated by a distance δx (fig. 2.9).

If X is the stress acting across the plane at A, then

$$q' = \frac{X}{\partial\xi/\partial x}.$$

$$\therefore X = q'\frac{\partial\xi}{\partial x}.$$

Thus for unit area, the force acting across A is

$$X = q'\frac{\partial\xi}{\partial x}.$$

Similarly, the force acting across B is given by

$$q'\frac{\partial\xi}{\partial x} + \frac{\partial}{\partial x}\left(q'\frac{\partial\xi}{\partial x}\right)\delta x = q'\left(\frac{\partial\xi}{\partial x} + \frac{\partial^2\xi}{\partial x^2}\delta x\right).$$

Therefore the resultant force acting on the element between the planes is

$$q'\frac{\partial^2\xi}{\partial x^2}\delta x.$$

Mass of element $= \rho\,\delta x$

$$\therefore \rho\delta x\,\frac{\partial^2\xi}{\partial t^2} = q'\,\frac{\partial^2\xi}{\partial x^2}\,\delta x,$$

or

$$\frac{\partial^2\xi}{\partial t^2} = \frac{q'}{\rho}\frac{\partial^2\xi}{\partial x^2}. \quad \ldots \ldots \quad (2.60)$$

$$\therefore c^2 = \frac{q'}{\rho}. \quad \ldots \ldots \ldots \quad (2.61)$$

In this particular case it may be shown* that if q is Young's modulus and σ is Poisson's ratio

$$q' = \frac{q(1-\sigma)}{(1-\sigma-2\sigma^2)}.$$

$$\therefore c = \sqrt{\frac{q'}{\rho}} = \sqrt{\frac{q(1-\sigma)}{\rho(1+\sigma)(1-2\sigma)}}. \quad \ldots \quad (2.62)$$

---

* Champion and Davy, *Properties of Matter*, p. 87 (Blackie & Son, Ltd., 1936).

14. Velocity of Longitudinal Waves in a Rod.

The only case in which the velocity of sound in solids is of much practical importance is the case of propagation in a rod.

If we assume the rod (fig. 2.10) to have density ρ, area of cross-section A and Young's modulus q, then, choosing two planes perpendicular to the length of the rod and initially at distances from the origin x and $x + \delta x$, we suppose them displaced by amounts ξ and $\xi + \delta\xi$ respectively.

The new distance between the planes $= \delta x + \delta\xi = \delta x + \dfrac{\partial\xi}{\partial x}\delta x.$

$\therefore$ Increase of distance $= \dfrac{\partial\xi}{\partial x}\delta x.$

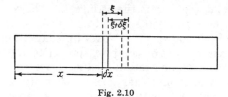

Fig. 2.10

$\therefore$ Extension of bar per unit length at this point $= \partial\xi/\partial x$. If P is the force acting on the element across the first face,

$$q = \frac{P/A}{\partial\xi/\partial x}.$$

$$\therefore P = qA\frac{\partial\xi}{\partial x}.$$

The force acting across the second face of the element is

$$qA\frac{\partial\xi}{\partial x} + \frac{\partial}{\partial x}\left(qA\frac{\partial\xi}{\partial x}\right)\delta x = qA\frac{\partial\xi}{\partial x} + qA\frac{\partial^2\xi}{\partial x^2}\delta x.$$

Therefore the resultant force acting on the element is

$$qA\frac{\partial^2\xi}{\partial x^2}\delta x.$$

But the mass of the element is $A\rho\delta x$ and its acceleration is $\partial^2\xi/\partial t^2$. Therefore

$$A\rho\delta x\frac{\partial^2\xi}{dt^2} = qA\frac{\partial^2\xi}{\partial x^2}\delta x$$

and velocity of propagation $= \sqrt{q/\rho}.$ . . . . . . (2.63)

CHAPTER III

Forced Vibration

1. Forced Vibration and Resonance.

Resonance in the narrower sense of the term is the response of an instrument capable of emitting a particular note when this note is sounded by some other means. If a key on a piano is depressed so as to remove the damper from the strings, and the corresponding note is loudly sung, the piano will respond and give out the note. Stories are told of the breaking of glass vases by singers able to produce a very pure and intense note of the pitch proper to the vase. Bouasse* regards this phenomenon as established by the multitude of witnesses who have testified to it, and then goes on to quote the Talmud to the following effect, although without giving a reference. "It has been said by Ramé, son of Jécheskel: when a cock shall have stretched his neck in the interior of a glass vase and shall have crowed therein in such a manner as to break it, the whole cost shall be payable." It seems difficult to believe that legislation should be designed to cover a situation that had never arisen, although Bouasse admits that he had reared a large number of cocks, none of which had acquired a habit of breaking glass vases.

The phenomenon has of course many applications in other spheres than that of acoustics, and we shall first of all consider it in its wider aspects. Most vibrating systems have several possible modes of vibration, and if disturbed and left to themselves they will, as a rule, oscillate in one of these modes or in a combination of several of them with an amplitude which gradually diminishes. If, for example, we displace a pendulum, strike a tuning-fork, or pluck a stretched string, we have this kind of vibration. It is called *free vibration*. The period is one of the natural or free periods of the system. The gradual decay of amplitude, which is known as damping, is due to the gradual dissipation of the energy communicated in the initial displacement, this energy being used up in overcoming the frictional resistances to the motion.

It is possible to subject the vibrating system to the action of a periodic force. In this case it is said to be in a state of *forced vibration*. Its amplitude of vibration is, as a rule, small and its period of vibration

* *Acoustique Générale*, p. 157 (Delagrave, Paris, 1926).

is exactly that of the force. For example, take an empty bottle and, by blowing across the top of it so as to elicit its proper note in free vibration, tune it by pouring in water until the note of the bottle differs by about a semitone from the note of a particular tuning-fork. Now strike the tuning-fork and hold it over the neck of the bottle. The air in the bottle is set in vibration and a faint sound is heard which has the pitch of the fork—not that of the free vibration of the air in the bottle.

The term forced vibration should be reserved for cases where the responding system does not by its reaction modify the periodic force. Where this reaction is not negligible we are really dealing with a coupled system, a case to which reference will be made later (p. 401).

Fig. 3.1.—Unbalanced gyro-wheel with vibrating springs attached to frame

Resonance is a special case of forced vibration. When the period of the force coincides with the natural frequency of the vibrating system the amplitude of the forced vibration may become very large indeed. It is for this reason that troops are instructed to break step when crossing a bridge. There is a danger that the time of the tread should just happen to coincide with the natural period corresponding to one of the modes of vibration of the bridge. A very beautiful illustration of forced vibration and resonance is afforded by an unbalanced gyroscope to the frame of which is attached a series of springs of different lengths (fig. 3.1). Setting the gyro wheel in rapid rotation, and placing the instrument so that the images of the ends of the springs can be projected on to the screen, we notice that at first none of the springs shows marked vibration. They are all forced to vibrate with a frequency too high for their natural frequency and their response is small. As the speed of rotation of the wheel diminishes, however, the vibration which it communicates to the frame falls in frequency and presently coincides with the natural frequency of the shortest spring. This immediately takes up a vibration of large amplitude.

Presently the second shortest spring vibrates with increased amplitude while the vibration of the shortest dies away, and so on, each spring responding in turn with maximum amplitude when the frequency of vibration of the frame is close to its own natural frequency.

If the periodic force is sinusoidal—i.e. if it is a sine function of the time—then it can induce resonance only in a system which has one of its free periods the same. Thus it may excite a partial (p. 335) of the vibrating system. This partial, however, will have the period of the force. The force cannot excite resonance in a system having a period half, a third, a quarter, &c., of its own period. On the other hand, if the force is not strictly simple harmonic, it can be analysed into a series of simple harmonic components, and any one of these will be effective as a periodic force applied to the responding system. On this fact depends the possibility of distortion in the transmission of acoustic (or electric) vibrations. If natural frequencies of the responding (or transmitting) system lie close to frequencies of the harmonic components into which the original vibration can be analysed, then the components are selectively treated and the result is a vibration quite different in form from the original. The distortion of a complex sound by transmission through a horn having natural frequencies in the range covered by the components of the sound is a case in point.

One very important matter in connexion with resonance is what has been called the sharpness of resonance. If we take a bottle tuned to a particular frequency and hold a series of tuning-forks successively opposite its mouth, we shall find that it responds not merely to the fork which is in tune with its natural frequency, but to forks differing in pitch from this by a tone or more. On the other hand, in the case of two tuning-forks, where resonance is very marked when the forks are correctly tuned, the slightest mistuning—a tenth of a tone or less—makes the response almost negligible. Thus we find, in the case of the bottle, a response to all neighbouring pitches without very marked response to any, and in the case of the forks a highly selective action involving very marked response for correct tuning, and almost no response for quite small differences in pitch from the correct value.

This difference is bound up with the damping of the system, i.e. the rate at which its free vibrations die out when it is disturbed and left to itself. In the case of the bottle we can produce a tone by blowing across the neck, but the tone ceases almost at the instant at which the air blast is stopped. On the other hand, in the case of the fork we start the free vibrations by plucking or bowing the prongs, and the sound persists for quite a long time afterwards. A system which is highly damped is one which has a broad continuous spectrum of natural frequencies, and it is only to be expected that resonance should occur for the whole range of frequencies present in the free vibrations.

Further reference to this will be made in connexion with the analysis of sounds (Chapter XIII).

For the sake of completeness it is necessary at this point to refer also to the "transient" vibrations called out in the early stages of the action of a periodic force on a vibrating system. These transient vibrations are damped free vibrations of the system and consequently have one of the free periods of the system; they may be neglected in considering the steady motion finally reached.

2. Analytical Discussion of Forced Vibration and Resonance.

The most important practical case is that in which a system capable of resisted simple harmonic motion is subjected to a force varying harmonically.

Let $2\pi/\omega$ be the free period of the system, and $2r$ the resisting force per unit mass per unit velocity; then the equation for the free resisted motion is

$$\ddot{x} + 2r\dot{x} + \omega^2 x = 0. \quad \ldots \quad (3.1)$$

If now the system is subject to a periodic force of maximum value F per unit mass and of period $2\pi/n$, the equation of motion is

$$\ddot{x} + 2r\dot{x} + \omega^2 x = F \sin nt. \quad \ldots \quad (3.2)$$

The solution of (3.1) has already (equation 2.9, p. 48) been shown to be of the form

$$x = be^{-rt} \cos(\sqrt{\omega^2 - r^2} \cdot t - \epsilon). \quad \ldots \quad (3.3)$$

This is the complementary function of equation (3.2) and the complete solution is the sum of this function and a particular integral.

If we use the symbol D for the operation d/dt, in many algebraic transformations D can be treated as an ordinary algebraic quantity.*

That is, we have $\qquad Dx = \dfrac{dx}{dt}, \ D^2 x = \dfrac{d^2 x}{dt^2};$

and $\qquad D^2 \sin nt = \dfrac{d^2}{dt^2}(\sin nt) = -n^2 \sin nt,$

$$\therefore \ \psi(D^2) \sin nt = \psi(-n^2) \sin nt,$$

where ψ represents any polynomial function.

The equation $\qquad \ddot{x} + 2r\dot{x} + \omega^2 x = F \sin nt$

becomes $\qquad (D^2 + 2rD + \omega^2)x = F \sin nt,$

---

* See Piaggio, *Differential Equations*, p. 30 (Bell, 1929).

or, from the above,
$$(-n^2 + \omega^2 + 2rD)x = F \sin nt;$$

multiplying by the operator $(\omega^2 - n^2 - 2rD)$, we get
$$[(\omega^2 - n^2)^2 - 4r^2 D^2]x = F(\omega^2 - n^2 - 2rD) \sin nt$$

or $\quad [(\omega^2 - n^2)^2 + 4r^2 n^2]x = (\omega^2 - n^2) F \sin nt - 2rn F \cos nt.$

Hence $\qquad\qquad\qquad x = a \sin(nt - \delta) \quad \cdot \cdot \cdot \cdot \cdot \quad (3.4)$

where $\qquad\qquad\qquad \delta = \tan^{-1} \dfrac{2rn}{\omega^2 - n^2}, \quad \cdot \cdot \cdot \cdot \cdot \quad (3.5)$

and $\qquad\quad a = \dfrac{F \sin \delta}{2rn} = \dfrac{F}{\sqrt{\{(\omega^2 - n^2)^2 + 4r^2 n^2\}}}, \quad \cdot \cdot \quad (3.6)$

$$\therefore \ x = be^{-rt} \cos(\sqrt{\omega^2 - r^2}.t - \epsilon) + \frac{F \sin(nt - \delta)}{\sqrt{\{(\omega^2 - n^2)^2 + 4r^2 n^2\}}}. \quad (3.7)$$

Alternatively, if we assume a solution of equation (3.3) to be of the form
$$x = a \sin(nt - \delta),$$

then $\qquad \dot{x} = an \cos(nt - \delta), \ \ddot{x} = -an^2 \sin(nt - \delta).$

Substituting these values in equation (2) and putting
$$\begin{aligned} F \sin nt &= F \sin(nt - \delta + \delta) \\ &= F \sin(nt - \delta) \cos \delta + F \cos(nt - \delta) \sin \delta, \end{aligned}$$

we have
$$\begin{aligned} -an^2 \sin(nt - \delta) &+ 2r \, an \cos(nt - \delta) + \omega^2 a \sin(nt - \delta) \\ &= F \sin(nt - \delta) \cos \delta + F \cos(nt - \delta) \sin \delta. \end{aligned}$$

Equating coefficients of $\sin(nt - \delta)$ and $\cos(nt - \delta)$ we have
$$\left. \begin{aligned} F \cos \delta &= a(\omega^2 - n^2), \\ F \sin \delta &= 2rna, \end{aligned} \right\} \quad \cdot \cdot \cdot \cdot \quad (3.8)$$

$\therefore \ x = a \sin(nt - \delta)$ is a solution of the original equation if
$$a = \frac{F \sin \delta}{2rn} = \frac{F}{\sqrt{\{(\omega^2 - n^2)^2 + 4r^2 n^2\}}},$$

and $\qquad\qquad\qquad \delta = \tan^{-1} \dfrac{2rn}{\omega^2 - n^2},$

as before.

To this value of x we may add any value which makes the left-hand side of the original equation vanish. Such a value is given by

$$x = be^{-rt} \cos(\sqrt{\omega^2 - r^2} . t - \epsilon),$$

where $\omega > r$.

Thus the complete solution is, as before,

$$x = \frac{F \sin \delta}{2rn} \sin(nt - \delta) + be^{-rt} \cos(\sqrt{\omega^2 - r^2} . t - \epsilon).$$

We can therefore think of the motion as made up of two components. The first term represents a simple harmonic vibration of constant amplitude which has the same period as the force $(2\pi/n)$ and differs in phase from the force by an angle δ representing a retardation. The second term represents a free vibration of the natural period of the vibrating system, decaying at a rate determined by r —a rate which is the same as that of the system when no force is acting. This is the transient previously referred to.

Initially these two vibrations may be expected to give beats (p. 195) —beats whose frequency is the difference of frequency of the two vibrations, i.e. the difference between $n/2\pi$ and $\omega/2\pi$. The less the natural damping of the vibrating system, the more marked and the more prolonged will the beats be. This beating can be actually observed, as will be pointed out later. In time, however, the free vibration is damped out and only the forced vibration is left, so that the steady state is one in which we have only the vibration given by

$$x = \frac{F \sin \delta}{2rn} \sin(nt - \delta). \quad \ldots \quad (3.9)$$

3. Phase of Forced Vibration.

With regard to δ, the phase difference between the force and the vibration, we have, from (3.8),

$$F \sin \delta = 2rna,$$
$$\therefore \sin \delta \text{ is positive,}$$
$$\therefore 0 < \delta < \pi.$$

The vibration is therefore always less than half a cycle behind the force.

Also we have, from (3.8),

$$F \cos \delta = a(\omega^2 - n^2).$$

If $\omega > n$, $\cos \delta$ is positive,

$$\therefore 0 < \delta < \pi/2.$$

If, therefore, the period of the system is less than the period of the force, the vibration is less than one-quarter cycle behind the force.

If $\omega < n$, $\cos \delta$ is negative,

$$\therefore \ \pi/2 < \delta < \pi.$$

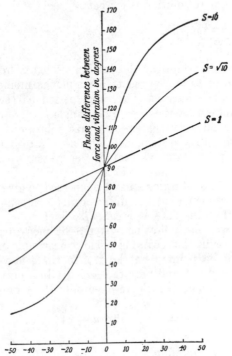

$n < \omega$ *Mistuning of force and system in centioctaves* $n > \omega$

Fig. 3.2

In this case the period of the system is greater than that of the force and the vibration is from one-quarter to one-half cycle behind the force.

If $\omega = n$, then $\cos \delta = 0$ and $\delta = \pi/2$.

In this case the period of the system is identical with that of the force, and the vibration is in quadrature with the force, i.e. one-quarter cycle behind.

If r is very small,

then $\sin \delta \fallingdotseq 0$

and $\delta \fallingdotseq 0$ or π.

For $\omega > n$, δ will be nearly zero, which means that if the period of the system is less than that of the force the two will be practically in phase.

On the other hand, if $\omega < n$, δ will be nearly equal to π, so that if the period of the system is greater than the period of the force the system is almost in opposition.

In discussing the variation of phase difference, displacement amplitude and velocity amplitude with the frequency of the applied force, it is convenient to use the ratio $\omega/r = S$. The main interest centres in values of the frequency of the applied force which are nearly equal to the free undamped frequency of the system. We can measure the mistuning of the force by the ratio ω/n or, better still, by the logarithm of this ratio. Since if $\omega/n = 2$ or $\frac{1}{2}$ the interval is an octave, the interval will be a centi-octave if

$$\log \frac{\omega}{n} = \pm \frac{1}{100} \log 2.$$

Fig. 3.2 shows for various values of S the variation of δ with n plotted in this way. $S = 1$ represents a system heavily damped. $S = 10$ represents a system lightly damped.

4. Amplitude Resonance.

The amplitude of the forced vibration, a, is given (3.6) by

$$a = \frac{F}{\sqrt{\{(\omega^2 - n^2)^2 + 4r^2 n^2\}}}.$$

This may be put in the form

$$a = \frac{F}{n\sqrt{\{\omega^2(\omega/n - n/\omega)^2 + 4r^2\}}}. \quad \cdot \ \cdot \ \cdot \quad (3.10)$$

If we regard ω/n as indicating the amount of mistuning, then if this ratio is fixed the quantity $(\omega/n - n/\omega)^2$ has the same value no matter which of the two frequencies is the greater. Since ω^2 and r^2 are constant, it follows that for given mistuning, a is less when n is greater. The amplitude of the forced vibration is therefore less for a given ratio of the frequencies when the frequency of the force is greater, and the curves showing for various values of S the variation of a with n are not symmetrical. They are plotted in fig. 3.3 for the same three values of S as in fig. 3.2.

The condition for maximum amplitude of the forced vibration is easily found. It corresponds to the minimum value of the denominator of the expression for a. Treating ω as constant and n as variable, for a minimum value we have

$$\frac{d}{dn}[(\omega^2 - n^2)^2 + 4r^2n^2] = 0$$

or

$$-4(\omega^2 - n^2)n + 8r^2n = 0,$$

$$\therefore n^2 = \omega^2 - 2r^2.$$

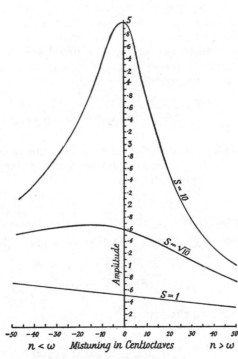

$n < \omega$ Mistuning in Centioctaves $n > \omega$

Fig. 3.3

Hence the amplitude is a maximum when the period of the force is $2\pi/\sqrt{(\omega^2 - 2r^2)}$. It is to be noted that this is not the unresisted period of the system, $2\pi/\omega$, nor is it the resisted period $2\pi/\sqrt{(\omega^2 - r^2)}$ but a still longer period. For this resonance period of the force,

$$a = \frac{F}{2r\sqrt{(r^2 + n^2)}}.$$

5. Velocity Resonance.

If
$$x = a \sin(nt - \delta),$$
$$\dot{x} = an \cos(nt - \delta).$$

Thus $\dot{x}$ is a maximum when
$$\cos(nt - \delta) = 1,$$

i.e.
$$\sin(nt - \delta) = 0,$$

i.e.
$$x = 0.$$

The corresponding value of $\dot{x}$ is the velocity amplitude

$$\hat{\dot{x}} = an = \frac{F}{\sqrt{\{\omega^2(\omega/n - n/\omega)^2 + 4r^2\}}}, \quad \cdot \quad \cdot \quad (3.11)$$

by (3.10). For any given value of r this is a maximum when

$$\left(\frac{\omega}{n} - \frac{n}{\omega}\right) = 0,$$

i.e. when
$$\omega = n.$$

This, then, is the condition for maximum velocity amplitude, i.e. for velocity resonance. Note that it is not the same as the condition for displacement resonance. Velocity resonance occurs when the frequency of the force is the same as the *undamped* frequency of the vibrating system. For the case of resonance we have, from (3.11),

$$\hat{\dot{x}} = \frac{F}{2r}. \quad \cdot \quad \cdot \quad \cdot \quad \cdot \quad \cdot \quad \cdot \quad 3.12$$

To see how the velocity amplitude varies when $n \neq \omega$, i.e. when the force is mistuned, we take

$$\frac{R}{100} = \frac{\text{Velocity amplitude for any value of } n}{\text{Velocity amplitude at resonance } (n = \omega)}$$

$$= \frac{F}{\sqrt{\{\omega^2(\omega/n - n/\omega)^2 + 4r^2\}}} \div \frac{F}{2r}$$

$$= \frac{1}{\sqrt{\{(\omega^2/4r^2)(\omega/n - n/\omega)^2 + 1\}}},$$

where R is the percentage response. In this expression n occurs only in the bracket and its value is the same for any given ratio of ω and n, no matter which happens to be the larger quantity. Thus if we measure the mistuning by the ratio ω/n or its logarithm as before, the resulting curve will be symmetrical about the line $n = \omega$.

If we put $S = \omega/r$ as before, and $y = \log_e \omega/n$,

then
$$\frac{\omega}{n} = e^y, \quad \frac{n}{\omega} = e^{-y},$$

and
$$\frac{1}{2}\left(\frac{\omega}{n} - \frac{n}{\omega}\right) = \frac{e^y - e^{-y}}{2} = \sinh y,$$

$$\therefore R = \frac{100}{\sqrt{(1 + S^2 \sinh^2 y)}}.$$

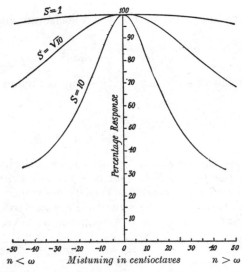

Fig. 3.4

When $\sinh y = 1/S$ the velocity amplitude falls to $1/\sqrt{2}$ of its value at resonance and the kinetic energy falls to half value. This may be taken as a measure of the sharpness of resonance, and we see that the sharpness is most marked for large values of S, i.e. for large values of ω and small values of r.

Since ω/n is considered in the neighbourhood of correct tuning $(n = \omega)$, $\log_e(\omega/n)$ is small,

$$\therefore \sinh y \doteqdot y,$$

$$\therefore R \doteqdot \frac{100}{\sqrt{(1 + S^2 y^2)}}.$$

The form of the response curves is shown in fig. 3.4, where R is plotted against the mistuning measured in centi-octaves.

To get the actual value of the velocity amplitude for these cases we have

$$\hat{\hat{x}} = \frac{R}{100} \times [\hat{\hat{x}}]_{n=\omega},$$

$$= \frac{R}{100} \times \frac{F}{2r} = \frac{RSF}{200\omega}.$$

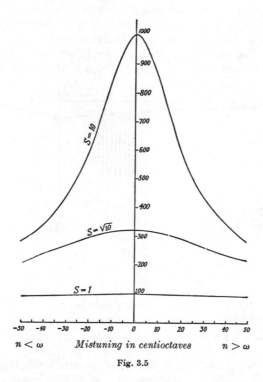

Fig. 3.5

For simplicity in plotting put $F = 200\omega$; the velocity amplitude curves for the same three values of S are shown in fig. 3.5.

6. Energy of Forced Vibration.

During part of the cycle in each vibration the system is drawing energy from the applied force and in the remaining part of the cycle it does work against the force. Thus the energy of the system varies, and in any discussion it is necessary to specify the conditions in which it is to be measured. If we measure it when the system is in the position of zero displacement, all the energy is kinetic and it is proportional to the square of the velocity amplitude found in the preceding section.

7. Experimental Illustrations of Forced Vibration.

The main features of the foregoing analysis can be illustrated by a very simple arrangement due to Barton* (fig. 3.6). From a stretched horizontal cord a number of light pendulums are suspended. These pendulums vary in length and consist of small paper cones attached to threads. At some distance from them is suspended a heavy iron bob, forming a pendulum of length intermediate between the longest and shortest of the light pendulums. If now the heavy pendulum is set swinging, its motion is communicated by the cord to the light pendulums. The reaction of the light pendulums is negligible, so that their vibrations are forced. If one of them is set in free vibration its

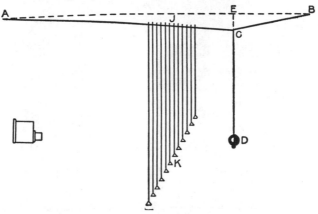

Fig. 3.6.—Barton's pendulums

ACB, stretched cord. D, heavy pendulum bob suspended from the cord. K, light paper cones suspended by threads from the same cord and set in motion when D is made to swing. DE is the effective length of the driving pendulum.

amplitude dies out rapidly, so that it represents a vibration for which r is large. The forced vibrations can be studied most conveniently by placing a source of light to the left of the diagram so that a shadow of the vibrations is projected on a screen placed to the right of the diagram. When the heavy pendulum is set swinging it will be noticed that the vibrations of the light pendulums show beats. These beats rapidly disappear and the light pendulums settle down to steady vibration. The distribution of phase is shown in fig. 3.7. The left-hand side shows the instantaneous positions of the small pendulums at the instant when the driving pendulum is passing its mid-point towards the right. Short and long pendulums are nearly in the same phase or nearly in opposite phase. The pendulum in resonance is

* *Phil. Mag.*, Vol. 36, p. 169 (1918).

obviously about $\pi/2$ behind. The right-hand side shows the positions an instant later. Obviously the shorter pendulums have moved to the right and so are in phase with the driving pendulum. The long pendulums have moved to the left and so are in the opposite phase. Fig. 3.8 (a) shows a time exposure of the swinging pendulums; though one pendulum shows maximum amplitude the selectivity is not great and neighbouring pendulums show an amplitude nearly as large.

If now split brass curtain rings are slipped on to the paper cones they become systems for which the damping is much less; if they are displaced and left to themselves the amplitudes decay much less

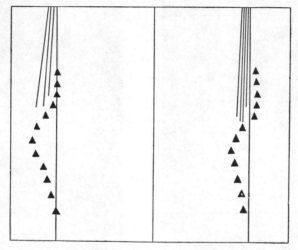

Fig. 3.7.—Pendulums in forced vibration

rapidly, owing to the fact that the work done against air resistance is now a much smaller proportion of the total energy of the swing. This time the initial beats are much more obvious and much more prolonged. When steady motion is finally established the phase distribution is markedly different from that of the previous case. *All* the shorter pendulums are very nearly in phase, and *all* the longer pendulums are very nearly in the opposite phase. The pendulum in resonance is, as before, $\pi/2$ behind the driving pendulum. A photograph of the system of pendulums shows that the selectivity is much more pronounced and the amplitudes fall off much more rapidly as the error in tuning increases (fig. 3.8 b, p. 90).

8. Singing Flames.

If a small jet of inflammable gas is ignited and inserted into a wider tube open at both ends then in certain conditions a steady and intense note is produced having the natural frequency of the wider tube.

The early history of this discovery is given by Tyndall* and is thus summarized by Jones †.

" The first person who observed a singing flame may have been Dr. Bryan Higgins. He found the effect in 1777, but it was not until about twenty-five years later that he wrote, for publication in Nicholson's *Journal*, the letter in which he described his discovery. The letter appeared in Nicholson's *Journal of Natural Philosophy*, 50, 129 (1802).

 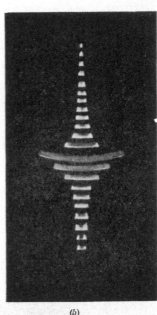

(a)   (b)

Fig. 3.8.—Photograph of moving pendulums, showing variation of amplitude

(a) Cones unloaded and therefore heavily damped, showing little selective resonance
(b) Cones loaded with curtain rings, giving small damping and selective resonance

" In the meantime the effect may have been discovered independently by others. J. A. DeLuc described it in his *Idées sur la Météorologie*, Vol. 1 (1796), p. 171, but did not say whether he discovered it himself or learned of it from someone else. Professor Hermbstädt of Berlin (Crell's *Chemische Annalen*, p. 355 in Part I for 1793) says that the Russian Count von Moussin Bouschkin (Pusch-kin (?)) showed him the experiment and told him that it was described by DeLuc. Chladni (*Ges. Naturforschender Freunde zu Berlin, Neue Schriften*, I, 125, 1795) speaks of the singing flame as having been discovered by DeLuc. Charles Gaspard Delarive (*Journ. de Physique*, 55, 165, 1802) and Michael Faraday (*Quarterly Journ. of Science and the Arts*, 5, 274, 1818) say that Pictet described the experiment at Geneva, and both William Nicholson (Editor of the *Journ. of Nat. Philos.*)

---

* *Sound*, p. 238.   † *Sound*, Appendix 6 (Chapman and Hall, 1937).

and Delarive refer to an article on singing flames by Professor Brugnatelli, probably Luigi Valentino Brugnatelli of Pavia. I have not found the papers by Pictet and Brugnatelli."

The experiment works quite well with ordinary coal-gas but better with hydrogen. The phenomenon has been widely studied and its real nature was established by Rayleigh,* who showed that it depends on the intermittent supply of heat by the jet. To get the greatest efficiency it is necessary that the maximum heat supply should occur at the instant of greatest compression of the air at the node adjoining the jet.

The action is analogous to that of a simple pendulum whose point of attachment is movable through a short horizontal distance. If at the instant when the bob has its maximum displacement to the right we suddenly move the point of suspension to the left, we increase the amplitude of the swing, but owing to the isochronism of the pendulum we leave its period unchanged. When the bob reaches the end of its swing to the left we move the point of suspension to the right and again the amplitude of the vibration is increased. On the other hand, if the direction of movement of the point of suspension is reversed, i.e. if it is moved to the right when the bob is on the right, the pendulum is soon brought to rest. The effect of moving the point of suspension when the bob is passing through its mean position is different. In this case there is a small effect on the period but none on the amplitude.

If, now, we think of a column of air closed at one end with a piston in the open end executing vibrations, the analogy is obvious. Any change in temperature of the air alters the mean position of the piston. If, when the piston is in the position giving maximum compression of the contained air, heat is suddenly supplied, the mean position about which the piston vibrates is moved outwards and the amplitude of the vibration is increased. Thus the condition favouring maintenance of the vibrations is that the heat supply should be in phase with the compression of the air. When the air in the wide tube of the singing flame is in vibration in its fundamental mode the node at the middle of the tube acts as a closed end and the conditions of the piston and closed tube are reproduced.

A model illustrating the action has been devised by Bragg.† Fig. 3.9 shows a bulb containing air, fixed by means of a cork to one end of a U-tube containing mercury. Inside the bulb is a spiral of fine platinum wire through which a battery can send a current of electricity, raising it to a bright red heat. The current runs from one end of the battery by way of a wire passed through the cork, goes through the spiral, and down inside the U-tube by means of a wire which just dips into the mercury. Then the current runs to the other end of the mercury, and out by a wire which dips well in, and so back to the battery.

As soon as the battery is connected the spiral becomes hot, the air inside

---

* *Theory of Sound*, Vol. 2, p. 226.   † *The World of Sound*, p. 92 (Bell, 1920).

becomes heated and expands so that it presses the mercury down on the bulb side. But this breaks the electrical connexion, because the mercury drops below the wire; the spiral grows cold, the air contracts, and the mercury comes back: the same series of events then repeats itself.

The various possible cases of singing flames are illustrated graphically * in fig. 3.10.

With correct timing the increase in the amplitude of vibration will of course continue until the amount of energy supplied at each vibration is equal to that dissipated in the vibration. The correct phase relationship can only be maintained if there are stationary vibrations not only in the air tube but in the gas supply tube; this means that if the gas supply tube is a short narrow tube terminating in a wider one, its length ought to be such that it has a node at the jet and an antinode at the junction with the wider tube. Thus the best lengths are $\lambda/4$, $3\lambda/4$, $5\lambda/4$, . . . , where λ is the wavelength of the sound in the gas.

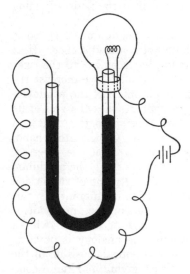

Fig. 3.9.—Oscillations maintained by electrical heating

By stroboscopic examination of the flame Richardson † has shown that its vibrations are in phase with the compression of the air at the node and has verified the fact, originally noted by Wheatstone, that not only does the size of the flame vary but in some cases it is actually withdrawn periodically into the supply tube.

Even when the conditions are right the tube will not always sing spontaneously and may require to be encouraged by tapping or by blowing across the top.

9. Gauze Tones.

These tones were discovered by Rijke ‡ in 1859, who found that if a piece of gauze is inserted into the lower half of a wide tube and heated by a bunsen flame the tube sounds loudly for a few minutes after the flame is withdrawn. The sound can be maintained indefinitely if the gauze is heated by an electric current. In this case

---

* A. B. Wood, *Sound*, p. 201 (Bell, 1930).   † *Proc. Phys. Soc.*, Vol. 35, p. 47 (1922–3).
‡ *Ann. d. Physik*, Vol. 107, p. 339 (1859); see also Lehmann, *Ann. d. Physik*, Vol. 29, p. 527 (1937).

there is no intermittence in the source of heat; the intermittence is supplied by the motion of the air in the tube. The air flow near the gauze consists of an alternating flow due to the vibrations in the tube superimposed on a steady flow due to convection. When the air is moving in towards the node to form a compression cold air

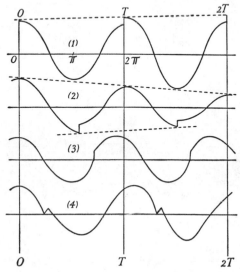

Wave form of resultant vibrations

Phase of Heat Supply relative to Phase of Pressure	Effect on	
	Amplitude	Frequency
(1) In phase . . .	increasing	none
(2) Opposite phase . .	decreasing	none
(3) Quarter period before	none	increase
(4) Quarter period after .	none	decrease

Fig. 3.10.—Maintenance of oscillations by heat and phase of heat supply

flows over the gauze and there is a maximum communication of heat. When the air is moving out, air which has already passed across the gauze returns through it, and as this air is already relatively warm the heat communicated is a minimum. Thus the phase of the heat supply is favourable for the maintenance of vibrations.

The converse case was studied by Bosscha and Riess.* Here the gauze is placed in the upper half of the tube, but it is a cold gauze—preferably water-cooled—and the current of air is hot.

With metal tubes a few centimetres in diameter and about a metre

* Ann. d. Physik, Vol. 109, p. 145 (1860).

in length some very impressive sounds can be produced by Rijke's method.

10. Work done in the Maintenance of Forced Vibrations.

The work done by the force per unit mass in maintaining a vibration is given by

$$W = \int F \sin nt \, dx$$

$$= \int F \sin nt \frac{dx}{dt} \, dt.$$

From (3.9), p. 81, $\dfrac{dx}{dt} = \dfrac{F \sin \delta}{2r} \cos (nt - \delta)$

$$= \frac{Fn}{\sqrt{\{(\omega^2 - n^2)^2 + 4r^2n^2\}}} (\cos nt \cos \delta + \sin nt \sin \delta).$$

Also, from (3.5), $\sin \delta = \dfrac{2rn}{\sqrt{\{(\omega^2 - n^2)^2 + 4r^2n^2\}}}$

and $\cos \delta = \dfrac{\omega^2 - n^2}{\sqrt{\{(\omega^2 - n^2)^2 + 4r^2n^2\}}},$

$\therefore \dfrac{dx}{dt} = \dfrac{Fn}{(\omega^2 - n^2)^2 + 4r^2n^2} [(\omega^2 - n^2) \cos nt + 2rn \sin nt],$

$\therefore W = \dfrac{F^2n}{(\omega^2 - n^2)^2 + 4r^2n^2} \int [(\omega^2 - n^2) \cos nt \sin nt$
$$+ 2rn \sin^2 nt] dt.$$

If we integrate over a complete period, we have

$$\int_0^{2\pi/n} \cos nt \sin nt \, dt = 0,$$

$$\int_0^{2\pi/n} \sin^2 nt \, dt = \frac{\pi}{n}.$$

$$\therefore W = \frac{F^2n}{(\omega^2 - n^2)^2 + 4r^2n^2} \cdot 2r\pi,$$

and the mean power $= \dfrac{W}{2\pi/n} = \dfrac{F^2n^2r}{(\omega^2 - n^2)^2 + 4r^2n^2}.$ . . . (3.13)

The same result can also be obtained by integrating the work done against the damping resistance. We then have

$$W = \int 2r\dot{x} \, dx = 2r \int \dot{x}^2 \, dt.$$

If T is the kinetic energy per unit mass, $T = \frac{1}{2}\dot{x}^2$,

$$\therefore\ W = 4r \int T\, dt.$$

But $\int T\, dt$ taken over a complete period $= \bar{T} \cdot \dfrac{2\pi}{n}$,

where $\bar{T}$ is the average kinetic energy over the period;

$$\therefore\ W = \frac{8\pi r}{n}\, \bar{T}.$$

Now the average kinetic energy over the period is half the maximum kinetic energy. Hence, from equation 3.9 (p. 81),

$$\frac{\dot{x}^2}{4} = \bar{T} = \frac{F^2 \sin^2 \delta}{16r^2}$$

and

$$W = \frac{\pi}{n}\, \frac{F^2 \sin^2 \delta}{2r}$$

$$= \frac{\pi F^2}{2rn}\, \frac{4r^2 n^2}{(\omega^2 - n^2)^2 + 4r^2 n^2}$$

$$= \frac{\pi F^2 \cdot 2rn}{(\omega^2 - n^2)^2 + 4r^2 n^2}.$$

Hence $\dfrac{W}{2\pi/n}$, the mean rate of working, is

$$\frac{F^2 n^2 r}{(\omega^2 - n^2)^2 + 4r^2 n^2}.$$

11. Oscillations in an Electrical Circuit.

If we have an electrical circuit containing resistance R, inductance L and capacity C in series and apply to the circuit an E.M.F. varying sinusoidally, we can obtain an expression for the current j in the circuit at any instant as follows.

The fall of potential round the circuit, Rj, will be the applied E.M.F., $E_0 \cos \omega t$, less the back E.M.F. due to the inductance, $L(dj/dt)$, and to the charge on the condenser, q/C. Hence, using the fact that $j = dq/dt$, we have

$$L\frac{d^2q}{dt^2} + R\frac{dq}{dt} + \frac{q}{C} = E_0 \cos \omega t. \quad . \quad . \quad . \quad (3.14)$$

But $E_0 \cos \omega t$ is the real part of $E_0(\cos \omega t + i \sin \omega t)$, where i is $\sqrt{-1}$. It is therefore the real part of $E_0 e^{i\omega t}$, and we may write

$$L \frac{d^2q}{dt^2} + R \frac{dq}{dt} + \frac{q}{C} = E_0 e^{i\omega t}. \quad \ldots \quad (3.15)$$

For our purpose the use of complex numbers is only a convenient device for performing differentiation and integration with the least trouble. It need cause no confusion if we remember that the derivative of an expression like $u + iv$, where u and v are real functions of the time t, is given by $\left(\dfrac{du}{dt} + i \dfrac{dv}{dt}\right)$, so that it does not matter whether

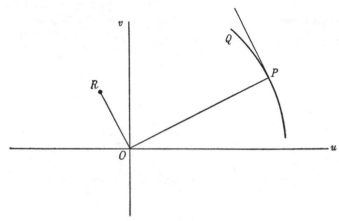

Fig. 3.11

we take the real and imaginary parts before or after differentiating. This may be verified in a particular case by considering

$$e^{i\omega t} = \cos \omega t + i \sin \omega t$$

of which the derivative is $i\omega e^{i\omega t}$ by the ordinary rule for the exponential function.

Now $$i\omega(e^{i\omega t}) = i\omega \cos \omega t - \omega \sin \omega t,$$

so that the real part, $-\omega \sin \omega t$, is, as we expect, the derivative of $\cos \omega t$.

In the general case we write $(u + iv)$ as $Z(t)$ and represent $Z(t)$ by a point P in the complex plane, or by the displacement OP. Then as t varies, P moves along some curve in this plane, PQ, say (fig. 3.11).

The derivative of Z is defined as $\displaystyle \lim_{\delta t \to 0} \frac{Z(t + \delta t) - Z(t)}{\delta t}$ as for ordinary real numbers, and will be represented by a displacement OR parallel to the tangent at P. In the important special case in which $u + iv = e^{i\omega t}$, the time derivative is at right angles to the original displacement OP. In the language of complex numbers, the operation represented by $L(d/dt)$, where L is a real constant, is in this special case given by $iL\omega$, that is by (a) multiplication by the real constant $L\omega$, (b) turning through a right angle counterclockwise.

The inverse operation of integration with respect to time is represented by dividing by $i\omega$, or by multiplying by $-i/\omega$, that is (a) multiplying by $1/\omega$, (b) turning through a right angle clockwise.

These considerations apply directly to alternating currents and

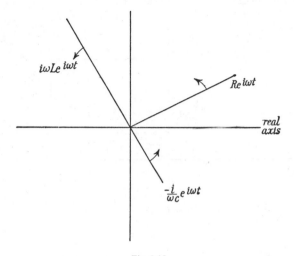

Fig. 3.12

analogous problems (fig. 3.12), since the calculation of E.M.F.s due to resistances, capacities and inductances, normally a process of differentiation and integration, is now reduced to the combination of complex numbers. Relations of *phase* are readily seen simply as angles between displacements such as OP and OR. Variation of t merely rotates the diagram as a whole (the operation $\times \exp i\omega(t - t_0)$ ensures this). In this way the phase relations remain obvious in the picture, and we can also avoid explicit reference to t in discussing the problem. The diagram has become a diagram of *impedances* (fig. 3.13), rather than of E.M.F.s.

The impedance diagram is a picture of such operators as that which is included in the bracket in the equation

$$\left(L\frac{d}{dt} + R + \frac{1}{C}\int dt\right)j = E_0 e^{i\omega t},$$

where j is the current, and the integration sign operates on whatever *follows dt.*

It should be emphasized that by reducing the problem to one of division and multiplication we fail to obtain a complete solution of the equation; our solution has no arbitrary constants. We fail to introduce any sinusoidal functions of periods differing from that of the E.M.F.; this is only a particular integral, and the complementary function is required to complete the solution. Often this particular integral is required to the exclusion of the complete solution, because usually the complementary function contains only transient terms which become negligible as t increases.

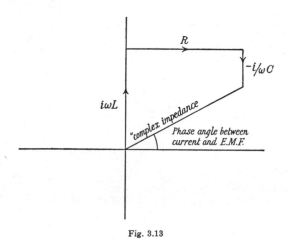

Fig. 3.13

The impedance diagram enables us to see immediately that a solution of the above equation is

$$j = \frac{E_0 e^{i\omega t}}{R + i\omega L - i/\omega C} \quad \cdots \cdots \quad (3.16)$$

and this is equivalent to assuming a trial solution for j of the form $Ae^{i\omega t}$.

Thus returning to equation (3.15) in terms of q (it does not matter which we solve first), namely,

$$L\frac{d^2q}{dt^2} + R\frac{dq}{dt} + \frac{q}{C} = E_0 e^{i\omega t}$$

we may put $\qquad\qquad\qquad q = Ae^{i\omega t},$

and therefore $\qquad\qquad \dot{q} = i\omega Ae^{i\omega t}, \quad \ddot{q} = -\omega^2 Ae^{i\omega t}.$

Substituting in the equation, we have

$$-\omega^2 L A e^{i\omega t} + Ri\omega A e^{i\omega t} + \frac{A e^{i\omega t}}{C} = E_0 e^{i\omega t}$$

$$\therefore A\left(-\omega^2 L + Ri\omega + \frac{1}{C}\right) = E_0.$$

Hence
$$q = \frac{E_0 e^{i\omega t}}{-\omega^2 L + Ri\omega + 1/C}$$

$$= \frac{E_0 e^{i\omega t}}{i\omega[R + i(\omega L - 1/C\omega)]}, \quad \cdot \quad \cdot \quad \cdot \quad \cdot \quad (3.17)$$

and the instantaneous value of q is the real part of this complex expression. Further,

$$\dot{q} = i\omega q = \frac{E_0 e^{i\omega t}}{R + i(\omega L - 1/C\omega)} \quad \cdot \quad \cdot \quad \cdot \quad (3.18)$$

The ratio $E_0 e^{i\omega t}/\dot{q}$ is the instantaneous value of the ratio of E.M.F. and current. It therefore plays the same part in an oscillating circuit as resistance for steady currents. It is called the *complex impedance* of the circuit and is equal to $R + i(\omega L - 1/C\omega)$.

R is the resistance and $(\omega L - 1/C\omega)$ is called the *reactance R'*, ωL being the inductive reactance and $1/C\omega$ the capacity reactance.

The value of $\dot{q}$ is the real part of the complex expression (3.18). To find this put Z for the positive square root $\sqrt{(R^2 + R'^2)}$ and ϵ for $\tan^{-1} R'/R$. The complex impedance is then $Z e^{i\epsilon}$ or $Z(\cos\epsilon + i\sin\epsilon)$,

and
$$\dot{q} = \frac{E_0 e^{i\omega t}}{Z e^{i\epsilon}} = \frac{E_0}{Z} e^{i(\omega t - \epsilon)}.$$

Hence

$$\text{real part of } \dot{q} = \frac{E_0}{Z} \cos(\omega t - \epsilon).$$

In the same way the real part of $\dot{q}/i\omega$ is

$$\frac{E_0 \sin(\omega t - \epsilon)}{\omega Z},$$

and this is the appropriate value of q.

Thus it will be seen that

(*a*) There is a phase difference of $\pi/2$ between q and $\dot{q}$.

(*b*) There is a phase difference of ϵ between the applied E.M.F. and the current, where

$$\epsilon = \tan^{-1} \frac{R'}{R} = \tan^{-1} \frac{\omega L - 1/C\omega}{R}.$$

(c) The impedance Z has a minimum value and therefore the current $\dot{q}$ a maximum value if $\omega L - 1/C\omega = 0$. In this case the frequency—the resonance frequency—is given by

$$f = \frac{\omega}{2\pi} = \frac{1}{2\pi\sqrt{LC}}. \quad \ldots \ldots \quad (3.19)$$

At this frequency ϵ obviously vanishes.

12. Analogy between Mechanical and Electrical Quantities.

The close analogy between electrical and mechanical oscillations can be clearly brought out if we apply to the mechanical system the same method of treatment as that just given for the electrical circuit.

Suppose we have a mass m (fig. 3.14), subject to frictional forces opposing motion, and acted on by a spring and by an applied force F. Let the spring develop a restoring force S per unit displacement, and let the frictional forces develop a retarding force r per unit velocity.

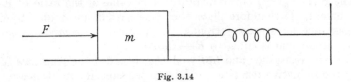

Fig. 3.14

The equation of motion is

$$m\ddot{\xi} + r\dot{\xi} + S\xi = F. \quad \ldots \ldots \quad (3.20)$$

Putting $F = F_0 \cos\omega t$ and using complex quantities as before, we have

$$m\ddot{\xi} + r\dot{\xi} + S\xi = F_0 e^{i\omega t}. \quad \ldots \ldots \quad (3.21)$$

Here we have an equation identical in form with that for the oscillations in an electrical circuit, with m substituted for L, r substituted for R, S substituted for $1/C$, and F for E. In other words, we have the following analogies:

Electrical	Mechanical
Inductance	Mass
Resistance	Resistance
Capacity	$\dfrac{1}{\text{Stiffness}}$
E.M.F.	Force
Charge	Displacement
Current	Velocity

If we introduce a new mechanical term, *compliance* (C), where $C = 1/S$, then we have

$$\text{Compliance} = \frac{1}{\text{Force per unit displacement}}$$
$$= \text{Displacement per unit force}.$$

Obviously the solution will have the same form as before, and we shall have

$$\xi = \frac{F_0 e^{i\omega t}}{i\omega [r + i(\omega m - 1/C\omega)]}, \qquad \cdots \quad (3.22)$$

$$= \frac{F_0 e^{i\omega t}}{i\omega Z_M}, \qquad \cdots \cdots \cdots \quad (3.23)$$

where Z_M is the mechanical impedance, so named from analogy with the electrical case. It consists of a pure resistance and a mechanical reactance which depends on the applied frequency and comprises two terms, one involving the mass and the other the compliance of the spring. Here again we have

$$\dot{\xi} = \frac{F_0 e^{i\omega t}}{Z_M},$$

and the phase relations of driving force, displacement and velocity are the same as those for E.M.F., charge and current. Also, the resonance frequency is given by

$$\omega m - \frac{1}{C\omega} = 0, \text{ or } \omega = \frac{1}{\sqrt{Cm}},$$

so that

$$f = \frac{1}{2\pi\sqrt{Cm}}$$

where f is the frequency of the free vibrations of the loaded spring.

To complete the analogy we may compare the properties of the transformer and the lever. Just as the transformer couples two circuits in such a way that the E.M.F. is stepped up or down in a fixed ratio, so the lever transmits force from one mechanical system to another, stepping it up or down in a fixed ratio.

Thus, in the diagram (fig. 3.15, p. 102), if we consider velocities, we have $\dot{x}_1/\dot{x}_2 = d_1/d_2$; and for currents in the transformer, if n_2, the number of turns in the secondary, is small compared with n_1, the number of turns in the primary, we have $j_1/j_2 = n_2/n_1$. Also if C (fig. 3.15) is fixed and a force F_1 is applied at A then the force at B will be F_2, where $F_1/F_2 = d_2/d_1$; and an E.M.F. E_1 in the primary of a transformer gives an E.M.F. E_2 in the secondary, where $E_1/E_2 = n_1/n_2$. The analogy is therefore complete, provided that $d_1/d_2 = n_2/n_1$.

It is accordingly possible to utilize the results which have been obtained from an intensive study of electrical systems and apply these to the design of mechanical systems. A notable instance of this was the epoch-making improvement in the mechanical gramophone in-

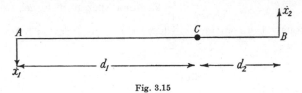

Fig. 3.15

troduced by Maxfield and Harrison with a view to obtaining a uniform response over a large frequency range. Fig. 18.20, p. 523, shows the sound-box and the equivalent electrical circuit. Before we can fully appreciate this equivalence, however, we must go on to consider the acoustical analogy.

CHAPTER IV

Resonators, Filters and Horns

1. The Helmholtz Resonator.

In his analysis of musical sounds Helmholtz (1821–1894) made use of an air resonator. It is made of brass or glass, and has two apertures, the narrower being inserted into the ear and the wider being presented to the source of sound. If a tone of the natural frequency of the contained air is present in the sound to be analysed, the resonator responds and this response is detected by the ear. This system may be treated as an example of an acoustical system which has one degree of freedom.

We shall proceed to consider a simplified resonator as shown in fig. 4.1.

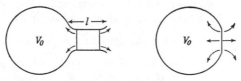

Fig. 4.1.—Simple Resonators

Let V_0 be the volume of the resonator, l the length of neck, S the area of cross-section of neck, ρ the density of air, and, as before, let ξ be the displacement and s the condensation.

As the motion is mainly confined to the air in the neck we may take the mass-acceleration as $lS\rho\ddot{\xi}$. The excess pressure acting on this mass is given by

$$p = Ks = c^2\rho s$$

$$= -c^2\rho\frac{dV}{V_0} = c^2\rho\frac{\xi S}{V_0}.$$

$$\therefore \text{ Force acting} = pS = \frac{c^2\rho\xi S^2}{V_0}.$$

The dissipation of energy is mainly that due to the energy radiated, and this corresponds to a resisting force * given by

$$\frac{\rho \omega k}{2\pi} S^2 \dot{\xi}, \text{ where } k = \frac{2\pi}{\lambda}.$$

We may therefore write the complete equation as

$$lS\rho\ddot{\xi} + \frac{\rho\omega k S^2}{2\pi}\dot{\xi} + \frac{c^2\rho S^2}{V_0}\xi = S\hat{P}e^{i\omega t},$$

where $\hat{P}$ is the pressure amplitude due to an external applied force.

It is convenient to choose a new quantity X called the volume displacement and defined by the relation $X = S\xi$. Then $\dot{X} = S\dot{\xi}$, $\ddot{X} = S\ddot{\xi}$, and we have

$$\frac{l\rho}{S}\ddot{X} + \frac{\rho\omega k}{2\pi}\dot{X} + \frac{\rho c^2}{V_0}X = \hat{P}e^{i\omega t}. \quad . \quad . \quad . \quad (4.1)$$

By analogy with (3.18), p. 99, the steady state solution is

$$\dot{X} = \frac{\hat{P}e^{i\omega t}}{\dfrac{\rho\omega k}{2\pi} + i\left(\dfrac{\rho\omega l}{S} - \dfrac{\rho c^2}{V_0\omega}\right)}. \quad . \quad . \quad . \quad (4.2)$$

Here again the analogy with the electrical case is obvious and a similarity in nomenclature is desirable. Accordingly, the quantity $\frac{\rho\omega k}{2\pi} + i\left(\frac{\rho\omega l}{S} - \frac{\rho c^2}{V_0\omega}\right)$ is called the *acoustical impedance* and is denoted by Z_A. It is defined as the ratio of the sound pressure at a source of sound and the strength of the sound U, and the strength of a sound is defined in turn as the rate of volume displacement of the surface which constitutes the source. Thus $\dot{X} = U$,

$$Z_A = \frac{\hat{P}e^{i\omega t}}{U} = \frac{\hat{P}e^{i\omega t}}{S\dot{\xi}}. \quad . \quad . \quad . \quad . \quad (4.3)$$

It is to be distinguished from the unit area impedance at a point in the medium in which sound waves are being propagated. This is defined as the complex ratio of the sound pressure and the sound particle velocity, and is denoted by $Z_u = \frac{p}{\dot{\xi}} = \frac{p}{v}$.

The *acoustical resistance*, which is the real component of the acoustical impedance, is given by $R_A = \frac{\rho\omega k}{2\pi}$.

* See Rayleigh, *Sound*, Vol. 2, § 311.

The *acoustical reactance* is the magnitude of the imaginary component of the acoustical impedance. It is equal to $\left(\dfrac{\rho \omega l}{S} - \dfrac{\rho c^2}{V_0 \omega} \right)$. It is composed of a mass reactance $\rho \omega l / S$ and a stiffness reactance $\rho c^2 / V_0 \omega$. The *acoustical mass* is the mass reactance *divided* by the pulsatance ω, in this case $\rho l / S$, and the *acoustical stiffness* is the stiffness reactance *multiplied* by the pulsatance, in this case $\rho c^2 / V_0$.

The resonance frequency is that corresponding to the value of ω for which the reactance disappears, that is, for which

$$\frac{\rho \omega l}{S} = \frac{\rho c^2}{V_0 \omega}.$$

Hence

$$\omega = c \sqrt{\frac{S}{l V_0}} \quad \cdots \cdots \quad (4.4)$$

and

$$f = \frac{\omega}{2\pi} = \frac{c}{2\pi} \sqrt{\frac{S}{l V_0}}. \quad \cdots \cdots \quad (4.5)$$

Thus the frequency is directly proportional to the square root of the aperture area and inversely proportional to the square root of the volume and to the square root of the length of the neck.

The quantity S/l is known as the *conductivity* (C) of the opening. As the motion is not strictly confined to the neck the effective length of the neck l' is always greater than the true length l by an amount $l' - l$ known as the " end correction " (see also § 6, p. 253, and § 9, p. 406). When the opening is a circular aperture in a thin wall it has been shown by Rayleigh [*] that the effective mass of moving air is $\rho S^2 / 2a$, where a is the radius of the aperture. Hence

$$\frac{\rho S^2}{2a} = \rho S l',$$

$$\therefore \frac{S}{l'} = 2a. \quad \cdots \cdots \quad (4.6)$$

The analogy with electrical conductivity holds, and conductivities may be combined in series or in parallel. Thus in the case of a short neck we may treat it as two conductivities in series: that of the neck and that of the aperture. We therefore have

$$\frac{1}{C} = \frac{1}{C_1} + \frac{1}{C_2},$$

[*] *Sound*, Vol. 2, § 306.

where C is the effective conductivity, C_1 the conductivity of the neck, and C_2 the conductivity of the aperture;

$$\therefore \ C = \frac{C_1 C_2}{C_1 + C_2} = \frac{2a \cdot \pi a^2/l}{2a + \pi a^2/l} = \frac{\pi a^2}{l + \pi a/2}.$$

In this discussion it has been assumed that the linear dimensions of the resonator are small compared with the wave-length of the sound, so that the air in the neck moves as a whole and the pressure at any instant is nearly uniform throughout the interior.

A horn of varying cross-section may be treated as a chain of conductors in series and its conductivity will be C, given by

$$\frac{1}{C} = \int_0^l \frac{dx}{S},$$

where S is the cross-section at a distance x from the origin.

Now consider the case where the vibrations of the air are forced by the impact of waves from another source, the pressure due to these waves at the neck of the resonator being given by $\hat{P}e^{i\omega t}$.

The rate of volume flow $\dot{X}$ at resonance is given by $\dfrac{\hat{P}e^{i\omega t}}{\rho\omega k/2\pi}$, by (4.3).

The particle velocity in the neck of the resonator will therefore be

$$\frac{\dot{X}}{S} = \frac{2\pi \hat{P}e^{i\omega t}}{\rho\omega k S},$$

and the amplitude or maximum value of this quantity will be

$$\hat{\vartheta} = \frac{2\pi \hat{P}}{\rho\omega k S}. \quad \ldots \ldots \quad (4.7)$$

But for the wave $\qquad \hat{\vartheta} = \dfrac{\hat{P}}{c\rho}$

(equation 11.12, p. 290). Therefore the magnification is given by

$$M_v = \frac{2\pi c}{\omega k S}. \quad \ldots \ldots \quad (4.8)$$

This type of magnification applies to all measuring apparatus which depends on velocity, e.g. the Rayleigh disc.

To find the pressure magnification we put $\hat{X}$ for the amplitude of the volume displacement; then, since by analogy with 3.17 (p. 99), we have at resonance

$$X = \frac{\hat{P}e^{i\omega t}}{i\omega(\rho\omega k/2\pi)},$$

it follows that
$$\hat{X} = \frac{2\pi \hat{P}}{\omega^2 \rho k}. \qquad \ldots \ldots (4.9)$$

The pressure excess, p, in the resonator is given at any instant by
$$p = Ks = c^2 \rho \frac{X}{V_0}.$$

Therefore the pressure amplitude in the resonator is given by
$$\hat{P}_r = c^2 \rho \frac{\hat{X}}{V_0} = \frac{2\pi c^2 \hat{P}}{\omega^2 k V_0}. \qquad \ldots \ldots (4.10)$$

But
$$\omega^2 = \frac{c^2 S}{l' V_0},$$

from (4.4). Hence the pressure magnification is given by
$$M_p = \frac{\hat{P}_r}{\hat{P}} = \frac{2\pi l'}{kS}, \qquad \ldots \ldots (4.11)$$

and as the loudness in the ear depends on the pressure amplitude, it is on this factor that the use of the Helmholtz resonator depends.

The ratio of the two magnifications is given by
$$\frac{M_p}{M_v} = \frac{\omega l'}{c} = \frac{2\pi l'}{\lambda}. \qquad \ldots \ldots (4.12)$$

As l' is usually much smaller than λ it follows that M_p is small compared with M_v.

If for instance we consider a note of frequency 256, then λ is about 129 cm. and if the aperture is circular of radius 1·5 cm. and there is no neck, we have, from (4.6),
$$l' = \frac{S}{2a} = \frac{\pi a}{2},$$

and
$$\frac{M_p}{M_v} = \frac{14·8}{129} = 0·115.$$

Since
$$M_p = \frac{2\pi l'}{kS} = \frac{\lambda}{2a},$$

we have
$$M_p = 43,$$

and
$$M_v = \frac{M_p}{0·115} = 374.$$

In this discussion it is assumed that viscosity-losses in the neck are negligible compared with radiation-losses, and this is not true for narrow apertures.

2. Impedance of Pipes.

As a preliminary to the study of acoustical filters we shall now consider the propagation of sound in a tube. Following the method of treatment suggested by Irons * we have for the propagation (neglecting frictional dissipation)

$$\frac{\partial^2 \xi}{\partial t^2} = c^2 \frac{\partial^2 \xi}{\partial x^2},$$

and if the motion is simple harmonic,

$$\frac{\partial^2 \xi}{\partial x^2} + \omega^2 \xi = 0.$$

The solution may be written in the form

$$\xi = \left(A \sin \frac{\omega x}{c} + B \cos \frac{\omega x}{c} \right) e^{i(\omega t + \epsilon)}.$$

Hence

$$\dot{\xi} = i\omega \xi,$$

$$\frac{\partial \xi}{\partial x} = \frac{\omega}{c} \left(A \cos \frac{\omega x}{c} - B \sin \frac{\omega x}{c} \right) e^{i(\omega t + \epsilon)},$$

$$p = Ks = -c^2 \rho \frac{\partial \xi}{\partial x} = -c\rho\omega \left(A \cos \frac{\omega x}{c} - B \sin \frac{\omega x}{c} \right) e^{i(\omega t + \epsilon)}.$$

The impedance at any point is given (4.3, p. 104) by

$$Z = \frac{p}{S\dot{\xi}} = \frac{-c\rho\omega \{ A \cos(\omega x/c) - B \sin(\omega x/c) \} e^{i(\omega t + \epsilon)}}{Si\omega \{ A \sin(\omega x/c) + B \cos(\omega x/c) \} e^{i(\omega t + \epsilon)}}$$

$$= \frac{ic\rho \{ A \cos(\omega x/c) - B \sin(\omega x/c) \}}{S \{ A \sin(\omega x/c) + B \cos(\omega x/c) \}}, \qquad . \quad . \quad (4.13)$$

$\therefore$ at $x = 0$ we have

$$Z_0 = \frac{ic\rho A}{SB}, \qquad . \quad . \quad . \quad . \quad . \quad (4.14)$$

and at $x = l$ we have

$$Z_l = \frac{ic\rho \{ A \cos(\omega l/c) - B \sin(\omega l/c) \}}{S \{ A \sin(\omega l/c) + B \cos(\omega l/c) \}}.$$

* *Journ. Sci. Inst.*, Vol. 8, p. 89 (1931).

Dividing numerator and denominator by B and substituting $A/B = Z_0 S/ic\rho$ (from 4.14), we have

$$Z_l = \frac{ic\rho\{(S/ic\rho)Z_0 \cos(\omega l/c) - \sin(\omega l/c)\}}{S\{(S/ic\rho)Z_0 \sin(\omega l/c) + \cos(\omega l/c)\}}$$

$$= \frac{ic\rho}{S} \left\{ \frac{Z_0 \cos(\omega l/c) - (ic\rho/S) \sin(\omega l/c)}{Z_0 \sin(\omega l/c) + (ic\rho/S) \cos(\omega l/c)} \right\}.$$

If the end of the pipe is at $x = l$ and this end is open, then a small pressure excess produces a large volume displacement and $Z_l = 0$:

$$\therefore \ Z_0 = \frac{ic\rho}{S} \tan\frac{\omega l}{c}.$$

If the end at $x = 0$ is also open we have

$$Z_0 = 0,$$

$$\tan\frac{\omega l}{c} = 0,$$

$$\therefore \ \frac{\omega l}{c} = m\pi,$$

where m is any integer, and the possible stationary modes of vibration for the air in the pipe are given by

$$f_m = \frac{\omega}{2\pi} = \frac{cm}{2l}, \quad \ldots \ldots \quad (4.15)$$

in agreement with equation 15.11 (p. 397); the possible wave-lengths are

$$\lambda_m = \frac{c}{f_m} = \frac{2l}{m}. \quad \ldots \ldots \quad (4.16)$$

If the pipe is stopped at $x = l$, then we have at that point $\dot{\xi} = 0$ and $Z_l = \infty$,

$$\therefore \ Z_0 \sin\frac{\omega l}{c} + \frac{ic\rho}{S} \cos\frac{\omega l}{c} = 0$$

or

$$Z_0 = -\frac{ic\rho}{S} \cot\frac{\omega l}{c}.$$

If the end at $x = 0$ is open, then we have

$$Z_0 = 0,$$

$$\cot\frac{\omega l}{c} = 0.$$

Hence $$\frac{2\pi f_m l}{c} = (2m - 1)\frac{\pi}{2},$$

or $$f_m = \frac{(2m - 1)c}{4l}, \quad \ldots \ldots (4.17)$$

as given later in equation 15.12 (p. 398).

Hence $$\lambda_m = \frac{4l}{2m - 1}. \quad \ldots \ldots (4.18)$$

3. Electrical Filters.

The analogy between electrical quantities and acoustical quantities outlined on p. 100 enables us to devise acoustical filters analogous to electrical filters. These electrical filters were first introduced by G. A. Campbell * and consist of ladder networks, each element of the ladder being a similar elementary circuit. By a proper adjustment of the

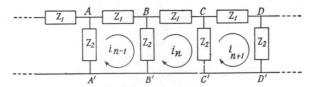

Fig. 4.2.—Electrical filter circuit

impedances of these circuits the filter can be made to transmit high frequencies only (high-pass filter), or low frequencies only (low-pass filter), or any given band of frequencies (band-pass filter). The electrical filters themselves have important acoustic applications. Thus if they are inserted between the pick-up and the loud-speaker of an electrical gramophone, the effect on the reproduction of filtering out certain ranges of frequency may be tested (p. 362).

Let fig. 4.2 represent three successive elements of the filter circuit, having impedances Z_1 in series in the line and Z_2 in shunts. Let the currents in the elements be as shown and the E.M.F.s across the shunts be e_{n-1}, e_n, &c.

Then if we consider the element $BCC'B'$ and take the E.M.F. round the mesh, we have

$$i_n Z_1 + (i_n - i_{n+1})Z_2 + (i_n - i_{n-1})Z_2 = 0.$$

$$\therefore \; i_n(Z_1 + 2Z_2) = Z_2(i_{n-1} + i_{n+1})$$

or $$\frac{i_{n-1}}{i_n} + \frac{i_{n+1}}{i_n} = 2 + \frac{Z_1}{Z_2}.$$

* U.S. Patent No. 1,227,113, 22nd May, 1917.

As all the elements are exactly similar we may assume that the current ratio is constant, i.e. that

$$\frac{i_{n-1}}{i_n} = \frac{i_n}{i_{n+1}} = \ldots = e^y \text{ (say)}.$$

Then
$$e^y + e^{-y} = 2 + \frac{Z_1}{Z_2}$$

$$\therefore 1 + \frac{1}{2}\frac{Z_1}{Z_2} = \cosh y \quad \ldots \ldots \quad (4.19)$$

If y is purely imaginary ($\lambda = iy$) the currents in adjacent sections differ only in phase and there is no attenuation. In this case we have

$$\cosh i\lambda = \cos \lambda, \quad \ldots \ldots \ldots \quad (4.20)$$

so that $\left(1 + \frac{1}{2}\frac{Z_1}{Z_2}\right)$ lies between $+1$ and -1 and there is no attenuation between the limiting values

$$\frac{Z_1}{Z_2} = 0 \text{ and } \frac{Z_1}{Z_2} = -4.$$

1. *Low-pass Filter.*

Let Z_1 consist of inductance L only, and Z_2 of capacity C only.

Then
$$Z_1 = \omega L, \ Z_2 = -\frac{1}{\omega C} \text{ (see p. 99)},$$

$$\therefore \frac{Z_1}{Z_2} = -\omega^2 LC.$$

When
$$\frac{Z_1}{Z_2} = 0, \ \omega = 0.$$

When
$$\frac{Z_1}{Z_2} = -4, \ \omega = \frac{2}{\sqrt{LC}}.$$

That is, the filter passes low frequencies and cuts off at a frequency $\frac{\omega}{2\pi} = \frac{1}{\pi\sqrt{LC}}$. This is just twice the natural frequency of a series circuit containing inductance L and capacity C.

The transmission of vibrations along a stretched string loaded with equal masses, equally spaced, affords a mechanical analogy.*

* See Crandall, *Vibrating Systems and Sound*, p. 64 (Van Nostrand Co, 1926).

2. *High-pass Filter.*

If the series impedances are capacities only and the shunt impedances are inductances only, we have

$$Z_1 = -\frac{1}{\omega C}, \; Z_2 = \omega L,$$

$$\therefore \; \frac{Z_1}{Z_2} = -\frac{1}{\omega^2 LC}.$$

When $$\frac{Z_1}{Z_2} = 0, \; \omega = \infty.$$

When $$\frac{Z_1}{Z_2} = -4, \; \omega = \frac{1}{2\sqrt{LC}}.$$

That is, the filter passes high frequencies and cuts off at a frequency

$$\frac{\omega}{2\pi} = \frac{1}{4\pi\sqrt{LC}}.$$

3. *Band-pass Filter.*

If Z_1 and Z_2 each contain both capacity and inductance,

$$Z_1 = \omega L_1 - \frac{1}{\omega C_1} \text{ and } Z_2 = \omega L_2 - \frac{1}{\omega C_2},$$

$$\therefore \; \frac{Z_1}{Z_2} = \frac{\omega L_1 - 1/\omega C_1}{\omega L_2 - 1/\omega C_2}.$$

When $$\frac{Z_1}{Z_2} = 0, \; \omega = \frac{1}{\sqrt{L_1 C_1}}.$$

When $$\frac{Z_1}{Z_2} = -4, \; \frac{\omega^2 L_1 C_1 C_2 - C_2}{\omega^2 L_2 C_1 C_2 - C_1} = -4,$$

or $$\omega = \sqrt{\left(\frac{4C_1 + C_2}{C_1 C_2 (L_1 + 4L_2)}\right)}.$$

That is, the filter passes the range of frequencies lying between

$$\frac{1}{2\pi}\frac{1}{\sqrt{L_1 C_1}} \text{ and } \frac{1}{2\pi}\sqrt{\left(\frac{4C_1 + C_2}{C_1 C_2 (L_1 + 4L_2)}\right)}.$$

4. Acoustical Filters.

The electrical wave filters suggested to Stewart * the possibility of devising acoustical filters on similar lines and of course under similar limitations, i.e. any section of the line must be short compared with the wave-length of the sound concerned in order that the phase may be regarded as uniform throughout it, and the line must be a tube or conduit confining the waves in transmission.

A filter consists essentially of a main transmission tube with side branches placed at intervals along it. The displacement at a junction will be propagated partly down the main tube and partly through

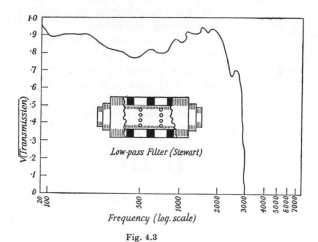

Fig. 4.3

the branch. Low-pass filters are made by two concentric cylinders joined by equally spaced partitions perpendicular to the axis. Each chamber thus formed has a ring of holes connecting the air in the inner tube which acts as the transmission line with the air in the space between the cylinders. Using four sections each of length 1·6 cm. with an inner tube of radius 1·2 cm. Stewart obtained a high transmission up to about 3000 cycles per second with almost no transmission above that frequency, although at certain high frequencies transmission again appeared. High-pass filters are made with a straight transmission tube having small side tubes fixed at regular intervals. When six sections were used these were found to cut out frequencies below about 800 and give large transmission for higher frequencies. By combining these types a band-pass filter is constructed. The efficiency of these filters is indicated in fig. 4.3, which applies to the

* *Phys. Rev.*, Vol. 20, p. 528 (1922).

low-pass filter. They show a marked lack of precision as compared with electrical filters.

An approximate value of the cut-off frequency can be calculated in each case by a direct application of the analysis suitable for the electrical analogue, but some uncertainty is introduced by the difficulty of determining whether in any given case the mass reactance and capacity reactance are to be treated as in series or in parallel.

5. Propagation of Sound in Horns.

In considering the propagation of sound in horns we shall assume that the conditions are uniform over any transverse section of the horn, that the disturbance is small and that the wave-length is large compared with the diameter of the section.

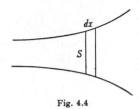

Fig. 4.4

We shall first derive the equation of continuity. If S is the area of the horn at distance x from the origin (fig. 4.4) then the mass of air entering the element defined by two transverse sections at distance dx will be $S\rho\dot\xi\,dt$ and the mass leaving across the other face will be greater by $(\partial/\partial x)(S\rho\dot\xi)\,dx\,dt$. This decrease of mass must be

$$-\frac{\partial}{\partial t}\,(\rho S\,dx)\,dt.$$

Equating these two expressions we have

$$\frac{\partial}{\partial t}\,(\rho S) + \frac{\partial}{\partial x}\,(S\rho\dot\xi) = 0,$$

or

$$S\frac{\partial\rho}{\partial t} + \rho\dot\xi\frac{\partial S}{\partial x} + S\frac{\partial}{\partial x}\,(\rho\dot\xi) = 0. \quad . \quad . \quad (4.21)$$

Putting $\rho = \rho_0(1 + s)$ and neglecting $s\dot\xi$ as compared with $\dot\xi$, we have

$$\rho_0 S\frac{\partial s}{\partial t} + \rho_0\dot\xi\frac{\partial S}{\partial x} + S\rho_0\frac{\partial\dot\xi}{\partial x} = 0,$$

$$\therefore S\frac{\partial s}{\partial t} + \frac{\partial}{\partial x}\,(S\dot\xi) = 0. \quad . \quad . \quad . \quad (4.22)$$

As on pp. 59, 60, we have

$$\dot\phi = c^2 s \text{ and } \dot\xi = -\frac{\partial\phi}{\partial x};$$

$$\therefore \ddot\phi - \frac{c^2}{S}\frac{\partial}{\partial x}\left(S\frac{\partial\phi}{\partial x}\right) = 0,$$

or
$$\ddot{\phi} = c^2 \frac{\partial^2 \phi}{\partial x^2} + c^2 \frac{\partial \phi}{\partial x} \frac{\partial}{\partial x} (\log S). \quad . \quad . \quad . \quad (4.23)$$

In the simplest approximation, where the length l of the horn is small compared with the wave-length, this equation can be integrated directly, for, neglecting $\ddot{\phi}$, we have

$$\frac{\partial^2 \phi}{\partial x^2} + \frac{\partial \phi}{\partial x} \frac{\partial}{\partial x} (\log S) = 0, \quad . \quad . \quad . \quad . \quad (4.24)$$

$$\text{or} - \frac{\partial \phi}{\partial x} S = \dot{\xi} S = \text{constant} = \dot{X}, \text{ say.}$$

Thus to this approximation the medium is to be regarded as incompressible.

Then
$$\phi_1 - \phi_2 = \dot{X} \int_0^l \frac{dx}{S} = \dot{X}/C$$

$$\dot{X} = C(\phi_1 - \phi_2),$$

where C is the conductivity as previously defined on p. 105, and $\dot{X}$ is the volume flow.

The above equation $\ddot{\phi} = c^2 \frac{\partial^2 \phi}{\partial x^2} + c^2 \frac{\partial \phi}{\partial x} \frac{\partial}{\partial x} (\log S)$, which is essentially the same as that derived by Webster [*], has been made the foundation of subsequent discussion of the function of the horn. Its solution depends on the relation of S and x. Obviously in the case of a cylindrical pipe S is constant. Then $\partial(\log S)/\partial x = 0$, and we have the equation for the propagation of plane waves,

$$\ddot{\phi} = c^2 \frac{\partial^2 \phi}{\partial x^2}.$$

The next simplest case is the case of the exponential horn, for which $S = S_1 e^{mx}$,

or
$$\frac{\partial}{\partial x} (\log S) = m$$

and
$$\ddot{\phi} = c^2 \left[m \frac{\partial \phi}{\partial x} + \frac{\partial^2 \phi}{\partial x^2} \right]. \quad . \quad . \quad (4.25)$$

If we confine our attention to the case of simple harmonic waves we can put

$$\ddot{\phi} = -\omega^2 \phi \ .$$

[*] *Proc. Nat. Acad. Sci.*, Vol. 5, p. 275 (1919).

and the equation takes the form

$$\frac{\partial^2 \phi}{\partial x^2} + m \frac{\partial \phi}{\partial x} + \frac{\omega^2}{c^2} \phi = 0, \quad \ldots \quad (4.26)$$

the solution of which we have already (p. 48) found to be of the form

$$\phi = A_1 e^{r_1 x} + A_2 e^{r_2 x}, \quad \ldots \quad (4.27)$$

where r_1, r_2, are the roots of the equation

$$r^2 + mr + \frac{\omega^2}{c^2} = 0.$$

If
$$\frac{\omega^2}{c^2} > \frac{m^2}{4},$$

$$r_1 = -\frac{m}{2} + i \sqrt{\left(\frac{\omega^2}{c^2} - \frac{m^2}{4}\right)},$$

$$r_2 = -\frac{m}{2} - i \sqrt{\left(\frac{\omega^2}{c^2} - \frac{m^2}{4}\right)}.$$

If
$$\frac{\omega^2}{c^2} < \frac{m^2}{4},$$

$$r_1 = -\frac{m}{2} + \sqrt{\left(\frac{m^2}{4} - \frac{\omega^2}{c^2}\right)},$$

$$r_2 = -\frac{m}{2} - \sqrt{\left(\frac{m^2}{4} - \frac{\omega^2}{c^2}\right)}.$$

There is thus a critical frequency for the functioning of the horn given by

$$\omega = \frac{cm}{2},$$

i.e.
$$f = \frac{cm}{4\pi} \quad \text{or} \quad \lambda = \frac{4\pi}{m}.$$

The greater the value of m, i.e. the more rapid the flare of the horn, the shorter is the wave-length at which this critical change in the functioning takes place.

Let
$$k = \frac{\omega}{c} = \frac{2\pi}{\lambda};$$

then
$$\frac{\omega^2}{c^2} - \frac{m^2}{4} = k^2 - \frac{m^2}{4} = \tfrac{1}{4}(4k^2 - m^2).$$

Hence for the case of $\dfrac{\omega^2}{c^2} > \dfrac{m^2}{4}$

$$r_1 = -\frac{m}{2} + \frac{i}{2}\sqrt{(4k^2 - m^2)} = -a + i\beta, \text{ say,}$$

$$r_2 = -\frac{m}{2} - \frac{i}{2}\sqrt{(4k^2 - m^2)} = -a - i\beta,$$

$$\therefore \ \phi = e^{-ax}[A_1 e^{i\beta x} + A_2 e^{-i\beta x}]e^{i\omega t}$$
$$= e^{-ax}[A_1 \cos(\omega t + \beta x) + A_2 \cos(\omega t - \beta x)]. \quad (4.28)$$

If there is an open end of fairly large area the reflection from it can be neglected and we have

$$\phi = e^{-ax}A_2 \cos(\omega t - \beta x). \quad \ldots \ldots \quad (4.29)$$

The dissipation factor e^{-ax} is due not to frictional dissipation, which has been neglected, but to the change in cross-section of the horn. It increases as m increases, since $a = m/2$.

The effective velocity is given by ω/β, instead of $\lambda f = \dfrac{\lambda \omega}{2\pi} = \dfrac{\omega}{k}$ if there had been no dissipation.

Hence $\qquad \dfrac{c'}{c} = \dfrac{k}{\beta} = \dfrac{k}{\sqrt{(k^2 - m^2/4)}}, \quad \ldots \ldots \quad (4.30)$

so that as the critical frequency given by $k^2 = m^2/4$ is approached c' becomes very large and the vibrations in the horn are almost in phase throughout.

It can be shown * that the mean rate of radiation of energy from the open end of the horn is given by

$$\frac{dW}{dt} = \frac{\rho c A^2}{2S_1 S_2}\sqrt{\left(1 - \frac{m^2 c^2}{4\omega^2}\right)}. \quad \ldots \ldots \quad (4.31)$$

In this expression S_1, S_2 are the areas of cross-section of the two ends of the horn and A is the strength of the source operating at the narrow end. This expression brings out the real importance of the critical value of the frequency and wave-length already found. For $f < cm/4\pi$ or $\lambda > 4\pi/m$ the horn transmits no radiation at all. The frequency $cm/4\pi$ is therefore the cut-off frequency and the horn is a high-pass filter which suppresses all radiation of low frequency. We shall later consider what this means in the practical design of horns.

---

* See Crandall, *Theory of Vibrating Systems and Sound*, p. 161 (Van Nostrand Co., New York, 1926).

Meantime it may be noted that a similar discussion of the conical horn * gives

$$\frac{dW}{dt} = \frac{\rho c A^2}{2 S_1 S_2} \frac{k^2 x_1^{\,2}}{1 + k^2 x_1^{\,2}}. \quad \cdots \cdots \quad (4.32)$$

Here A, S_1, S_2 have the same significance as for the exponential horn and x_1 is the distance of the narrow end from the vertex of the

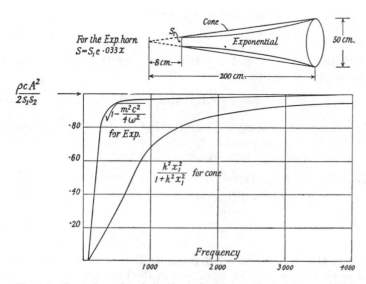

Fig. 4.5.—Comparison of conical and exponential horns having the same initial and final openings

cone of which the horn is a truncated section. Fig. 4.5 shows a comparison for two horns, one conical and the other exponential. Both have the same length, 192 cm., and the same initial and final areas. The larger end has a diameter of 50 cm. and the narrow end a diameter of 2 cm. This means that for the conical horn $x_1 = 8$ cm. and for the exponential horn $m = 0.033$. The immense superiority of the exponential horn over the conical form is evident from the fact that for similar dimensions—length and areas of initial and final sections all equal—the exponential horn radiates more energy, and above its cut-off frequency it radiates energy with almost equal efficiency from this frequency upwards.

The performances of the two types of horn may be compared with one another and with the cylindrical tube by using a summary given

* See Crandall, loc. cit.

by Davis.* Pressures and volume displacements at the two ends of the horn are related by the equations

$$p_2 = ap_1 + bX_1,$$
$$X_2 = fp_1 + gX_1,$$

where a, b, f, g depend on the shape of the horn and have the following values:

	Tubular Conduit	Conical Conduit $S = S_0 x^2$	Exponential Horn $S = S_0 e^{mx}$
a	$\cos kl$	$\dfrac{x_1}{x_2}\dfrac{\sin k(l + \epsilon_1)}{\sin k\epsilon_1}$	$e^{-(ml/2)}\left[\dfrac{m}{2\gamma}\sin\gamma l + \cos\gamma l\right]$
b	$\dfrac{\beta}{S}\sin kl$	$\dfrac{\beta}{S_1}\dfrac{x_1}{x_2}\sin kl$	$\dfrac{\beta k}{S_1 \gamma}e^{-(ml/2)} . \sin kl$
f	$-\dfrac{S}{\beta}\sin kl$	$-\dfrac{S_2 x_1}{\beta x_2}\cdot\dfrac{\sin k(l + \epsilon_1 - \epsilon_2)}{\sin k\epsilon_1 . \sin k\epsilon_2}$	$-\dfrac{S_2 k}{\beta \gamma}e^{-(ml/2)} . \sin\gamma l$
g	$\cos kl$	$-\dfrac{S_2 x_1}{S_1 x_2}\cdot\dfrac{\sin k(l - \epsilon_2)}{\sin k\epsilon_2}$	$-\dfrac{S_2}{S_1}e^{-(ml/2)}\left[-\dfrac{m}{2\gamma}\sin\gamma l + \cos\gamma l\right].$

Here l is the length of the conduit $= x_1 - x_2$; $\beta = kc^2\rho_0$, $kx_1 = \tan k\epsilon_1$, $kx_2 = \tan k\epsilon_2$, and $\gamma^2 = k^2 - m^2/4$. (The suffix 1 relates to one end of the conduit and the suffix 2 to the other).

If Z_1 and Z_2 are the impedances at the two ends,

$$Z_1 = \frac{p_1}{\dot{X}_1} = \frac{p_1}{i\omega X_1}, \quad Z_2 = \frac{p_2}{\dot{X}_2} = \frac{p_2}{i\omega X_2},$$

and substituting from the above equations, we have

$$Z_1 = \frac{i\omega g Z_2 - b}{i\omega a + \omega^2 f Z_2} \quad\quad . \quad . \quad . \quad . \quad . \quad (4.33)$$

from which the impedance at one end of a horn can be deduced when that at the other end is given. The relation already deduced for the cylindrical tube is a particular case.

6. Design of Horns.

The horn is used mainly in association with a loud-speaker element or a gramophone sound-box. At the time it was first used its real function was not understood; the small horn on the old type of gramophone is a fairly clear indication of this. It was incapable of trans-

* *Modern Acoustics*, p. 206 (Bell, 1934).

mitting low frequencies and in the old gramophone the inadequacy of the bass was notorious. The horn is not primarily for confining the emitted sound to one direction, although it has some directive effect. Nor is it a resonator; the existence of resonances is fatal to good reproduction. Its primary purpose is to load the diaphragm at the narrow end by increasing the pressure against which it has to work and to deliver the energy it receives to the atmosphere over an area sufficiently large to avoid reflection back into the horn with consequent stationary vibration and resonance.

First of all, the throat of the horn must be small, and it is usually designed so that it opens out of a small chamber, of which the vibrating diaphragm constitutes the opposite side. The impedance of the air in this chamber may be adjusted to that of the diaphragm. The area of throat may be from 1 to 2 sq. cm.

Now we have seen that if there is no reflection from the open end, the exponential horn will give a nearly constant load for all frequencies above the cut-off. It will therefore give reproduction without distortion where it gives reproduction at all. Let us assume that we are going to make large demands on the horn and require that it shall transmit down to a frequency of 55. This is still about an octave above the lowest audible frequency. The corresponding wave-length is $\dfrac{1100}{55} = 20$ ft., and in order that the horn may transmit frequencies down to this we must have

$$\lambda \leqq \frac{4\pi}{m},$$

i.e.
$$m \leqq \frac{4\pi}{\lambda} = \frac{\pi}{5} \text{ ft.}^{-1} = 0 \cdot 63 \text{ ft.}^{-1}$$

In the discussion of the performance of the horn, however, it was assumed that there was no reflection from the open end, and this in turn may be regarded as a matter of adjusting the specific impedance, i.e. the impedance per unit area at the open end, to that of the open air. Crandall * has shown that the mouth of the horn may be treated approximately as part of a spherical source whose radius r_0 bears the following relation to R, the radius of the mouth:

$$S_2 = \pi R^2 = 1 \cdot 39 \, \pi r_0{}^2.$$

In this case the impedance is $\rho c S_2 (X' + iY')$,

where
$$X' = \frac{k^2 r_0{}^2}{k^2 r_0{}^2 + 1} \quad \text{and} \quad Y' = \frac{k r_0}{k^2 r_0{}^2 + 1};$$

* *Vibrating Systems and Sound*, p. 171.

obviously as k increases X' approaches 1, and Y' has a maximum for $kr_0 = 1$, after which it diminishes. The terms are set out with those for the flat piston in fig. 4.6, taken from Crandall's book. It is the resistance term which is increasing and the reactance term which is diminishing. When $X' = 1$, Y' is negligible, and the impedance is a pure resistance, $\rho c S_2$. Now for plane waves

$$p = Ks = c^2\rho s = c\rho v.$$

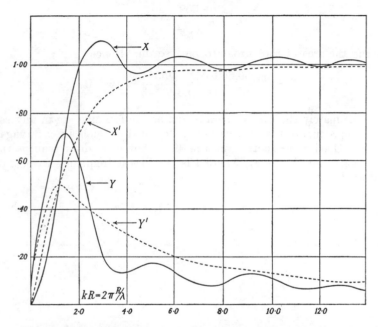

Fig. 4.6.—Impedance for piston, and for "equivalent" spherical surface (Crandall)

COMPARATIVE DATA

	Piston		Spherical Surface
Area	$\pi R^2 = S_2$	$=$	$1\cdot39\pi r_0^2$
Impedance	$\rho c\, S_2(X + iY)$		$\rho c\, S_2(X' + iY')$
Resistance Factor	$X = \left\{1 - \dfrac{\mathcal{J}_1(2kR)}{kR}\right\}$		$X' = \left\{\dfrac{k^2r_0^2}{k^2r_0^2 + 1}\right\}$
Resistance Factor	$Y = \left\{\dfrac{K_1(2kR)}{2k^2R^2}\right\}$		$Y' = \left\{\dfrac{kr_0}{k^2r_0^2 + 1}\right\}$

Note: $0\cdot85kR = kr_0$

Hence the unit area impedance $= p/v = c\rho$, so that in this case the impedance per unit area at the mouth of the horn is approximately the unit area impedance of the medium into which the waves are being radiated; there is little reflection and little resonance but a uniform radiation of all frequencies down to that corresponding to $X' = 1$.

As an approximation we can take our limit where $X' \doteqdot 0 \cdot 92$ and $2\pi R/\lambda = 4$, that is, $R = 2\lambda/\pi$.

Taking the same value of λ as before, we see that the radius of the mouth must be nearly 13 ft. Then $S_2 = \pi R^2 = 509$ sq. ft.

But
$$\log_e \frac{S_2}{S_1} = ml.$$

$$\therefore \ \log_e \frac{509}{1/72} = \cdot 63l,$$

taking the area of the throat to be 2 sq. in. Hence

$$l = \frac{\log_e 36,650}{\cdot 63} = \frac{4 \cdot 56}{\cdot 63 \times \cdot 43} = 16 \cdot 8 \ \text{ft.}$$

Fortunately the ear is tolerant and as the formulæ are in any case only approximate the horn is rarely designed on such an extravagant scale. Good reproduction in the bass, however, does require that $m \leqq 4\pi f/c$ and $R \geqq c/\pi f$, where f is the lowest frequency to be fully radiated.

CHAPTER V

Dissipation of Energy of Sound Waves

1. Causes of Dissipation of Energy.

Dissipation of energy in sound waves may be traced to three main causes. The first of these is viscosity. Whenever the layers of a medium are in relative motion the viscous forces opposing this relative motion must be overcome, and this involves the transformation of the mechanical energy of the waves into heat.

The second cause of dissipation of energy is heat conduction. When layers of air are compressed during the propagation of the waves their temperature is raised, while the temperature of the neighbouring layers which are in a state of rarefaction is correspondingly lowered. There is thus a tendency for heat to be conducted from the compression to the rarefaction, and this passage of heat down a temperature gradient means an increase of entropy and so a dissipation of energy. Stokes showed that this dissipation of energy could only be avoided if the compressions and rarefactions took place either under strictly adiabatic conditions or under strictly isothermal conditions. The velocity of sound as determined experimentally corresponds to transformations of the former type. It was supposed that the changes are so rapid that there is no time for transfer of heat to occur. It has been pointed out, however, by Herzfeld and Rice * that the rate of heat conduction is proportional to the temperature gradient and that for a given amplitude of wave this is inversely proportional to the square of the wave-length and therefore directly proportional to the square of the frequency. In travelling equal distances waves of given displacement amplitude will undergo changes in s which are proportional to the change of temperature due to conduction, and therefore proportional to $f^2 \div 1/f$, since the thermal capacity per wave varies as $1/f$. The compression s itself, however, varies directly as f and is therefore subject to a percentage change depending on f^2. It should be noticed, therefore, that adiabatic conditions are approximately maintained *because of the slowness of the oscillations*, and at high frequencies interesting phenomena of dispersion and absorption may be expected.

* *Phys. Rev.*, Vol. 31, p. 691 (1928).

The third cause of dissipation of energy is radiation of heat from the compressions to the rarefactions. Here again we have heat running down a temperature gradient, with consequent dissipation of energy.

A further cause of absorption is to be found in intermolecular exchanges of energy, either between molecules of different gases, or between different degrees of freedom of one gas.

We have seen that the equation

$$\frac{\partial^2 \xi}{\partial t^2} = c^2 \frac{\partial^2 \xi}{\partial x^2} \qquad \ldots \ldots \ldots \quad (5.1)$$

is satisfied by a plane wave of simple harmonic type for which the equation (2.20, p. 55) is

$$\xi = a \sin \omega \left(t - \frac{x}{c} \right)$$

where c, the phase velocity, is equal to λ / T.

This type of wave can also be represented by the real part of

$$\xi = a e^{i\omega(t - x/c)}. \qquad \ldots \ldots \ldots \quad (5.2)$$

Similarly, a wave proceeding in the opposite direction may be represented by

$$\xi = a e^{i\omega(t + x/c)}. \qquad \ldots \ldots \ldots \quad (5.3)$$

For sound waves where damping is assumed negligible we have the differential equation (2.22, p. 56),

$$\frac{\partial^2 \xi}{\partial t^2} = \frac{K}{\rho} \frac{\partial^2 \xi}{\partial x^2}$$

or alternatively (2.27),

$$\frac{\partial^2 \dot{\xi}}{\partial t^2} = \frac{K}{\rho} \frac{\partial^2 \dot{\xi}}{\partial x^2}, \qquad \ldots \ldots \ldots \quad (5.4)$$

and

$$c = \sqrt{\frac{K}{\rho}}.$$

In considering the effect of viscous damping we shall follow the treatment of Crandall.*

At any point x in the cylindrical element of the medium under consideration the excess pressure $p = Ks = -K(\partial \xi / \partial x)$. The resultant pressure on a transverse lamina of thickness δx is therefore given by $(\partial p / \partial x) \delta x$ or $-K(\partial^2 \xi / \partial x^2) \delta x$. In part this excess pressure is used to generate momentum amounting to $\rho(\partial^2 \xi / \partial t^2) \delta x$ per second, and in part to overcome frictional resistance.

* *Vibrating Systems and Sound*, p. 96.

If $R_1(\partial\xi/\partial t)$ is equal to the component of the pressure gradient $\partial p_f/\partial x$ which is in phase with the particle velocity, then the resultant force due to this is $R_1\dfrac{\partial\xi}{\partial t}\delta x$,

$$\rho\frac{\partial^2\xi}{\partial t^2}\delta x + R_1\frac{\partial\xi}{\partial t}\delta x - K\frac{\partial^2\xi}{\partial x^2}\delta x - 0$$

or, alternatively,

$$\rho\frac{\partial^2\dot\xi}{\partial t^2} + R_1\frac{\partial\dot\xi}{\partial t} - K\frac{\partial^2\dot\xi}{\partial x^2} = 0. \quad\ldots\quad (5.5)$$

This is the original wave equation with the addition of a friction term and may be compared with the electrical equation

$$L\frac{\partial^2 j}{\partial t^2} + R\frac{\partial j}{\partial t} - \frac{1}{C}\frac{\partial^2 j}{\partial x^2} = 0.$$

Assuming a solution of the form

$$v = ae^{i\omega(t - x/c_1)}$$

we have

$$-\omega^2\rho + iR_1\omega = -\frac{K}{c_1^2}\omega^2,$$

$$\therefore\quad \frac{1}{c_1^2} = \frac{\rho}{K} - \frac{iR_1}{\omega K} = \frac{1}{c^2}\left(1 - \frac{iR_1}{\omega\rho}\right). \quad\ldots\quad (5.6)$$

If $R_1/\omega\rho$ is a small quantity,

$$\frac{1}{c_1} = \frac{1}{c}\left(1 - \frac{iR_1}{2\omega\rho}\right). \quad\ldots\ldots\quad (5.7)$$

A complex value for the wave " velocity " is the natural consequence of the dissipation:

$$v = ae^{i\omega(t - x/c + iR_1 x/2\omega\rho c)}$$

$$= ae^{-ax}e^{i(\omega t - \beta x)} \quad\ldots\ldots\quad (5.8)$$

where $\beta = \omega/c$ and $a = R_1/2\rho c$; a is called the *attenuation constant*.

2. Effect of Viscosity.

In the case of a gaseous medium it has been shown by Stokes * and Rayleigh † that the differential equation for the wave motion becomes

$$\rho\frac{\partial^2 v}{\partial t^2} = K\frac{\partial^2 v}{\partial x^2} + \frac{4}{3}\eta\frac{\partial^3 v}{\partial x^2\partial t}.$$

* *Trans. Cambr. Phil. Soc.*, Vol. 8, p. 297 (1845).   † *Sound*, Second Ed., Vol. II, § 346.

This equation is identical with that just discussed if

$$R_1 v = -\frac{4}{3}\eta\,\frac{\partial^2 v}{\partial x^2} = \frac{4}{3}\eta\,\frac{\omega^2}{c^2}\,v,$$

since

$$\frac{\partial^2 v}{\partial x^2} = -\frac{\omega^2}{c^2}\,v.$$

Putting the solution in the form

$$v = a e^{-a_1 x} e^{i\omega(t - x/c)} \quad \cdots \quad (5.9)$$

we have

$$a_1 = \frac{R_1}{2\rho c} = \frac{2}{3}\cdot\frac{\eta}{\rho}\cdot\frac{\omega^2}{c^3} = \frac{2}{3}\frac{\nu\omega^2}{c^3} \quad \cdots \quad (5.10)$$

where $\nu = \eta/\rho$ is the coefficient of kinematic viscosity.

It will be seen from this that when a correction term is inserted in the wave equation an approximate solution is obtained of the type $e^{i(\omega t - k_1 x)}$, where in general the constant k_1 is complex and may be written in the form $\beta - ia$. The velocity has become $c' = \omega/\beta$ and the attenuation constant for amplitude is a.

In general it may happen that c' depends on the frequency, in which case we get dispersion, but in the particular case of viscous damping the effect on the velocity is negligible, and that on the amplitude may be estimated by putting

$$a_x = a_0 e^{-a_1 x}$$

where (from 5.10)

$$a_1 = \frac{2\pi^2 f^2}{c^3}\cdot\frac{4\nu}{3} \quad \cdots \quad (5.11)$$

Here a_0 is the initial amplitude of a plane wave, a_x the amplitude after traversing distance x, c the velocity of sound, f the frequency, and ν the kinematic viscosity, i.e. the ratio of viscosity to density. Since $c = f\lambda$, $f^2/c^2 = 1/\lambda^2$, and we may write $a_x = a_0 e^{-(a_1'/\lambda^2)x}$, where $a_1' = a_1 \lambda^2 = 8\pi^2\nu/3c$.

For air at 15° C. we have $\nu = 0\cdot146$ c.g.s., $c = 3\cdot4 \times 10^4$ cm./sec.

$$\therefore \ a_1' = 1\cdot13 \times 10^{-4} \doteqdot 10^{-4}.$$

If l represents the value of x during which the amplitude falls off in the ratio of 1 to $1/e$, we have

$$e^{-1} = \frac{a_l}{a_0} = e^{-(l/10^4\lambda^2)}$$

$$\therefore \ l = 10^4\lambda^2.$$

From this expression we see at once that attenuation from this cause is very small for ordinary wave-lengths but increases very rapidly for short wave-lengths.

Thus for the shortest audible waves $\lambda \fallingdotseq 1\cdot7$ cm., $l \fallingdotseq 300$ metres.

For the longest audible waves $\lambda \fallingdotseq 1700$ cm., $l \fallingdotseq 3 \times 10^{10}$ cm., or about 190,000 miles.

3. Effect of Heat Conduction.

This was first treated by Stokes [*] and subsequently by Kirchhoff [†] (1824-1887) and Rayleigh.[‡]

In this case the effect may be similarly expressed by a relationship of the form $a_x = a_0 e^{-a_2 x}$, where

$$a_2 = \frac{2\pi^2 f^2}{c^3} \cdot \frac{(\gamma - 1)k'}{\gamma}. \quad \ldots \ldots \quad (5.12)$$

Here k' is the thermometric conductivity

$$= \frac{\text{Heat conductivity}}{\text{Heat capacity per unit volume}} = \frac{k}{C_v \rho},$$

k the heat conductivity, C_v the specific heat at constant volume, ρ the density, γ the ratio of specific heats.

It is worth noting that the kinetic theory of gases gives us $k = F\eta C_v$, where η is the viscosity and F is a constant equal to $1\cdot78$ for air.[§] It follows that the thermometric conductivity is $F\eta C_v / \rho C_v = F\nu$, where ν is the kinematic viscosity. The two effects are therefore in the ratio

$$\frac{\gamma - 1}{\gamma} F\nu : \frac{4\nu}{3}$$

i.e.
$$\frac{\gamma - 1}{\gamma} \cdot \tfrac{3}{4}F : 1 \quad \text{or} \quad 0\cdot38 : 1,$$

so that conduction contributes less than internal friction.

Substituting $\quad \dfrac{1}{\lambda^2} = \dfrac{f^2}{c^2}$ as before,

we have $\quad a_x = a_0 e^{-a_2' x/\lambda^2}$

where $\quad a_2' = a_2\lambda^2 = \dfrac{2\pi^2}{c} \cdot \dfrac{\gamma - 1}{\gamma} k'. \quad \ldots \ldots \quad (5.13)$

Inserting the appropriate values for air we have $k = 5\cdot49 \times 10^{-5}$ c.g.s., $C_v = 0\cdot172$ calories/gm., $\rho_0 = 1\cdot23 \times 10^{-3}$ gm./c.c., $\gamma = 1\cdot4$, $k' = 0\cdot26$, $a_2' = 4\cdot3 \times 10^{-5}$.

---

[*] *Phil. Mag.*, Vol. 1, p. 305 (1851).   [†] *Pogg. Ann.*, Vol. 134, p. 177 (1868).
[‡] *Phil. Mag.*, Vol. 47, p. 308 (1899).
[§] Roberts, *Heat and Thermodynamics*, 3rd. ed., p. 225 (Blackie & Son, Ltd., 1939).

Hence the distance traversed while the amplitude falls as before in the ratio $e : 1$ is given by $l = 23,000\lambda^2$. Combining these two effects, which both vary with λ in the same way, we have

$$a_x = a_0 e^{-(\alpha_1' + \alpha_2')x/\lambda^2},$$

$$\therefore l = \frac{\lambda^2}{\alpha_1' + \alpha_2'} = \frac{\lambda^2}{11\cdot3 \times 10^{-5} + 4\cdot3 \times 10^{-5}}$$

$$= \frac{\lambda^2}{1\cdot56 \times 10^{-4}}$$

$$= 6\cdot4 \times 10^3 \lambda^2.$$

The very great variation of penetration with wave-length is here shown if we consider again the two special cases

$$\lambda = 1\cdot7 \text{ cm.}; \qquad l \doteqdot 200 \text{ metres,}$$

and $\qquad\qquad \lambda = 1700 \text{ cm.}; \qquad l \doteqdot 200,000 \text{ kilometres.}$

4. Effect of Heat Radiation.

This factor is more difficult to evaluate. Stokes * puts the amplitude relation in the form

$$a_x = a_0 e^{-(\gamma-1)/\gamma \cdot (q/2c)x}, \quad \ldots \ldots \quad (5.14)$$

where q is defined by the rate of cooling, at constant volume, of a mass of gas. If θ_t is the excess temperature at time t, θ_0 the excess temperature at time 0, then $\theta_t = \theta_0 e^{-qt}$.

Rayleigh has experimented directly on the cooling of a mass of air, using it as a constant-volume thermometer. The diameter of the sphere used was 35 cm. and the time taken to reduce the excess temperature to half was 26 seconds. Assuming the mass of air heated in a wave to be that corresponding to half a wave-length, we might apply this figure to waves of wave-length 70 cm. This gives

$$26q = \log_e 2 = 0\cdot692,$$

$$\therefore q = 0\cdot027,$$

$$\therefore \frac{\gamma-1}{\gamma} \cdot \frac{q}{2c} = 1\cdot14 \times 10^{-7} \text{ for a wave-length of 70 cm.}$$

Subsequent experiments † with the apparatus of Clement and Désormes did not indicate any modification in the order of magnitude of this correction.

Here again we have an attenuation factor of the same order as the other two, but one which does not vary in the same way with the wave-length.

---

* *Phil. Mag.*, Vol. 1, p. 305 (1851).   † Rayleigh, *Phil. Mag.*, Vol. 47, p. 314 (1899).

5. Audibility and Pitch.

The variation of penetrative power with wave-length suggested by this discussion does not at first sight seem to be borne out by common observations. This, however, is due to the fact that the atmosphere can rarely, if ever, be regarded as a still homogeneous medium, and that the ear is more sensitive to frequencies of about 2000 cycles/sec. than to any others. Observations by Stewart,[*] for instance, indicate that in the case of the noise of an aeroplane low-pitched sounds are the best heard when hearing conditions are bad and high-pitched sounds when hearing conditions are good. In the first case the atmospheric irregularities have a much greater scattering effect on the shorter wave-lengths. In the second case the good audibility of the high-pitched notes is to be ascribed to the properties of the ear rather than to those of the medium.

6. Direct Measurement of Attenuation.

This measurement has been attempted by Duff.[†] He used a series of eight whistles and assumed that for two sounds of the same pitch and equality the same intensity will be given at the point where they cease to be heard.

If
$$a_x = a_0 e^{-ax},$$

then
$$I_x = I_0 e^{-2ax},$$

where I_x and I_0 are the intensities, i.e. the rates of flow of sound energy per unit area perpendicular to the direction of propagation.

Using eight whistles and two whistles and assuming that the intensities at the source are in the ratio of four to one for the two cases, we have, if R, r are the distances,

$$\frac{4e^{-2aR}}{R^2} = \frac{e^{-2ar}}{r^2}$$

or
$$e^{-2a(R-r)} = \frac{R^2}{4r^2},$$

whence
$$a(R - r) = \log_e \frac{2r}{R}$$

and
$$a = \frac{\log_e (2r/R)}{R - r}.$$

---

* *Phys. Rev.*, Vol. 14, p. 376 (1919).   † *Phys. Rev.*, Vol. 6, p. 129 (1898).

If there were no dissipation the inverse square law would hold and we should have $a = 0$, $R = 2r$.

In an actual experiment Duff obtained $R = 754$, $r = 634$ metres, whence $\alpha \doteqdot 4\cdot3 \times 10^{-5}$. His mean result was $4\cdot2 \times 10^{-5}$. It is interesting to compare this with the results of the theoretical calculations. For the combined effects of viscosity and conduction we found (p. 128)

$$\alpha = (\alpha_1' + \alpha_2')/\lambda^2 = \frac{1\cdot56 \times 10^{-4}}{\lambda^2}.$$

In this experiment $\lambda = 5$ cm.; hence $\alpha = 6\cdot24 \times 10^{-6}$.

If Duff's experimental value for α is $4\cdot2 \times 10^{-5}$ then the fraction of this contributed by radiation must be the difference of these two numbers, i.e. $3\cdot6 \times 10^{-5}$. This is very much greater than the value obtained by Rayleigh ($1\cdot2 \times 10^{-7}$). In discussing this discrepancy Rayleigh * maintains that some other factor must be operating and that Duff's value for the radiation correction is impossibly high. Duff later repeated his experiments † and confirmed his value for α.

Experiments were subsequently made by Hart ‡, using a small siren as a source and measuring the intensity at different points with resonating hot-wire microphones. The working pressure of the siren in these experiments never rose above 4 or 5 lb. per square inch, but the experiments showed that very considerable losses occurred. In particular, it was found that between two points 40 cm. and 100 cm. from the source respectively the intensity was reduced in the ratio of about $7\cdot4$ to 1. Correcting this value for the divergence of the waves we get $7\cdot4 \times (40)^2/(100)^2 = 1\cdot18$. But since the intensity ratio is given by $e^{2\alpha(100 - 40)}$, we have

$$1\cdot18 = e^{120\alpha},$$

so that
$$\alpha = \frac{\log_e 1\cdot18}{120} = \frac{\cdot165}{120} = 1\cdot4 \times 10^{-3}.$$

This gives a still higher value for α and suggests that in the neighbourhood of the source energy losses are much higher; but the theory of the experiments is open to grave criticism.

7. Absorption of High-frequency Waves in Gases.

Taking into account all the foregoing causes of dissipation we may write

$$a_x = a_0 e^{-(\alpha'/\lambda^2)\, x}.$$

If by I_x, I_0 we indicate the corresponding values of the intensity, then $I_x = I_0 e^{-mx}$, where

$$m = \frac{2\alpha'}{\lambda^2}. \qquad \ldots \ldots \ldots \quad (5.15)$$

This quantity $2\alpha'$ was called by Lebedew § the absorption constant, but he obtained for it a theoretical expression containing a term involving dissipation within the molecule and effective only at very

---

* *Phil. Mag.*, Vol. 47, p. 308 (1899).
‡ *Proc. Roy. Soc.*, A, Vol. 105, p. 80 (1924).
† *Phys. Rev.*, Vol. 11, p. 64 (1900).
§ *Ann. d. Physik*, Vol. 35, p. 171 (1911).

high frequencies. Experiments using a wave-length of the order of 1 mm. were carried out by Neklepajev [*] and led to a value of the absorption coefficient twice the theoretical value.

A great deal of experimental work has since been done, particularly in America.

Rich and Pielemeier [†], using a piezo-quartz generator and a torsion vane receiver, obtained a value lying between the theoretical one of Lebedew and the experimental one of Neklepajev. They found the absorption enormously increased when carbon dioxide was present in any considerable proportion.

This high absorption for carbon dioxide was also noticed by Pierce [‡] and was further investigated by Abello [§]. Abello worked with a frequency of 612,000 cycles/sec. and found that the intensity of the waves transmitted through a short tube fell in the ratio of 100 to 10 while the volume percentage of carbon dioxide was increased from 0 to 25. A similar effect was discovered in the case of hydrogen, the intensity of the transmitted waves falling from 100 to 5 while the volume percentage of hydrogen increased from 0 to 50. These results were confirmed and extended to the case of nitrous oxide [||]. Argon was found to show no trace of the effect.

Pielemeier [¶] has carried out a very complete series of experiments on oxygen. His source was a slab of quartz having the two large faces sputtered with platinum, and his receiver an interferometer which could be replaced by a torsion pendulum.

These results have been collected by Bergmann [**] in the following table of values for A, where $A = \dfrac{a}{f^2} = \dfrac{a'}{c^2} = \dfrac{m}{2f^2}$.

TABLE I

Measured and Calculated Values of Sound Absorption Coefficients in different Gases

Gas	Author	Frequency kc.	10^{-13} cm.$^{-1}$ sec.^{2}	
			a/f^2 Measured	a/f^2 Calc. by Class. Theory
Air	Neklepajev	132–415	2·94–3·99	1·45
	Pielemeier	1158–1408	1·67–1·99	1·45
	Grossmann	178	2.72	1·45
O_2	Pielemeier	655–1219	3·47–1·90	1·78
CO_2	Abello	612	46·5	1·60
	Grossmann	64	277	1·60
		99	540	1·60
		178	240	1·60
A	Abello	612	0	2·0

[*] *Ann. d. Physik*, Vol. 35, p. 175 (1911).   [†] *Phys. Rev.*, Vol. 25, p. 117 (1925).
[‡] *Proc. Amer. Acad. Arts and Sci.*, Vol. 60, p. 271 (1925).
[§] *Proc. Nat. Acad. Sci.*, Vol. 13, p. 699 (1927).
[||] *Phys. Rev.*, Vol. 31, p. 1083 (1928).
[¶] *Phys. Rev.*, Vol. 35, p. 1417 (1930); Vol. 36, p. 1006 (1930).
[**] *Ultrasonics* (Bell, 1938).

It will be seen that at high frequencies the classical causes of absorption become negligible compared with intra-molecular causes.

Meantime the matter was being approached from another angle. It had been noticed by P. E. Sabine * during experiments on reverberation time for rooms that for frequencies of 2000 and over the absorption increases rapidly when the relative humidity of the air is low. A similar observation had been made by Meyer †. Knudsen ‡ in a series of experiments on reverberation time for a frequency of 6000 and a relative humidity of 20 per cent found

$$m = 1\cdot 6 \times 10^{-4}\,\text{cm}^{-1}.$$

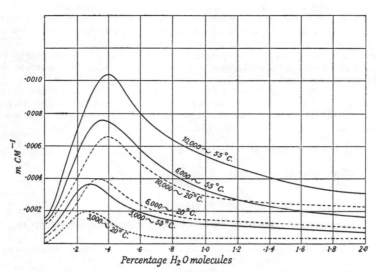

Fig. 5.1.—Curves showing the values of the absorption coefficient m for different concentrations of water vapour in air at temperatures of 20° C. and 55° C., for tones of 3000, 6000 and 10,000 cycles.

Returning to the method with improved apparatus and technique, Knudsen § used frequencies from 500 to 11,000 and relative humidity varying from 0 to 100 per cent. He found that for all frequencies the absorption is least for dry air, reaches a maximum at a relative humidity of from 5 to 20 per cent, according to the frequency, and diminishes for higher humidities. Fig. 5.1 shows the values of m deduced.

Extension of the experiments to include moist oxygen gave similar results, with larger maximum values for m (fig. 5.2). In the case of nitrogen, on the other hand, the value of m is much less and is independent of the humidity. Thus a large proportion of the absorption of audible sounds in air seems to be attributable to an interaction between the molecules of oxygen and of water.

* *Journ. Frankl. Inst.*, Vol. 207, p. 347 (1929).
† *Zeits. f. techn. Physik.*, Vol. 7, p. 253 (1930).
‡ *Journ. Amer. Soc. Acoust.*, Vol. 3, p. 126 (1931).
§ *Journ. Amer. Soc. Acoust.*, Vol. 5, p. 112 (1933).

As a result of all this experimental work the theoretical study of the phenomenon began to attract a good deal of attention. A useful clue had been given by Jeans,* who suggested that some of the absorption of sound might be attributed to an exchange of energy between the internal degrees of freedom of the molecules of a gas and the translational degrees of freedom. Jeans concluded that the effect was very small at ordinary frequencies. The explanation was developed and applied to the supersonic frequencies by Herzfeld and Rice † on the lines of classical theory. Bourgin ‡ applied quantum theory to the energy exchange, as did also Henry.§

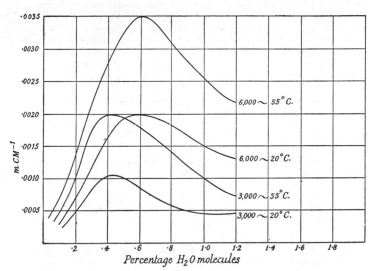

Fig. 5.2.—Curves showing values of m in oxygen and water vapour at temperatures of 20° C. and 55° C. Note that the maximum values of m are approximately five times as large as the corresponding maximum values for air shown in fig. 5.1.

Kneser ‖ explains the matter as follows: "When a gas is compressed adiabatically a certain amount of the energy supplied passes into the interior of the molecule as vibrational energy. In reversing the process the total amount of energy is regained if the cycle is performed sufficiently slowly. If the cycle is performed very rapidly no energy passes into the interior and so no energy is absorbed. If, however, the period of the cycle is comparable with the time required to establish thermal equilibrium between normal and vibrating molecules,

* *Dynamical Theory of Gases*, 2nd Ed., p. 374 (Cambridge University Press, 1916).
† *Phys. Rev.*, Vol. 31, p. 691 (1928).
‡ *Phil. Mag.*, Vol. 7, p. 821 (1929); *Phys. Rev.*, Vol. 34, p. 521 (1929).
§ *Proc. Cambr. Phil. Soc.*, Vol. 28, p. 249 (1931–2).
‖ *Journ. Amer. Soc. Acoust.*, Vol. 5, p. 122 (1933).

then a certain fraction of vibrational energy is retained in the molecule and does not reappear as mechanical energy in the wave. This appears as a rise in temperature of the gas."

The analysis given in this paper is based on Einstein [*] and is similar to that given by Henry [†] and Rutgers.[‡] With the insertion of known constants the expressions give values in close agreement with the experimental values of Knudsen, on the assumption that it is the vibrational energy of the oxygen molecule that is responsible. Since the absorption rises to about five times its value when pure oxygen is substituted for air and disappears almost completely in pure nitrogen, the absorption must be associated with the oxygen molecule. The equilibrium between rotational and translational energy is known to be reached in less than 10^{-6} sec. and therefore cannot affect sound waves of period greater than 10^{-4} sec. Kneser deduces from Knudsen's data that the "mean life" time of the vibrating molecule, or, more exactly, the "mean life" of a quantum of vibrational energy, is 4×10^{-5} sec. in oxygen at 20° C. with relative humidity 21·6 per cent. As the time between two successive collisions is about 3×10^{-10} sec. the quantum endures during about $1·3 \times 10^5$ collisions, of which 650 are with water molecules. Curiously enough, the results indicate that two water molecules are in each case involved in the process of transforming energy. The quantized vibrational energy is rarely transformed into any other kind of energy by means of collisions unless water molecules participate.

A valuable series of experimental investigations has been carried out by Richards and Reid.[§] These papers discuss experimental data which are not fully in accordance with the theory developed by Kneser.

The absorption coefficients in air and oxygen have been calculated by Kneser and Knudsen [||] for various frequencies and temperatures and are shown in the following table, where $a' = a\lambda^2$ and $I = I_0 e^{-2ax}$.

TABLE II

Sound Absorption Coefficients in Air and Oxygen as Measured and Calculated for different Temperatures (Kneser and Knudsen)

Gas	Temperature °C	Frequency kc.	$a'_{max} \times 10^4$	
			Observed	Calculated
Air	20	3	21·7 ± 2	21·8
	20	6	20·6 ± 1	21·8
	20	10	21·1 ± 1	21·8
	55	3	41·0 ± 6	39·4
	55	6	44·4 ± 4	39·4
	55	10	35·9 ± 4	39·4
Oxygen	20	3	106·0 ± 10	104·0
	20	6	103 ± 10	104·0
	55	3	201 ± 20	188·0
	55	6	189 ± 19	188·0

[*] *Ber. d. Berl. Akad.*, p. 380 (1920).   [†] *Proc. Cambr. Phil. Soc.*, Vol. 28, p. 249 (1932).
[‡] *Ann. d. Physik*, Vol. 16, p. 350 (1933).
[§] *J. Chem. Phys.*, Vol. 1, pp. 114, 737, 863 (1933); Vol. 2, pp. 193, 206, 263 (1934).
[||] *Ann. Phys. Lpz.*, Vol. 21, p. 682 (1934).

That is, $1/2a$ is the distance in wave-lengths passed over by the sound waves before the intensity is reduced in the ratio $1 : 1/e$; a'_{max} is the value of a' for the frequency giving maximum absorption. It will be seen that the agreement between calculation and observation is very good.

Associated with this abnormally high absorption are abnormally high values for the velocity of the supersonic waves. When the time period of vibration becomes comparable with the relaxation time or

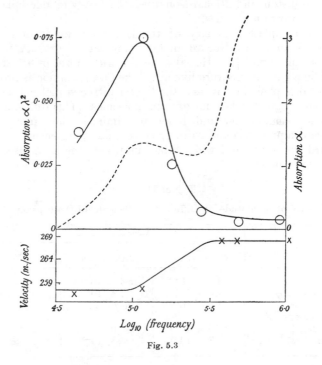

Fig. 5.3

mean life of a sound quantum there is an absorption of energy from the wave and an associated rise in γ, the ratio of specific heats.

This relation is shown clearly in fig. 5.3, which is based on the results of Kneser (l. c.) and Grossmann.*

There is, of course, an alternative explanation of some of the experimental results so far discussed; they may be attributed to a form of resonant absorption. On the theory developed by Kneser the form of the dispersion curve would be as shown above. On the resonant absorption theory we should expect with increasing frequency a moderate fall in velocity on both sides of a rather steep rise.

* *Phys. Zeits.*, Vol. 33, p. 202 (1932); *Ann. Phys. Lpz.*, Vol. 13, p. 681 (1932).

Tentative support is given to this latter view by Railston and Richardson in the discussion of experimental results obtained by them on the effect of pressure on dispersion.* This explanation also receives some support from the experiments of Pearson on dispersion in air,† the results of which will be considered together with the technique of measurement of velocity of sound at supersonic frequencies in § 7, p. 257. Measurements of absorption have for the most part been made by some form of acoustic interferometer (p. 258), although Railston and Richardson used the hot-wire microphone to compare velocity amplitudes.

A very complete summary of the factors in absorption so far considered is given by Rocard in his pamphlet on propagation and absorption of sound ‡. He also deals with absorption due to diffusion in a gaseous mixture like air. When a rarefaction is produced diffusion takes place into it, and the lighter nitrogen molecules diffuse more rapidly than the heavier oxygen molecules. This diffusion is an irreversible phenomenon and tends to diminish the amplitude of successive compressions and so to produce a damping effect.

Rocard gives the following table, in which the data used were collected by Kneser.

TABLE III

Order of Magnitude of Different Coefficients of Absorption

Cause	Value of m in c.g.s. at		
	6000 Cycles per sec.	8×10^5 Cycles per sec.	∞
Viscosity	3.6×10^{-6}	6.4×10^{-2}	∞
Heat conduction	4×10^{-7}	7×10^{-3}	6×10^4
Heat radiation	1.5×10^{-8}	negligible	negligible
Internal energy of molecules	1.16×10^{-5}	10^{-1}	2×10^{-1}
Diffusion	3×10^{-7}	5×10^{-3}	∞

8. Propagation of Sound Waves in Liquids.

The propagation of sound waves in water has recently assumed very great importance. Methods of production and reception of submarine sounds were greatly improved during the war of 1914–18, and the importance of submarine signals for the safety of shipping in times of peace is now being widely recognized.

Comparing water with air from this point of view, we note that the velocity in water is about 4·3 times as great, and consequently the

* *Proc. Phys. Soc.*, Vol. 47, p. 533 (1936). † *Proc. Phys. Soc.*, Vol. 47, p. 136 (1935).
‡ *Propagation et Absorption du Son* (Hermann et Cie., Paris, 1935).

wave-length of a sound of given frequency about 4·3 times as long as in air.

We shall see later (p. 289) that the energy flux across unit area normal to the propagation of the waves is given by

$$I = \frac{2\pi^2 a^2 \rho c^3}{\lambda^2} = 2\pi^2 a^2 \rho f^2 c.$$

Hence, if we assume the same energy flux and a note of the same frequency,

$$a_1{}^2 \rho_1 c_1 = a_2{}^2 \rho_2 c_2,$$

$$\therefore \frac{a_1}{a_2} = \sqrt{\left(\frac{\rho_2 c_2}{\rho_1 c_1}\right)}.$$

If the suffix 1 refers to water and the suffix 2 to air, then

$$\frac{\rho_2}{\rho_1} = 1·29 \times 10^{-3}, \quad \frac{c_2}{c_1} = \frac{1}{4·3} = 2·3 \times 10^{-1},$$

$$\therefore \frac{a_1}{a_2} = 1·7 \times 10^{-2} \doteqdot \frac{1}{60}.$$

The pressures will be in the inverse ratio, i.e. the pressures developed in the water will be about 60 times as great as those developed in the air.

Even more important is the comparative penetration of waves in air and water. We have seen (p. 126) that as limited by viscosity the penetration of waves in air is given by $l = 0·88 \times 10^4 \lambda^2$, where l is the distance in which the amplitude is reduced in the ratio $e : 1$.

If we insert the values for water in the corresponding formula we have $c = 1·45 \times 10^5$ cm./sec., $\nu = 0·0114$ c.g.s., $l = 3c\lambda^2/8\pi^2\nu = 4·9 \times 10^5\lambda^2$. Hence for the same wave-length the penetration in water is about 55 times as great. If we take heat conduction into account we find that it is practically negligible for water waves, while for air we have $l = 6·4 \times 10^3\lambda^2$, so that the penetration is probably something like 77 times as great when this factor is taken into consideration. This is for the same wave-length. For the same frequency the wave-length is 4·3 times as great and the penetration $(4·3)^2 \times 77 \doteqdot 1400$ times as great. From this point of view the advantage of compression waves in water over electromagnetic waves in water is even more remarkable. For salt water $l \doteqdot \sqrt{\lambda}/61$. Consequently if we take $\lambda = 15,000$ metres, we have $l \doteqdot 2$ metres.

Biquard * gives a comparison of the values of A (p. 131) for various liquids as calculated from the classical formulæ. It will be seen that the effect of heat conduction is almost negligible in every case.

TABLE IV

Sound Absorption Coefficients ($A \times 10^{17}$) as calculated for different
Liquids (Biquard)

| Liquid | $A \times 10^{17}$ | | |
	Viscosity	Heat Conduction	Combined
Acetone	6·54	0·5	7·04
Ether	8·48	0·49	8·97
Benzene	8·36	0·3	8·66
Chloroform	10·045	0·057	10·1
Ethyl acetate ..	7·95	0·31	8·26
Methyl acetate ..	6·34	0·44	6·78
Meta-xylene ..	8·13	0·24	8·37
Toluene	7·56	0·28	7·84
Water	8·5	0·0064	8·5

Biquard made measurements of the absorption by using a torsion pendulum
to determine the radiation pressure at various distances and calculating the
intensity from the radiation pressure (see p. 154). Other measurements based
on determinations of radiation pressure have been made by Sörensen *. The
use of the torsion pendulum of course involves some disturbance of the wave
system, and in order to avoid this source of error Biquard † made use of the diffraction of light by ultrasonic waves (see Chap. X, p. 273). His apparatus was
similar to that of Wyss (fig. 10.18, p. 278). The trough containing the liquid in
which the waves are being propagated is moved across the beam of light and the
intensity of the sound waves calculated from observations on the diffracted light.
The following table gives the calculated and observed values of the coefficient
of absorption α for a frequency of 7958 kilocycles per second. It will be noticed
that the observed value is in every case much greater than the calculated value,
but the reason for this still awaits satisfactory elucidation.

TABLE V

Calculated and Measured Sound Absorption Coefficients
of different Liquids

Liquid	t	$\alpha \times 10^2$ Calculated	t	$\alpha \times 10^2$ Measured
Acetone	20	0·44	17	2
Benzene	20	0·54	17	58
Chloroform	20	0·66	18	30
Ether	20	0·57	18	3·5
Ethyl acetate ..	15	0·67	15	4·9
Meta-xylene ..	20	0·78	20	4·7
Methyl acetate ..	20	0·53	17	6·9
Toluene	20	0·49	20	5·4
Water	20	0·538	20	1·6

* *Ann. Phys. Lpz.*, Vol. 26, p. 121 (1936), Vol 27, p. 70 (1936).
† *Comptes Rendus*, Vol. 197, p. 309 (1933).

9. Reception of Sound Waves in Water.

The reception of sound waves in water offers no serious difficulty. Leonardo da Vinci (1452–1519) has been credited with listening to underwater sounds by applying his ear to the handle of an oar whose blade was immersed in the water. Francis Bacon describes an experiment in which a man descends under water with an inverted bucket over his head so that his mouth and nose are kept free from water. "Then let him speak; and any that shall stand without shall hear his voice plainly; but yet made extreme sharp and exile, like the voice of puppets: but yet the articulate sounds of the words will not be confounded." * The Abbé Nollet conducted experiments on the transmission of sound in water, as a preliminary accustoming himself to keeping his head immersed. There was at that time a controversy as to whether or not water was compressible, and upon the answer to this question hung the decision as to whether it could conduct sound. Nollet tried the method of direct attack. With his ears immersed four inches under water he heard a pistol shot, a small bell and a whistle, and understood loud speech, the sounds all being produced in air. The intensity he found to vary little with the depth, showing that most of the loss occurred at the surface. An alarm clock sounding in water was not audible when he had his head in the air, but with his ears immersed he found the sound extremely loud.

Practical experiments on submarine signalling were carried out in the United States Navy in 1894, and later practical tests were initiated and carried out by the Submarine Signal Company under the direction of the General Manager, Millet.† The microphones were immersed in liquid in two tanks fixed on the inside of the ship below the waterline. Signals from submarine bells could be heard over long distances under all sorts of weather conditions. With two tanks, one on each side of the ship, it was easily possible to compare the strengths of the two signals received and get a rough idea of the bearing of the source. It was possible to keep a course direct for the source by keeping the signal strengths equal. These tests also demonstrated the important fact that a bell in a water-tank in the forepeak of one vessel can be heard by another vessel at a distance of three or four nautical miles. The possibility of locating submarines by their water noises was suggested in the paper referred to, and the importance of this suggestion was fully realized during the war of 1914–18.

Colladon and Sturm in their pioneer experiments on the Lake of Geneva used a large horn, the open end of which was immersed in the water and the narrow end held to the ear. A simple form of receiver is the Broca tube. This was originally a stethoscope capable of

---

* Buckingham, *Matter and Radiation*, p. 5 (Oxford Univ. Press, 1930).
† *Trans. Inst. Naval Architects*, Vol. 47, p. 256 (1905).

being immersed in water. It consisted of a flat circular metal box, one of whose sides was a thin metal plate. A tube fixed into the centre of the opposite face led to the ear of the observer. The box may be replaced by the closed end of a rubber tube, the open end being inserted into the ear. The closed end is sometimes enlarged so as to form a spherical cavity. The rubber transmits the vibrations to the enclosed air. An arrangement similar in principle is the geophone, which consists of two metallic plates between which is compressed a flexible rubber ring. The upper plate is made massive to give it inertia, while the lower one is made light in order that its inertia may not seriously interfere with its motion. There is a shallow air space between the two plates which communicates by tube with the ear. In these methods

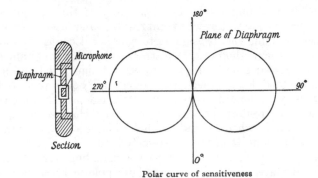

Polar curve of sensitiveness

Fig. 5.4.—Bidirectional hydrophone

of reception the vibrations remain mechanical throughout and the reception is not very efficient.

The most efficient methods are those which transform the mechanical vibrations into electrical. In the magnetophone, the vibrations of a thick rubber diaphragm are transmitted to a coil in a non-uniform magnetic field. The vibrations of the coil in this field generate an alternating E.M.F. which can be conveyed to a telephone. An electrostatic condenser with a movable plate can obviously be used in a similar way. The vibration of the movable plate gives rise to a variation of capacity which with a fixed charge causes a varying E.M.F. By far the most useful general method, however, is some form of carbon microphone (p. 512) such as is used in the telephone transmitter. There are two types: (a) the button type, (b) the solid type. In the first of these the carbon granules are loosely packed between two carbon plates, and the shaking of the granules causes variations in the conductivity of the mass of granules separating the plates. In the second type the granules are not free to move, but one plate is exposed to the varying pressure due to the waves and this pressure, transmitted to the granules, varies their resistance. In either case if the microphone is in series with a telephone and battery the variations of current will operate the telephone.

It is obviously very desirable not only to be able to hear a sound produced in water but to be able to locate its direction. A form of hydrophone * which offers possibilities of this kind and proved of service during the war of 1914–18 is shown in fig. 5.4. It consists of a heavy metal ring closed by a metal diaphragm. To the centre of this diaphragm is fixed a small chamber containing a button microphone. Connecting wires are led up an attached rod to a telephone head-piece. This hydrophone is bidirectional. When its edge is presented to the source of sound the pressures on the two sides of the diaphragm are equal and the microphone gives no response. The response is a maximum when it is rotated through 90°. The setting for zero response can be made with fair accuracy, but there is no in-dication in which direction along this line the source is to be sought. The intensity curve is as shown. By fitting one of these bidirectional hydrophones with a "baffle plate" supported a few inches away from one face of the diaphragm a single maximum can be observed when the other face points to the source. The intensity curve is now as shown

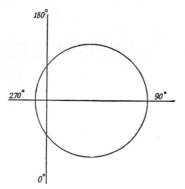

Fig. 5.5.—Polar curve of sensitiveness of hydrophone with baffle plate

in fig. 5.5. The hydrophone is unidirectional, but the maximum is not sharp enough for accurate setting. If the two types are com-bined, however, the bidirectional one can be used to fix the line in which the source lies and the unidirectional one then gives without ambiguity the direction along this line in which the source must be sought. The great practical disadvantage of this method is that though it works extremely well for fixed stations or for ships at rest, the noises produced by the motion of a moving ship makes listening with these hydrophones extremely difficult.

The action of the baffle plate is a little obscure, as it is too small to cast a true shadow with waves of the wave-length normally used.†

Propagation in the sea has, from the point of view of signalling, numerous advantages over propagation in the atmosphere. Not only is there much less dissipation of energy, as we have just seen, but in the sea we have a medium bounded above and below. Reflection at

* *Journ. Inst. Elect. Engineers*, Vol. 58, p. 572 (1919–20).
† *Proc. Roy. Soc.*, Vol. 100, p. 261 (1921–2).

the surface takes place almost without loss and reflection from the bottom is fairly copious. Then in the atmosphere temperature gradients refract the waves, air currents deflect them and eddies break them up. In the case of the sea all these effects are greatly diminished. Though the temperature gradient is small, its effects are noticeable and manifest themselves in a seasonal variation.

CHAPTER VI

Reflection of Sound Waves

1. Echoes.

The reflection of sound waves on a large scale is familiar to us in the echo frequently found from a cliff, the edge of a wood or the gable of a house. In a fog, if the audibility is good, a ship can be navigated along a cliff-bound coast by timing the interval between the sounding of a blast on the whistle and the receipt of an echo. Echoes are occasionally met with in large buildings. In every room there is a continual process of reflection taking place from floor, walls and ceiling whenever a sound is produced, but as a rule this gives the prolongation of sound known as *reverberation*. A separate and distinct echo can be heard only when a fairly pronounced reflection follows the initial sound at an interval sufficiently long for the ear to appreciate the two as distinct. This requires an interval of about 1/15 of a second and therefore a path difference of about 1120/15 or 75 feet. A large hall with curved surfaces which may act as concave mirrors for the sound beams is always liable to this defect, and glaring instances are on record. Where such defects exist they may be cured by covering the reflecting surface with a material which absorbs the sound waves and so diminishes the intensity of the echo. This subject will be more fully dealt with later (Chap. XIX).

Another type of reflection is illustrated by the Whispering Gallery of St. Paul's Cathedral. Here, as was suggested by Lord Rayleigh,* a sound emitted tangentially to the circular wall is carried round by successive reflections and is clearly heard at the opposite side. The phenomenon is assisted by the fact that the walls are dome-shaped and so hinder the spread of the sound upwards. The investigations carried out by Sutherland and Raman † show that the phenomenon is in reality more complicated than Rayleigh indicates, periodic changes of intensity occurring both round the wall and radially, but they corroborate Rayleigh's explanation in essentials.

The so-called " echelon " echo from a flight of steps belongs more

---

* *Phil. Mag.*, Vol. 20, p. 1001 (1910); Vol. 27, p. 100 (1914).
† *Proc. Roy. Soc.*, Vol. 100, p. 424 (1922).

properly to the class of phenomenon studied under diffraction and will be dealt with later (p. 235).

Echoes from atmospheric discontinuities are not uncommon. Arago reported the observation of echoes from clouds. Rayleigh on one occasion observed the return of an echo from the sea after twelve seconds, and Tyndall noted similar phenomena in the course of his work on transmission of sound in the atmosphere. He repeated the phenomenon on an experimental scale by reflecting the sound of a high-pitched whistle on to a sensitive flame, using a gas flame as reflector.

2. Multiple Echo.

A multiple echo repeated at sufficiently short intervals may give rise to a musical note. An instance of this is the multiple reflections which follow the sound of a footstep in a narrow passage between two houses or two walls. A source of sound at S (fig. 6.1) will produce an

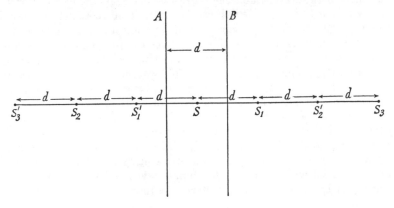

Fig. 6.1

image in wall B at S_1 and this in turn at S_2 in wall A, and this at S_3 in wall B. Similarly S will produce an image at S_1' in A and at S_2' and S_3'. These images are equally spaced at a distance d apart. The echoes will therefore arrive at S with a time interval of d/c between each successive pair, where c is the velocity of sound. The frequency of the note is therefore c/d. The observer being also the source of sound, the whole system of images moves with him and the pitch of the note remains constant if the walls are parallel. Appel records a case where he noticed a change of pitch as he walked down a narrow lane. He found for the extreme widths 1·32 metres and 1·78 metres. Taking the velocity of sound as 345 m./sec. these lengths give frequencies 261 and 194, in good agreement with the observed change of pitch. Where the observer is stationed at one end and the source moves down the passage the predominant pitch alters, but the distance of the observer from successive images does not vary by a constant amount, so the apparent wave-length varies and the pitch is indefinite. If the sound is some way from the observer the paths from the nearer images vary very little and the pitch of the notes becomes correspondingly high.

3. Analytical Treatment of Reflection.

The reflection of waves incident normally on a plane boundary may be treated by using the general equation of wave motion.

(a) Rigid Boundary.

Let the rigid boundary be at $x = 0$. Then here there can never be any displacement.

Let the incident wave be $\xi_1 = f(ct - x)$; then if the displacement of the medium is represented by

$$\xi = f(ct - x) + F(ct + x)$$

and we impose the condition that $\xi = 0$ at $x = 0$ for all values of t, we have

$$0 = f(ct) + F(ct)$$

$$\therefore \ F(ct) = -f(ct)$$

$$\therefore \ F(ct + x) = -f(ct + x)$$

$$\therefore \ \xi = f(ct - x) - f(ct + x). \ . \ . \ . \ (6.1)$$

That is, in addition to the positively travelling wave $\xi_1 = f(ct - x)$ there is a negatively travelling wave $\xi_2 = -f(ct + x)$, the displacement ξ at any point being $\xi_1 + \xi_2$. This negatively travelling wave is the reflected wave.

For the incident wave

$$\dot{\xi}_1 = cf'(ct - x). \ . \ . \ . \ . \ . \ (6.2)$$

For the reflected wave

$$\dot{\xi}_2 = -cf'(ct + x). \ . \ . \ . \ . \ . \ (6.3)$$

At the boundary, $x = 0$, so that

$$\dot{\xi}_1 = cf'(ct), \ \dot{\xi}_2 = -cf'(ct),$$

that is, the velocities are equal and opposite.

A wave is therefore reflected from a rigid boundary with its particle velocity reversed. As the velocity of the wave has also been reversed, the relation of the particle velocity to the wave velocity remains unchanged. The same is true of the displacement.

Again, we have for the incident wave

$$\frac{\partial \xi_1}{\partial x} = -f'(ct - x),$$

and for the reflected wave

$$\frac{\partial \xi_2}{\partial x} = -f'(ct + x).$$

At the boundary $x = 0$, so that

$$\frac{\partial \xi_1}{\partial x} = -f'(ct), \quad \frac{\partial \xi_2}{\partial x} = -f'(ct),$$

that is, the condensations are equal and of the same sign.

(b) Free Boundary.

If we suppose the boundary to have no inertia, then for all values of t the resultant condensation there must be zero. Putting as before

$$\xi = f(ct - x) + F(ct + x),$$

we have

$$\frac{\partial \xi}{\partial x} = -f'(ct - x) + F'(ct + x).$$

Hence at the boundary $x = 0$

we have

$$0 = -f'(ct) + F'(ct),$$

that is,

$$F'(ct) = f'(ct),$$
$$F'(ct + x) = f'(ct + x),$$
$$F(ct + x) = f(ct + x) + \text{const.},$$
$$\therefore \ \xi = f(ct - x) + f(ct + x) + \text{const.} \quad . \quad . \quad (6.4)$$

Since the constant represents a displacement of the medium as a whole we may make it equal to zero, and we have

$$\xi = f(ct - x) + f(ct + x).$$

Here the reflected wave is

$$\xi_2 = f(ct + x),$$

and obviously $\dfrac{\partial \xi_1}{\partial x} = -f'(ct - x) = -f'(ct)$ at $x = 0$,

$$\frac{\partial \xi_2}{\partial x} = f'(ct + x) = f'(ct) \text{ at } x = 0.$$

That is, in the case of a boundary having no inertia the wave is reflected with its condensation reversed, i.e. a compression is reflected as a rarefaction, and conversely.

Also $\quad \dot{\xi}_1 = cf'(ct - x) = cf'(ct)$ at $x = 0$,

and $\quad \dot{\xi}_2 = cf'(ct + x) = cf'(ct)$ at $x = 0$,

that is, the velocity is unchanged. This case is nearly realized at the open end of an organ pipe.

In both the above cases the reflection is obviously complete.

It will be seen that if we consider the direction of displacement and velocity in space we can summarize the effect of reflection as follows:

Rigid Boundary.
Displacement reversed.
Particle velocity reversed.
Condensation unchanged.
Pressure difference unchanged.

Free Boundary.
Displacement unchanged.
Particle velocity unchanged.
Condensation reversed.
Pressure difference reversed.

As was suggested earlier, the matter is simplified if we consider the direction of the displacement and the particle velocity relative to the direction of the wave, which is of course always reversed. In that case we may say that reflection at the rigid boundary takes place with no change of displacement, particle velocity, condensation or pressure difference, while at the free boundary all these quantities are reversed.

We have seen that for a positively travelling wave $\dot{\xi} = +cs$, while for a negatively travelling wave $\dot{\xi} = -cs$. Hence for a reflected wave either $\dot{\xi}$ or s must change sign, the direction of $\dot{\xi}$ being referred to a direction fixed in space.

4. Partial Reflection at Normal Incidence.

We shall take the case where the waves impinge normally. Let the incident wave be denoted by the suffix i, the reflected wave by the suffix r, and the wave transmitted in the second medium by the suffix t.

Continuity at the boundary requires that the velocities of the media on opposite sides shall be equal. That is,

$$\dot{\xi}_i + \dot{\xi}_r = \dot{\xi}_t.$$

The pressures on opposite sides of the boundary must also be equal. That is,

$$K_1 s_i + K_1 s_r = K_2 s_t, \quad . \quad . \quad . \quad . \quad . \quad (6.5)$$

where K and s represent elasticity and condensation.

But
$$\dot{\xi}_i = c_1 s_i,$$
$$\dot{\xi}_r = -c_1 s_r$$

(since the reflected wave is travelling in the negative direction),

and
$$\dot{\xi}_t = c_2 s_t,$$

where c_1, c_2 are the velocities of the waves in the two media.

Hence
$$c_1 s_i - c_1 s_r = c_2 s_t,$$

or
$$c_1(s_i - s_r) = c_2 s_t,$$

and from (6.5)
$$K_1(s_i + s_r) = K_2 s_t,.$$

$$\therefore \frac{s_i - s_r}{s_i + s_r} = \frac{K_1 c_2}{K_2 c_1},$$

and
$$s_r = s_i \cdot \frac{c_1 K_2 - c_2 K_1}{c_1 K_2 + c_2 K_1} \quad . \quad . \quad . \quad . \quad (6.6)$$

This gives the condensation in the reflected wave in terms of the condensation in the incident wave.

Also
$$s_t = s_i \cdot \frac{2 c_1 K_1}{c_1 K_2 + c_2 K_1}, \quad . \quad . \quad . \quad . \quad (6.7)$$

which gives the condensation in the transmitted wave in terms of that in the incident wave.

If the inertia of the second medium is infinite (which is the case of the rigid boundary), $c_2 = 0$. Hence $s_r = s_i$, and the wave is completely reflected without reversal of the sign of its condensation.

If the inertia of the second medium is zero, $c_2 = \infty$. Hence $s_r = -s_i$, and reflection is complete with the sign of the condensation reversed.

Again, since $K_1 = \rho_1 c_1^2$ and $K_2 = \rho_2 c_2^2$,

we have
$$\frac{s_r}{s_i} = \frac{c_1 \rho_2 c_2^2 - c_2 \rho_1 c_1^2}{c_1 \rho_2 c_2^2 + c_2 \rho_1 c_1^2}$$

$$= \frac{c_2 \rho_2 - c_1 \rho_1}{c_2 \rho_2 + c_1 \rho_1} = \frac{R_2 - R_1}{R_2 + R_1}, \quad . \quad . \quad . \quad (6.8)$$

where $R_1 = c_1 \rho_1$ and $R_2 = c_2 \rho_2$. The product $c\rho$ for a medium is the *unit area impedance* or *characteristic impedance* of the medium (see p. 290).

For the case of reflection at an air/water surface we may take for the values of the velocities of sound

$$c_1 = 3.43 \times 10^4 \text{ cm./sec. in air,}$$
$$c_2 = 1.45 \times 10^5 \text{ cm./sec. in water,}$$

and for the densities

$$\rho_1 = 1.2 \times 10^{-3} \text{ gm./c.c. for air,}$$
$$\rho_2 = 1.0 \text{ gm./c.c. for water.}$$

We therefore have

$$R_1 = c_1\rho_1 = 41.2,$$
$$R_2 = c_2\rho_2 = 1.45 \times 10^5,$$
$$\therefore \frac{s_r}{s_i} = 0.9994,$$

so that the water surface is practically a perfect reflector. This is obviously true no matter whether the sound originates in the water or in the air.

Transmission from liquids to solids or vice versa is much easier and reflection less copious, because the characteristic impedances are more nearly equal.

For steel the characteristic impedance is 3.9×10^6. In this case we have for a water-steel boundary

$$\frac{s_r}{s_i} = 0.928,$$

and the percentage of energy reflected is $(0.928)^2 \times 100 = 86$ per cent, giving a transmission of 14 per cent.

For oak $R = 3.4 \times 10^5$ and for a water-oak boundary we have $s_r/s_i = 0.4$, giving a reflection of 16 per cent and a transmission of 84 per cent.

If we consider the case of two gases for which γ is the same, then, since they must be at the same pressure, K must be the same. From (6.6) and (6.7) we therefore have

$$\frac{s_r}{s_i} = \frac{c_1 - c_2}{c_1 + c_2}, \quad \frac{s_t}{s_i} = \frac{2c_1}{c_1 + c_2}.$$

Let

$$\frac{c_1}{c_2} = \mu, \text{ say;}$$

then

$$\frac{s_r}{s_i} = \frac{\mu - 1}{\mu + 1}, \quad \frac{s_t}{s_i} = \frac{2\mu}{\mu + 1}.$$

For a wave in hydrogen reflected at a surface separating this gas from oxygen

$$\mu = \frac{c_1}{c_2} = \sqrt{\frac{\rho_2}{\rho_1}} = 4.$$
$$\therefore \frac{s_r}{s_i} = \frac{3}{5}, \quad \frac{s_t}{s_i} = \frac{8}{5}.$$

In order to find the relation between the amplitudes we may put $\hat{s}$ for the maximum condensation and $\hat{v}$ for the maximum particle velocity.

Then

$$c_1\hat{s} = \hat{v} = 2\pi f a,$$

where f is the frequency and a the amplitude. Hence

$$\frac{a_r}{a_i} = \frac{c_1 \dot{s}_r}{c_1 \dot{s}_i} = \frac{\dot{s}_r}{\dot{s}_i} = \frac{3}{5},$$

$$\frac{a_t}{a_i} = \frac{c_2 \dot{s}_t}{c_1 \dot{s}_i} = \frac{1}{4} \cdot \frac{8}{5} = \frac{2}{5}.$$

5. Partial Reflection for any Angle of Incidence.

An application of Huygens' principle leads at once to Snell's law

$$\frac{\sin i}{\sin r} = \frac{c_1}{c_2},$$

where c_1 is the velocity of the waves in the medium in which they are incident and c_2 the velocity in the medium into which they are refracted.

Let a_i, a_r, a_t be the displacement amplitudes of the incident, reflected, and transmitted waves respectively. These will be proportional to the velocity amplitudes, which must have equal components normal to the surface of separation on both sides of the surface. Then

$$(a_i + a_r) \cos i = a_t \cos r.$$

Let $a_r = m a_i$; then

$$a_i (1 + m) \cos i = a_t \cos r.$$

If now we express the fact that all the energy of the incident wave must divide itself between the reflected and transmitted beams, we shall get another relation between these. The mean energy per unit volume in a beam is proportional (1) directly to the square of the amplitude, (2) directly to the normal density, (3) directly to the square of the frequency.

Let the density of the first medium be ρ_1 and that of the second ρ_2. The frequency need not be considered, as that is the same for all the beams. The cross-section of the incident beam is AB $\cos i$, if we consider the beams to have unit depth perpendicular to the plane of the diagram (fig. 6.2). The reflected beam has the same cross-section, but the transmitted beam has cross-section AB $\cos r$. The energy of the incident beam reaching the surface per unit time is contained in a column of length c_1. This is distributed between a reflected column of the same length and a transmitted column of length c_2. We therefore have

$$c_1 a_i^2 \rho_1 \cdot \text{AB} \cos i = c_1 m^2 a_i^2 \rho_1 \cdot \text{AB} \cos i + c_2 a_t^2 \rho_2 \cdot \text{AB} \cos r,$$

$$\therefore \quad c_1 a_i^2 \rho_1 \cos i (1 - m^2) = c_2 a_t^2 \rho_2 \cos r.$$

Dividing this equation by the square of the previous one, we have

$$\frac{(1 - m^2)\rho_1 c_1}{(1 + m)^2 \cos i} = \frac{\rho_2 c_2}{\cos r}$$

or
$$\frac{1 - m}{1 + m} = \frac{\rho_2}{\rho_1} \frac{\cos i}{\cos r} \frac{c_2}{c_1}. \quad \cdots \quad (6.9)$$

But
$$\frac{c_2}{c_1} = \frac{\sin r}{\sin i},$$

$$\therefore \quad \frac{1 - m}{1 + m} = \frac{\rho_2}{\rho_1} \cdot \frac{\cot i}{\cot r},$$

or
$$m = \frac{\rho_1 \cot r - \rho_2 \cot i}{\rho_1 \cot r + \rho_2 \cot i}$$

$$= \frac{\rho_1/\rho_2 - \cot i/\cot r}{\rho_1/\rho_2 + \cot i/\cot r}. \quad \cdots \quad (6.10)$$

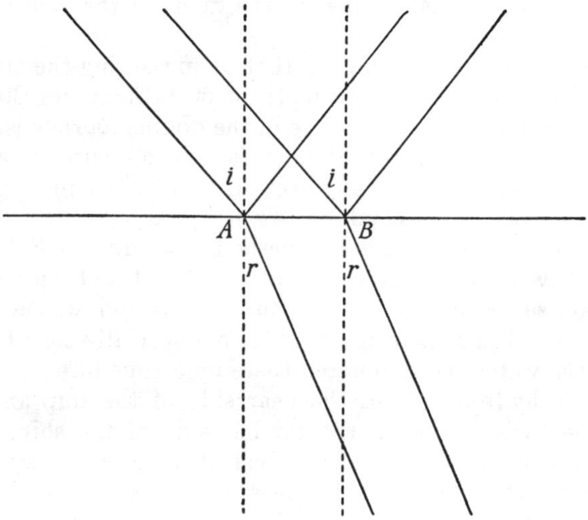

Fig. 6.2

This gives the ratio of the reflected and incident amplitudes. A more rigorous derivation of this relation will be found in Rayleigh's *Sound* (Vol. II, § 270).

For perpendicular incidence (6.9) reduces to

$$m = \frac{\rho_1/\rho_2 - c_2/c_1}{\rho_1/\rho_2 + c_2/c_1}, \text{ as before.} \quad \cdots \quad (6.11)$$

The condition for no reflection is obviously

$$c_1\rho_1 = c_2\rho_2. \quad . \; . \; . \; . \; . \quad (6.12)$$

Since the frequency is the same in both media, $c_1/c_2 = \lambda_1/\lambda_2$; that is, the condition for no reflection may be stated as

$$\lambda_1\rho_1 = \lambda_2\rho_2. \quad . \; . \; . \; . \; . \quad (6.13)$$

6. Echo-Sounding.

In the course of the early experiments on the transmission of sound in water the possibility of detecting an echo from the sea bottom suggested itself and was at once realized by experiment.* Here was the basis of a very simple method of depth sounding. The immemorial practice of heaving the lead is still in use, but it has many disadvantages. It is a slow process, cannot be carried out in a ship travelling at speed, and for survey work in deep water requires an elaborate mechanical outfit. Measurement of the time interval between the production of a sound at the surface of the sea and the receipt of the echo from the bottom at once gives us a value for the depth if the velocity of sound in sea-water is known.

The chief practical difficulty is that of measuring the time interval with sufficient accuracy. In a depth of 50 fathoms (or 300 feet) the total time taken by the sound wave in the double journey is only about one-eighth of a second. If this distance is to be measured to an accuracy of 1 per cent (or an error of 3 feet in depth) the interval must be measured to 1/800 of a second.

One of the earliest successful methods was due to Behm †, whose experiments were begun in 1911. Ships were fitted with two hydrophones, one on each side. The source of sound was a detonating charge contained in a cartridge fired from a specially constructed firing head into the water and detonated there by a time fuse. The explosion actuated the hydrophone on the near side of the ship and the echo affected the hydrophone on the further side of the ship, which had been shielded by the hull from the effect of the original explosion. The time interval was recorded and measured by a special device. The necessary outfit is extremely portable, and one was carried by Amundsen on his polar expedition. A modified type adapted for use in air was carried on the Zeppelin ZR 111 on her trial flights over Germany, and soundings were taken when the airship was flying at a height of 600 feet and a speed of 60 miles per hour.

Experiments conducted by the Research Department of the British Admiralty led to another form of apparatus, which has several advantages over the Behm type and is now manufactured under licence.

---

* See *Nature*, Vol. 113, p. 462 (1924).   † *Engineering*, Vol. 120, pp. 595, 629 (1925).

The whole apparatus and its arrangement is shown in fig. 6.3. The sound waves used are damped trains emitted by striking a metal diaphragm. The transmitter is fitted on one side of the hull and consists of a diaphragm, a metal hammer, and a solenoid. The hammer is held back against a spring by the solenoid, whose

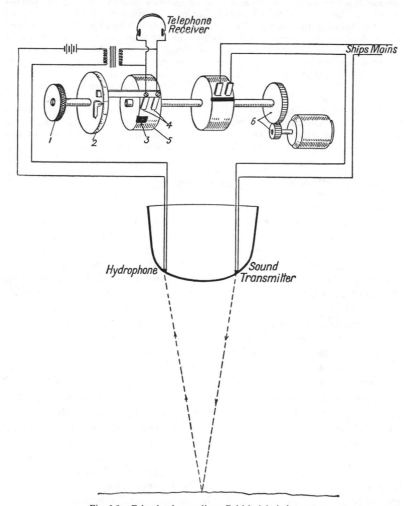

Fig. 6.3.—Echo depth sounding: British Admiralty system

1, Screw by which adjustment is made. **2,** Graduated wheel reading depth directly

circuit is completed through two brushes bearing on the revolving metal disc shown on the right of the diagram. Once in each revolution of this disc the ebonite piece (shown in black) comes under the brushes, the circuit of the solenoid is broken, and the spring drives the hammer down on to the diaphragm, sending out a damped train of waves of frequency about 1250. On the other side of the ship is a button microphone, the circuit of which is linked through a transformer to the headphones. The circuit containing these phones is short-circuited through the switch contacts bearing on the rotating metal disc carried by the revolving shaft and shown on the left of the diagram. Once in each revolution of the disc the insulated segment comes under one of the switch contacts and the phones are thrown into operation. If at this instant the hydrophone receives a sound it will be heard in the phones. The switch contacts can be adjusted by the hand wheel shown on the extreme left. When the apparatus is working all that is necessary is to adjust the hand wheel until the echo is heard. The position of the hand wheel will depend on the time interval to be measured and therefore on the depth, and it is accordingly possible to attach to the hand wheel a scale reading depth directly in fathoms or feet. In this method there are no cartridges to be carried and as the apparatus can be worked with the ship at full speed a continuous record of depths can be obtained throughout a voyage. As an adjunct for purposes of navigation and as an instrument of research in charting ocean depths the instrument is of very great value. Alternative methods of sounding which have special advantages will be discussed later (pp. 191, 225).

7. Pressure of Sound Waves on a Surface.

That electromagnetic waves must exert a pressure on a perfectly conducting and therefore perfectly reflecting boundary was Maxwell's deduction from his general equations of the electromagnetic field, and the existence of this pressure was experimentally confirmed by Lebedew and measured by Nichols and Hull and by Poynting. Theory and experiment indicate that the pressure on a surface normal to the incident waves is equal to the energy-density of the radiation in front of the surface. If the surface is perfectly absorbing the pressure equals the energy-density of the incident radiation. If the surface is perfectly reflecting the pressure equals the energy-density of the incident and reflected radiation. Thus the pressure on a perfectly reflecting surface is twice that on a perfectly absorbing surface.

The pressure due to sound waves was discussed by Rayleigh.* He deduced the relation $\bar{P} = \frac{1}{2}(\gamma + 1)E$, where E is the total energy per c.c. in front of the surface, $\bar{P}$ the mean pressure, γ the ratio of specific heats. This relation is obtained by first of all deriving a general expression for the mean pressure without making any assumption as to the relation between the pressure and volume of any given mass of the fluid during the transformations. When the adiabatic relation is inserted the expression reduces to that given above; γ enters into the expression as the power of v in the adiabatic relation

$$pv^\gamma = \text{const.}$$

If we assume Boyle's law we have

$$pv = \text{const.}$$

* *Phil. Mag.*, Vol. 3, p. 338 (1902); Vol. 10, p. 364 (1905).

and we must substitute 1 for γ in the expression for $\bar{P}$. This gives

$$\bar{P} = E.$$

It may be observed that the formula indicates a zero pressure only for the hypothetical case $\gamma = -1$, which is incompatible with the statical stability of the medium.

Larmor has obtained this result for any propagated disturbance in which the energy-density is inversely proportional to the wave-length. The method is to consider the energy change due to the motion of a reflector, taking into account the Doppler effect of its speed on the wave-length of the reflected beam. The change is equated to the work done by the forces moving the reflector. This argument, however, cannot be correctly applied to sound waves. The equivalent result for a progressive wave is an erroneous calculation of the momentum, the average per unit volume being $\overline{\rho_0(1 + s)v}$, where v is the particle velocity and the bar indicates that a spatial mean is taken. Then as $s = v/c$, we have $\frac{1}{2}\rho_0 v^2/c$ or E/c. This is of the second order in v, and therefore the result itself shows that second order effects are not negligible; the equations we have used are not of this accuracy. It is mentioned by Rayleigh * that the discrepancy between the equation $\bar{P} = E$ and the relation deduced by Rayleigh and Lamb for sound waves, $\bar{P} = (\gamma + 1)E/2$, has the same causes as the progressive distortion of the waves. $\bar{P}$ vanishes for the hypothetical fluid which has a linear relation between pressure and volume,

$$p = p_0 - c^2\rho_0^2/\rho.$$

In such a medium waves of finite amplitude are propagated without distortion.

Rayleigh's result is obtained by applying to a stationary wave eqn. 2.32 (p. 59), which involves no approximation. He also shows that the momentum of a progressive wave, for a cylindrical element of fluid of length c in the direction of propagation, is $(\gamma + 1)E'/4$ per unit area, assuming the mean density of the fluid to be unaltered by the presence of the wave. In this expression E' denotes the appropriate energy-density. The reflection of the wave would be expected to require a pressure $2(\gamma + 1)E'/4$ or $(\gamma + 1)E/4$, in disagreement with the formula already given. It is to be noted, however, that the momentum of a progressive wave is to some extent an arbitrary quantity, so far as the equations of motion are concerned.

An accurate solution † of equation 2.57 (p. 71) is

$$v = f\left(y - ct - \frac{\gamma + 1}{2}vt\right),$$

* *Phil Mag.*, Vol. 10, p. 364 (1905).   † See Ramsey, *Hydrodynamics*, p. 360 (Bell, 1935)

where v is the particle velocity at the point y. An approximately sinusoidal solution is of the form

$$v = \hat{v}\sin k\,(ct - y) + \frac{\gamma+1}{4}\,\hat{v}^2 kt\sin 2k\,(ct - y) + \frac{\gamma-1}{4}\frac{\hat{v}^2}{c},$$

where the constant term is chosen for the wave emerging from one end of a tube in which a stationary wave has been established.

The momentum per unit area for length c is now given by the equations

$$s = \frac{v}{c} + \frac{3-\gamma}{4}\frac{v^2}{c^2},$$

$$\overline{\rho v} = \rho_0 \overline{(1+s)\,v}$$

$$= \rho_0\bar{v} + \tfrac{1}{2}\rho_0\hat{v}^2/c, \text{ to the second order in } v;$$

Hence momentum $= \tfrac{1}{2}\rho_0\hat{v}^2\left(\dfrac{\gamma-1}{2}+1\right)$

$$= \frac{\gamma+1}{2}E';$$

that is, the momentum generated is equal to the impulse of the mean pressure previously given for the stationary wave.

Both relations have been used in calculating the energy-density of sound waves from the observed pressure (see section 10, p. 298). Zernov * used powerful waves of frequency 512 and energy-density about 0·5 erg/cm.³ and found that $\bar{P} = (\gamma + 1)E/2$ gave results agreeing with a maximum discrepancy of 3 per cent with those given by a vibration manometer method developed by Wien.† Altberg made measurements on sound waves whose energy content was about half the above value, and he used the relation $\bar{P} = E$, but his experiments unfortunately provide no means of checking the applicability of the formula.

8. Acoustic Repulsion.

This phenomenon may be conveniently demonstrated by the apparatus shown in fig. 6.4, which is taken from a paper by Dvořák.‡ A small glass resonator tuned to the note of the fork is fastened by sealing-wax to the end of a light wooden rod, the other end of which carries a small lead counterpoise. To the centre of the rod is fixed a glass cap which rests on a vertical needle point. When the fork is

---

* *Ann. d. Physik*, Vol. 21, p. 131 (1906).   † *Wied. Ann.*, Vol. 36, p. 835 (1889).
‡ *Phil. Mag.*, Vol. 6, p. 225 (1878).

strongly bowed and the open end of the resonance box presented to the open end of the resonator the wooden arm rotates on the needle point. The phenomenon is associated with the unbalanced pressure on the interior wall of the resonator opposite to its open end. For

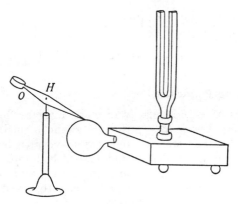

Fig. 6.4.--Acoustic Repulsion

convenience of construction, a cylindrical resonator of stiff paper may be substituted for the glass resonator and tuned by adjusting a short paper neck. If four such resonators are combined to form a small mill a continuous rotation may be maintained. Other similar experiments will be found in the original paper.

CHAPTER VII

Refraction of Sound Waves

1. Experiments on Refraction.

Early refraction experiments were made on gases by Sondhauss[*] and Hajech,[†] but the results, although giving a qualitative indication of the phenomenon, were to some extent vitiated by the fact that the gases constituting the lenses and prisms had to be contained in thin membranes and these membranes must have vibrated as a whole. Tyndall[‡] cites experiments made with a concertina reed as source and a sensitive flame as receiver. Between source and receiver were inserted soap-bubbles blown with nitrous oxide or hydrogen. In the first case the action was that of a converging lens and in the second case that of a diverging lens. Refraction through a prism has been demonstrated by Pohl[§] using a whistle as source and a radiometer as detector.

If the velocity of sound in air is assumed to be 340 m./sec. at ordinary temperatures and the velocity in carbon dioxide 269 m./sec., the refractive index from carbon dioxide to air will be $\mu = 269/340 = 0.79$. Measuring the angles of incidence and refraction, Pohl obtains

$$\mu = \frac{\sin 30°}{\sin 39.8°} = \frac{0.5}{0.64} = 0.78.$$

Here again a containing membrane is used.

Gezechus[‖] got over the difficulty of the containing membrane by using a hemispherical network of wire enclosing wool, down or similar substances, fixed like a lens over a circular aperture in a board. The source of sound was a high-pitched whistle (Galton whistle), and the refracted beam was explored with a sensitive flame. A true image was obtained for which the relationship of the distances from the lens

$$\frac{1}{p} + \frac{1}{p'} = \frac{1}{f}$$

[*] Phil. Mag., Vol. 5, p. 73 (1853).
[†] Pogg. Ann., Vol. 103, p. 163 (1857).   [‡] Sound, pp. 264–7.
[§] Physical Principles of Mechanics and Acoustics, p. 288 (Blackie & Son Ltd., 1932).
[‖] Journ. d. Russ. Phys.-chem., Vol. 22, p. 233 (1890).

was roughly verified. If the velocity of the sound in the cotton wool is taken as c and the velocity in the air as c_0, then $\mu = c_0/c$.

If R is the radius of the hemisphere (about 25 cm. in these experiments) then, as for light waves,

$$\frac{1}{f} = \frac{\mu - 1}{R},$$

$$\therefore \ \mu = \frac{R + f}{f}$$

and

$$c = \frac{c_0}{\mu} = \frac{c_0 f}{R + f}.$$

Working with wave-lengths from 2 cm. to 6 cm. Gezechus found that the velocity in the medium diminishes as the average density increases, and for a given density it increases with frequency, e.g. $\lambda = 6$ cm. gives $c = 160$ m./sec.; $\lambda = 2$ cm. gives $c = 250$ m./sec.

2. Audibility of Sounds from Distant Sources.

When the extreme sensitiveness of the ear is considered in relation to the amount of power put into certain sources of sound, the inaudibility of these sources at quite short distances is remarkable. Thus the high note of a Scottish siren tested by Lord Rayleigh * at St. Catharine's required 600 h.p. to maintain it. The distance at which the siren should be audible if all this power were converted into energy of sound waves and spread uniformly over a hemispherical diverging wave is easily calculated. The minimum audible intensity corresponds to a transmission of power amounting to 10^{-16} watt/cm.^{2}; 1 h.p. $= 746$ watts. It follows that if x is the distance of audibility in cm.

$$\frac{600 \times 746}{2\pi x^2} = 10^{-16}$$

or $\quad\quad x = 2 \cdot 67 \times 10^{10}$ cm. $= 267,000$ kilometres (about),

a distance more than six times the circumference of the earth.

Perhaps fortunately, this range of audibility is not achieved even under the most favourable conditions. The maximum range is only a few kilometres, and in unfavourable conditions it may drop to one or two kilometres. One obvious reason for this is the inefficiency of the source of sound as a transformer of mechanical energy into sound —a subject to which we shall return later. The second reason is the dissipation in the atmosphere, but this, as we have already seen, is small. A third reason is the dissipation of sound at the edge of the

* Phil. Mag., Vol. 6, p. 289 (1903).

wave as it travels over the ground. There is little accurate experiment to guide us here, but Osborne Reynolds * has shown by direct experiment that sounds are heard at much greater distances across a snow-covered field than across the same field in ordinary circumstances, and the frictional absorption due to long grass, shrubs, trees, &c., is probably very great. The exceptionally good audibility of sounds over water is probably due to the comparatively small surface absorption.

3. Effect of Heterogeneity in the Atmosphere.

The factors noted in the preceding paragraph are quite insufficient by themselves to account for recorded instances of low range of audibility of high-power sources.

The following example is given by Tyndall:†

" On July 3 we first steamed to a point 2·9 miles S.W. by W. of the signal station. No sounds, not even the guns, were heard at this distance. At 2 miles they were equally inaudible. But this being a position at which the sounds, though strong in the axis of the horn, invariably subsided, we steamed to the exact bearing from which our observations had been made on July 1. At 2.15 p.m., and at a distance of 3¾ miles from the station, with calm clear air and a smooth sea, the horns and whistle (American) were sounded, but they were inaudible. Surprised at this result, we signalled for the guns. They were all fired, but, though the smoke seemed close at hand, no sound whatever reached us. On July 1, in this bearing, the observed range of both horns and guns was 10½ miles, while on the bearing of the Varne light-vessel it was nearly 13 miles. We steamed in to 3 miles, paused, and listened with all attention: but neither horn nor whistle was heard. The guns were again signalled for: five of them were fired in succession, but not one of them was heard. We steamed on in the same bearing to 2 miles, and had the guns fired point-blank at us. The howitzer and the mortar with 3-lb. charges yielded a feeble thud, while the 18-pounder was wholly unheard. Applying the law of inverse squares, it follows that, with the air and sea, according to accepted notions, in a far worse condition, the sound at 2 miles' distance on July 1 must have had more than forty times the intensity which it possessed at the same distance at 3 p.m. on the 3rd."

Tyndall afterwards learned that in the evening of the same day the sounds had been heard at the Varne Lightship 12¾ miles from the signal station.

Tyndall was of opinion that the main factor involved was the heterogeneity of the atmosphere. In his view ascending currents of air at a temperature different from that of the surrounding air and, over water, ascending currents of air charged with water vapour, cause successive reflections of the sound waves which render the atmosphere opaque. This view was reinforced by various experiments with a whistle and sensitive flame, showing that the air over a series of flames is opaque, as is also a region of air where there are alternate descending streams of carbon dioxide and ascending layers of coalgas. Very probably this heterogeneity plays a considerable part in

* *Proc. Roy. Soc.*, Vol. 22, p. 531 (1874).   † *Sound*, pp. 303–4.

diminishing audibility, but it is fairly certain that Tyndall exaggerated its rôle. It was no doubt the cause of the controversy as to whether a fog is detrimental to audibility. This is a question of first-rate importance in connexion with fog signals, in relation to which this whole subject was first systematically studied. If the fog which obscures the light from the lighthouse also damps out the sound waves from the siren, then before the days of submarine sounds and ordinary wireless the navigator was in a sorry plight. There seems to be no *a priori* reason to expect that a fog should affect the audibility of sounds of ordinary frequency, the wave-lengths being much too long for the water particles to act as obstacles, and the air being usually still and probably homogeneous. Fog, however, occurs frequently in banks which mark discontinuities, and with the source in one bank and the observer outside of it or even in another bank, the reflection may be considerable and diminution of intensity correspondingly great. The importance of heterogeneity in the atmosphere was rather minimized by Reynolds, who assigned the major rôle to refraction due to wind and temperature gradients. Tucker,* however, from observations on aeroplanes made with Service sound locators, confirms Tyndall's view. He finds that acoustic clouds are most common on warm sunny days with good visibility and that uniform fog banks are acoustically clear. It is of course highly probable that the " turbulence " in the air is an important contributor to the effect.†

4. Effect of Wind Gradient.

Another factor was first suggested by Stokes,‡ and its importance subsequently explained by Osborne Reynolds.§ It is a fact of common experience that sound is heard better down wind than up wind. What is not generally realized is that very long distance records for sounds are frequently made up wind. Both these facts can be explained by considering the refraction of sound waves due to wind gradient. Wind is practically without effect on the audibility of sound if it blows at the same speed at all heights. Even with very high winds the wind velocity is very small compared with the velocity of sound. But if there is a wind gradient, i.e. if the wind velocity is a function of the height above the ground, then sound waves will suffer a change of direction which, although not due to a true refraction, is similar in its effects. If we take the obvious case of a wind velocity increasing with height, it is easy to see qualitatively what its effect will be on the propagation of sound waves. If plane waves arrive from a distant source the effect of a wind gradient is to deflect waves travelling with the wind towards the ground and waves travelling against it away

* *Nature*, Vol. 114, p. 689 (1926).
† Devik, *Chr. Michelsons Inst. Beretninger*, Vol. 6, p. 2 (1936).
‡ *B. A. Report*, p. 22 (1857).   § *Proc. Roy. Soc.*, Vol. 22, p. 531 (1874).

from the ground. Thus an observer may fail to hear a sound, not because it has died away, but because it has been refracted and is passing over his head.

The way in which sound waves are affected by wind gradient is shown in fig. 7.1. The waves, but for the wind, would appear in the diagram as semicircles surrounding the source. They are actually distorted as shown, the tops being carried forward more than the lower edges. If now we remember that the sound rays are always perpendicular to the waves, we see that to windward the rays are directed upwards and tend to leave the surface of the earth, while to leeward they are bent down and so directed along the ground. This, then, is a case of refraction similar to that which we studied in the case of water ripples (p. 24), and the relation between the two

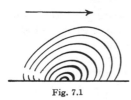

Fig. 7.1

phenomena becomes still clearer when it is mentioned that fig. 7.1 is actually from a sketch, made by Reynolds, of the ripples spreading out from drops falling into a stream which flowed past a vertical wall. Near the wall the velocity of the stream is retarded, so that farther from the wall it moves more rapidly, and what would be a semicircular set of ripples if the water were at rest becomes the set of ripples actually shown in the diagram.

Furthermore, as the wave travelling down wind is kept close to the surface and is subject to frictional dissipation, while the wave travelling up wind is kept above the ground, it may well be that *looked for in the proper place* the wave travelling up wind will be found to be more intense than that travelling down wind at the same distance from the source. These considerations were established by some simple observations of Osborne Reynolds (loc. cit.). He placed a bell on a box in the middle of a field and tested its audibility at different distances and at different heights with and against the wind. Against the wind the sound was lost at 20 yards with the head on the ground, lost at 30 yards with the head 3 feet up, lost at 70 yards with the head 6 feet up, and heard at 70 yards with full intensity at a height of 12 feet. In this position the sound was as intense as that at 70 yards to lee of the bell, if not more intense. This fact explains the tradition of the sportsman who approaches his prey up wind. The sound waves due to his footsteps will miss a bird on the ground until he is quite close up.

If we leave out of account the divergence of the wave, we may form some idea of the path which the bottom of the wave or the limiting ray would follow. If the variation of the speed of the wind were uniform from the surface upwards, the rays of sound would at first move upwards in nearly circular paths of radius $1100 \times h/(v_1 - v_2)$ feet, where 1100 is the velocity of sound in feet per second and $(v_1 - v_2)/h$ is the velocity gradient in feet per second per foot vertical height. As the gradient is in fact greatest at the ground and diminishes upwards, the actual path would be more nearly parabolic.

Further observations on the variation of audibility with wind direction are recorded by Tyndall * and the explanation in terms of wind gradient is accepted.

The following more detailed treatment of the phenomenon is given by Barton.† Here the wind velocity is assumed to vary regularly with height and Huygens' principle is applied.

Let AB (fig. 7.2) be the surface of separation, u_0 and u_1 the wind velocities on opposite sides. Let AC be the incident wave-front making

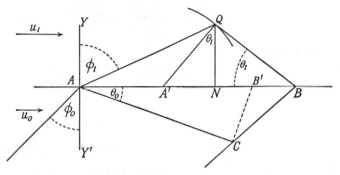

Fig. 7.2

an angle θ_0 with the surface, and ϕ_0 the angle of incidence between the ray and the normal. The ray will not be perpendicular to the wave-front. We require the position of the wave-front at a time t when the wavelet from C has just reached B.

Draw CB′ perpendicular to AC and lay off B′B, making $B'B/CB' = u_0/c$.

A spherical wavelet from A will at time t have its centre at A′, where $AA' = u_1 t$, and radius $A'Q = ct$. Then BQ is the refracted wave-front.

$$\operatorname{cosec} \theta_1 = \frac{BA'}{A'Q} = \frac{B'A - A'A + BB'}{A'Q} = \frac{B'A}{B'C} - \frac{u_1 t - u_0 t}{ct}$$

$$= \operatorname{cosec} \theta_0 - \frac{u_1 - u_0}{c}$$

$$\therefore \ \operatorname{cosec} \theta_0 - \operatorname{cosec} \theta_1 = \frac{u_1 - u_0}{c} = \text{constant.} \quad . \quad . \quad (7.1)$$

This gives the inclination of any refracted wave-front.

* *Sound*, pp. 343–7.   † *Textbook of Sound*, p. 99 (Macmillan, 1908).

For the direction of the ray we have

$$\tan \phi_1 = \tan AQN = \frac{NA}{NQ} = \frac{NA'}{NQ} + \frac{AA'}{A'Q \cos \theta_1}$$

$$= \tan \theta_1 + \frac{u_1}{c} \sec \theta_1. \quad \ldots \quad (7.2)$$

For a laminated medium the final directions of the wave-front and the ray will, from the form of the equations, be independent of the constants of the intervening layers, and we shall have

$$\operatorname{cosec} \theta_n = \operatorname{cosec} \theta_0 - \frac{u_n - u_0}{c} \quad \ldots \quad (7.3)$$

$$\tan \phi_n = \tan \theta_n + \frac{u_n}{c} \sec \theta_n. \quad \ldots \quad (7.4)$$

If the equation gives for $\operatorname{cosec} \theta_n$ a value lying between $+1$ and -1 the wave cannot penetrate the layer in question.

If we take the limiting case and put $\theta_n = \pi/2$ (wave-front vertical), we have

$$\operatorname{cosec} \theta_0 - \frac{u_n - u_0}{c} = 1.$$

Any pair of values of θ_0 and $u_n - u_0$ which makes the left-hand side less than 1 gives total reflection.

If the wind velocity increases with height indefinitely, such a layer must ultimately be reached, provided that the initial value of θ_0 is not zero.

If, however, $\theta_0 = 0$ (wave-front horizontal), then $\operatorname{cosec} \theta_0 = \infty$, and all values of θ_n are zero. Thus the wave-front is always horizontal, but the ray deviates without limit from the vertical, since

$$\tan \phi_n = \tan \theta_n + \frac{u_n}{c} \sec \theta_n$$

$$= 0 + \frac{u_n}{c}.$$

In the case where the wind velocity is proportional to the height and the wind gradient therefore uniform, we have

$$\frac{u}{c} = b + ay,$$

where y is measured vertically upwards.

For possible values take $b = \cdot 02$, $a = \cdot 0001$, $c = 1100$ ft. per sec., $u_0 = 22$ ft. per sec. $= 15$ m.p.h.

If we assume $\theta_0 = 60°$, and let the suffix n refer to the layer where total reflection takes place, we have

$$\operatorname{cosec} 60° = \frac{u_n - u_0}{c} + 1.$$

But

$$\frac{u_n - u_0}{c} = ay_n,$$

where y_n is the height of the totally-reflecting layer,

$$\therefore \; ay_n = \operatorname{cosec} 60° - 1$$
$$= 0 \cdot 1547,$$

or

$$y_n = 1547 \text{ ft.}$$

We can obtain the horizontal distance to the point at which the sound ray becomes horizontal by obtaining the equation to the ray:

$$\frac{dx}{dy} = \tan \phi = \tan \theta + (b + ay) \sec \theta.$$

But

$$\operatorname{cosec} \theta = \operatorname{cosec} \theta_0 - \frac{u - u_0}{c}$$
$$= \operatorname{cosec} \theta_0 - ay.$$

Put $\operatorname{cosec} \theta_0 = f$; then

$$\sec \theta = \frac{f - ay}{\sqrt{\{(f - ay)^2 - 1\}}}, \quad \tan \theta = \frac{1}{\sqrt{\{(f - ay)^2 - 1\}}},$$
$$\frac{dx}{dy} = \frac{1 + (b + ay)(f - ay)}{\sqrt{\{(f - ay)^2 - 1\}}}.$$

Put

$$z = f - ay = \operatorname{cosec} \theta;$$

then

$$dz = -a \, dy,$$
$$-a \, dx = \frac{1 + (b + f - z)z}{\sqrt{(z^2 - 1)}} \, dz,$$

or

$$-ax = \int \frac{dz}{\sqrt{(z^2 - 1)}} + \int \frac{(b + f)z \, dz}{\sqrt{(z^2 - 1)}} - \int \frac{z^2 dz}{\sqrt{(z^2 - 1)}} + C,$$

where C is to be determined from the condition that the trajectory passes through the origin, i.e. when $x = 0$, $y = 0$.

This gives

$$-ax = \log\{z + \sqrt{(z^2 - 1)}\} + (b + f)\sqrt{(z^2 - 1)}$$
$$- \tfrac{1}{2} z \sqrt{(z^2 - 1)} - \tfrac{1}{2} \log\{z + \sqrt{(z^2 - 1)}\} + C.$$

When $$y = 0, \quad z = f;$$

$$\therefore C = -\tfrac{1}{2}\log\{f + \sqrt{(f^2 - 1)}\} - \left(b + \tfrac{f}{2}\right)\sqrt{(f^2 - 1)},$$

$$\therefore 2ax = \log \frac{f + \sqrt{(f^2 - 1)}}{z + \sqrt{(z^2 - 1)}}$$
$$+ (f + 2b)\sqrt{(f^2 - 1)} - (f + 2b + ay)\sqrt{(z^2 - 1)}.$$

To find the horizontal distance to leeward at which the sound ray is horizontal we have to find the value of x for which $y = 1547$ ft. and $ay = \cdot 1547$.

We have
$$f = \operatorname{cosec} 60° = 1\cdot 1547,$$
$$z = f - ay = 1,$$
$$\sqrt{(z^2 - 1)} = 0.$$

Substituting these values in the equation we get

$$x = 6070 \text{ ft.}$$

A more detailed theoretical discussion is given by Milne.* He assumes the following principle:

The motion of a wave-front is the same as if at each moment each point on it were moving with a velocity compounded of (1) the velocity of sound at the point considered, taken in the direction of the normal to the wave-front at this point drawn in the direction in which the wave-front is progressing, and (2) the velocity of the medium at the point.

This principle is sufficient to determine the successive positions of the wave-front, given the motion of the medium and the velocity at each point. A sound ray is then defined as a curve such that the tangent at each point is in the direction of the resultant velocity given by the above principle, taken at the moment when the wave-front passes through the point.

It is to be noted that the type of variation of wind velocity with height here assumed is not universal. Occasionally in the layers near the surface of the earth, and frequently in higher layers, the velocity diminishes with height, and this reverses the phenomenon, giving greater audibility against the wind.

5. Effect of Temperature Gradient.

A similar effect must follow from the existence of a temperature gradient, as was pointed out by Reynolds.† Sound travels more rapidly in warm air than in cool air. It follows that if the temperature decreases as we rise above the surface of the earth, the velocity of sound also decreases and we get a refraction of sound rays away from the

* *Phil. Mag.*, Vol. 47, p. 97 (1921).
† *Proc. Roy. Soc.*, Vol. 22, p. 531 (1874); *Phil. Trans.*, Vol. 166, p. 315 (1876).

earth, as in the case of sound travelling against an adverse wind. In the case of temperature, however, the effect is the same in all directions and all rays are bent upwards. This particular kind of temperature gradient is the normal one, and is probably most marked in the middle of a hot sunny day. The rays of the sun are absorbed by the ground, which becomes hot and heats the layers of air immediately in contact with it, the upper layers being relatively cool. Audibility is therefore poor. On the other hand, in the evening after a hot day the earth cools quickly if the sky is clear, and so cools the layers of air in contact with it. Thus temperature increases with height, the velocity of the sound also increases with height, and all rays are refracted downwards. This accounts for the good audibility which so often obtains in the evening.

It will be obvious that the range of audibility is greatly increased if the point of observation is high, and the same result is obtained if

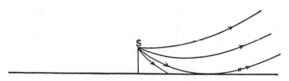

Fig. 7.3 —Refraction of sound as a result of temperature gradient

the source is high. This will be seen from fig. 7.3. Rays which leave the source in a downward direction are deviated so as to become horizontal and finally move upwards again, so that if source and observer are at the same height the range is double that for the observer at this height and the source on the ground.

The effect of this increasing range of audibility with increasing height of the source is to give a definite acoustic horizon, and this has been observed by Tucker in the case of experiments on the location of aeroplanes by sound.*

In fig. 7.4 we have two neighbouring rays approximately horizontal, along which the velocity of sound is c and $c + \delta c$ respectively, and whose distance apart is δR, where R is the radius of curvature of the rays. Then, measuring s along the ray, we have

$$\frac{\delta s'}{R + \delta R} = \frac{\delta s}{R}$$

$$\therefore \quad \delta s' = \delta s \left(1 + \frac{\delta R}{R}\right).$$

* *Nature*, Vol. 114, p. 689 (1926).

Since AB, CD are successive positions of an element of the wave-front the time taken to describe the paths δs, $\delta s'$ is the same; that is,

$$\frac{\delta s'}{c + \delta c} = \frac{\delta s}{c},$$

$$\therefore \frac{1}{R} = \frac{1}{c}\frac{dc}{dR}. \quad \cdots \cdots \quad (7.5)$$

But $\quad c = c_0\sqrt{(1 + a\theta)} = c_0(1 + \tfrac{1}{2}a\theta)$ approximately.

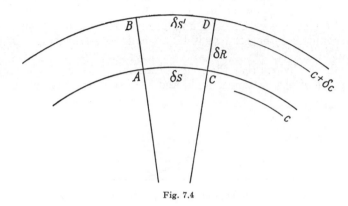

Fig. 7.4

Assuming the temperature to vary linearly with the height, and considering rays which are nearly horizontal, we have

$$\frac{1}{R} = \frac{1}{c}\frac{dc}{dh} = \frac{1}{c}\frac{dc}{d\theta}\frac{d\theta}{dh} = \frac{1}{c}\frac{c_0 a}{2}\frac{\theta_2 - \theta_1}{h}$$

$$= \frac{a}{2}\frac{\theta_2 - \theta_1}{h} \quad \cdots \cdots \quad (7.6)$$

$$\therefore R = \frac{546\,h}{\theta_2 - \theta_1}. \quad \cdots \cdots \quad (7.7)$$

The gradient actually observed in the lower strata of the atmosphere varies with the time of day and with the state of the sky. If we assume 2° C. per 1000 ft. as a reasonable value we have

$$R = \frac{546 \times 1000}{2 \cdot 0} = 273,000 \text{ ft. or about 52 miles.}$$

The range of audibility, neglecting diffraction, for a source on the ground and an observer standing (head 6 ft. up) would be given by

$$x^2 = 2 \times R \times 6,$$

i.e. $\qquad\qquad x = \sqrt{2 \times 273,000 \times 6} \doteqdot 1800 \text{ ft.,}$

or about $\tfrac{1}{3}$ of a mile.

For a source 6 ft. up the range would be doubled—this shows the importance of a high position for the source—and the range would of course be considerably increased by diffraction.*

It is suggested by A. B. Wood † that in view of this effect of temperature a seasonal variation of the audibility of sounds over the sea may reasonably be expected. The maximum sea temperature occurs later in the year than the maximum air temperature. In the Straits of Dover the maximum temperature occurs about September and the minimum in March. Thus from March to August the sea temperature is on the whole lower than the air temperature and the gradient is positive upwards, while from September to February the conditions are reversed. Thus we should expect good audibility in summer and poor audibility in winter. Wood cites the observations of Player ‡ made from the North Foreland on the sound of a siren from a light-vessel several miles away. From May to September the siren was audible on six occasions and inaudible on two: from October to March it was audible on two occasions, inaudible on nine.

6. Abnormal Audibility of Sound.

In 1666 there was an engagement between the English and Dutch fleets in the Channel which was heard in London but not at Deal, Dover, or on the Downs.

The fact is recorded by John Evelyn in his Diary under date 1st June, 1666. " Being in my garden at six o'clock in the evening, and hearing the great guns go thick off, I took horse and rode that night to Rochester: thence next day towards the Downs and sea-coast, but meeting the Lieutenant of the Hampshire frigate, who told me what passed, or rather what had not passed, I returned to London, there being no noise, or appearance, at Deal, or on that coast of any engagement. Recounting this to his Majesty, whom I found at St. James's Park, impatiently expecting, and knowing that Prince Rupert was loose about three at St. Helen's Point at N. of the Isle of Wight, it greatly rejoiced him: but he was astonished when I assured him they heard nothing of the guns in the Downs, nor did the Lieutenant who landed there by five that morning."

The same fact is recorded by Samuel Pepys in his Diary under dates 2nd and 3rd June and summarized under the date 4th June, 1666, as follows: " And so far as to yesterday it is a miraculous thing that we all Friday and Saturday and yesterday did hear everywhere most plainly the guns go off, and yet at Deal and Dover, to last night, they did not hear one word of a fight, nor think they heard one gun. This, added to what I have set down before, the other day, about the Catharine, makes room for a great dispute in philosophy, how we should hear it and they not, the same wind that brought it to us being the same that should bring it to them: but so it is."

Similar references to this phenomenon on the same large scale are to be found in connexion with explosions and gun-fire, and on a much

---

* Mallock, *Proc. Roy. Soc.*, Vol. 91, p. 71 (1914).
† *A Textbook of Sound*, p. 292.   ‡ *Journ. Roy. Met. Soc.*, Vol. 52, p. 354 (1926).

smaller scale the silent zone has been observed in connexion with fog sirens on the coast. So far as these small-scale instances are concerned it seems probable that the silent area owes its origin to wind. Near the surface of the earth the wind velocity increases with height, but this positive wind-velocity gradient does not persist indefinitely, and if it is reversed at a moderate height the curvature of the rays will be reversed. Thus rays proceeding against the wind will first be concave upward, and, later, becoming concave downward, will return to the ground. These silent areas occur to windward as reckoned from the surface wind and are variable in distance and in distribution. They are of no great theoretical interest.

The case of the large-scale phenomena is quite different. Here the inner zone is generally lopsided and sometimes quite small. It is called the area of normal audibility, because the velocity of sound as calculated from the observed time and distance agrees with the theoretical value for the given atmospheric conditions. The outer zone is usually completely detached from the inner. It shows signs of symmetry about the source and its inner boundary is at a distance from the source between 100 km. and 200 km. More important still, it is an area of abnormal audibility, the calculated velocity of the audible sound being very much less than that to be expected from the atmospheric conditions. This suggests that the path of the rays is a long one, reaching perhaps a considerable height in the atmosphere.

Three possible explanations suggest themselves: (1) reversal of wind gradient, (2) reversal of temperature gradient, (3) variation in composition of the atmosphere.

The first of these fails by itself to account for the regularities which are observed and for the degree of symmetry. In 1899 the " isothermal layer " in the atmosphere was discovered by Teisserenc de Bort. He showed that the temperature in the atmosphere, after falling steadily with increasing height, becomes steady about 10 or 12 km. above the surface of the earth. The atmosphere below this is called the troposphere, the region in which convection keeps the composition and temperature gradient constant. Above this lies the stratosphere, where the temperature is constant and where the absence of convection may be presumed to allow the atmosphere to stratify, each constituent gas forming its own atmosphere according to Dalton's law of partial pressures; the result is a mixed atmosphere richest in heavy gases in its lower layers and becoming progressively richer in hydrogen and helium as the height is increased.

A large explosion at Förde in Westphalia in 1904 was discussed by G. v. d. Borne.* He discounted the possibility of explaining the observations by wind and invoked instead an increase of sound velocity with height in the stratosphere due to the high proportion

* *Phys. Zeits.*, Vol. 11, p. 483 (1910).

of helium with its large value of γ. This explanation was later supported by van Everdingen,* who made observations during the war of 1914–18 and published maps of the areas of audibility for naval and military engagements. Against this explanation must be placed the fact that it requires a trajectory the highest point of which may lie at 115 km. to 120 km. above ground level, and the time elapsed would be much greater than those actually observed. In addition to this, the direct experimental evidence for the variation of composition of the atmosphere is wanting at such levels as have been reached.† The hypothesis has been modified by Eropkin ‡ so as to apply to the atomic form of oxygen, which he believes to be the only possible form at altitudes greater than 35 km.

On 17th January, 1917, a severe explosion took place at a munition factory in Silvertown, involving heavy loss of life and immense material damage. Owing to the war censorship, the details were suppressed, but the magnitude of the explosion may be gauged from the fact that nearly half a million windows were broken. Records were collected by Davison § and formed the basis of maps of the areas of audibility. One of these is reproduced in fig. 7.5. It will be seen that the area of abnormal audibility is completely detached and that in places the boundary is very well marked. The inner margin of the outer zone is about 100 km. from the source.

In 1922 an important paper was published by Lindemann and Dobson ‖ in which they suggested that the temperature in the stratosphere increases with height. This conclusion was based on observations which had been made at various times on the heights at which meteorites become incandescent. They deduced a temperature of about 300° K. at about 60 km. height. This reversed temperature gradient at once suggested itself as a possible explanation of the silent zone. In 1923 a series of large explosions was arranged at La Courtine in France and observers in neighbouring countries were notified in advance of the times at which firing would take place. This made possible much more accurate timing than had ever been available before. A map for one of the explosions is shown in fig. 7.6. A rough symmetry around the source is indicated for the area of abnormal audibility. The numbers are (1) distance in km., (2) elapsed times in sec., (3) velocities in km./sec. corresponding to distances measured· along the ground.

Maurain ¶ published the discussion and maps, and concluded that to account for the calculated velocities the temperature at a height

* *Proc. Roy. Acad. Sci. Amsterdam*, Vol. 18, p. 923 (1915).

† Paneth, *Nature*, Vol. 139, p. 220 (1937).

‡ *Journ. Roy. Met. Soc.*, Vol. 62, Supp. 68 (1936).

§ *Proc. Roy. Soc. Edin.*, Vol. 38, p. 115 (1918).

‖ *Proc. Roy. Soc.*, A, Vol. 102, p. 411 (1922).

¶ *Sur la Propagation des Ondes Aeriennes: Annales de l'Institut de Physique du Globe*, (1926).

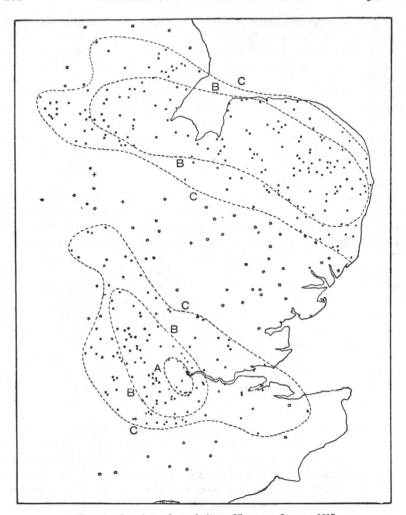

Fig. 7.5.—Sound map for explosion at Silvertown, January, 1917

Dots indicate place where the sound was heard.   Circles indicate places where no sound was heard.   Crosses represent two places in the silent area which are on high ground and where the sound was heard.   Dotted lines give a rough idea of intensity, and similar intensities in the inner and outer areas are indicated by the letters A, B, C.

of 60 km. must be greater than 300° K. or else v. d. Borne's hypothesis must be invoked.   Whipple subjected this report to detailed criticism.*
He assumed:

(1) Ground air temperature 290° K., falling by 6·7° per km. to 210° K. at 12 km. in accordance with the known data.

* *Nature*, Vol. 118, p. 309 (1926).

(2) Uniform temperature of 210° K. from a height of 12 km. to an undetermined height H_2.

(3) Uniform positive temperature gradient until the ground temperature recurs at an undetermined height H_3.

By computing the paths of the rays for various assumed values of H_2 and H_3 he found good agreement for $H_2 = 32$ km., $H_3 = 46$ km.

Vast explosions like that at La Courtine are very expensive, and

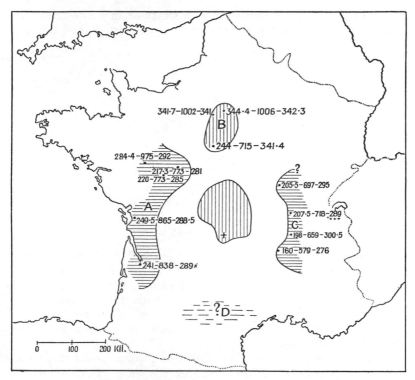

Fig. 7.6.—Sound map for an explosion at La Courtine

in 1926 Whipple * explored the possibility of using gunfire. He found that guns at Shoeburyness could be heard at Grantham, a distance of 185 km. Since then long-distance experiments have been organized, using hot-wire microphones connected to string galvanometers to record the receipt of the sound. Gunfire takes place at Yantlet, Shoeburyness and Woolwich, and sounds are received at Birmingham, Bristol, Cardiff, Nottingham, Exeter, and North Walsham. By using three microphones at a station and measuring the time intervals between the

* *Journ. Roy. Meteor. Soc.*, Vol. 61, p. 289 (1935).

reception of the sound at successive pairs the angle of descent of the sound rays may be estimated. The time signals corresponding to the instant of firing are superimposed on B.B.C. programmes. In order to compute the paths of the rays the following relationship is used:
Starting with equation (7.5),

$$\frac{1}{R} = \frac{1}{c}\frac{dc}{dR},$$

let us assume that the atmosphere is stratified in horizontal layers, and that in any layer the ray makes an angle ψ with the horizontal. Then

$$\frac{\partial c}{\partial R} = -\frac{dc}{dy} \cdot \cos\psi,$$

$$\frac{\partial c}{\partial s} = \frac{dc}{dy} \cdot \sin\psi.$$

Hence, we have

$$\frac{d\psi}{ds} = \frac{1}{R} = \frac{1}{c}\frac{\partial c}{\partial R} = -\frac{1}{c}\frac{dc}{dy}\cos\psi$$

$$= -\frac{1}{c}\frac{\partial c}{\partial s}\cot\psi.$$

$$\therefore \ c\sec\psi = \text{const.} = c_m. \quad . \quad . \quad . \quad . \quad . \quad (7.8)$$

Here c and ψ are corresponding values, and it is obvious that c_m is the velocity when $\sec\psi = 1$, i.e. when the ray is horizontal at the vertex of its path. The law may be stated by saying that the velocity of the trace of any wave-front on a horizontal plane is constant. If we know the velocity at ground level and ψ for the received sound ray, c_m is known. The height of the summit of the trajectory is calculated on the following assumptions:

(1) The temperature gradient and wind gradient in the troposphere are known from observations made at the time. From there both ends of the trajectory of the ray so far as they lie in the troposphere may be computed on the assumption that the trajectory is symmetrical. It is found that, as a rule, ignoring the effect of wind in the troposphere introduces very little error.

(2) The height of the tropopause or transition layer between the troposphere and stratosphere is known, also the temperature of the lower layers of the stratosphere. It is assumed that this temperature is maintained steady to an unknown height H_2, the velocity of sound being constant and the ray straight.

(3) At this height H_2 the temperature starts to rise again at a uniform rate so as to give the velocity c_m at the top of the trajectory.

When these assumptions are fitted in with the known elapsed time a hypothetical trajectory can be traced. The conclusion drawn from the experiments so far made is that the isothermal layer in the strato-sphere extends from the tropopause to a height of about 30 km.; the ground temperature recurs at about 40 km., and the heights reached by the sound rays vary between about 45 km. and 60 km. In some cases the recorded angle of descent is as much as 35°, which implies a value for c_m of something like 420 m./sec. This means either a tem-perature of 440° K. (167° C.) or a very strong wind in the stratosphere, or a combination of both.

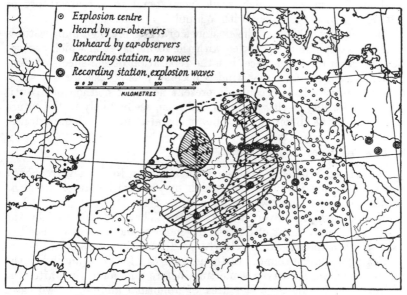

Fig. 7.7.—Map for an explosion at Oldebroek, December, 1932

That wind in the stratosphere plays some part is strongly suggested by the fact that the areas of abnormal audibility always lie to the west of the source in summer and to the east of the source in winter. This is borne out by all the English observations and also by the work of observers in Germany. Excellent records were obtained from four explosions at Oldebroek in Holland carried out by the International Commission for the Investigation of the Upper Atmosphere.* The map for one of these is shown in fig. 7.7. It will be noted that the explosion took place in December, and that the outer area of audibility lay to the east. Whipple has established the probability of a seasonal

---

* Duckert, &c., *Zeits. für Geophysik*, Vol. 10, p. 119 (1934).

wind in the stratosphere by a comparison of pressures at a height of 20 km. above England and above Lapland.

A systematic series of experiments has been carried out by the *Notgemeinschaft der Deutschen Wissenschaft*. These experiments show a marked seasonal effect, the minimum distance of audibility in the outer zone being 110 km. in winter and 190 km. in summer. The velocity for the inner zone is normal for the temperature of the air at ground level, but as in the case of the La Courtine explosions the apparent velocity for the outer zone is much less and suggests a much longer path through the upper atmosphere. Analysis of the observations leads to the conclusion that the velocity of sound at about 40 km. is about 340 m./sec., which would correspond to a temperature of 290° K., in good agreement with Whipple's results.

It seems probable that the existence of relatively high temperatures in the stratosphere is associated with the ozone layer in which absorption of radiation takes place, but the separation of the effects of temperature from the effects of wind is necessary as a basis for any satisfactory theory. It is because at present no other method of investigation is possible at these heights and none seems likely in the future that work on the abnormal audibility of sound assumes such importance.

7. Low-frequency Sound Waves.

Associated with all explosions there seem to be low-frequency waves which are inaudible and which may travel before or after the audible waves. These waves are discussed by Davison (loc. cit.) in connexion with the Silvertown explosion. They are indicated by the rattling and movement of doors and windows, and their responsibility for this phenomenon can be clearly fixed when it occurs either before or after the audible sound. In the inner area of normal audibility the phenomenon was observed some time before and some time after the audible sound. In the outer area of abnormal audibility two cases were recorded where the phenomenon occurred before the audible sound. A novel recorder of these inaudible sound waves was provided by the pheasants in the outer area. Records of the disturbance of pheasants were received from 116 places in the outer area, and in 19 of these the behaviour of the birds was observed before the sound was heard. Dr. Davison attributes their agitation to the low-frequency waves. It is interesting to notice that either the shaking of windows or the agitation of the pheasants or both were observed in sixteen places lying in the silent area.

These low-frequency sounds are discussed by Gowan.* They are easily recorded by instruments. The hot-wire microphone may be made to serve this purpose, and in Germany an instrument known as

---

* *Nature*, Vol. 124, p. 452 (1929).

the undograph is now widely used. It consists of a steel fibre fastened to a thin mica sheet along an axis of symmetry. The sheet swings freely—one half with as little clearance as possible in an opening in the wall of an air-tight box and the other in a small damping chamber. The movement of the mica vane is recorded by a spot of light from a mirror attached to the suspension. In the matter of sensitiveness there is little to choose between the hot-wire microphone and the undograph, but the latter is more self-contained and therefore more portable.

CHAPTER VIII

Superposition or Interference

1. Superposition of Simple Harmonic Vibrations in the same direction.

Suppose we have a series of wave trains of the same period and wave-length arriving by nearly parallel paths at a point. Then at this point the vibrations due to the several members of the series will be superposed and we shall have a series of vibrations, which may be written as

$$\xi_1 = a_1 \sin(\omega t + \epsilon_1),$$
$$\xi_2 = a_2 \sin(\omega t + \epsilon_2),$$

$$\cdot \quad \cdot \quad \cdot \quad \cdot \quad \cdot \quad \cdot$$

$$\begin{aligned} \xi = \xi_1 + \xi_2 + \xi_3 + \cdots \\ = a_1 \sin\omega t \cos\epsilon_1 + a_1 \cos\omega t \sin\epsilon_1 \\ + a_2 \sin\omega t \cos\epsilon_2 + a_2 \cos\omega t \sin\epsilon_2 + \cdots \\ = \sin\omega t \, \Sigma a \cos\epsilon + \cos\omega t \, \Sigma a \sin\epsilon. \quad \cdots \quad (8.1) \end{aligned}$$

If we put $\Sigma a \cos\epsilon = A \cos\phi$ and $\Sigma a \sin\epsilon = A \sin\phi$, we have

$$\begin{aligned} \xi = A \sin\omega t \cos\phi + A \cos\omega t \sin\phi \\ = A \sin(\omega t + \phi). \quad \cdots \quad \cdots \quad (8.2) \end{aligned}$$

Thus the resultant vibration is simple harmonic: its amplitude is A and its phase angle ϕ, where

$$A = \sqrt{\{(\Sigma a \sin\epsilon)^2 + (\Sigma a \cos\epsilon)^2\}} \quad \cdots \quad (8.3)$$

and
$$\tan\phi = \frac{\Sigma a \sin\epsilon}{\Sigma a \cos\epsilon}. \quad \cdots \quad \cdots \quad (8.4)$$

One case of special interest is that where only two vibrations are concerned and they have the same amplitude. Here

$$A = a\sqrt{\{2 + 2\cos(\epsilon_1 - \epsilon_2)\}},$$

and $\epsilon_1 - \epsilon_2$ is the phase difference.

If $\epsilon_1 - \epsilon_2 = 0$ or $2K\pi$, where K is any integer, $A = 2a$;

if $\epsilon_1 - \epsilon_2 = (2K - 1)\pi$, $A = 0$.

178

Thus the vibration at the point in question may have double amplitude or zero amplitude, or any value between, according to the value of $(\epsilon_1 - \epsilon_2)$.

The phase difference may arise partly as a result of a difference of phase between two sources, each sending a train of waves to the point. This, however, is unusual. It is commoner for the two sources to be in the same phase and for the difference in phase at the point in question to arise owing to the difference in length of path from the two sources. If this path difference is δ, then $\epsilon_1 - \epsilon_2 = 2\pi\delta/\lambda$, and we have $A = 2a$ if $\delta = 0$ or $K\lambda$, $A = 0$ if $\delta = (2K - 1)\lambda/2$. This case corresponds to the experiment described on p. 185. The difference of phase may also arise through the train of waves being led from the *same* source to the point of observation by two different paths. Numerous instances of this will appear later.

Another case of special interest with reference to diffraction is that of the superposition of a series of vibrations of the same amplitude and period but with a common phase difference. If this phase difference is ϵ and the common amplitude is a, we have

$$\Sigma a \sin\epsilon = a[\sin\epsilon + \sin 2\epsilon \ldots + \sin m\epsilon]$$

$$= a \frac{\sin m\epsilon/2}{\sin\epsilon/2} \sin \frac{m + 1}{2} \epsilon,$$

$$\Sigma a \cos\epsilon = a[\cos\epsilon + \cos 2\epsilon \ldots + \cos m\epsilon]$$

$$= a \frac{\sin m\epsilon/2}{\sin\epsilon/2} \cos \frac{m + 1}{2} \epsilon,$$

$$\therefore A = \frac{a \sin m\epsilon/2}{\sin\epsilon/2}. \qquad \ldots \ldots \ldots \quad (8.5)$$

If now m becomes very large and ϵ very small and if the phase difference between the last vibration and the first is $2a = m\epsilon$, we have

$$A = \frac{a \sin a}{\sin a/m} = \frac{ma \sin a}{a}, \text{ since } a/m \text{ is small,}$$

$$= R \frac{\sin a}{a}, \qquad \ldots \ldots \ldots \quad (8.6)$$

where R is the algebraic sum of the amplitudes when all the disturbances are assumed to be in phase, i.e. when $\sin a = a$ since $a = 0$.

2. Graphical Composition of Simple Harmonic Vibrations of the same Period in the same Direction.

All the results just obtained analytically can be quite simply obtained graphically. Let P_1, P_2 (fig. 8.1) be the positions at time $t = 0$ of the two points which by projection on to OY generate the two motions

$$\xi_1 = a_1 \sin(\omega t + \epsilon_1),$$
$$\xi_2 = a_2 \sin(\omega t + \epsilon_2).$$

Then $OP_1 = a_1$, $OP_2 = a_2$, $\angle XOP_1 = \epsilon_1$, $\angle XOP_2 = \epsilon_2$.

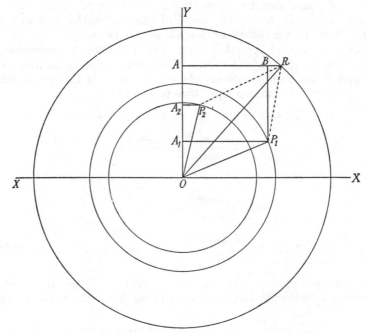

Fig. 8.1.—Composition of simple harmonic motions of the same period and direction

Complete the parallelogram OP_1RP_2 and draw the diagonal OR and the perpendiculars P_1A_1, P_2A_2, and RA. Then at time $t = 0$

$$\xi_1 = OA_1, \ \xi_2 = OA_2 = A_1A,$$
$$\xi = \xi_1 + \xi_2 = OA.$$

Then, since P_1 and P_2 have the same period, the parallelogram rotates with OR unchanged and A describes the resultant simple harmonic vibration which has the same period as the constituent vibrations.

Hence $\xi = A \sin(\omega t + \phi)$,

where $A = \mathrm{OR} = \sqrt{(a_1{}^2 + a_2{}^2 - 2\,a_1 a_2 \cos \mathrm{OP_1 R})}$
              $= \sqrt{(a_1{}^2 + a_2{}^2 + 2\,a_1 a_2 \cos \mathrm{P_1 OP_2})}$
              $= \sqrt{\{(a_1{}^2 + a_2{}^2 + 2\,a_1 a_2 \cos(\epsilon_1 - \epsilon_2)\}}$,

$\tan \phi = \tan \mathrm{ARO}$

              $= \dfrac{\mathrm{OA}}{\mathrm{AR}}$.

Draw $\mathrm{P_1 B}$ perpendicular to AR; then

$$\tan \phi = \frac{\mathrm{OA_1} + \mathrm{A_1 A}}{\mathrm{AB} + \mathrm{BR}} = \frac{a_1 \sin \epsilon_1 + a_2 \sin \epsilon_2}{a_1 \cos \epsilon_1 + a_2 \cos \epsilon_2}.$$

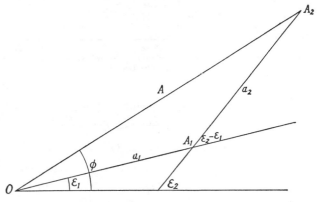

Fig. 8.2.—Composition of two simple harmonic motions of the same period and direction

The method is obviously capable of extension to any number of vibrations. As just derived for two, it is known as Fresnel's rule.

Draw $\mathrm{OA_1}$ (fig. 8.2) to represent a_1 and from $\mathrm{A_1}$ draw $\mathrm{A_1 A_2}$ proportional to a_2 and making with $\mathrm{OA_1}$ an angle $\epsilon_2 - \epsilon_1$. Then $\mathrm{OA_2}$ is proportional on the same scale to the amplitude of the resultant vibration and $\angle \mathrm{A_1 O A_2}$ is $\phi - \epsilon_1$.

To extend the method to any number of vibrations we may choose a datum line OX (fig. 8.3). Draw $\mathrm{OA_1}$ to represent a_1, making $\angle \mathrm{XOA_1} = \epsilon_1$, and so on for all the component vibrations. Then join A_n to O to close the polygon so formed. OA_n is the amplitude of the resultant vibration and $\angle \mathrm{A}_n \mathrm{OX}$ is its phase angle ϕ.

If we take the particular case already treated analytically, where $a_1 = a_2 = a_3 \ldots = a$ and $\epsilon_1 = \epsilon$, $\epsilon_2 = 2\epsilon$, $\epsilon_3 = 3\epsilon, \ldots$, then applying the graphical method we see that the lines representing the displacements to be compounded become the sides of a regular polygon, usually

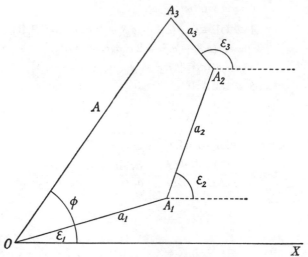

Fig. 8.3.—Composition of any number of simple harmonic vibrations of the same period and direction

incomplete. The resulting displacement is the line closing this incomplete polygon. Let OP be this line (fig. 8.4). Then

$$\angle \text{PTX} = m\epsilon = 2a, \quad \angle \text{POT} = a,$$
$$A = \text{OP} = 2R \sin a$$
$$= 2R \sin \tfrac{1}{2} m\epsilon,$$

where R is the radius of the circle touching TP and TO.

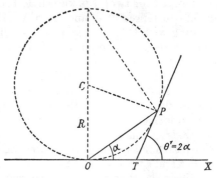

Fig. 8.4.—Composition of any number of simple harmonic vibrations of the same amplitude, period and direction and common phase difference $\epsilon = 2a/m$.

But
$$a = 2R \sin \tfrac{1}{2}\epsilon.$$

$$\therefore A = a \frac{\sin \tfrac{1}{2} m\epsilon}{\sin \tfrac{1}{2}\epsilon}$$

$$= a \frac{\sin a}{\sin a/m}.$$

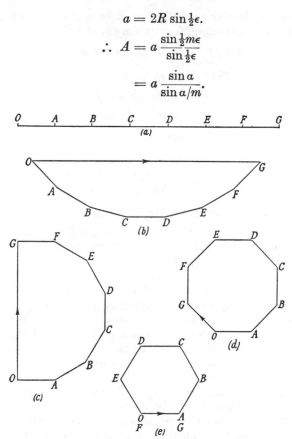

Fig. 8.5.—Composition of seven simple harmonic vibrations of the same period, amplitude and direction with a common phase difference ϵ: (a) $\epsilon = 0$; (b) $\epsilon = 15°$; (c) $\epsilon = 30°$; (d) $\epsilon = 45°$; (e) $\epsilon = 60°$.

Fig. 8.5 represents the superposition for seven constituent vibrations when the common phase difference is (a) $0°$, (b) $15°$, (c) $30°$, (d) $45°$, (e) $60°$. Obviously the magnitude of the resultant depends on the difference in phase between the first and last vibrations. It is a maximum if this is zero, i.e. if all the vibrations are in the same phase. Measurement of the resultant OG gives the resultant amplitude in each case.

Obviously, if as already suggested the number m of components becomes very large and ϵ very small, the parts of polygons become in the limit segments of circles. If ds is the amplitude of each vibration and ϵ is a small increment of phase $d\theta'$ we have

$$\frac{ds}{d\theta'} = \text{constant} = R, \text{ or } s = R\theta',$$

which defines a circular arc of radius R tangential to OX at O (see fig. 8.4). The resultant amplitude is the chord OP.

$$\angle \text{ PTX} = m\epsilon = 2a \text{ as before}$$

and $\angle \text{ POT} = a$, so that

$$A = \text{chord OP} = 2R \sin a.$$

But $ma = \text{arc OP} = 2aR.$

$$\therefore R = \frac{ma}{2a}$$

$$\therefore A = \frac{2ma \sin a}{2a} = \frac{ma \sin a}{a}.$$

3. Experimental Illustrations of Interference.

We have seen in Chapter I (p. 32) how the phenomenon of super-position or interference may be illustrated using short sound waves. The variations of intensity due to superposition may usually be observed with ease if the observer walks about in a church when the organ is being tuned. It is often possible also to while away an idle few minutes at a railway station by locating what correspond to Lloyd's fringes in optics—the maxima and minima of sound due to the superposition of waves coming direct from a locomotive whistle and those coming from its image as formed by the platform, i.e. the waves reflected from the platform. In an ordinary room with a high-pitched whistle sounding the phenomenon is remarkably distinct, especially with one ear closed, and there are many types of detector by means of which the variations of intensity can be demonstrated. The failure of the ear to detect the variations due to superposition of direct and reflected waves under ordinary circumstances probably arises from a variety of causes. In the first place, we very rarely deal with pure tones and as each constituent tone of a musical note produces its own super-position-pattern of intensity we nowhere get silence—only a differ-ence of quality difficult to appreciate. Then again our hearing is bin-aural. For the shorter waves, at any rate, there may be very different intensities at the two ears, and those intensities are averaged.

Instances of the experimental arrangements necessary for observing interference patterns with short waves have already been given. With sounds of ordinary pitch interference patterns may be shown by a tuning-fork. If the fork is made to sound and rotated in front of the ear with its shaft vertical it will be found that there are four positions of maximum loudness and four of minimum loudness in each complete rotation.

The phenomenon may also be demonstrated by an apparatus first suggested by J. Herschel (1792–1871), the principle of which will be clear from fig. 8.6. Wave trains travelling from B to D will arrive at D in opposite phase if the path difference along the two branches is $(2K - 1)\lambda/2$, where K is any integer. The experiment was not actually

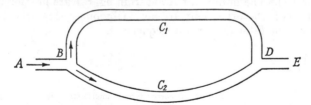

Fig. 8.6.—One type of Herschel-Quincke interference tube

attempted by Herschel, but was later carried out by Quincke (1834–1924).* The apparatus can be modified so as to contain a trombone slide for altering the path difference. Stewart † showed that the simple Herschel explanation is inadequate, and by taking account of the fact

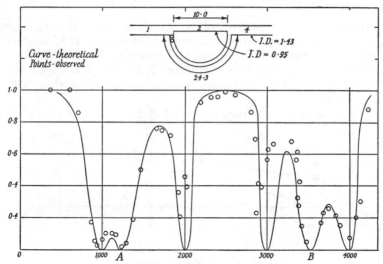

Fig. 8.7.—Transmission of sound through a Herschel-Quincke interference tube (Stewart). Instead of changing the length of one branch and keeping the wave-length of the sound the same, Stewart kept the lengths of the branches the same and changed the frequency. The wave-lengths can be obtained from the relation $c = f\lambda$; c was taken as 343 m./sec. The inset in the upper part of the figure gives the dimensions of the apparatus in centimetres; I.D. stands for inner diameter.

that the sound arriving at D by the path C_2 divides so that some goes on through E while some returns to B by C_1 and, similarly, of the sound arriving at D by C_1, some travels back to B by C_2, he developed a more complete theory which he verified by observation. Fig. 8.7 shows the

* *Pogg. Ann.*, Vol. 128, p. 177 (1866).   † *Phys. Rev.*, Vol. 31, p. 696 (1928).

dimensions of his apparatus and gives a comparison of the theoretical relation between the frequency and the intensity at E (as indicated by the continuous curve) and the actual observations (as indicated by the circles). The minima at A and B in fig. 8.7 are predicted by the simple theory; the other four are not. Obviously this branched tube acts as a simple filter for certain frequencies.

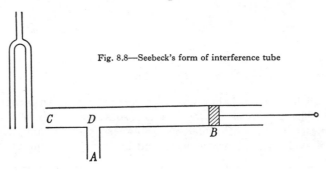

Fig. 8.8—Seebeck's form of interference tube

Another arrangement by Seebeck is used in one of the stationary-wave methods for determining the velocity of sound. It is illustrated in fig. 8.8. Sound waves from the fork travel to A either directly by the path CDA or, after reflection from B, by the path CBA. If we adjust the piston B we shall find minimum loudness at A when $2DB = (2K - 1)\lambda/2$.

It may be mentioned that if the end of A is closed and we remove

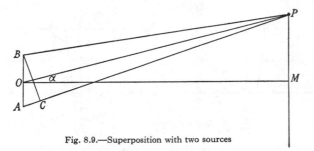

Fig. 8.9.—Superposition with two sources

the piston and transmit the sound waves along the tube from C to B, all components will be weakened for which $2AD = (2K - 1)\lambda/2$, and the side tube will act as a filter.

The simplest experimental case is that in which we have two sources of waves of the same frequency and we examine the effect in the neighbourhood of a plane bisecting at right angles the line joining the sources.

Let A and B (fig. 8.9) be the two point-sources and MP the plane in which observations are being made. Let MP $= z$ and AB $= s$, and draw BC perpendicular to AP. Let OM $= D$. Then

$$BP^2 = D^2 + (z - s/2)^2,$$

$$AP^2 = D^2 + (z + s/2)^2,$$

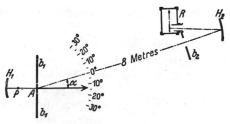

Fig. 8.10.—Double-slit interferometer

hence $AP^2 - BP^2 = 2sz,$

or $(AP - BP)\ 2OP = 2sz.$

That is, $\delta = s \,.\, \sin \alpha,$

where α is the angle POM.

$$\therefore\ \sin \alpha = \frac{\delta}{s}.$$

We get maxima for $\delta = 2K\lambda/2$ and minima for $\delta = (2K - 1)\lambda/2$.

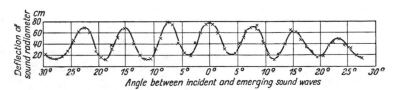

Fig. 8.11.—Results of measurements with the double-slit interferometer of fig. 8.10

Using his whistle as a source of sound and the acoustic radiometer as a detector, R. W. Pohl * applies this formula to determine the wave-length of the sound given by the whistle. In fig. 8.10, b_1 is a double slit, each slit being about 1 cm. in width and the centres of the slits about 11 cm. apart; P is the whistle directed to the concave mirror H_1 which reflects a parallel beam on to the slits. This part of the apparatus can rotate about a vertical axis through the centre of b_1. The beam issuing from the double slit falls on a concave mirror H_2 and is focused on the radiometer R. In fig. 8.11 the radiometer deflections are plotted against the angle α between the normal to the slits and the direction from them to the slit b_2 admitting the beam to the mirror of the radiometer. The curve shows well-

* *Physical Principles of Mechanics and Acoustics*, p. 296.

marked maxima and minima distributed fairly symmetrically. The mean value for α for the third minimum is $19 \cdot 2°$ and since

$$\sin \alpha = \frac{(2K - 1)}{s} \frac{\lambda}{2}.$$

we have $\lambda = 1 \cdot 45$ cm.

4. Location of Direction of Source of Sound by application of Principle of Superposition.

The application to aerial listening has been made by J. Perrin in the design of an instrument called the myriaphone. This consists (fig. 8.12) of a large number of horns with their wide ends arranged in a plane. Cylindrical tubes of equal length conduct the sound collected in these by groups to another set of horns, which in turn deliver the sound to a single horn connected to the ear. When the plane of the instrument is at right angles to the direction from which the sound is received each horn in the first set collects the sound which falls on it, and as the length of path is the same from all the horns to the ear the sounds arrive at the ear in phase, with great reinforcement. The amplitude at the ear is approximately proportional (the dissipation of sound in the tubes being neglected) to the number of collecting horns, and the intensity of the sound to the square of this number. On the other hand, the instrument is highly selective with respect to direction. If the dimensions of the instrument are comparable with the wave-length of sound, then sounds coming from a direction off the axis of the instrument will arrive at the various collecting horns with marked differences of phase and these will be preserved unchanged in their passage to the ear, so that the resulting sound will be considerably weakened.

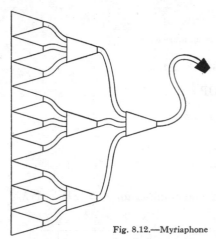

Fig. 8.12.—Myriaphone

Binaural Superposition.

If a length of rubber tubing is arranged at random on the table and the two ends are inserted in the ears, then a tap delivered on the tube at any point will give rise to a sound which will appear to come from left or right, according to which ear is nearer to the point tapped.

When the sound is " centred " it appears to come from a point in the median plane of the head, the instant of arrival at the two ears being the same.   If proper precautions are taken this adjustment can be made with very great accuracy, a difference in time of arrival amounting to no more than 10^{-5} sec. being appreciated by an untrained observer.

This faculty of the ear is used in determining the direction of a source of sound, e.g. an aeroplane at night. If RL (fig. 8.13) represents the line joining the two ears, and LA an advancing plane wave-front, then the difference in time of arrival at the two ears will be given by AR/c, where c is the wave velocity. If Δt is this time difference,

$$\Delta t = \frac{AR}{c} = \frac{RL \cdot \sin a}{c} = \frac{b \sin a}{c},$$

where b is the distance between the two ears and a the angle which the direction of the source of sound makes with the normal to the line joining the ears.   Hence

$$\sin a = \frac{c \Delta t}{b}.$$

Obviously, then, the sensitiveness depends on b.   The distance between the ears cannot be increased, but R and L may be replaced by two horns, each connected separately to one ear and mounted on a framework which can be rotated about an axis so as to " centre " the sound; b now becomes the distance between the horns and can be greatly increased, with a corresponding gain in sensitiveness.   One pair of horns can be used to give azimuth and another pair to give altitude, the four horns giving the line to the source, or at least the line to the point where the source was when the sound waves were emitted.

The principle was first applied in a practical instrument known as the Claude orthophone, which was in use in the French army during the war of 1914–18.*   It is shown diagrammatically in fig. 8.14.

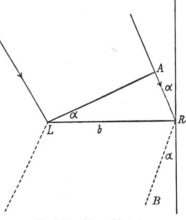

Fig. 8.13.—Binaural listening

The sound is received through the open ends O_1, O_2 of two tubes T_1, T_2 bent as shown and connected to a stethoscope.   It was used for the determination of

* Paris, *Science Progress*, Vol. 27, p. 457 (1933).

the direction of gun-fire, so that only an azimuthal bearing was required. For aircraft location four collecting horns are mounted in a framework as in fig. 8.15,

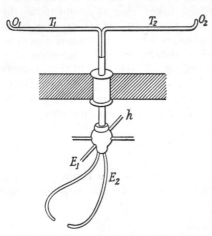

Fig. 8.14.—Instrument for binaural listening

the altitude setting being made by an observer using E_1, E_2 and centring by rotation about the axis A_1, A_2, while a second observer uses the horns A_1, A_2 and sets for azimuth by rotating about the vertical axis X. The horns give increased accuracy of discrimination, since the sound transmitted to the ear by the horn is a maximum when the axis of the horn points towards the source, or at least is normal to the wave-front being received. This tends to cut out other sounds, and if the trumpet mouths are coplanar and are arranged to lie in the plane of the wave-fronts of the received sound, then the time difference is zero, so that zero time difference and maximum loudness occur together. In the Exponential Sound Locator of American origin the trumpets are exponential and about 15 ft. long. The base length is about 9 ft. In the French Telesitemètre each sound collector is a myriaphone consisting of forty-two small conical trumpets.

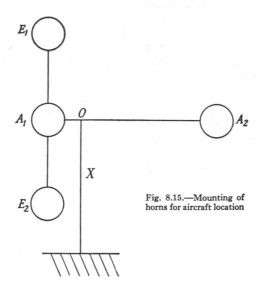

Fig. 8.15.—Mounting of horns for aircraft location

The accuracy of setting corresponds to a path difference of about 1 cm., which, on a 9-ft. base, means an angular error of about $\frac{1}{270}$ of a radian or about 12·5 minutes.

There remains the application of the necessary corrections to give the position of the aeroplane at the instant when observations are made. Some of these are concerned with atmospheric refraction and need not concern us here. When they have been applied we have the position of the aeroplane when the sound waves then being received were emitted. Meanwhile, however, the aeroplane has moved. For an aeroplane at 10,000 ft. the time taken by the sound to reach the observers may be about 15 sec., and in this time the aeroplane may have moved half a mile. If the path of the aeroplane is a horizontal line, then the line along which the sound is received (the line of sound) will be a past line of sight, and all past lines of sight lie in the plane containing the track of the aeroplane and the point of observation.

Let OT_1, OT_2 (fig. 8.16) be two successive lines of sound. Then if t is the time

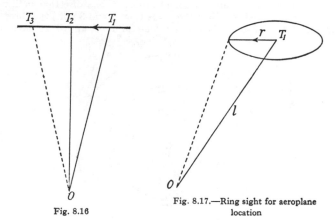

Fig. 8.16

Fig. 8.17.—Ring sight for aeroplane location

for the sound to reach O from T_2, $OT_2 = ct$, and if v is the velocity of the aeroplane and T_3 its position when the sound is received, $T_2T_3 = vt$,

$$\therefore \frac{T_2T_3}{OT_2} = \frac{v}{c}.$$

Since the directions OT_2 and T_2T_3 are known the direction OT_3 can be determined.

The correction is actually applied by using a "ring sight" (fig. 8.17). Let O be the position of the point of observation and T_1 a point on the line of sound to the aeroplane. Let the length of OT_1 be l, and with centre T_1 draw a circle of radius r such that $r/l = v/c$. Then the line of sight will always pass through some point in this circle, and the circle will move parallel to itself so that its centre moves parallel to the track of the aeroplane. In this case the corrected sight line will join the point O to the point of the ring which is leading.

The same principle may be applied to the determination of the direction of a source of sound in water. The method was first applied in this country, but it has been developed chiefly in the United States, where it has been used with great success. If R and L are two acoustic receivers connected by tubes of equal length to the two ears, then by rotating the frame to which they are attached the sound can be centred and the direction determined. An alternative method of adjustment is more convenient. Keeping the direction RL constant, the source of sound may be centred by lengthening the path to the left ear and shortening the path to the right ear. This method of compensation is carried out by the apparatus shown in fig. 8.18.

The method is rendered more accurate by the development shown in fig. 8.19. The arrangement known as the MV tube consists of twelve equally spaced acoustic receivers. The paths from 1, 2, and 3 to A are equal, so that for a sound coming from a direction normal to the line of receivers the sounds reaching A from the three receivers arrive in the same phase and reinforce one another; *ac* is a circular compensator, and if the source of sound is not in the direction indicated the compensator can be used to adjust the paths from 1 and 3 until the three sounds arrive in the same phase. If the same is done for B, C, and D we have the four

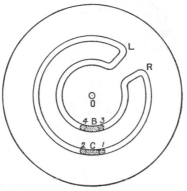

Fig. 8.18.—Diagram of circular compensator

Rotation of upper disc displaces the stops B, C and alters the relative lengths of the sound paths R and L leading to the right and left ears respectively

sets of receivers centred on 2, 5, 8, and 11. The compensator EF is now adjusted so that the combined sounds from the first receivers leave E in phase with those from the next three leaving F. A similar adjustment is made for GH. These combined sounds are now led separately through the last compensator MN to the ears at L and R. If all the compensators had to be set separately the method would be extremely slow and cumbersome. This is not so, however; the amount of compensation required is proportional to the base line in each case, i.e. the distance of the receivers to which the compensation is applied. If s is the distance between successive receivers this base line for A, B, C, and D is $2s$ in each case, so that these four all have the same setting. For E and F it is $3s$, and for the last compensator it is $6s$. Thus one circular compensator in which the grooves have their radii in the ratio of $2:3:6$, with the appropriate connexions, carries out all the settings in one operation and can be graduated to give the direction by direct reading.

Considerable advantages may be obtained by substituting button microphones for acoustic receivers. The connexions from the microphones are made to two earphones through transformers, in the secondaries of which are placed retardation units for the compensation. The retardation lines are of the type known as capacity coupling. In a circuit of this type there is a change of phase from unit to unit without appreciable attenuation. The time interval introduced per section is $\sqrt{L_1 C_2}$.

This electrical arrangement has several notable advantages. The system of acoustic receivers has to be screwed to the hull of the observing ship, usually one row of twelve receivers on each side of the keel, and repair of defective units is difficult. The electrical type may consist of twelve microphones strung to a cable (the " eel ") and towed behind the ship, and they can be pulled on board with comparative ease. In the case of acoustic receivers, again, the compensator

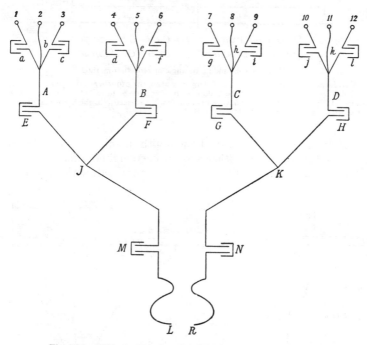

Fig. 8.19.—MV tube for submarine detection by binaural listening

must be close to the receivers. In the electrical installation it may be anywhere convenient for the operator.

It may be noticed in fig. 8.13 that there is an ambiguity between sounds arriving along the direction AR and those arriving along BR. In order to eliminate this, two eels are towed in parallel and by special compensators six microphones of one can be centred with six of the others so as to give a check observation and eliminate the ambiguity.

Using this type of direction-finder a submarine bell has been picked up at 37 miles, and its bearing fixed to within two degrees. As applied to echo-sounding, the method consists in the solution of an isosceles triangle in which the base and one of the angles is known and the

height is required. Fig. 8.20 shows the case in which a ship picks up her
own propeller sound. An interesting further possibility is indicated in

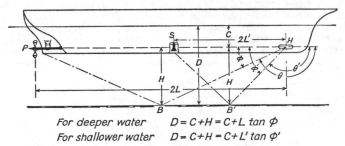

For deeper water $D = C + H = C + L \tan \phi$
For shallower water $D = C + H = C + L' \tan \phi'$

Fig. 8.20.—Sounding by angle of reflection method

For deeper water the angle ϕ is made larger by using the propeller as the source of sound.
For shallower water a source at the middle of the ship may be used. D is the depth of the
water; C the depth of source and hydrophone below the surface; 2L the horizontal distance
of source from hydrophone.

fig. 8.21 in which, having found the depth, a ship is able to locate by
bearing and distance any other ship in her neighbourhood.

Very remarkable results have been obtained with this type of

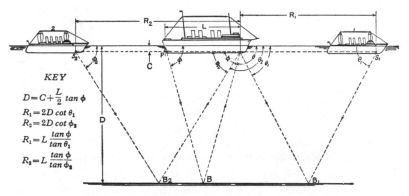

KEY

$$D = C + \frac{L}{2} \tan \phi$$
$$R_1 = 2D \cot \theta_1$$
$$R_2 = 2D \cot \phi_2$$
$$R_1 = L \frac{\tan \phi}{\tan \theta_1}$$
$$R_2 = L \frac{\tan \phi}{\tan \phi_2}$$

Fig. 8.21.—Location of other ships by echo-sounding method

D, the depth, is first obtained from the direction of the sound from the ship's own propeller
reflected from the bottom. The distances of the other ships are then found in terms of D and
of the angles at which the sounds of their submarine bells are received by the observing ship.

hydrophone.* It has been shown to facilitate rapid navigation in
shallow water, the channel being picked out entirely by means of the
sounding apparatus and chart.

* Proc. Amer. Phil. Soc., Vol. 59, pp. 1, 371 (1920); Journ. Frankl. Inst., Vol. 197,
p. 323 (1924).

5. Beats.

When two sources of nearly equal frequency are sounded simultaneously, the resulting sound shows marked variation of intensity, alternately swelling and lulling. The effect may be well demonstrated by two tuning-forks originally of the same pitch, one of which has been flattened somewhat by loading the ends of its prongs with a little wax. If a couple of open organ pipes giving the same note are mounted together on a wind-chest and the pitch of one of them is flattened by shading the open end with the hand, a strong beating is heard. The effect is not unpleasing and is utilized in the *voix celeste* stop, which consists of a series of mistuned pipes giving the characteristic fluctuations. The qualitative explanation of the phenomenon is fairly simple. The source of higher frequency gains on the source of lower frequency and is alternately in the same phase and in the opposite phase. Thus, if we assume the simple law of superposition to hold, the amplitude is alternately the sum and difference of the amplitudes of the two sources. Obviously the beat cycle is completed every time the sharper source gains a whole vibration on the flatter source, so that the number of beats per second is the difference in frequency of the two sources.

The phenomenon is a very important one. The mistuning of an interval is made evident at once by the resulting beats and the tuning may be made exact by adjusting either source until the beats disappear. Again, the unknown frequency of a source may be determined by counting the beats it makes with a source of known frequency. This is the principle used in Scheibler's tonometer (p. 318).

Further, according to the Helmholtz theory of dissonance, the roughness of dissonant intervals is always due to the beats occurring between pairs of tones which may be either the fundamentals or partials (p. 335) or combination tones (p. 478) or any selection of these.

Let the two sources have frequencies $p + \epsilon/2$ and $p - \epsilon/2$. Choose the time origin so that at the point considered the two component sounds are in phase. Then we have

$$\xi_1 = A_1 \sin 2\pi[(p + \epsilon/2)t - \phi],$$
$$\xi_2 = A_2 \sin 2\pi[(p - \epsilon/2)t - \phi],$$
$$\xi = \xi_1 + \xi_2 = (A_1 - A_2) \sin 2\pi[(p + \epsilon/2)t - \phi]$$
$$+ 2A_2 \cos \pi \epsilon t \sin 2\pi(pt - \phi). \quad (8.7)$$

If $A_1 \geqslant A_2$ the first term is a simple sine term with the frequency of the stronger source and amplitude given by the difference of the amplitudes of the sources. The second term is the product of two variable factors, one of which has a longer period than the other, since ϵ is small compared with p. This term may be interpreted as a sound of frequency p and of variable amplitude. If the two sources have the same intensity the first term becomes equal to zero and only the second term remains. Its amplitude has a frequency ϵ, which is the difference of the frequencies of the two sources, the sign of the cosine term being ignored. (The reason for ignoring the sign is that the intensity, which the ear appreciates, varies as ξ^2. It therefore varies as $A_2{}^2 (1 + \cos 2\pi\epsilon t)$ and has the frequency ϵ.)

If $A_1 \neq A_2$, then at instants when the second term is zero we hear only the sound of frequency $p + \epsilon/2$ and amplitude $A_1 - A_2$. For the rest of the time we should expect to hear with varying intensities two sounds of frequencies $p + \epsilon/2$ and p. If ϵ is small these frequencies will not be distinguished. Indeed, an alternative to (8.7) is

$$\xi = (A_2 - A_1) \sin 2\pi[(p - \epsilon/2)t - \phi] + 2A_1 \cos \pi\epsilon t \sin 2\pi(pt - \phi),$$

indicating a frequency $p - \epsilon/2$ at the moment of least amplitude. Thus the approximation of supposing $\cos \pi\epsilon t$ to vanish for more than one consecutive instant is sufficient to blur the residual frequency to the extent of ϵ.

There is some disagreement among experts as to the variation in pitch experienced with beats, which Helmholtz claimed to hear. According to the analysis given by Becquerel, if the more intense sound is the sharper, then when the intensity of the resultant sound passes from its minimum to its maximum the pitch falls from $p + \epsilon/2$ to $p + \dfrac{A_1 - A_2}{A_1 + A_2}\dfrac{\epsilon}{2}$. If the more intense sound is the flatter the pitch rises from $p - \epsilon/2$ to $p - \dfrac{A_1 - A_2}{A_1 + A_2}\dfrac{\epsilon}{2}$.

Beats are so familiar a phenomenon that it is hardly necessary to indicate further experimental illustrations. Two valve-operated telephones in one of which the frequency can be varied are very convenient for purposes of demonstration. Beating with two forks in strict unison can also be demonstrated if one is moved in the direction of the observer. The difference in this case is due to the Doppler effect.

6. Stationary Vibration due to Direct and Reflected Plane Waves.

We have already seen (Chapter VI, section 3, p. 145) that a direct wave given by

$$\xi_1 = f(ct - x)$$

gives rise at the surface $x = 0$ to a reflected wave

$$\xi_2 = \pm f(ct + x),$$

the sign depending on whether reflection takes place at an " open " or a rigid boundary.

Taking the case of the rigid boundary, we have for the displacement ξ at any point in front of the surface

$$\xi = \xi_1 + \xi_2 = f(ct - x) - f(ct + x).$$

For sine waves we may write

$$\xi = a[\sin(\omega t - kx) - \sin(\omega t + kx)]$$
$$= -2a \cos\omega t \sin kx. \quad \ldots \ldots \ldots \quad (8.8)$$

Then
$$v = \dot\xi = 2a\omega \sin\omega t \sin kx, \quad \ldots \ldots \quad (8.9)$$

$$s = -\frac{\partial\xi}{\partial x} = 2ak \cos\omega t \cos kx. \quad \ldots \ldots \quad (8.10)$$

The particle velocity is zero for all values of t for $\cos kx = 1$
or
$$kx = \pm K\pi, \text{ where } K = 0, 1, 2, \ldots,$$
that is, for $x = 0, -\lambda/2, -\lambda, \&\text{c.},$

negative values of x being taken for planes in front of the surface.

The particle velocity has maximum amplitude for $\cos kx = 0$
or
$$kx = \pm(2K - 1)\pi/2,$$
that is, for $x = -\lambda/4, -3\lambda/4, -5\lambda/4, \ldots.$

We therefore have a series of planes parallel to the surface at distances from it of $\lambda/4$, $\lambda/2$, $3\lambda/4$, &c. If we regard the surface itself as the first of the series, the odd numbered planes are nodal planes for particle velocity and the even ones are antinodal planes.

Consider these nodal planes at any fixed instant. For example, when $\sin\omega t = 1$ and v is therefore greatest, we have

$$v = 2a\omega \sin kx.$$

As we pass through the first nodal plane at $x = -\lambda/2$,

(1) $kx = -\pi,$

so that $\sin kx = 0$;

(2) kx is increasing numerically and $\sin kx$ changes from negative to positive. Therefore v changes sign as we cross this nodal plane. At each of the other nodal planes v again changes sign.

Considering the condensation, we note that it has maximum amplitude for

$$\cos kx = 1$$
or
$$kx = \pm K\pi,$$
that is, for $x = 0, -\lambda/2, -\lambda, -3\lambda/2, \ldots.$

These are the antinodal planes for s. Also, the condensation is zero for all values of t where

$$\cos kx = 0,$$

or $$kx = \pm (2K - 1)\pi/2$$

that is, for $$x = -\lambda/4,\ -3\lambda/4,\ -5\lambda/4,\ \ldots$$

The condensation also changes sign as we cross a nodal plane.

Taken together these planes form a series in front of the rigid reflecting surface, spaced at a distance $\lambda/4$ apart. If we regard the surface itself as the first of the series, then the odd members of the series are nodal planes for velocity and antinodal planes for pressure, while the even members are nodal planes for pressure and antinodal planes for velocity. If the reflection had taken place at a free boundary the nodal and antinodal planes would have had their positions interchanged.

It should be noted that owing to the dissipation of energy in the wave, the reflected wave is never in practice equal in amplitude to the direct wave, so that displacement amplitude is never zero at the one set of planes, nor is pressure amplitude ever zero at the other set, even if the surface is a perfect reflector.

In a single plane wave train *pressure* and *particle velocity* are in phase. *Displacement* and *velocity-potential* are in phase, but at 90° to the former two quantities. Just as velocity and pressure behave differently on reflection and so give rise to alternating nodes, the nodes of pressure occurring at the velocity antinodes, so it is with displacement and velocity-potential; they too part company in a stationary wave system. This is consistent with the necessary conditions (Chap. II, p. 60) that

$$v = \dot{\xi},\ \frac{p}{\rho} = \phi,$$

which imply that any relation between pressure (p) and velocity (v) will have a counterpart in a relation between displacement (ξ) and velocity-potential (ϕ). A free boundary, for example, is an antinode for displacement and velocity and a node for pressure and velocity-potential.

It can be shown that a solution of the equation of wave propagation (2.35) corresponding to a point source of sound at P may be expressed in the form

$$4\pi\phi = \frac{Ae^{ik(r-ct)}}{r},\ \ \ldots \ldots \ (8.11)$$

where the factor 4π is inserted to make A represent the " strength " of the source in the hydrodynamical sense, and r is the distance measured from P.

The value of $\partial\phi/\partial n$ can be made to vanish over the whole of a plane surface of which n is the normal by adding a term

$$\frac{Ae^{ik(r_1-ct)}}{r_1}$$

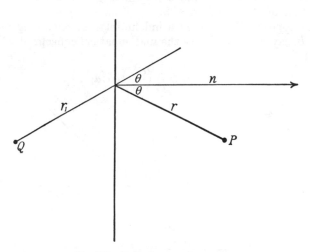

Fig. 8.22.—Reflection at a plane surface

to the right-hand side of the above equation, where r_1 is measured from a point at the geometrical image of P in the plane (fig. 8.22). The solution on the same side of the plane is then

$$4\pi\phi = \frac{Ae^{ikr}}{r} + \frac{Ae^{ikr_1}}{r_1}, \quad . \quad . \quad . \quad . \quad (8.12)$$

the time factor being omitted.

This is the type of disturbance which will result if a rigid perfect reflector is placed at the plane in question, so far as the result on the same side as P is concerned. So far, this is analogous to the formation of an image in optics. In acoustics, however, it may happen that the distance of P from the reflector is small compared with the wavelength, so that we may also examine the result for small values of $r_1 - r$, when r_1 and r are both large. Equation (8.12) shows that the amplitude is doubled and the intensity quadrupled by the reflector, on the same side as P. The case is interesting for a " free " boundary for which

$$4\pi\phi = \frac{Ae^{ikr}}{r} - \frac{Ae^{ikr_1}}{r_1}$$

$$\doteqdot A\frac{\partial}{\partial r}\left(\frac{e^{ikr}}{r}\right)\delta r = A\frac{\partial}{\partial r}\left(\frac{e^{ikr}}{r}\right)l\cos\alpha, \quad . \quad . \quad (8.13)$$

where l is written for PQ, and α for the angle between the direction of r and that of PQ, as in fig. 8.23.

If we suppose PQ to diminish indefinitely, Al remaining finite and equal to B, say, then we derive the mathematical concept of a " double source ":

$$4\pi\phi = B\frac{\partial}{\partial r}\left(\frac{e^{ikr}}{r}\right)\cos\alpha, \quad . \quad . \quad . \quad . \quad (8.14)$$

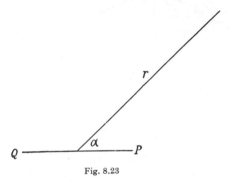

Fig. 8.23

and this is the form in which the idea of double sources finds many practical applications. The disturbance resulting from an oscillating rigid sphere of small dimensions approximates closely to this type, because the compressions in front or behind are in opposite phase, and act as " object " and " reversed image ".

Measurements based on Stationary Vibration.

If the medium in front of the reflecting surface is explored with a small funnel connected by rubber tubing to the ear, the existence of nodal planes may be experimentally demonstrated and the further interesting fact established that audibility is a maximum at the pressure antinodes, i.e. the ear is sensitive to changes of pressure and not to air displacement.

These facts explain a common phenomenon to which attention seems first to have been attracted by Baumgarten. On listening to the noise of a waterfall reflected from a rock close to his head, he noticed that the pitch of the note seemed to alter with the distance of his head from the reflecting surface, being higher when his head was nearer to the surface. The effect may easily be observed in the reflection of the noise of a motor-car from a wall or the noise of an aeroplane from the ground. It is most marked if the ear remote from the reflecting surface is closed. It can of course be detected only

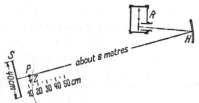

Fig. 8.24.—Interferometer with moving mirror

with impure sounds. Each constituent tone produces its own spacing of nodal planes, and the predominant pitch heard is that of the tone for which the ear is situated in the pressure antinode. Savart investigated the phenomenon and found that with his ear at 130 cm. from the reflecting surface the predominant pitch gave a frequency of about 128. As the first pressure antinode is $\lambda/2$ cm. from the wall this gave $\lambda = 260$ cm. For the velocity of sound in metres per second

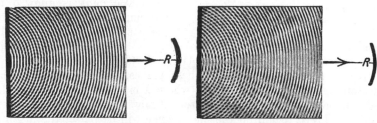

Fig. 8.25.—To illustrate the waves produced by the interferometer with moving mirror; both waves in phase in the direction of observation.

Fig. 8.26.—Like fig. 8.25, except that there is a phase difference of 180° between the two waves in the direction of motion.

this gave $128 \times 2{\cdot}6 = 333$ m./sec., which is a sufficient verification.

An application of the phenomenon is shown in fig. 8.24. P marks the position of the whistle and S is a large sheet of metal acting as a plane reflector, the distance of which from P can be altered. If x is the distance from the whistle to the plane reflector, then $2x = K\lambda$ gives agreement in phase between direct and reflected waves at P, and the sound beam proceeds as shown in fig. 8.25. If $2x = (2K - 1)\lambda/2$, the direct and reflected waves will be in opposite phase at P and there will be no beam along the axis of symmetry, as is seen in fig. 8.26.

It follows that as x is varied the deflection of the radiometer will go through a series of maxima and minima equally spaced. These are very clearly shown in fig. 8.27. The distance between the mirror and whistle changes by $(14\cdot1 - 9\cdot8) = 4\cdot3$ cm. while six successive minima in the sound occur. Hence $2 \times 4\cdot3 = 6\lambda$, or $\lambda = 1\cdot43$ cm.

These features are of course only part of a system of hyperbolic fringes similar to that referred to on p. 10; the only difference is that here one source is virtual, being the image of the real source in the reflecting surface. When the reflector moves the virtual source moves and the whole system of fringes moves in consequence. At any point in the medium alternations of intensity are produced, giving the effect of beats, and it can easily be shown that these beats may equally well be regarded as due to the simultaneous sounding of the real source and of its image, the frequency of the sound from the image being modified by the Doppler effect due to its motion with a velocity twice that of the reflecting surface.

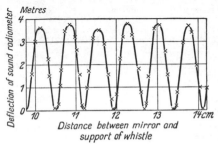

Fig. 8.27.—A series of measurements with the interferometer of fig. 8.26

If a photographic plate is silvered on the surface on which the film is deposited, stationary waves are set up when monochromatic light is allowed to fall normally on it, and the silver salt on the film is subjected to maximum photo-chemical activity at a series of antinodal planes equally spaced. When the plate is developed and fixed we have the metallic silver deposited in these planes, which become partial reflectors spaced at distances $\lambda/2$, where λ is the wave-length of the light originally incident on the plate. If now light of the same wavelength is allowed to fall on the plate, some will be reflected and some transmitted at each successive plane. The reflected waves will follow one another at intervals of λ and will be exactly in phase, so that reflection will be copious. For any other wave-length this will not hold and the light will be suppressed owing to destructive interference. This is the principle of the Lippmann colour photography process. At each point in the plate the spacing of the reflecting planes will be appropriate to the colour of the light falling on the plate at that point, and when white light is subsequently used to illumine the plate only the appropriate component will be copiously reflected.

This phenomenon accounts also for the very pure and intense colours sometimes developed by chlorate of potash crystals. A succession of partially reflecting equally spaced planes is developed in the crystal. Rayleigh has obtained the same effect with short sound waves, using muslin reflectors. The muslin is mounted on a series of rings carried on a framework, which allows of the spacing being altered but maintained equal. When these are correctly adjusted for the wave-length of the sound waves impinging on them, the reflection is copious and can be detected by a sensitive flame.

A case of great practical importance occurs when a sound source is placed just under the surface of water. In this case reflection takes place without change of velocity phase but with reversal of pressure phase, the conditions being opposite to those for reflection from a rigid boundary. It follows that the surface is a pressure node and that the pressure antinode does not occur until a depth of $\lambda/4$ below the surface is reached. As the wave-length of a sound in water is nearly

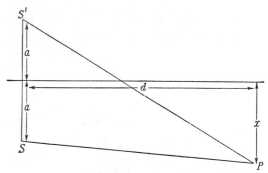

Fig. 8.28.—Reflection of waves in water from an air surface

five times that in air, this depth may be considerable. If a hydrophone is sensitive to pressure it may fail entirely to pick up submarine sounds if used too near the surface. On one occasion a ship was listening to the sound of her own propeller, lost it entirely when she got into deep water, and found that she had been listening all the time to the echo of the propeller sound from the bottom, the direct sound being suppressed by the superposition of the waves reflected with change of pressure phase from the surface.

The phenomenon is equivalent to the superposition of waves from two sources equidistant from the surface and in opposite phase.

The pressure amplitude is zero at the surface and is a maximum for $S'P - SP = \lambda/2$ (fig. 8.28).

But
$$S'P - SP \doteq \frac{2ax}{d}$$

∴ depth of the first maximum is given by

$$\frac{\lambda}{2} = \frac{2ax}{d}, \text{ or } x = \frac{\lambda d}{4a}.$$

If this is to be near the surface λ must be small and a large.

7. Stationary Waves with Partial Reflection.

In this case we have

$$\xi_1 = a \sin(\omega t - kx), \quad \xi_2 = ma \sin(\omega t + kx),$$

$$\xi = \xi_1 + \xi_2 = a(1+m) \sin\omega t \cos kx - a(1-m) \cos\omega t \sin kx. \quad (8.15)$$

If $m = +1$ we have the case of reflection from an " open end " without reversal of displacement phase, and

$$\xi = 2a \sin\omega t \cos kx.$$

If $m = -1$ we have the case of reflection from a rigid boundary with reversal of displacement phase, and

$$\xi = -2a \cos\omega t \sin kx,$$

which is the case already considered (p. 197).

If $m = 0$ we have

$$\xi = a \sin(\omega t - kx)$$

and only the incident wave exists.

Considering the complete equation again, we see that it consists of two sets of stationary waves both of period $2\pi/\omega$, with a quarter-period phase difference and amplitudes varying from point to point and given by $a(1+m) \cos kx$ and $a(1-m) \sin kx$ respectively.

The first of these amplitudes has maxima for $x = 0, -\lambda/2, -\lambda, \ldots,$ and these maxima are all given by $a(1+m)$. At these points the amplitude of the second vibration is zero.

The second vibration has maximum amplitudes for $x = -\lambda/4, -3\lambda/4, -5\lambda/4, \ldots,$ and these maxima are all given by $a(1-m)$. At these points there is no amplitude due to the first stationary vibration. Hence we again have a series of equally spaced planes which are alternately planes of maximum and planes of minimum vibration, and the ratio of the displacement amplitudes is given by $(1+m)/(1-m)$.

In this case m is the coefficient of reflection for amplitude, and if a_1 is the amplitude at a displacement antinode and a_2 that at a displacement node,

$$\frac{1+m}{1-m} = \frac{a_1}{a_2}$$

or

$$m = \frac{a_1 - a_2}{a_1 + a_2}. \quad \ldots \ldots \quad (8.16)$$

If the coefficient of reflection for intensity is R, and the coefficient of absorption A,

$$R = m^2 = \left(\frac{a_1 - a_2}{a_1 + a_2}\right)^2,$$

so that
$$A = 1 - R = \frac{4a_1 a_2}{(a_1 + a_2)^2}. \quad \cdots \quad (8.17)$$

The determination of the coefficient of absorption of a surface is a very important measurement in connexion with the acoustic absorbents used to reduce the time of reverberation in a room or building,

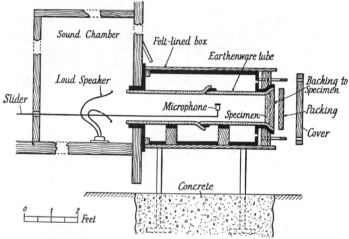

Fig. 8.29.—Stationary-wave apparatus for measuring reflecting powers of materials (Paris)

and a method based on this principle was devised and used by Taylor.* (See also p. 550).

A slab of the material is used to close the end of a long tube in which standing waves are formed by the reflection from the slab, and the nodes and antinodes are explored by means of a Rayleigh disc. The method has also been used by Paris † and the apparatus is shown in fig. 8.29. The experimental pipe in which the stationary waves are produced is 1 foot in diameter and is closed at one end by a specimen of the acoustic plaster under test. The source of sound is a loud-speaker completely enclosed and the nodes and antinodes are explored by a hot-wire microphone moved by a sliding rod from outside the enclosure. A similar method has been used in the National Physical Laboratory.‡ A full theoretical discussion of the method is given by the Bureau of Standards.§

* *Phys. Rev.*, Vol. 2, p. 270 (1913).   † *Proc. Phys. Soc.*, Vol. 39, p. 274 (1927).
‡ *Annual Report*, p. 67 (1924).   § *Scientific Papers*, Vol. 21, p. 53 (1926–7).

8. Interference in Plates.

It is well known that if homogeneous light is allowed to fall on a thin plate, comparable in thickness with the wave-length of the light, then the amount of light reflected or transmitted varies periodically as the thickness of the plate is increased. In the case of an air film between plane parallel glass plates the reflected light is zero for thicknesses of the air film equal to 0, $\lambda/2$, λ, $3\lambda/2$, ... This is due to the superposition on the incident wave train of the series of trains caused by multiple reflection at the front and back boundaries of the film. There is no transmission and nearly complete reflection for thicknesses given by $\lambda/4$, $3\lambda/4$, $5\lambda/4$, ...

The corresponding problem for sound waves has been treated by Rayleigh,* assuming that at a boundary the velocities perpendicular to the boundary must be the same in each of the two media and that the pressures on the two sides of the boundary must be equal. For the case of perpendicular incidence Rayleigh derived the expression

$$R^2 = \frac{(R_1/R_2 - R_2/R_1)^2}{4\cot^2 kd + (R_1/R_2 + R_2/R_1)^2}. \qquad . \quad . \quad (8.18)$$

In this expression R represents the fraction of the incident sound energy which is reflected, R_1, R_2 are the characteristic impedances (pp. 148, 290) of the media, d is the thickness of the plate, λ is the wave-length of the sound in the material of the plate, and $k = 2\pi/\lambda$.

It is obvious that if $kd = (2K + 1)\pi/2$ (where $K = 0, 1, 2 \ldots$), then $\cot kd = 0$ and R is a maximum. In this case $d = (2K + 1)\lambda/4$.

On the other hand, if $kd = K\pi$ then $\cot kd = \pm \infty$ and $R = 0$. In this case $d = K\lambda/2$ and the reflected energy is zero, the plate being acoustically transparent. This transparency is of course confined to particular wave-lengths and is associated with the resonances of the plate for vibrations along the direction of its thickness. The same kind of transparency may occur for flexural vibrations, and this phenomenon has been cited by Constable and Aston † to explain their observations on the transmission of sound by the walls of a room. The plate is of course transparent also if $(R_1/R_2 - R_2/R_1) = 0$, i.e. if $R_1 = R_2$, as was found in the case of reflection from a rigid boundary.

This expression does not seem to have been tested experimentally until the discovery of ultrasonic waves, probably owing to the large thicknesses of material required in order that d may be comparable with λ for ordinary sound waves. In the case of ultrasonic waves the test has been applied by Boyle and Lehmann.‡ The experiments were made by determining the energy-density in front of a torsion pendulum from measurements of the pressure on it.

---

* *Sound*, Vol. II, § 271.   † *Phil. Mag.*, Vol. 23, p. 166 (1937).
‡ *Trans. Roy. Soc. Canada*, Vol. 21, p. 115 (1927).

The vane of the pendulum is placed normal to the direction of the beam, and after the beam is allowed to impinge on it the torsion head is rotated until the vane is again normal to the beam. The torsion in the wire then measures the pressure. The energy-density of the reflected beam is RE and that of the transmitted beam $(1 - R)E$, where E is the energy-density of the incident beam. The transmitted beam produces a recoil pressure and therefore, since the pressure is equal to the energy-density $\times (\gamma + 1)/2$,

$$p = [E + RE - (1 - R)E] \times \frac{\gamma + 1}{2} = (\gamma + 1)RE.$$

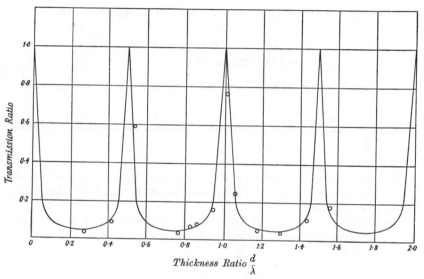

Fig. 8.30.—Transmission through a plate

The vane is of lead and is suspended in water. For water we have $R_1 = 1 \times 1\cdot5 \times 10^5 = 1\cdot5 \times 10^5$. For lead we have $R_2 = 11\cdot3 \times 2\cdot06 \times 10^5 = 23\cdot4 \times 10^5$. From these values R can be calculated for various values of d/λ. Nine different vanes with thicknesses between 0·0018 cm. and 0·777 cm. were used, and the calculated and observed values of R compared. These showed good agreement up to $d = \lambda/4$, when the reflection is nearly complete, and a sharp minimum for $d = 0\cdot765$ cm. This was assumed to be $\lambda/2$ and the velocity of sound in lead was calculated from this, the frequency being known to be 135,000 cycles/sec. An application of the formula to the case of air ($R_2 = 43$) confined between thin metal plates in water ($R_1 = 1\cdot5 \times 10^5$) shows that for a film of thickness 0·01 cm. and a frequency of 1000 ($\lambda = 33$ cm. in air) about 91 per cent of the incident energy would be reflected.

The calculation of the velocity of sound in lead just given yields a method of determining the velocity of sound in solids first suggested by Rayleigh.* Boyle and Rawlinson † amplified Rayleigh's analytical treatment and applied it directly to ultrasonic waves. Later they

---

* *Sound*, Vol. II, p. 86.   † *Trans. Roy. Soc. Canada*, Vol. 22, p. 55 (1928).

verified by experiments their theoretical conclusions *, showing that at normal incidence transmission is a maximum when the thickness of the plate is an integral number of half wave-lengths. This maximum is extremely sharp, as is shown in fig. 8.30, which refers to type metal. The thickness is kept constant and the frequency varied until the transmission is a maximum, an approximate value having previously been worked out to avoid any ambiguity due to whole multiples of $\lambda/2$.

In the case of aluminium † the best transmission frequency is 122×10^3 and $d = 0.825$ in. $= \lambda/2$. Hence the velocity required

$$= 122 \times 10^3 \times 0.825 \times 2.54 \times 2$$
$$= 5.11 \times 10^5 \, \text{cm./sec.}$$

This may be compared with the values given on p. 284.

9. Composition of Simple Harmonic Vibrations in Directions at Right Angles.

This phenomenon is more important in optics than in sound, owing to its application in connexion with polarized light, but in sound it has an important historical application in connexion with the exact comparison of frequencies (p. 213).

We shall assume first of all that the two vibrations to be compounded have the same period. By suitably choosing the instant $t = 0$ we can represent them by

$$\xi = a_1 \sin \omega t,$$
$$\eta = a_2 \sin (\omega t + \phi)$$
$$= a_2 \sin \omega t \cos \phi + a_2 \cos \omega t \sin \phi,$$

where ξ and η are the simultaneous co-ordinates of the point which traces the resulting motion. To find the path of this point we must eliminate t from the two equations

$$\sin \omega t = \frac{\xi}{a_1},$$

$$\cos \omega t = \frac{1}{\sin \phi} \left(\frac{\eta}{a_2} - \frac{\xi}{a_1} \cos \phi \right),$$

obtaining $\dfrac{\eta^2}{a_2{}^2} - \dfrac{2\xi\eta}{a_1 a_2} \cos \phi + \dfrac{\xi^2}{a_1{}^2} - \sin^2 \phi = 0.$ . . (8.19)

---

* *Canadian Journ. of Research*, Vol. 1, p. 405 (1929); Vol. 2, p. 1 (1930).
† Klein and Hershberger, *Phys. Rev.*, Vol. 6, p. 760 (1931).

This is in general an ellipse inscribed in the rectangle $\xi = \pm a_1$, $\eta = \pm a_2$. The principal axes make with the axes of reference angles given by ψ in the equation

$$\tan 2\psi = \cos\phi \tan 2\theta,$$

where
$$\tan\theta = \frac{a_2}{a_1}$$

and θ is the angle made by a diagonal of the rectangle in question with the axis of ξ. The diameter OA (fig. 8.31), where A is a point of

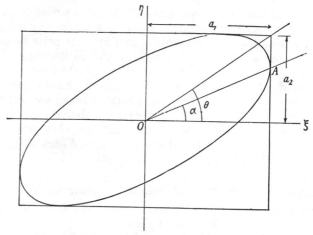

Fig. 8.31.—Composition of two simple harmonic vibrations of same period at right angles

contact of the ellipse with one of the vertical sides of the rectangle, is conjugate to the y-axis and is therefore given by

$$y = \left(\frac{a_2}{a_1}\cos\phi\right) x$$

or
$$\tan\alpha = \cos\phi \tan\theta.$$

Hence the angle α changes from θ when $\phi = 0$ to 0 when $\phi = \pi/2$. This may be seen also from the equation given above, which becomes simpler for these special values of ϕ:

(1) *Two vibrations in phase,* $\phi = 0$.

Here
$$\left(\frac{\eta}{a_2} - \frac{\xi}{a_1}\right)^2 = 0, \quad \cdots \cdots \quad (8.20)$$

and we have two coincident straight lines through the origin.

(2) *Two vibrations in quadrature,* $\phi = \pi/2$.

Here $$\frac{\eta^2}{a_2{}^2} + \frac{\xi^2}{a_1{}^2} - 1 = 0. \quad \ldots \ldots \quad (8.21)$$

This is an ellipse referred to the directions of the constituent vibrations as axes and with the amplitudes of the vibrations as its semi-axes.

In the special case where $a_1 = a_2 = a$,

$$\xi^2 + \eta^2 - a^2 = 0, \quad \ldots \ldots \quad (8.22)$$

and we have a circle of radius a.

This composition of two vibrations of the same period in directions at right angles may be illustrated by using a fairly long simple pendulum. The pendulum is set swinging and at some point in its swing the bob is given a quick blow at right angles to its plane of swing. It immediately begins to describe an ellipse. If the blow is delivered at the instant when the bob passes through its middle position the orbit is linear, the plane of swing being rotated by an amount depending on the strength of the blow. If the blow is delivered at the end of the swing the bob describes an ellipse, the axes of which are along and at right angles to its original line of swing. With a little care the blow may be adjusted so as to give the circle.

10. Graphical and Experimental Methods of Composition.

For unequal periods the analytical discussion becomes more difficult, but a graphical method is easily applied.

Construct a rectangle ADBC (fig. 8.32) whose sides are $2a_1$ and $2a_2$, the double amplitudes of the vibrations to be compounded. Let the periods of the two vibrations be T_1 and T_2 and let $T_1/T_2 = p/q$, where p and q are the smallest whole numbers which can express the ratio. On BC and AB describe semicircles. Divide the semicircle AB into $2q$ equal arcs and BC into $2p$. Through the points of subdivision draw lines parallel to AB and BC as shown. The time taken by the point executing the first vibration to move from B to C is $\frac{1}{2}T_1$, and since the lines drawn through the points of subdivision of the semicircle constructed on this side divide BC into paths described in equal increments of time, each division of the side BC occupies time $\frac{1}{2}T_1/2p$.

Similarly each division of the side AB occupies time $\frac{1}{2}T_2/2q$. Since $T_1/T_2 = p/q$, the divisions are described in equal times. It follows that if we start at any intersection in the rectangle the end of a time $T_1/4p$ or $T_2/4q$ finds the point describing the combined motions at the opposite angle of the elementary rectangle. Fig. 8.32 applies to the case $p/q = 2/3$ and the tracing of the curve was started from A.

If E had been chosen as the starting-point the curve would have been as shown by the dotted line. The initial phase relation is different in this case. With less simple ratios for the periods of the two motions very beautiful and attractive patterns result.

For demonstration purposes Wheatstone's kaleidophone (fig. 8.33) gives quite good results. It consists of two strips of steel placed end to end with their planes at right angles to one another. A bright metallic bead is attached to the end of one strip while the other end of the

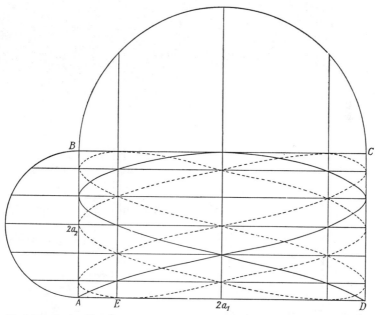

Fig. 8.32.—Composition of two simple harmonic motions with frequencies in the ratio 2:3 in directions at right angles

other strip is gripped in an adjustable clamp. The figure shows the appearance from two directions at right angles. The strips are nearly rigid for bending couples in their own planes and bend easily for couples at right angles. Thus in the first position shown the strips oscillate with length l_1 in the plane of the paper and with length l_2 in the plane perpendicular to the paper. If the system is given an initial displacement in a direction making an angle with these two planes, the motion of the bead is compounded of two vibrations of different periods executed at right angles, the ratio of the periods being adjusted by varying the length of the strip projecting from the clamp. The bead may be strongly illuminated and its motion projected on a screen.

Another experimental method is that of the Blackburn pendulum. This pendulum is suspended as shown in fig. 8.34. According to A. T. Jones [*] the first suggestion for a pendulum of this type was due to James Dean, Professor of Mathematics and Natural Philosophy at Vermont.[†] It was invented independently by Blackburn, Professor of Mathematics at Glasgow, probably in 1844, the year before he took his B.A. at Cambridge. When the bob swings in the plane of the

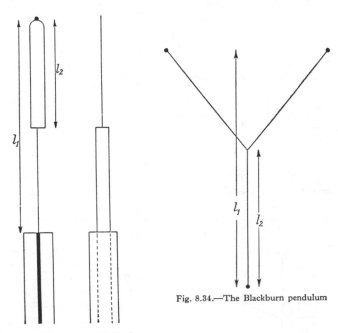

Fig. 8.33.—Wheatstone's kaleidophone

Fig. 8.34.—The Blackburn pendulum

paper the effective length of the pendulum is l_2. When it swings at right angles to the plane of the paper the effective length is l_1. Then

$$\frac{T_1}{T_2} = \sqrt{\frac{l_1}{l_2}}.$$

The Blackburn pendulum can be improved for demonstration purposes by substituting for the bob a funnel with small nozzle, filled with very fine sand. If a blackboard is placed close below the nozzle the track of the pendulum bob is marked by a thin trickle of sand. If the pendulum is suspended by two strings passing through a ring

[*] *Sound* (Chapman and Hall, 1937).

[†] *Amer. Acad. Arts and Sci., Memoirs* 3, p. 241 (1815).

the ratio T_1/T_2 may be modified by altering the position of the ring.

Various types of harmonograph are also used for the same purpose. These consist essentially of two rigid pendulums vibrating in planes at right angles. One carries a tracing point and the other a surface on which the trace is made. The periods of the pendulums can be adjusted and the curves obtained are very beautiful and interesting.

In all these experimental methods the difficulty is to adjust the two periods to a ratio expressible as the ratio of two small whole numbers. If this is not exactly achieved the pattern is not steady but gradually changes and goes more or less rapidly through the whole series of possible curves. We may regard this as the case of two vibrations exactly adjusted but subject to a small progressive change of phase difference each time the pattern is completed.

The application of the foregoing to the comparison of frequencies is due to Lissajous. For the case of tuning-forks small mirrors can be mounted on the prongs and a spot of light projected on a screen by successive reflection from the two mirrors when the planes of vibration of the forks are at right angles. When the frequencies of the forks are in exact adjustment a perfectly steady pattern is produced, and the method is extremely sensitive. It can be extended to the case of a string or other vibrating system by attaching a speck of starch and observing it under a strong illumination through a microscope, the object glass of which is attached to the comparison fork. The fork is arranged so that the vibration of the object glass is at right angles to the motion of the point observed.

CHAPTER IX

Diffraction

1. Diffraction.

It is well known that when Newton was considering the relative merits of the corpuscular and wave theories of light, the factor which determined his support of the corpuscular theory was the phenomenon of rectilinear propagation. As was established later, the departure from rectilinear propagation, which is known as diffraction, occurs for all types of wave motion. Wherever the wave-front is unobstructed each element of the wave-front travels along a straight line or ray. Wherever the wave-front is obstructed by the interposition of an obstacle or a perforated screen, propagation ceases to be rectilinear and we have diffraction. The shorter the wave-length the less obvious is the phenomenon of diffraction; thus for light it is much less obvious than for sound. It is impossible in the case of sound waves to discuss the radiation from a disc or a horn without knowing the ratio which the wave-length of the sound bears to the linear dimensions of the disc or the end of the horn. Short waves may be radiated almost as a " pencil " of sound rays, while under the same conditions long waves are propagated in every direction.

The quantitative study of diffraction is based on Huygens' principle. An instantaneous position of the wave-front is considered which passes through the obstacle or aperture whose effect is to be determined. Every point on this wave-front is then considered as a point-source and the effect of the wave at any point in space is obtained by summing the effects contributed by all the point-sources. A convenient method of simplifying this process was suggested by Fresnel, who was the first to give any adequate account of the phenomena of diffraction.

2. Diffraction of Plane Waves through a Slit.

We have already seen that the narrower the slit which is interposed in the path of a train of waves the more widely does that train diverge on the farther side of the slit. We shall now consider the theory of this phenomenon in greater detail. Let AB (fig. 1.8) be a slit whose length is perpendicular to the plane of the diagram in a screen whose plane is also perpendicular to that of the diagram. Let a plane wave fall on the screen from the left. Consider the effect of the wave at a distant point P such that the lines proceeding to it from A and B may be considered parallel. Divide the wave-front at the instant it fills the slit into a series of equal elementary strips parallel to the length of the slit. The contributions of these to the disturbance at P will be approximately equal but will differ in phase. Graphically we can compound them as on p. 182. Analytically we can compound them by using the formula on p. 179,

$$A = \frac{ma \sin a}{a},$$

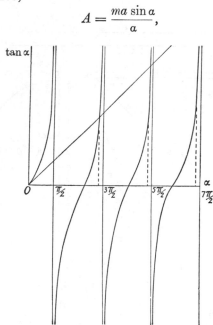

Fig. 9.1.—Tan a plotted against a

where A is the resultant amplitude, a is the amplitude due to each of the m elementary strips into which the unobstructed part of the wave front is divided, and $2a$ is the difference in phase at P between the wave trains from the first and last strips.

In this case $2a = 2\pi AC/\lambda = 2\pi e \sin \theta/\lambda$, where e is the width of the slit and θ is the angle between the normal to the slit and the direction to P.

For the direction normal to the slit $\theta = 0$, $a = 0$, $(\sin a)/a = 1$, and $A = ma$.

Let A_0 denote this value of A. Then in general

$$A = \frac{A_0 \sin a}{a}.$$

Obviously $A = 0$ for $a = K\pi$, i.e. $e \sin\theta = K\lambda$, or $\sin\theta = K\lambda/e$.

The maximum values for A (ignoring sign) are given by the values of a for which $dA/da = 0$, i.e. for which $a = \tan a$. We can easily find the values of a for which this is true by plotting $\tan a$ against a and then drawing a line through the origin making an angle of $45°$ with the axes (fig. 9.1). Where the straight line cuts the graph, $a = \tan a$. It will be seen that this happens at values of a near to $3\pi/2$, $5\pi/2$, $7\pi/2$, ... , and also of course at $a = 0$.

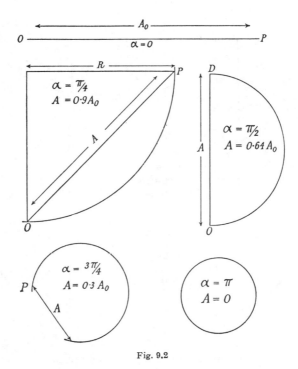

Fig. 9.2

Graphically, as we saw on p. 183, the problem is that of the varying length of the chord A of a circular arc of fixed length when the curvature of that arc is varied. The angle between the tangents at the extremities of the arc is $2a$, the extreme difference of phase. It follows that for $a = 0$ the arc is a straight line and the chord coincides with it, the length of both being $A_0 = ma$. For $a = \pi/4$ the arc is a quadrant, for $a = \pi/2$ the arc is a semicircle and so on. For $a = \pi$ the arc is a circle and the chord vanishes. These values are shown in fig. 9.2. The relation of A/A_0 to a is shown in fig. 9.3 by the dotted line. The continuous line shows the relation of A^2/A_0^2 to a, and as the intensity is proportional to the square of the amplitude this curve gives the intensity. For the first (central) maximum $A = A_0$.

For the second maximum $A = A_0 \dfrac{\sin \alpha}{\alpha}$

$$= A_0 \frac{\sin 3\pi/2}{3\pi/2} \text{ nearly}$$

$$= \frac{2A_0}{3\pi}.$$

That is, the ratio of the intensities is $9\pi^2/4$, i.e. approximately 22.

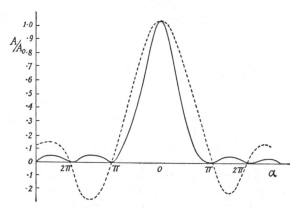

Fig. 9.3.—Diffraction pattern for a slit

It follows that the energy is almost entirely concentrated in directions for which $\alpha < \pi$, i.e. for which

$$\frac{\pi e \sin \theta}{\lambda} < \pi \text{ or } \sin \theta < \frac{\lambda}{e}.$$

That is, $\sin \theta$ is a measure of the divergence of the waves from the slit, and we see that the smaller the width (e) of the slit the larger the divergence; if $e = \lambda$, $\theta = \pi/2$, and the wave diverges in all directions.

It can be shown that for a circular aperture * $\sin \theta = 0.61\lambda/r$, where r is the radius of the aperture.

---

* Airy, *Trans. Cambr. Phil. Soc.*, Vol. 5, p. 283 (1834).

3. Experimental Investigation of Diffraction of Sound Waves through a Slit.

For sound waves in air, measurements have been made by Pohl, * using a high-pitched whistle and radiometer.

The whistle is mounted at P (fig. 9.4) at the focus of a concave mirror H_1. The slit, in this case 11·5 cm. wide, is placed at b_1b_1 so that slit, whistle, and mirror may be rotated about an axis through A. The receiving mirror is at H_2 and the radiometer at R. The wave-length of the note of the whistle is 1·45 cm.

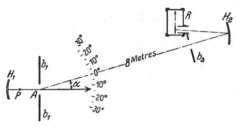

Fig. 9.4.—Limitation of a bundle of plane sound waves by a slit (Fraunhofer diffraction); R the sound radiometer with receiving mirror H_2.

Fig. 9.5 shows the radiometer readings plotted against θ. As a numerical check we may notice that the minimum occurs for $\theta = 7\cdot2°$. Then $\sin 7\cdot2° = \lambda/11\cdot5$, so that $\lambda = 1\cdot44$ cm.

Fig. 9.6 shows the same results plotted in polar co-ordinates, the radius vector r showing the intensity of the sound in that particular direction. Both methods of plotting show how the sound is concentrated into a comparatively narrow beam. A narrower slit would yield a wider maximum in fig. 9.5 and a correspondingly wider spread of the sound.

Experiments of the same kind have been made for ultrasonic waves in water by Boyle and Reid † and a fair quantitative agreement with the formula has been obtained.

4. Divergence of Beams.

From the discussion in the last section it appears that if sound waves are started by a vibrating piston or emerge from a circular aperture on which plane waves are incident they travel as a diverging beam. Most of the energy is contained within a cone whose semi-angle is given by $\theta = 0\cdot61\lambda/r$, where λ is the wave-length of the radiation and r the radius of the disc of the piston or of the aperture. This relation between the divergence of the beam and the dimensions of the source is of great practical importance. In the method of echo-sounding already described (p. 152) only a small fraction of the sound energy returns by reflection, since the waves are diverging in every direction and continue

---

* *Mechanics and Acoustics*, p. 290.   † *Trans. Roy. Soc. Canada*, Vol. 20, p. 233 (1926).

to diverge after reflection from the bottom. The result, too, is only a mean value of the depth over a considerable area. If the sound could be sent out as a nearly parallel beam it could be concentrated like the beam of a searchlight on a small area of sea bottom and the intensity of the reflected beam would show comparatively little loss. In this way minor irregularities, such as a sunken ship lying on the bottom, could be detected. Attention was directed to the phenomenon in another connexion by Lewis Richardson at the time of the loss of the *Titanic*

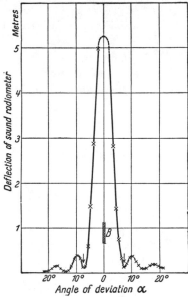

Fig. 9.5.—Fraunhofer's diffraction curve (sound-peak) for wave-length 1·45 cm., and the slit shown in fig. 9.4. The shaded region B indicates the geometrical boundaries of the ray.

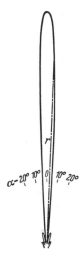

Fig. 9.6. — The Fraunhofer diffraction curve of fig. 9.5 plotted in polar co-ordinates.

by collision with an iceberg, and he pointed out that if by a right relation of wave-length to diaphragm area the divergence of the sound beam could be controlled, icebergs might be detected by the reflection of a horizontal beam of sound. A further possibility developed during the war. In the early stages submarines could be detected by listening to the sound which they made. In the later stages submarines were almost silent and detection depended on the possibility of detecting the reflected beam of sound sent out by the searching ship—a possibility which could be realized only in the case of beams of small divergence.

If we limit the semi-angle of the cone to 10° and substitute in the expression obtained, we have

$$\frac{0 \cdot 61\lambda}{r} \leqq \sin 10° \text{ or } 0 \cdot 174.$$

$$\therefore \ \frac{\lambda}{r} \leqq 0 \cdot 28.$$

If c is the velocity in sea-water $= 1 \cdot 55 \times 10^5$ cm./sec., f the frequency of the note, then, since $\lambda = c/f$, we have

$$r \geqq \frac{\lambda}{0 \cdot 28} \text{ or } \frac{c}{0 \cdot 28f}.$$

If we take $f = 1000$ we find that the minimum value of r to give a beam of the divergence desired is

$$r = \frac{1 \cdot 55 \times 10^5}{2 \cdot 8 \times 10^2} = 550 \text{ cm.}$$

It would be impossible to communicate to a diaphragm of this radius a vibration which had the same phase all over.

If we set as the maximum value for r the value 10 cm. then

$$\lambda \gtreqless 2 \cdot 8 \text{ cm.}$$

$$f \lesseqgtr \frac{1 \cdot 55 \times 10^5}{2 \cdot 8} \gtreqless 55,000 \text{ cycles/sec.}$$

This result presents another difficulty—that of communicating to a diaphragm of radius 10 cm. a frequency of 55,000, far above the limit of audible sound.

The earliest suggestion was to use a diaphragm excited by a magnet through which was passed an alternating current of the desired frequency, but the inductance offered insuperable difficulties if the required power was to be obtained. Progress only became possible when Langevin * suggested using the reversed piezo-electric effect (see below).

5. Supersonic Generators.

The piezo-electric effect was discovered in the case of quartz by J. and P. Curie.† If a slice of quartz is cut from a crystal in the way indicated in fig. 9.7 and pressures are applied to the opposite faces of the slice, then these faces will develop equal and opposite electric charges, with consequent differences of potential. The long axis of the crystal, normal to which the first sections are made, is an optic axis. The portion cut from the crystal by two planes perpendicular to this axis has a hexagonal perimeter. Lines joining opposite angles of this hexagon give the direction of the electric axes. The final slice, as shown, is perpendicular to one of these axes. Any one of the three might have been chosen by cutting the final slice by planes perpendicular to any one of the three pairs of parallel sides.

---

* Brit. Pat. Specifications, N.S., 457, No. 145691 (1920).

† Comptes Rendus, Vol. 91, p. 294 (1880); Vol. 93, p. 1137 (1881).

The phenomenon can be very simply illustrated by the arrangement shown in fig. 9.8. The quartz slice is held between two metal plates, the lower of which is earthed. Pressure is applied to the upper plate

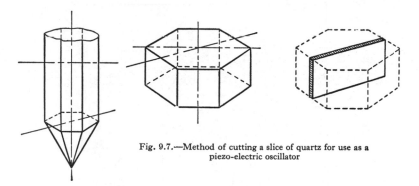

Fig. 9.7.—Method of cutting a slice of quartz for use as a piezo-electric oscillator

through an insulating layer, and the gold-leaf electroscope indicates a potential which varies with the pressure.

That this effect is reversible was predicted by Lippmann.* Just as elastic deformation of the quartz develops an electric field, so by

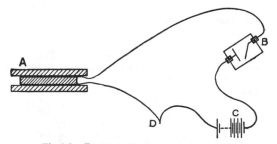

Fig. 9.8.—Demonstration of piezo-electric effect

A, slice of quartz placed between two metal plates between which pressure can be applied; B, Wilson tilted gold-leaf electroscope; C, battery; D, earth connexion. The upper metal plate is insulated and connected to the gold leaf. The lower metal plate is earthed, as is also one terminal of the high-potential battery. The other terminal of the battery is connected to the fixed plate of the electroscope.

placing the quartz in an electric field elastic deformations are developed in it. If the field is an alternating one, the quartz will be subject to oscillations along the electric axis, whose frequency is that of the applied field. If one face can be kept fixed the other will move to and fro, owing to the change in thickness. If this face is in contact with air, water, oil or any other fluid, waves will be generated in the fluid.

* *Ann. de Chim. et de Phys.*, Vol. 24, p. 145 (1881).

The type of circuit used by Pierce * is shown in fig. 9.9. The piezo-electric crystal vibrator C has one of its electrodes connected to the plate P of the valve and the other electrode to the grid G. The filament F is heated by the battery

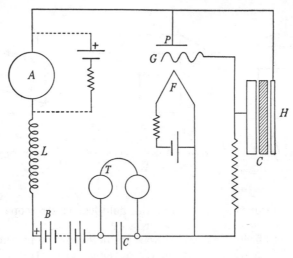

Fig. 9.9.—Quartz oscillator (Pierce)

shown and the plate current is supplied by the other battery B. A micro-ammeter A and a telephone T shunted by a condenser C are included in the plate circuit. L is a resistance of about 30,000 ohms or a large inductance of about 20 milli-henries. This system produces oscillations in the circuit and mechanical oscillations of the crystal with a frequency equal to the natural frequency of the vibration parallel to its thickness. An aperture H in the front electrode allows the train of waves to emerge. This system was used by Pierce for the determination of the velocity of sound (p. 258). It is very useful for experiments in gases, but cannot be used for experiments on liquids, as the powerful damping of the crystal by the liquid stops the reaction.

Another simple and effective circuit is that due to Hartley and shown in fig. 9.10. Here the frequency of vibration is not controlled by the free vibration of the

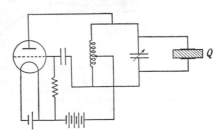

Fig. 9.10.—Circuit of a valve oscillator of Hartley type, and the connexions to the piezo-quartz.

crystal as is the case in the Pierce circuit. The vibrations of the oscillating circuit containing an inductance and a variable condenser are imposed on the crystal and adjusted to resonance by altering the capacity. This arrangement gives more powerful vibrations and is suitable for experiments with liquids.

* Proc. Amer. Acad. Arts and Sci., Vol. 60, p. 275 (1925).

The natural frequency of vibration of the crystal is determined by its dimension parallel to the direction of vibration. The density of quartz is 2·654 gm./c.c. and Young's Modulus measured in the appropriate direction is 8×10^{11} dyne/cm.[2] The velocity of compressional waves in the quartz is therefore

$$\sqrt{\left(\frac{8 \times 10^{11}}{2·654}\right)} = 5·5 \times 10^5 \text{ cm./sec.}$$

The wave-length in the quartz corresponding to any given frequency is therefore obtained from the relation

$$\lambda = \frac{5·5 \times 10^5}{f}.$$

If both faces are free to move, the fundamental mode of vibration will have a nodal plane in the middle of the slice and the thickness of the slice will be $\lambda/2$. It follows that the approximate frequency given by a plate of thickness e vibrating in its fundamental mode will be

$$f = \frac{5·5 \times 10^5}{2e} = \frac{275}{e} \times 10^3 \text{ c.p.s.}$$

Young's Modulus is not strictly applicable either to the thickness vibration of a plate or to the longitudinal vibration of a rod (see p. 281). Hund * gives for the experimental values

Thickness vibration of quartz plate $\left\{ f = \dfrac{287 \pm 5}{e} \times 10^3 \text{ c.p.s.} \right.$

Longitudinal vibration of quartz rod $\left\{ f = \dfrac{278·5 \pm 30}{l} \times 10^3 \text{ c.p.s.} \right.$

Using quartz, frequencies of 5×10^7 c.p.s. may be attained, but if this is the fundamental frequency the plate is only 0·055 mm. thick and very fragile. Tourmaline plates can be produced which give $1·5 \times 10^8$ c.p.s. Higher frequencies are of course attainable by using partial tones, and this has the further advantage that a number of different frequencies may be obtained from the same plate, although the intensity is never so great. If the surface of the plate is large compared with the thickness the partial tones are very nearly harmonic.

Another method of generating supersonic waves is based on the phenomenon of *magnetostriction*. The fact that a rod or tube of ferromagnetic material undergoes a change of length when subjected to a magnetic field parallel to its length seems to have been observed first

* *Proc. Inst. Radio Eng.*, Vol. 14, p. 447 (1926).

by Joule.* The effect is very small, amounting only to a few parts in a million, and has been studied by Bidwell † and others.

The application of the phenomenon of magnetostriction in order to maintain mechanical oscillations in a magnetic rod was made by Pierce.‡ The rods used were of various ferromagnetic metals and alloys. The arrangement is designed so that an oscillating electric current in the circuit stimulates the rod to longitudinal vibration, while the vibrations of the rod react on the electric circuit so as to maintain the frequency of oscillation constant. Frequency standards covering the range from 25,000 downwards can be obtained—a range lower than that in which the quartz standard can be more advantageously used. The arrangement is shown in fig. 9.11.

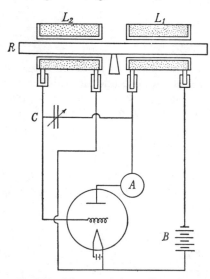

Fig. 9.11.—Magnetostriction oscillator circuit

Two magnetizing coils L_1 and L_2 are used, one in the plate circuit and one in the grid circuit. The vibrating rod R is clamped at the centre so that it lies axially in the coils. The rod may be magnetized permanently or by the plate current or by a permanent magnet placed near it. A direct-current milliammeter at A indicates the plate current and the change of this current with change of the variable capacity C indicates the presence of oscillations. The direct effect of static magnetization on length is very small. In the case of nickel it amounts only to about one part in a million for one gauss. On the other hand, when the magnetizing current is oscillatory of a frequency equal to the natural frequency of the rod the changes in length may be more than 100 times as great.

In addition to the direct effect there is also an inverse effect, i.e. when a magnetized bar is stretched its state of magnetization is changed. It is the association of these two effects that makes the maintenance of oscillations possible. Any change in the plate current causes a change of length at the right-hand end of the rod. This change is propagated to the left-hand end, where it effects a change of magnetization and so induces an electromotive force in L_2. This acts on the grid and produces an amplified current change in the plate circuit and in L_1. Thus the oscillating current builds up to a large amplitude with a frequency determined by the frequency of longitudinal mechanical vibration of the rod. The frequency of the standards was determined by comparison with a standard clock. The frequency is essentially independent of vacuum tube voltages and

* *Phil. Mag.*, Vol. 30, p. 76 (1847).

† *Proc. Roy. Soc.*, Vol. 40, p. 109 (1886); *Phil. Trans.*, A, Vol. 178, p. 205 (1888).

‡ *Amer. Acad. Arts and Sci. Proc.*, Vol. 63, p. 1 (1927-8): *Journ. Amer. Soc. Acoust.*, Vol. 9, p. 185 (1938).

characteristics, and the temperature coefficient of frequency $\frac{1}{f}\frac{\partial f}{\partial \theta}$ is only $-0.000107/\text{deg. cent.}$ for nichrome.

6. Applications of Supersonic Waves.

Supersonic waves can be used for a great variety of purposes, and accounts of these have been given by Boyle * and Hopwood.† More recently a very complete treatment of their production, measurement and use has appeared by Bergmann.‡ One of the practical uses of supersonic waves in liquids is that of transforming immiscible liquids such as water and oil into homogeneous stable emulsions. This property was first pointed out by R. W. Wood and Loomis.§ The tube containing the mixture of liquids is dipped into an oil-bath transmitting the waves. The process of emulsification is partly due to agitation at the interface, but Richards ‖ has shown that the solid boundaries are particularly active and that the shattering effect of the radiation is so great that minute fragments of the glass walls are colloidally dispersed through the liquid. Claus ¶ has succeeded in producing very fine dispersions of metals by bombarding the anode with supersonic waves during the process of electrolysis. Szalay ** used the waves to disintegrate polymerized molecules and split the chain of starch molecules into five or six fragments. In contrast to the dispersive effect which the waves produce in the case of liquids or hydrosols is the coagulative effect which they produce in the case of aerosols, i.e. suspensions in gases. Smoke is quickly coagulated and the large particles so produced cannot remain in suspension. This phenomenon has been studied by Brandt and others.†† Numerous chemical effects have been observed and the disruptive effect of the waves on pathogenic and other microorganisms has been studied. The heating effect of the waves is considerable and they may provide an alternative to the present methods of diathermy.

The effect, however, which has led to the discussion of supersonic waves at this point is the possibility of using them to produce a directed sound beam.

They have been so applied by Langevin to the development of a supersonic depth-finder. The frequency selected is about 40,000, which gives a wave-length in water of about 3.5 cm. A plate of diameter six to ten wave-lengths gives a pencil in which the divergence of the waves is comparatively small. There is a practical difficulty to be overcome. Plates of quartz so thick that their natural frequency is

* *Science Progress*, Vol. 23, p. 75 (1928).   † *Journ. Sci. Inst.*, Vol. 6, p. 34 (1929).
‡ *Ultrasonics and their Scientific and Technical Applications* (Bell, 1938).
§ *Phil. Mag.*, Vol. 4, p. 417 (1927).   ‖ *J. Amer. Chem. Soc.*, Vol. 49, p. 3086 (1927).
¶ *Zeits. f. tech. Phys.*, Vol. 16, p. 80 (1935); Vol. 16, p. 202 (1935).
** *Zeits. Phys. Chem.*, Vol. 164, p. 234 (1933).
†† *Zeits. f. Phys.*, Vol. 94, p. 348 (1935); *Trans. Faraday Soc.*, Vol. 32, p. 1101 (1936).

40,000 and having a diameter of 20 to 30 cm. would be very difficult to obtain and very expensive. The thickness difficulty is overcome by using as electrodes two steel plates cemented to the opposite faces of the quartz. These plates load the quartz and reduce its frequency, so that with a plate a few millimetres thick the necessary wave-length can be obtained. The use of these plates also enables us to substitute for the single quartz plate a mosaic of small pieces, provided these are all carefully cut and tested.

A spark is made to generate oscillations in a circuit containing a transmitter, and this circuit is tuned until its frequency is the natural frequency of the transmitter. Each spark then generates a damped train of electrical oscillations, which are transformed into mechanical oscillations of the transmitter, and so into a train of compressional waves in the water which is in contact with the face. The reflected wave-train is received again on the transmitter, which piles up the energy by resonance, and the resulting oscillations of the quartz plate generate an alternating E.M.F., which is amplified by a valve system. The output from the receiver is led to an oscillograph, and the depth found in one of two ways. The oscillograph is essentially a suspended magnet system round which an electric current can be led, so as to produce a deflection measured either by a beam of light reflected from a mirror attached to the magnet or by a pointer. By an ingenious arrangement a spot of light travels vertically downwards with uniform speed to the left of the depth scale. This spot receives a kick every time the oscillograph is put in action. This occurs at the instant of sending the signal and at the instant of receipt of the echo. The apparatus can be adjusted so that the first kick registers the depth of the transmitter below the surface of the water, and the second kick indicates on the scale the depth of the surface from which reflection occurs. These two points can be determined with great accuracy, and the sending of the signals is performed automatically at short intervals by a motor.

Instead of this optical method of observation, a mechanical record may be obtained by attaching to the oscillograph a long needle which bears on smoked paper revolving on a drum. The drum is geared to the sparking mechanism, so that a signal is sent once in each complete revolution of the drum. If the needle is at rest it produces an unbroken line on the smoked paper, but when a signal is sent or received the needle is suddenly deflected and the kick shows on the trace. Fig. 9.12 shows a photograph of one of these records. The white line on top represents the surface of the water, and the distance between that and the next white line represents the depth of the transmitter below the surface. This second white line is formed by the sudden deflection of the needle due to the sounding of the signal. The wavy line lower down is made up of the kicks due to the receipt of the echo, and the distance on the record between the two kicks on any one line measures the depth of the water at the instant at which the signal was sent and received. The strong white line represents increments of depth of 50 metres; thus, starting on the left with a depth of about 63 metres, the depth remains nearly constant at first, then increases to 90 at the centre of the trace, and then very rapidly to about 140, after which it gradually falls to 100.

It has already been shown that the reflecting power of the interface of two media depends on their respective characteristic impedances. The ratio of the reflected amplitude and the incident amplitude for

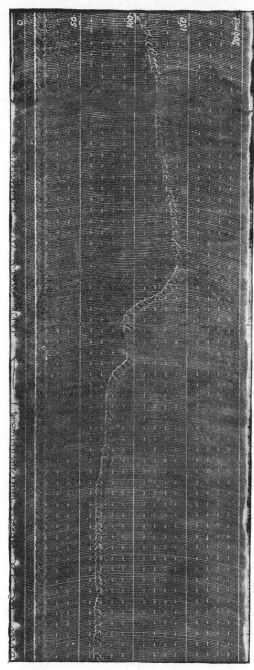

Fig. 9.12.—Portion of automatic record soundings taken by S.S. *Ile de France* in the neighbourhood of the Casquets
Depth in metres shown on extreme right

normal incidence has already been shown to be $(1 - a)/(1 + a)$, where a is the ratio of the impedances. For purposes of calculation we may use the following data:

Substance	Density (gm./c.c.)	Velocity of Sound (cm./sec.)	Characteristic Impedance
Sea-water	1·02	$1·55 \times 10^5$	$1·6 \times 10^5$
Steel	7·8	$5·2 \times 10^5$	$41·0 \times 10^5$
Granite	2·7	$4·0 \times 10^5$	11×10^5
Ice	0·92	$2·1 \times 10^5$	2×10^5

Using these values—which, in the case of granite and ice, are of doubtful accuracy—we obtain, following Boyle and Taylor,[*] these numbers:

Media	Ratio of Impedances ($1/a$)	Coefficient of Reflection
Sea-water/Steel	25·6	0·92
Sea-water/Granite	6·9	0·75
Sea-water/Ice	1·25	0·11

We thus see that a copious reflection may be expected from steel and from granite, but a comparatively small one from ice. Experiment, however, indicates that the reflecting power of ice is greater than these numbers would lead us to expect.

Another possible application of these sound beams deserves mention. They may obviously be used not only for ordinary depth determinations, but for detecting sunken obstacles, for they indicate the depth of a small patch of bottom and not the average depth over a considerable area, as is the case in the ordinary echo method. The beam may also be directed horizontally, and the reflection received from a submarine or from the hull of another ship. Boyle has carried out experiments on the reflection from icebergs and reflection has already been registered at considerable distances.

It is possible also to telephone under water along a supersonic beam by using the supersonic waves as carrier and modulating them by applying to the source an electromotive force which is varied by a microphone actuated by the voice. Experiments in this kind of telephony have been carried out successfully by Langevin.

By emitting from a harbour mouth an intense supersonic beam it would be possible to guide a ship. She would only have to pick up the beam and follow it, and the necessary information and instructions could be telephoned to her along the beam while she was being navigated. It is obvious, therefore, that we may look forward with confidence to increased ease and safety in navigation from the utilization of under-water sonic and supersonic radiation.

* *Proc. Roy. Soc. Canada*, Vol. 20, p. 246 (1926).

7. Fresnel Zones.

Many problems in diffraction can be most simply treated by the method of dividing the wave-front into half-period zones. The method is due to Fresnel and is based on Huygens' principle. If any element of area on an instantaneous position of the wave front may be treated as a source of waves and if the effect of the wave at any point is obtained by compounding the waves coming from these elementary sources, then the problem may be greatly simplified by suitable division of the wave-front into elementary areas or zones.

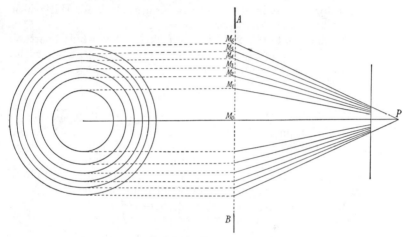

Fig. 9.13.—Half-period zones for a circular aperture

Let the plane of the wave-front at the instant considered cut the plane of the diagram in fig. 9.13 in the line AB, and let AB be the diameter of a circular aperture in a screen coinciding with the position of the wave-front. Let P, on the axis of the aperture, be the point at which the effect of the wave is to be determined. Let PM_0 be normal to the plane of the wave-front and of length b.

With centre P describe a series of spheres of radii b, $b + \lambda/2$, $b + 2\lambda/2$, $b + 3\lambda/2$, . . . , cutting the wave-front in a series of circles, as shown diagrammatically to the left of the figure.

Area of the centre zone $= \pi M_0 M_1{}^2 = \pi(PM_1{}^2 - PM_0{}^2)$

$$= \pi[(b + \lambda/2)^2 - b^2] = \pi\left(b\lambda + \frac{\lambda^2}{4}\right),$$

which is approximately $\pi b\lambda$, if λ is small compared with b. Similarly it can be shown that the area enclosed by the second circle (radius

M_0M_2) is $2\pi b\lambda$. Hence the area of the annular zone between the first and second circles is $\pi b\lambda$.

Similarly all the annular zones between successive circles have the same area, and this is the area of the central circular zone, $\pi b\lambda$. The radius of the central zone is $\sqrt{(b\lambda)}$, that of the second $\sqrt{(2b\lambda)}$, and so on. The radii of the successive circles are therefore in the ratio of the square roots of the integers.

Now the mean distance from P to points on the central zone differs from that for the surrounding annular zone by $\lambda/2$. If, then, we regard these zones as sources of waves travelling to P the waves will start in the same phase and arrive at P in the opposite phase. The same is true for each pair of consecutive zones. It is for this reason that they are known as " half-period zones ".

Let A be the resultant amplitude at P due to the whole aperture, A_1, A_2, A_3, . . . , the amplitudes due separately to the central circular zone and the successive annular zones respectively. Then

$$A = A_1 - A_2 + A_3 - A_4 + \ldots .$$

Now the amplitude due to any zone separately will depend on its area, its distance from P and the obliquity of the direction to P. All the zones have the same area and the distance and obliquity increase slowly. Therefore A_1, A_2, A_3, . . . , form a slowly diminishing series, and their differences also diminish steadily. Consider first the infinite series which applies when the aperture is of unlimited size.

Write $A_1 - A_2 = DA_1$, . . ., $A_n - A_{n+1} = DA_n$.
Then it appears from the actual form of the terms that

$$DA_1 > DA_2 > DA_3 \ldots .$$

The series of which A is the sum may also be put in the form

$$A = \tfrac{1}{2}A_1 + \tfrac{1}{2}(DA_1 - DA_2) + \tfrac{1}{2}(DA_3 - DA_4) + \ldots$$
$$= \tfrac{1}{2}A_1 + \text{(positive terms)},$$

or alternatively

$$A = \tfrac{1}{2}A_1 + \tfrac{1}{2}DA_1 - \tfrac{1}{2}(DA_2 - DA_3) - \tfrac{1}{2}(DA_4 - DA_5) - \ldots$$
$$= \tfrac{1}{2}A_1 + \tfrac{1}{2}DA_1 - \text{(positive terms)}.$$

Thus A lies between $\tfrac{1}{2}A_1$ and $\tfrac{1}{2}A_1 + \tfrac{1}{2}DA_1$. But DA_1 is generally very small and to a sufficient approximation $A = \tfrac{1}{2}A_1$.

Similarly, if the series began with A_n, its sum would be $\tfrac{1}{2}A_n$ if n were odd, $-\tfrac{1}{2}A_n$ if n were even. Hence the sum of n terms of the series is $\tfrac{1}{2}A_1 \pm \tfrac{1}{2}A_n$, according as n is odd or even.

If the elementary wavelets are represented on a vector diagram, the phase will increase indefinitely for points farther from M_0. The diagram will have the form of a spiral (fig. 9.14) beginning at M_0, which corresponds to the centre of the aperture in fig. 9.13. The points on a radius of the central zone of fig. 9.13 correspond to points on the first half-turn of the spiral, so that the diameter of this is A_1, the resultant amplitude due to the central zone. Similarly A_2, A_3, A_4, ..., are successive diameters of the spiral, which ends at a point corresponding to the edge of the circular aperture. If the aperture is very large the spiral approaches the centre and $A \doteqdot A_1/2$.

Thus the effect of the whole unobstructed wave-front at P (9.13) is but half that due to the uncovering of the first half-period zone only.

If a circular or spherical obstacle is placed so that P lies on its axis, Fresnel's method can be applied by commencing with an annular zone surrounding the obstacle. The effect at P will be half that due to this zone. If this zone is of a low order in the complete series (i.e.

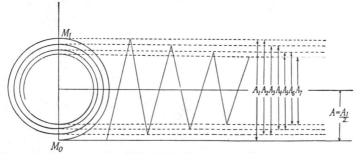

Fig. 9.14.—Vector diagram for circular aperture

if the obstacle is small or P is distant) this effect is not negligible and there will be wave disturbance at P. Thus we get wave disturbance at the centre of the shadow. The experimental demonstration of this has already been given (p. 33).

If the first unobstructed zone is of a high order, i.e. if the obstacle covers a large number of zones in the complete series, the effect at P is small and the shadow produced by the obstacle is effective.

A more detailed examination of the problem shows that in any plane perpendicular to the axis there is a central maximum where the axis cuts the plane, and surrounding this a series of concentric rings alternately of maximum and minimum intensity. The existence of these maxima and minima was demonstrated by Tucker and Paris [*] and their relative intensities measured and compared with theory for a circular disc of wood of diameter 6 feet and thickness 1 inch. The measurements were made by means of a hot-wire microphone tuned to the frequency of the source of sound. They showed that the location

[*] *Phil. Trans.*, Vol. 221, p. 389 (1921).

of the central maximum serves as an accurate means of locating the direction of the source of sound, even for low-frequency sounds.*

8. The Zone Plate.

One striking result which follows from these elementary considerations will be apparent if we assume the aperture AB to be adjustable. If it is initially very small, the amplitude of the wave motion at P increases as the aperture opens until the radius is $\sqrt{(b\lambda)}$. The amplitude then begins to diminish until, when the radius of the aperture is $\sqrt{(2b\lambda)}$, the amplitude is a minimum; since A_1 is nearly equal to A_2, this minimum is nearly zero. If the aperture is further opened the amplitude will again increase, reaching a second maximum when the radius is $\sqrt{(3b\lambda)}$. Thus the amplitude of the wave motion at P varies periodically as the aperture is opened.

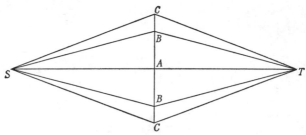

Fig. 9.15.—Zone plate

This phenomenon may be illustrated experimentally by the valve-operated telephone and sensitive flame. On a sheet of cardboard two circles are drawn with radii R and $R\sqrt{2}$. The cardboard is then cut so as to remove a central disc and a surrounding annular area, and these are suspended by strips of lantern-slide binding so as to lie in their proper positions. The sensitive flame S and telephone T are then correctly centred on opposite sides of the cardboard each at a distance d. The half-period zone condition will be fulfilled for waves coming from the telephone to the sensitive flame, if in fig. 9.15

$$\text{SB} + \text{BT} = \text{SA} + \text{AT} + \lambda/2$$
$$\text{or} \quad \text{SB} = \text{SA} + \lambda/4$$
$$= d + \lambda/4$$
$$R^2 = \text{SB}^2 - \text{SA}^2 = (d + \lambda/4)^2 - d^2$$
$$= \frac{\lambda d}{2} + \frac{\lambda^2}{16} \doteq \frac{\lambda d}{2},$$
$$\therefore \; d \doteq \frac{2R^2}{\lambda}.$$

---

* Rankine, *Ency. Britt.*, 13th ed., supp. vols., article *Sound*.

Here d can be adjusted to suit λ and R. Thus if $R = 10$ cm. and $\lambda = 2$ cm., $d = 100$ cm. The wave-length λ may be measured by the stationary-wave method. If the apparatus is properly adjusted and the flame not too sensitive it will roar when the central zone is removed and the annular zone left in position, and also when the annular zone is removed and the central one left hanging in position, but when both are removed simultaneously the flame is quiescent. This makes a very striking demonstration of the phenomenon.

If a series of circles are drawn on cardboard with radii R, $R\sqrt{2}$, $R\sqrt{3}$, $R\sqrt{4}$, ... , and if alternate zones commencing with the centre one are removed except for two strips forming two diameters at right angles, the resulting arrangement is a "zone plate" and with correct placing of S and T gives a very marked increase of intensity at S. This is due to the fact that the arrangement now allows to pass only the alternate terms of the series for A, and these all have the same sign.

9. The Diffraction Grating.

In optics the diffraction grating is a very important piece of apparatus for the production of spectra and for the measurement of wave-length. In acoustics the production of spectra is of little im-

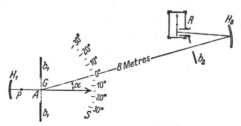

Fig. 9.16.—Diffraction grating for sound waves

portance, but the grating has been used as a method of determining the wave-length of a sound (see also p. 348). The action has been illustrated experimentally by Pohl, using the whistle and radiometer already referred to (p. 187).

The experimental arrangement is shown in fig. 9.16. G is the grating mounted with the whistle P and the concave mirror H_1, so that the whole apparatus can be rotated about a vertical axis through A. In this way the intensity of the sound transmitted in directions making various angles α with the incident beam may be measured on the radiometer R. The grating consists of wooden laths with seven slits and a distance of 5 cm. between consecutive centres.

The radiometer deflection was plotted against α and showed a strong central maximum with well-marked secondary maxima on each side.

If we draw rays from the centre of successive slits to a distant point (fig. 9.17) these rays will be approximately parallel, and the waves will arrive at the point in the same phase if the successive path differences are a whole number of wave-lengths. That is, $AC = K\lambda$. If $AB = e =$ grating space, $AC = e \sin a$,

$$\sin a = K \frac{\lambda}{e}$$

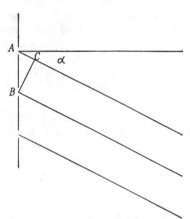

Fig. 9.17.—Principle of the grating

gives the successive maxima for the diffracted pencils ($K = 1, 2, 3, \ldots$). Applying this relation to the experiment just described and taking the first diffracted maximum, Pohl found $a = 16 \cdot 8°$, $\lambda = 1 \cdot 45$ cm.

Altberg * used this method to determine the wave-length of the sound from an oscillating circuit. The frequency was calculated from the electrical constants of the circuit and the wave-length, assuming 340 m./sec. as the velocity of sound, was 2·21 mm. The beam of sound was rendered parallel by reflection from a concave mirror and then directed on to a series of equally spaced rods. Consistent results were

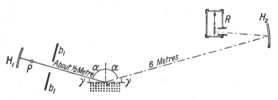

Fig. 9.18.—Glancing angle of a space lattice, demonstrated with sound waves

obtained although—probably owing to an error in the assumed value of the velocity of sound—they were too high.

e	α	$\sin \alpha$	$\lambda = e \sin \alpha$
1·18 cm.	11·7°	0·2028	2·39
0·79 ,,	17·7°	0·3040	2·40
0·62 ,,	23·3°	0·3955	2·45
0·41 ,,	35·2°	0·5764	2·36

The same method has been used by Neklepajev.†

* *Ann. d. Physik*, Vol. 23, p. 267 (1907).   † *Ann. d. Physik*, Vol. 35, p. 175 (1911).

Pohl has devised an experiment for sound waves to illustrate the investigation of crystal structure by reflection. Three or four plane gratings are placed parallel to one another, so that the distance between each successive pair is the grating space for an individual grating (fig. 9.18). The grating space chosen was 3 cm. and the wave-length of the sound was 1·45 cm. as before. Regular reflection takes place as for an ordinary plane reflector, but only at certain well-defined angles of incidence—in this case at $a_1 = 61°$ and $a_2 = 76°$. The complements of these angles—known by analogy with reflection from crystals as glancing angles—are $\gamma_1 = 29°$, $\gamma_2 = 14°$. From fig. 9.19 we see that reflection takes place when the retardation of the second sound path on the first is an integral number of whole wave-lengths. Hence $AB + BC = K\lambda$. But $AB = BC = e \sin\gamma$,

$$\therefore \; e = \frac{K\lambda}{2 \sin\gamma}.$$

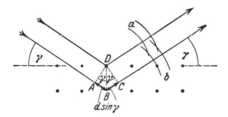

Fig. 9.19.—To illustrate how the phenomenon of the glancing angle arises

For $\lambda = 1·45$, $\gamma = 29°$, $K = 2$, we have $e = 3$ cm.

With crystals the plane gratings are replaced by the so-called "lattice planes" and the common distance between these planes is determined by finding the glancing angles for X-rays with a wave-length of something like 10^{-8} cm.

It is frequently noticed that the reflection of a short sharp sound such as is produced by a footstep on a pavement or the tapping of a walking-stick on the ground forms an echo which is a high ringing note. This phenomenon can usually be traced to a flight of steps, iron railing, wooden fence, or some other periodic structure. Each element of this structure scatters the incident wave, itself becoming the origin of a new wave, and these new waves arrive at the ear in succession and so give rise to the sensation of a musical note. In fig. 9.20 let S be a source of a simple wave and P the position of the observer. Let the periodic reflecting surface be perpendicular to PS and the common distance of its elements be e. Let $OA = pe$ and $OB = (p + 1)e$. Then

$$\text{Path PAS} = \sqrt{(a^2 + y^2)} + \sqrt{(b^2 + y^2)}.$$

If we call this path D_p, then the path from P to S by reflection from another point distant $y + dy$ from O will differ from D_p by an amount $\delta(D_p)$, where

$$\delta(D_p) = \frac{y\,\delta y}{\sqrt{(a^2 + y^2)}} + \frac{y\,\delta y}{\sqrt{(b^2 + y^2)}}.$$

If, however, reflection is from successive elements of the structure, then $\delta y = e$, and $y = pe$,

$$\therefore\ \delta(D_p) = pe^2\left[\frac{1}{\sqrt{(a^2 + p^2e^2)}} + \frac{1}{\sqrt{(b^2 + p^2e^2)}}\right].$$

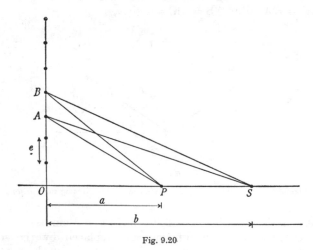

Fig. 9.20

If c is the velocity of sound, the time interval in arrival at P of the two successive reflections is $\delta(D_p)/c$. Hence

$$\text{Frequency} = \frac{c}{\delta(D_p)} = \frac{c}{pe^2\left[\dfrac{1}{\sqrt{(a^2 + p^2e^2)}} + \dfrac{1}{\sqrt{(b^2 + p^2e^2)}}\right]}.$$

Obviously the frequency varies with p.

For $\qquad\qquad\qquad p = \infty,\ \ f = \dfrac{c}{2e}.$

For $p = 0$ to 1, direct calculation gives $f = \dfrac{2c}{e^2(1/a + 1/b)}.$

Thus the highest frequency is the first to arrive.

If the observer and the source coincide in position, then $b = a$, and

$$f = \frac{c\sqrt{(a^2 + p^2e^2)}}{2pe^2}.$$

The highest and lowest frequencies are now ca/e^2 and $c/2e$, and their interval or ratio is $2a/e$. For $a = 0$, i.e. observer and source in the plane of the structure, f is constant at the value

$$f = \frac{c}{2e}.$$

10. General Theory of Diffraction.

Plane waves, and spherical waves spreading out symmetrically from point sources, correspond to special solutions of the wave equation

$$\nabla^2\phi - \frac{1}{c^2}\frac{\partial^2\phi}{\partial t^2} = 0. \quad \cdots \cdots \quad (9.1)$$

On p. 200, reference has also been made to a "double source", and the resulting value of ϕ is obtained by differentiating in a fixed direction that for a simple point source. That there is such a solution might be anticipated by examining (9.1), which holds after further differentiation. These straightforward results are only of value in a space where the validity of the parent equation is not interrupted. But we have seen in this chapter that in practice the results of interest are often very much less symmetrical and we have to deal with such things as screens and apertures. Often the problem is to study the distribution throughout space, given only the phase and amplitude of the disturbance at a certain surface, which is in a state of vibration either because it is a source or reflector of sound, or merely because it is an aperture through which sound is passing. We have seen that, contrary to the basic ideas of geometrical optics, the information given is necessary before the resulting amplitude can be found at even one point (P). Equation (9.1) remains valid at all points of the medium not occupied by obstacles, and mathematically the problem is that of finding solutions of this equation which will conform to the new boundary conditions. Fresnel's construction does this by applying the simple solution, in the form of elementary spherical wavelets, to the more general problem. In deriving an equation of which the elementary wavelets are the physical expression, we shall also find their amplitude, which hitherto we have not evaluated. In section 2, p. 215, A_0 is given only in terms of the unspecified a. It will be sufficient to state the answer with only an indication of the way in which it is obtained.*

* For a full treatment, see e.g. Jeans, *Electricity* (C. U. P., 1908); Lamb, *Dynamical Theory of Sound* (Arnold, 1910); Bateman, *Partial Differential Equations* (C. U. P., 1932).

The discussion may be confined to an oscillatory disturbance of the form $\phi e^{i\omega t}$, the wave equation becoming

$$\nabla^2 \phi + k^2 \phi = 0 \qquad \ldots \ldots \quad (9.2)$$

at all points of the medium where no source or obstacle is placed. ϕ is now a function of the co-ordinates only. The necessary link between the equation and the given data about the boundary surfaces of the medium is found in Green's theorem.

Green's theorem states that, for any two functions of position ϕ and ψ which with their first derivatives are continuous throughout a region bounded by a closed surface S,

$$\int (\psi \nabla^2 \phi - \phi \nabla^2 \psi)\, dv = \int \left(\psi \frac{\partial \phi}{\partial n} - \phi \frac{\partial \psi}{\partial n} \right) dS, \quad \ldots \quad (9.3)$$

where the left-hand side is an integral extended over all elements of volume enclosed by S, and the right-hand side is extended over the surface itself; and $\partial/\partial n$ denotes differentiation along the outward normal to S.

Consider a surface S surrounding the point P, and suppose that here is a distribution $\phi e^{i\omega t}$ of velocity-potential throughout the enclosed space, due to external sources only. Then apply Green's theorem to ϕ and the function e^{ikr}/r, where r is the distance of the element dv or dS from the fixed point P; both these functions satisfy the wave-equation in the form (9.2), except that at the origin P, from which r is measured, the latter function does not satisfy the conditions under which the theorem applies. To apply the theorem we therefore exclude from the volume a small sphere of radius ρ with P as centre, and then the surface integral must also include the surface of that sphere. The left-hand side of (9.3) now vanishes. On changing to the inward normal, and as $\rho \to 0$, we have

$$4\pi \phi_P = \int \left(\phi \frac{\partial}{\partial n} \frac{e^{ikr}}{r} - \frac{e^{ikr}}{r} \frac{\partial \phi}{\partial n} \right) dS \qquad \ldots \quad (9.4)$$

where the surface integral again refers only to the outer surface.

This is the formula from which the required result is to be derived. The same formula is to be applied in the case of a surface enclosing all the sources but excluding P; but n is then the outward normal.

Usually the disturbance is given on some surface which is not closed, and is zero over the rest of the surface S which may be imagined to surround P (fig. 9.21). An example is that of one or more apertures in a screen separating a source of sound from P; thus problems of interference are included in that of diffraction. Strictly speaking, in such cases the calculation should be applied to the actual potential and velocity at the aperture, and not that which would occur if the screen were absent. This correction may often be ignored. If the disturbance vanishes except over a very small aperture, equation (9.4) shows that the effect resembles that of a double source of strength ϕdS directed normally, together with a simple source of strength $-(\partial\phi/dn)dS$, where $-\partial\phi/\partial n$ is the particle velocity normal to dS. A small aperture behaves as a point-source and sound spreads from it in all directions.

It is to be noticed also that for apertures which are not small the potential at a distant point P may be regarded as due to

(1) a "double sheet", i.e. a uniform distribution of double sources, somewhat analogous to a magnetic shell, of strength ϕ per unit area normal to the surface S, together with

(2) a superficial source of strength $-\partial\phi/\partial n$ per unit area.

If kr is small, that is, if all the dimensions of the region considered are small compared with the wave-length, the problem is geometrically similar to that of static elec-tricity or of the flow of an incompressible perfect fluid. The wave equation in the form (9.2) reduces approximately to the form of Laplace's equation, $\nabla^2\phi = 0$. In such cases the "conduction" of the medium resembles that of an incom-pressible fluid, or the steady conduction of electricity in a metal. This justifies the use of the hydrodynamical con-ductivity of a bottle-neck, for

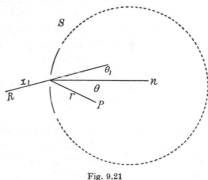

Fig. 9.21

sufficiently long waves, in finding the "end correction" (p. 105).

Both of the terms in (9.4) can be simply evaluated for a point-source R giving a velocity-potential Ae^{ikr_1}/r_1, where r_1 is the distance from R at which ϕ is measured. Here

$$4\pi\phi_P = \int\left[\frac{Ae^{ikr_1}}{r_1}\cos\theta\,\frac{e^{ikr}}{r^2}(1-ikr)+\frac{e^{ikr}}{r}\cos\theta_1\,\frac{Ae^{ikr_1}}{r_1^2}(1-ikr_1)\right]dS.$$

If kr and kr_1 are large, this becomes approximately

$$4\pi\phi_P = \int\frac{-iAke^{ikr+r_1}}{rr_1}(\cos\theta + \cos\theta_1)dS, \quad . \quad . \quad (9.5)$$

where θ, θ_1, are the angles shown in fig. 9.21, and the two terms will contribute *equally* if both angles are small. In most important appli-cations $\theta_1 = 0$, the surface S being taken as the wave-front itself. Then, in real terms, since $k = 2\pi/\lambda$,

$$\phi_P = \int\frac{A}{\lambda rr_1}\cdot\sin\frac{2\pi}{\lambda}\overline{r + r_1}\cdot\frac{1 + \cos\theta}{2}dS. \quad . \quad . \quad (9.6)$$

Thus no difficulty of calculation occurs with point-sources in known positions.

This equation is the embodiment of Huygens' principle (p. 5) modified by Fresnel, and its discussion is found in optical books. Huygens' principle states that the wave-front S may be regarded as generating a large number of secondary wavelets, which in turn combine to form the new wave-front. Equation (9.6) shows that a wave of amplitude a $(=A/r_1)$ gives a secondary wavelet from an element dS of mean strength $ka \cdot dS$ retarded $\pi/2$ in phase (because we have sin not cos in 9.6). The amplitude of each wavelet varies in proportion to $1/r$, and, according to direction, in proportion to $(1 + \cos\theta)$—so that in the forward direction the strength is twice the mean and in the backward direction $\theta = \pi$ it becomes zero. This is again the type of wave that would come from a combination of simple and double sources of equivalent strengths. The wavelet reaches P with the appropriate phase, the disturbance having travelled altogether a distance $(r_1 + r)$. Finally, the wavelets are compounded according to Fresnel's rule (p. 181), which takes account of their phases. The amplitude phase diagram will generally be some spiral curve, if the surface S is divided into elementary annuli in the way described in optical problems. It is often simpler to use the finite annuli called half-period zones (section 7, p. 229).

It is an interesting check of formula (9.6) to apply it to a simple point-source, using the half-period zones to evaluate the integral. The area of the first zone for a point P at a distance r from a spherical wave of radius r_1 is $\pi \lambda r_1 r/(r_1 + r)$. But for the internal variation of phase, this would represent a total amplitude at P of $\pi A/(r_1 + r)$. Fig. 9.14 shows that the true resultant amplitude A_1 is less, and that the final resultant of all the zones is less in the ratio $1/\pi$, giving the correct value $A/(r_1 + r)$. The figure also shows a gain of phase of $\pi/2$ between the wavelet which has a direct path to P and the resultant at P; this restores the expression $\sin k(r_1 + r)$ of equation (9.6) to its correct value $\cos k(r_1 + r)$.

Referring back to equation (9.4), we see that both ϕ and $\partial\phi/\partial n$ must be given in order to solve the problem of calculating ϕ_P at some other point by this method, and it may happen that only one is given.

It has been shown that, from (9.5), if only small inclinations are in question, the terms contribute equally, and either half of the integral may be used for calculation. A physical method of obtaining this result is given in Lamb's *Dynamical Theory of Sound*, § 79, where it is argued that as far as P is concerned the disturbance at the surface S is equivalent to either

(1) the production of fluid at each point of S at that rate which will produce a normal velocity $-\partial\phi/\partial n$, or

(2) the oscillation of a massless membrane at S constrained to

move so as to produce the actual velocity-potential on the side nearer to P.

The corresponding expressions for ϕ_P are

$$(1) \quad \phi_P = -\frac{1}{2\pi} \int \frac{\partial \phi}{\partial n} \frac{e^{ikr}}{r} dS, \quad \ldots \ldots \quad (9.7)$$

$$(2) \quad \phi_P = +\frac{1}{2\pi} \int \phi \frac{\partial}{\partial n} \left(\frac{e^{ikr}}{r} \right) dS, \quad \ldots \ldots \quad (9\cdot8)$$

and the full expression (9.4) is of course the mean of these two.

CHAPTER X

Measurement of the Velocity of Sound

1. Velocity of Plane Waves of Sound by Adverse-wind Method.

The velocity of sound may be deduced in terms of the physical constants of the medium by forming the differential equation as in Chapter II. It may be deduced more simply but rather less directly by supposing the communication to the medium of a velocity equal and opposite to that of the waves, so that the train of waves is brought to rest relative to the observer. If the waves are plane waves of constant type, then the velocity, pressure, density, &c., at each point in space will remain constant. Let us consider a region of the medium contained between two planes A and B at right angles to the direction of propagation and bounded by a cylinder of unit area of cross-section with its axis perpendicular to the planes. Since the motion is longitudinal it is always parallel to the axis of the cylinder and none of the medium crosses the sides of the cylinder.

Let the velocities, relative to the observer, of the medium at A and B, be u_1, u_2 respectively, and the densities ρ_1, ρ_2 respectively.

Mass of medium crossing A per second $= \rho_1 u_1$,
Mass of medium crossing B per second $= \rho_2 u_2$.

But the density at all points remains the same. Hence there is no accumulation of the medium between A and B;

$$\therefore \ \rho_1 u_1 = \rho_2 u_2.$$

Momentum crossing A per second $= \rho_1 u_1^2$.
Momentum crossing B per second $= \rho_2 u_2^2$.

$\therefore$ Rate of increase of momentum of the medium contained in the cylinder

$$= \rho_1 u_1^2 - \rho_2 u_2^2$$

$$= \rho_1 u_1^2 - \frac{\rho_2^2 u_2^2}{\rho_2}$$

$$= \rho_1 u_1^2 - \frac{\rho_1^2 u_1^2}{\rho_2}$$

$$= \rho_1 u_1^2 \left(\frac{\rho_2 - \rho_1}{\rho_2} \right).$$

Let p_1, p_2 be the pressures at A and B, V_1, V_2 the specific volumes at A and B; then

$$\frac{p_2 - p_1}{p_2} = \frac{V_1 - V_2}{V_1}.$$

Also $p_1 - p_2$ = resultant force acting on the medium in the cylinder = rate of change of momentum. Hence

$$p_1 - p_2 = \rho_1 u_1{}^2\left(\frac{V_1 - V_2}{V_1}\right),$$

$$\therefore\ V_1 \cdot \frac{p_1 - p_2}{V_1 - V_2} = \rho_1 u_1{}^2.$$

But $V_1 \cdot \dfrac{p_1 - p_2}{V_1 - V_2} = K$, the volume elasticity of the medium,

$$\therefore\ K = \rho_1 u_1{}^2.$$

Now u_1, the velocity of the medium at A relative to the observer, is made up of two parts:

(1) A velocity given to the medium as a whole, which we may call c,
(2) A velocity due to the passage of the wave (the particle velocity).

If we choose A so that it coincides with a plane of normal density (2) will be zero; then, calling the normal density ρ_0, we have $K = \rho_0 c^2$, and c, the velocity of the medium necessary to bring the waves to rest, is the velocity of the waves. Hence $c = \sqrt{(K/\rho_0)}$.

This formula can be checked dimensionally. K, like all moduli of elasticity, is the ratio of a stress and a strain. As a strain has no dimensions, the dimensions of K are those of a stress, i.e. of force per unit area, $ML^{-1}T^{-2}$. Density has the dimensions ML^{-3}. Hence the dimensions of K/ρ are $L^2 T^{-2}$, and the dimensions of $\sqrt{(K/\rho)}$ are LT^{-1}, the dimensions of a velocity.

It now remains for us to determine the exact meaning of K. In the case of a gas, if the bulk modulus or volume elasticity is measured isothermally, $K = K_\theta = P_0$, where P_0 is the normal pressure of the medium.

This choice does not seem to have been consciously present in Newton's mind, but he assumed Boyle's law. He shows [*] that the velocity is proportional to $\sqrt{\left(\dfrac{\text{Elastic Force}}{\text{Density}}\right)}$, and in the next proposition he shows that if H is the height of the homogeneous atmosphere, then in the time of one complete oscillation of a simple pendulum of length H, the pulses travel a distance $2\pi H$. This gives

* *Principia*, Book 2, Prop. 48.

That is, increase of velocity per degree centigrade $= \frac{1}{2}c_0 a$. Since $c_0 = 1090$ ft./sec., $\frac{1}{2}c_0 a \doteqdot 2$ ft./sec. Also $c_0 = 331$ m./sec., whence $\frac{1}{2}c_0 a \doteqdot 61$ cm./sec. That is, the velocity of sound increases by 2 ft./sec. or 61 cm./sec. for each degree centigrade rise of temperature.

3. Long-distance Experiments in the Open Air.

The simplest and most obvious method for determining the velocity of sound is to time the passage of a sound over as great a distance as possible. Mersenne (1588–1648) and Gassendi (1592–1655) both determined the velocity by noting the time which elapsed between the arrival of the flash and the report from a distant gun.

Mersenne quotes an echo giving back seven successive syllables (*Benedicam Dominum*), occupying in all one second and at a distance of 81 " toises ". He concludes that the velocity of sound is 162 toises per second or 316 metres/sec. He notes that it is the same for high-pitched and for low-pitched voices, and he can detect no difference in fog or clear weather, or up, down and across the wind.

In 1660 Borelli and Viviani carried out a series of cannon-firing experiments under the auspices of the *Academia del Cimento* of Florence. They used the method of Mersenne and Gassendi with certain improvements in technique, and obtained the value 361 metres/sec.

A very complete experimental study was made by Derham,[*] Vicar of Upminster in Essex, in 1704. He used for timing a very accurate portable movement with a pendulum beating half-seconds. He measured the time for guns fired at Blackheath to be heard in Upminster, and also timed the sound of bells, hammers, and guns over a measured mile. He found that, within the limits of the accuracy to which he could work, weather conditions were without any important influence, and gives as his mean value 1142 ft./sec. or 348 metres/sec.

In 1738 a new determination was made under the auspices of the *Académie des Sciences* of Paris. Cannons were fired and the retardation of the report on the flash was noted for a series of stations from Paris to Monthléry, a distance of 17 or 18 miles. By timing at intermediate stations the observers hoped to detect any change of velocity with intensity. An attempt was also made to eliminate the effect of wind by taking reciprocal observations. It will be seen from the following discussion that if the velocity of the wind is small compared with that of sound—as is always the case—the wind effect is approximately eliminated in this way.

Let S_1, S_2 (fig. 10.1) be two observing stations each equipped with sources of sound and recording apparatus. Let the wind, supposed constant, have a velocity v and let c be the velocity of sound. Let the time of transit of the sound from S_2 to S_1 be t_1 and that from S_1 to

[*] *Phil. Trans.* (1704).

S_2 be t_2. From S_1 lay off a distance S_1S_1' in the direction of the wind and equal to vt_2. Similarly lay off S_2S_2' equal to vt_1. Then the path of the sound from S_1 to S_2 is equivalent to $S_1S_1' + S_1'S_2$, where $S_1'S_2 = ct_2$. Similarly, the path from S_2 to S_1 is equivalent to $S_2S_2' + S_2'S_1$, where $S_2'S_1 = ct_1$. Then if $S_1S_2 = l$ we have

$$c^2t_1{}^2 = l^2 + v^2t_1{}^2 - 2vt_1l\cos a.$$

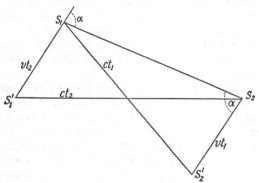

Fig. 10.1

As v is small compared with c we may neglect the term in v^2 and substitute l/c for t_1 in the term containing v. Then

$$c^2t_1{}^2 = l^2 - 2\,\frac{l^2v}{c}\cos a,$$

or

$$ct_1 = l\sqrt{\left(1 - \frac{2v}{c}\cos a\right)}$$

$$= l\left(1 - \frac{v}{c}\cos a\right),$$

$$\therefore\ t_1 = \frac{l}{c}\left(1 - \frac{v}{c}\cos a\right).$$

In the same way
$$t_2 = \frac{l}{c}\left(1 + \frac{v}{c}\cos a\right).$$

For a cross-wind, $a = \pi/2$ and $t_1 = t_2 = \dfrac{l}{c}$.

For any other wind, $t_1 + t_2 = \dfrac{2l}{c}$, or

$$c = \frac{l}{\tfrac{1}{2}(t_1 + t_2)}. \qquad \ldots \ldots \quad (10.3)$$

Hence to a first approximation we eliminate the wind effect by taking reciprocal observations and using the mean value of the time.

The final result of these observers was a value of 332 metres/sec. at 0° C.

A very careful series of experiments in which Arago took part was carried out in conjunction with the *Bureau des Longitudes* in 1822. The course was from Monthléry to Villejuif and the distance was determined by the *Bureau* with great precision. Arago pointed out that the wind was such a variable factor that the elimination of the consequent error by reciprocal observations was not effective unless the observations were simultaneous. After the necessary corrections had been made the value was found to be 340·8 metres/sec. at 16° C. or 331·2 metres/sec. at 0° C.

All the foregoing experiments are vitiated by one serious source of error: the uncertainty of the personal equation of the observer. The interval which elapses between the perception of the flash or report and the recording is not negligible in comparison with the quantity to be measured. Regnault (1810–1878) tried to evade this difficulty by electrically registering the firing of the gun and the motion of a membrane which received the report. He worked over a distance of 2850 metres, made reciprocal observations, and obtained a value of 330·7 metres/sec. corrected to *dry* air at 0° C.

The method, however, remains open to serious criticism. The membrane has inertia and therefore a " personal equation " of its own. This personal equation has the merit of being constant, but it has not been eliminated. Further, in order to register the receipt of the report on a membrane in the open air, an intense source of sound must be used and the distance cannot be very great. This means that the elapsed times are small and that the abnormal velocity of the intense sound near the source is a relatively important cause of error.

These difficulties can only be overcome by using a receiver which is sensitive and which has so little inertia that it is practically instantaneous in its action. To secure these conditions use has been made of the hot-wire microphone (p. 303). This instrument was developed during the war of 1914–18 for the location of guns. It consists essentially of a container with a fine resistance wire stretched across its mouth. This wire is heated by an electric current and is inserted as one arm of a balanced Wheatstone Bridge arrangement. So long as its temperature remains constant its resistance remains constant and the bridge remains balanced. If the wire is cooled the resistance drops and the balance is destroyed. When a sound wave passes across the mouth of the container the compression causes air to surge in and the rarefaction causes a return surge. This cools the wire, deflects the galvanometer, and gives a record of the instant at which the sound is received.

Using a detector of this kind Esclangon in 1919 obtained the value 330·9 metres/sec. for the velocity of sound in dry air at 0° C., and Angerer and Ladenburg * in 1921 obtained the value 330·8 ± 0·1 metres/sec. For air at 10° C. and humidity 67 per cent they obtained 337·4 metres/sec. or 1107 ft./sec.

Objections to the general principle of the method, however, still remain. No matter what care is taken in selecting suitable country and suitable weather conditions and in making the necessary wind, temperature and humidity observations, these latter quantities will always vary locally over the distance, and it will be impossible to allow for this variation.

4. Stationary-wave Method.

The principle used in this method is that of measuring the distance between successive nodes in a system of stationary waves and hence calculating the wave-length. The method is usually applied to waves in a tube, but a stationary wave method in free air and therefore independent of the corrections and uncertainties due to the use of tubes was proposed by Michelson and carried out by Hebb.†

The apparatus is shown in fig. 10.2. Two large paraboloidal mirrors A_1, A_{11}, made of plaster of Paris, are arranged co-axially facing one another. In the focus of one of these mirrors is placed a source of sound S and close to it a telephone transmitter or microphone T_1. A second microphone T_{11} is arranged at the focus of the other mirror. Each microphone is in series with a battery (B_1, B_{11}), and with

Fig. 10.2.—Velocity of sound by Hebb's method

a primary of an induction coil I wound with two primaries. A telephone receiver R is connected to the secondary of this coil. Waves from the source reach the adjacent microphone directly, and the further microphone after reflection from the two mirrors. Movement of one of the two mirrors in the direction of its axis will vary the relative phase of the waves at the two microphones and therefore the intensity of the sound heard in the receiver. The source of sound is a whistle blown at constant pressure. It was found possible to make over two hundred successive settings of the movable reflector for minima covering a total distance

* *Ann. d. Physik*, Vol. 66, p. 293 (1921).   † *Phys. Rev.*, Vol. 20, p. 91 (1905).

of over 100 ft. The pitch of the whistle was compared with a tuning-fork which was in turn compared with a pendulum, and this latter was rated against a standard clock.

The mean of six sets of observations gave 331·29 ± ·04 metres/sec. In a later paper * Hebb finds 331.44 and shows that this value leads to a value for the ratio of the specific heats of dry air at 0° C. which agrees well with the best direct determinations of that quantity.

5. Experiments on the Velocity of Sound in Gases in Pipes and Tubes.

It is obvious that some of the disadvantages attending determinations of the velocity of sound in the open air are avoided by making experiments in pipes. Wind effects are eliminated and the temperature and humidity are much more constant and more easily controlled. For these reasons Regnault was led in 1862 to take advantage of the new arrangements being made for the supply of water and gas in Paris. He made a long series of experiments on the conduction of sound in pipes. The origin of the sound as a rule was the firing of a pistol, and this was electrically recorded on a revolving drum. The movement of a diaphragm at the farther end of the pipe on receipt of the sound closed a circuit and was also recorded on the drum. The time scale was given by the trace of a tuning-fork of known frequency. The pipes varied in diameter from 11 cm. to 110 cm. and in length up to 4900 metres. By reflections from the ends distances up to 20,000 metres were obtained. The results were corrected for temperature and moisture by using the formula

$$c_0' = c \sqrt{\left(\frac{1 - 0 \cdot 38 f/h}{1 + at} \right)}, \quad \cdots \quad (10.4)$$

where c_0' is the velocity in dry air at 0° C., c the observed velocity, f the pressure of aqueous vapour, h the barometric height, t the temperature centigrade.

The more important conclusions reached by Regnault were as follows:

(1) In a cylindrical tube the intensity of the wave does not remain constant, but diminishes with the distance, and this diminution is the more marked the narrower the tube.

(2) The velocity diminishes with the intensity.

(3) The velocity tends towards a limit which increases with the diameter of the pipe. This limiting value after all corrections is given by Regnault as 330·6 metres/sec.

(4) The velocity is independent of the pressure. This was tested over a range from 247 mm. of mercury to 1267 mm. of mercury.

(5) The velocity varies inversely as the square root of the density.

* *Phys. Rev.*, Vol. 14, p. 74 (1919).

This was tested for hydrogen, carbon dioxide, nitrous oxide, and ammonia, and allowing for the difficulties of the experiment a fair verification of the law was obtained.

Another important series of experiments was carried out later by Violle and Vautier * in a double conduit constructed between Rochefort and Grenoble. The conduit had an internal diameter of 70 cm. and was 6342 metres long. By connecting the distant ends with a semi-circular tube, a U-shaped pipe 12,687 metres long was obtained with both ends under observation by one observer.

The main conclusions arrived at by these experimenters from this and other series of experiments were as follows:

(1) No matter what the nature of the initial disturbance, the sound wave in the course of propagation tends towards a simple determinate form.

(2) This form once attained, the different parts of the wave propagate themselves with the same uniform velocity, which must be regarded as the normal velocity of the wave.

(3) The disturbance provoked by a pistol shot at first presents a complex form and the various parts move with different velocities; but the crest of the wave (maximum condensation) soon assumes the normal velocity, while the front, starting with a velocity too great, slows down and tends towards this same normal value.

(4) The intensity of the pistol shot is without effect on the normal velocity; but the velocity of the wave-front increases with the intensity.

(5) Within the limits customary for the intensity of musical sounds the intensity is without effect on their velocity, which rapidly assumes the normal value.

(6) Differences of pitch are without effect on the velocity of musical sounds.

(7) The velocity of propagation of sound in the open air is greater than in a pipe, where the influence of the walls produces a retardation inversely proportional to the diameter of the pipe and exceeding 0·46 metres per second for a pistol shot in a pipe of 1 metre diameter.

The last of these conclusions calls attention to the weak point in the method. The action of the pipe wall is probably twofold: (1) mechanical friction between the interior face of the pipe and the air in contact with it must retard the movement of the air; (2) by conduction the walls take heat from the condensations and give it to the rarefactions, thus tending to equalize the temperature and to produce isothermal conditions. This tends to reduce the velocity to the isothermal value as a limit. The joint effect of these two processes is not easy to evaluate. The problem was tackled successively by Helmholtz

* *Ann. de Chimie et de Physique*, Vol. 19, p. 306 (1890); Vol. 5, p. 208 (1905); Vol. 8, p. 443 (1906); *Journal de Physique*, Vol. 5, p. 22 (1896); Vol. 9. p. 621 (1900).

and by Kirchhoff * and the Helmholtz-Kirchhoff correction is the result. The relation is in the form

$$c = c_0 \left(1 - \frac{k}{2r\sqrt{(\pi f)}} \right) \quad \ldots \quad (10.5)$$

where c is the velocity of sound in the pipe, c_0 the velocity of sound in free air, r the radius of the pipe, f the frequency of the sound; and k is a constant which has the value

$$k = \mu^{\frac{1}{2}} + \left(\frac{\nu}{\gamma} \right)^{\frac{1}{2}} (\gamma - 1) \quad \ldots \quad (10.6)$$

where μ is the kinematic viscosity, ν the thermal diffusivity, γ the ratio of specific heats. For measurements in metres, k is about 0·6.

This formula and the value of the correction have been the subject of a good deal of criticism by various experimenters. A very extensive series of determinations by Kaye and Sherratt † of the velocity of sound in gases based on measurements of stationary waves in tubes has yielded valuable information on this point. Using tubes of different materials (glass, copper and carbon), of different widths (0·88 cm. to 2·89 cm.) and making experiments on six different gases at a great variety of frequencies, they came to the conclusion that the form of the expression correctly represented their results within the limits of experimental error. For the numerical value of k they found that for the smooth tubes (glass and copper) they obtained values about 10 per cent too low as compared with the values calculated from the known constants for the gases. With the rough tubes (carbon), on the other hand, they obtained experimental values which were about 30 per cent too high. The correction is difficult to determine with accuracy, as it has to be calculated from the small difference of two large numbers, but Kaye and Sherratt conclude that apart from this effect of tube surface the formula for correction is reliable and the actual value of k for all smooth tubes may be found by multiplying its theoretical value by 0·9.

Similar conclusions were reached by Waetzmann and Keibs,‡ using a thermophone as source and frequencies from 400 to 1400 c./sec. In the supersonic region Norton § finds the correction to be 0·47 instead of the theoretical value 0·54, and this is in good agreement with the results of Kaye and Sherratt.

Violle and Vautier found as their observed value of the velocity of sound $c = 338·740$ metres/sec. Correcting this value for temperature and pressure by Regnault's formula, they obtained $c_0 = 330·331$ metres/sec. Using a value obtained by Kayser and open to

---

* *Pogg. Ann.*, Vol. 134, p. 177 (1868).
† *Proc. Roy. Soc.*, A, Vol. 141, p. 123 (1933). See also p. 255.
‡ *Ann. d. Phys.*, Vol. 22, p. 247 (1935).
§ *Journ. Amer. Soc. Acoust.*, Vol. 7, p. 16 (1935).

criticism, the correction to open-air conditions becomes $+0.676$ metre, giving as a final value $c = 331.007$ metres/sec. Applying the same correction to Regnault's results they obtained as the most probable value

$$c = 331.1 \pm 0.1 \text{ metres/sec.}$$

6. Velocity of Sound in Gases in Pipes and Tubes by Stationary-wave Methods.

These methods all depend on measurements made on a stationary-wave system with waves of known frequency, the wave-length being measured and the velocity calculated.

The simplest application of the method is the ordinary resonance tube experiment. A sounding tuning-fork is held over the end of a tube of adjustable length, one end of which is closed. The length of the tube is then adjusted until it gives with maximum loudness the tone of the fork. It is then vibrating in the frequency of the fork, and if its length is the shortest length which will resound to the fork, the length of the air column is one-quarter of the wave-length of the note. We then have $c = f\lambda = f \times 4l$.

The experiment can be most simply carried out by using a tube open at both ends and immersing the lower end in water. The result is corrected for temperature in the usual way. The correction for moisture is too small to be worth making in view of the other inaccuracies of the experiment. The most important of these is that the antinode does not occur exactly at the end of the tube but some little way above it. The correction which has to be added to the measured length in order to give $\lambda/4$ cannot be easily calculated. The correction for a tube ending in an infinite flange, however, has been calculated by Rayleigh, who found it to be $0.824r$, where r is the radius of the tube, supposed circular. Subsequently a more exact solution was given by L. V. King,* who obtains $0.821r$. The effect of removing a flange is found by experiment to be $.22r$ (Rayleigh obtained 0.25 and Bosanquet 0.20) so that for an ordinary open end it is usual to take the correction as $0.6r$. The factor calculated by A. E. Bate † is $1/\sqrt{2}$, giving $0.58r$. Inserting the usual correction in the formula we have $c = 4f(l + 0.6r)$. It is obvious that by using tubes of different radii the correction can be eliminated (see also p. 406). It may also be eliminated by raising the tube so that the water surface coincides with the second node in the tube. Clearly the distance between the two positions of the node is $\lambda/2$ and is independent of the end correction. The arrangement cannot be relied on for accurate results. The setting is difficult to make and the experiment is open to the same criticism as the previous method—the velocity obtained is the velocity in a pipe and a narrow one at that.

---

* *Phil. Mag.*, Vol 21, p. 128 (1936).   † *Phil. Mag.*, Vol 24, p. 453 (1937).

A more promising avenue was opened up by Kundt * (1839–1894) with his dust-tube method. The principle is very simple. A wide tube (fig. 10.3) is closed at one end by an adjustable piston and at the other end by a diaphragm fixed to a rod clamped at the centre. The diaphragm nearly fills the cross-section of the tube. The tube between the diaphragm and the adjustable piston contains a dry powder. When the rod is stroked with a wet cloth or resined rubber, or struck by a hammer, longitudinal vibrations are set up in it, which are communicated by the diaphragm to the gas in the tube. If the piston is now adjusted so that the length of the gas column gives an exact number of stationary waves, the dust will be violently disturbed at the antinodes and will form an unmistakable series of striations marking these positions. The frequency of the note given by the rod is determined and the wavelength of the sound in the tube is calculated by measuring the distance from the diaphragm to the piston and dividing by the number of

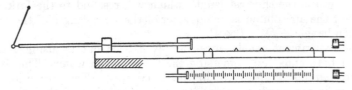

Fig. 10.3.—Kundt's tube

vibrating segments. This gives the half wave-length of the sound in the gas, and therefore the velocity. By using the same tube and various gases we can obviously get a series of comparative values for the velocities without knowing the frequency of the note, and if we know the pressure and density of the various gases and the frequency we can determine γ in each case. The method was used by Kundt to determine the velocity of sound in the solid rod (assuming the velocity in air), to determine the velocity of sound in gases other than air, and to measure the velocity in air at various temperatures from 0° C. to 100° C. It was used to determine γ for mercury vapour by Kundt and Warburg † and for argon and helium by Rayleigh and Ramsay.‡

Modifications of the Kundt's tube method were used by Behn and Geiger,§ by Partington,‖ by Shilling,¶ by Shilling and Partington,** and by Sherratt and Awbery.†† The most complete series of experiments on stationary waves in tubes are those of Kaye and Sherratt already referred to on p. 252.

* *Pogg. Ann.*, Vol. 127, p. 497 (1866).   † *Pogg. Ann.*, Vol. 157, p. 353 (1876).
‡ *Phil. Trans.*, Vol. 186, p. 187 (1895); *Proc. Roy. Soc.*, Vol. 8, p. 86 (1895).
§ *Ber. deutsch. phys. Ges.*, Vol. 5, p. 657 (1907).   ‖ *Phil. Mag.*, Vol. 43, p. 370 (1922).
¶ *Phil. Mag.*, Vol. 3, p. 273 (1927).   ** *Phil. Mag.*, Vol. 6, p. 920 (1928).
†† *Proc. Phys. Soc.*, Vol. 43, p. 242 (1931).

The apparatus used by these experimenters is shown in fig. 10.4. The resonating tube is mounted inside a longer brass tube. The source of the vibrations is either a telephone diaphragm supplied with alternating current from an oscillatory valve circuit controlled by a quartz oscillator, or a maintained quartz oscillator operating directly on the air column. The reflector is a massive cylinder occupying the whole cross-section of the resonating tube and carried by a steel rod, the displacement of which can be accurately measured. The temperature is determined by thermojunctions P_1, P_2, P_3, P_4. During a series of observations the frequency is kept constant and the steel piston moved. Variations in the E.M.F. across the telephone are correlated with variations in the position of the steel rod. These variations in E.M.F. are due to variations in phase of the reflected waves and the reaction of these reflected waves on the diaphragm. The kind of relationship obtained is shown in fig. 10.5. The displacement of the

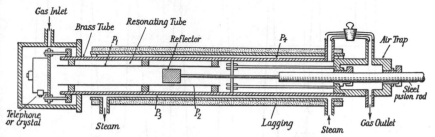

Fig. 10.4.—Sectional diagram of Kaye and Sherratt's apparatus

reflector corresponding to a complete cycle of values is equal to half the wavelength of the sound. The corrected values so obtained were as follows:

Gas				18° C.	100° C.
Air (dry and CO_2 free)	..	..	..	343·4 metres/sec.	387·3 metres/sec.
Hydrogen ..	..	..	..	1301	1463
Carbon dioxide	..	..	..	265·8	297·2
Sulphur dioxide	..	..	..	216·2	244·2
Ammonia ..	..	..	..	428·2	481·9
Ethyl chloride	..	..	..	203·8	230·6

The phenomena occurring in Kundt's tube are much more complex than early observers supposed. Between the nodes the powder arranges itself in striæ, of which no accurate measurements were made and about the formation of which no theory was suggested. Experimenters were handicapped by the fact that the stroked rod is an intermittent source of sound and measurements on the striæ and the nodal heaps can only be made after the sound has ceased.

A detailed study of the phenomena has been made by Irons,[*] Cook,[†] Henry,[‡] Andrade,[§] and Hutchisson and Morgan.[||] Using a valve-maintained diaphragm as the source of sound and fine smoke particles observed in scattered light as

[*] *Phil. Mag.*, Vol. 7, p. 523 (1929).   [†] *Phys. Rev.*, Vol. 36, p. 1099 (1930).
[‡] *Proc. Phys. Soc.*, Vol. 43, p. 340 (1931).
[§] *Nature*, Vol. 127, p. 438 (1931); *Proc. Roy. Soc.*, A, Vol. 134, p. 445 (1932); *Phil. Trans.*,
A, Vol. 230, p. 413 (1932).   [||] *Phys. Rev.*, Vol. 37, p. 1155 (1931).

tracing points, Andrade was able to measure the amplitude of the vibrations in the tube and establish the existence of the circulation that was predicted by Rayleigh. This circulation takes place from antinode to node in the neighbour-

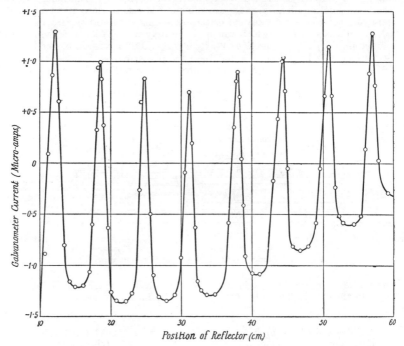

Fig. 10.5.—Air in glass tube. Frequency 2636 cycles/sec. Temperature 16·7° C.

hood of the walls and from node to antinode along the centre, as shown in fig. 10.6. The form of the circulation was given by Rayleigh in the formula

$$\psi = C(r^4 - r^2R^2) \sin \frac{2\pi x}{\lambda}, \qquad \ldots \ldots \quad (10.7)$$

Wall of tube

Centre of tube

Fig. 10.6—Circulation in a Kundt's tube; observed lines of flow on the left; lines plotted from Rayleigh's formula on the right

where ψ is the velocity potential, r the radial distance, x the axial distance, and R the radius of tube, and the observed circulation gave good agreement with Rayleigh's formula.

Very light objects like fine smoke particles follow almost exactly the motion of the air; round larger particles vortex systems are formed, and from observations of these considerable light is thrown on hydrodynamical problems. All the phenomena of Kundt's tube are explicable in terms of the vortex motion and the circulation. Two other figures taken from the same paper of Andrade are shown in figs. 10.7 and 10.8. When two particles come close enough together

Fig. 10.7.—One section, node to antinode, of the circulation with wave-length of 91·8 cm.

to coalesce they arrange themselves side by side across the tube. When a number do this they range themselves in striæ whose longitudinal spacing varies from node to antinode, the edges of the corresponding vortex systems being contiguous. The spacing depends on sound intensity, size of particles, gas pressure and density

Fig. 10.8.—The vortex system formed round a sphere, diameter 0·317 cm.

of particles. When the sound is very intense the centre stria coincides in position with a disc of particles extending right across the tube. These discs are very convenient for measurement. The particles rise up the walls of the tube and fall back across its whole section.

7. Velocity of Supersonic Waves in Gases.

An attempt to investigate the possible variation of velocity with frequency was made by Palaiologos * in 1923. Using as a source of sound a direct-current arc on which was imposed a high-frequency alternating current, he measured the wave-length in air of the resulting sound with a wire diffraction grating. For values of the frequency from 2×10^5 cycles/sec. to 2×10^6 cycles/sec., he obtained values of the wave-length varying from 1·7 mm. to 0·17 mm. and the calculated velocity of sound was constant and equal to 335 metres/sec. at 0° C.

* *Zeits. f. Phys.*, Vol. 12, p. 375 (1923).

Experiments were made by Pierce * in 1925 by a method which, with modifications, has become a most important instrument of research in high-frequency sound waves.

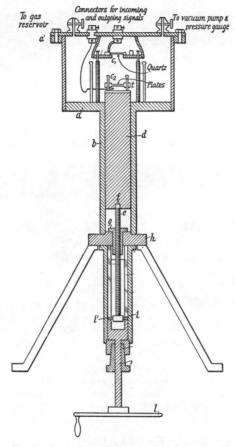

Fig. 10.9.—Gas chamber and auxiliary parts of triple-quartz-plate supersonic generating and receiving system

a, a' brass flanges soldered to the top and bottom of the air chamber, a brass cylinder of diameter 20 cm., b heavy-walled copper cylinder acting as guide for the piston, c_1 sending quartz plate, c_2 reflecting quartz plate, d piston, e micrometer screw, f friction contact through jewelled bearing, g split nut, h disc holding nut, i, i' lugs projecting into closely fitting vertical grooves, l vernier disc, t adjustable screws.

The source of waves (see fig. 9.9) is a quartz plate with one face presented to a parallel reflecting surface which can be moved at right angles to its plane by a fine screw. The reflected waves react on the quartz sufficiently to produce a periodic variation in the readings of the milli-ammeter as the distance of the reflector is gradually increased. The quartz plate in this experiment fulfils three distinct functions. (1) It controls the frequency of the oscillations and this frequency can be determined by standard wave-meter methods. (2) It acts as a source of waves and if its linear dimensions are sufficiently large compared with the wave-length radiated these waves will be sensibly plane. (3) It detects the variation in phase difference of the reflected waves as they impinge on its surface. The maxima can be located to 0·05 mm. and about 100 internodal distances can be measured, giving an order of accuracy in the wave-length measurement of about 1 in 3000.

The demand for increased accuracy in the measurement of velocity in order that dispersion may be investigated, and the desirability of making simultaneous measurements on velocity and absorption, have led to much more elaborate forms of the interferometer.

One of these forms is described by Yeagley * (fig. 10.9). The quartz system consists of three plates, one used as a frequency control, one as the sending plate and one as reflector.

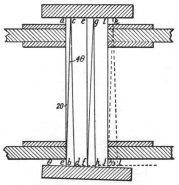

The temperature of the enclosure in which the whole apparatus is contained is controlled to 0·05° C. The effect of standing waves is eliminated by tilting the reflecting plate as shown in fig. 10.10, so that the portion under one edge of the lower aperture is $\lambda/3$ lower than the other. This means that a ray travelling between the plates near the left edge of the beam starting at a and doubly reflected at b and c will arrive at d just one wave-length out of phase with the ray travelling over the path $ijkl$. Thus the plate can be divided into two sets of corresponding points such that doubly reflected waves will arrive at these pairs of points in opposite phases. The reaction of the waves on c_2 leads to measurements of absorption, while the reaction on c_1 enables measurements of the wave-length to be made. The results show

Fig. 10.10.—Arrangement of piezo-quartz plates, showing destructive interference of twice-reflected portions of the supersonic waves.

a positive though small increase of velocity as the absorption constant increases.

A large number of researches have been carried out on the dispersion of super-sonic waves in gases by Hubbard,† Grabau,‡ using a magnetostriction oscillator, Richards and Reid,§ Pearson,‖ Railston and Richardson,¶ Penman,** Sinness and Roseveare,†† Brandt and Freund,‡‡ and others.

* *Rev. Sci. Inst.*, Vol. 6, p. 148 (1935).

† *Phys. Rev.*, Vol. 35, p. 1442 (1930); Vol. 36, p. 1668 (1930); Vol. 38, p. 1011 (1931); Vol. 41, p. 523 (1932).

‡ *Journ. Amer. Soc. Acoust.*, Vol. 5, p. 1 (1933-4).

§ *J. Chem. Phys.*, Vol. 2, pp. 193, 206 (1934).

‖ *Proc. Phys. Soc.*, Vol. 47, p. 136 (1935).   ¶ *Proc. Phys. Soc.*, Vol. 47, p. 533 (1935).

** *Proc. Phys. Soc.*, Vol. 47, p. 543 (1935).

†† *J. Chem. Phys.*, Vol. 4, p. 423 (1936).   ‡‡ *Zeits. f. Phys.*, Vol. 91, p. 415 (1935).

The existence of dispersion seems to be definitely established and to be associated with a relaxation time effect for internal degrees of freedom in the atom. It seems clear that investigations of this kind will throw a good deal of light on the constitution of the molecule.*

8. Abnormal Velocities for Intense Sounds.

It has already been shown that what is known as the velocity of sound is a limiting value which the velocity of intense sound waves approaches only as the intensity diminishes. It is accordingly to be expected that where measurements of velocity are made on intense sound waves considerable discrepancies from the ordinary values will arise. Regnault in the course of his experiments on the velocity of sound in pipes found that the velocity increased with the charge of powder used in generating the wave. A long and careful series of experiments was made by Angerer and Ladenburg,† using the sound waves from explosions and an electrical method of recording the time interval. The firing of the charge broke an electrical contact and the arrival at various microphones suitably disposed was recorded. In order to eliminate as completely as possible the variable effects of atmospheric conditions, the charges were fired from three points in fairly quick succession and the progress of the resulting waves was followed along the adjacent sides of the triangle in each case. Careful measurements were also made of wind velocity and direction, moisture content, &c., not only at ground level but for some distance above. The result of a large number of observations was to give the velocity of sound waves of small amplitude as 330·8 metres/sec. at 0° C. in dry air. When the charge exploded was 3 kg. this normal velocity was reached at about 100 metres from the source. With a charge of 200 kg. it was not reached until 200 metres from the source. Near the source the existence of abnormally high velocities was established; the figures given for a 3 kg. charge are:

Distance from Explosion	Velocity
3 metres	1150 metres/sec.
6 metres	470 metres/sec.
12 metres	380 metres/sec.

These observations establish that (1) near the source the wave velocity is very great—more than three times its normal value, (2) the velocity falls off very rapidly and 9 metres farther from the source it is only about 16 per cent above its normal value.

Similar results were obtained from experiments of Payman, Robinson and Shepherd ‡ on the behaviour of an explosive wave.

* See § 7, p. 135; see also Pielemeier, *Journ. Amer. Soc. Acoust.*, Vol. 10, p. 313 (1919); Richards, *Rev. Mod. Phys.*, Vol. 11, p. 366 (1939); and excellent discussions of the whole subject in Bergmann, *Ultrasonics*, and R. W. Wood, *Supersonics* (Brown Univ., 1939).

† *Ann. d. Physik*, Vol. 66, p. 293 (1933).

‡ *Safety of Mines Research Board*, Papers 18 and 29 (1926); Thompson and Riffolt, *Journ. Amer. Soc. Acoust.*, Vol. 11, pp. 233, 245 (1939).

A very complete investigation of the sound wave from a gun or rifle was made by Miller and others.* The actual wave-front was plotted by timing the arrival at a series of microphones in the line of fire and in directions making angles of $42\frac{1}{2}°$ and $81°$ with this line. The results (plotted in fig. 10.11) show that the wave-front is circular and behaves as if the wave emanated from a moving centre shot out of the gun. In the figure the dotted lines show the distances to which the sound would have travelled with normal velocity from the muzzle of the gun. The actual wave-fronts are these same circles displaced

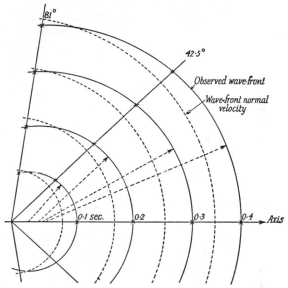

Fig. 10.11.—Wave-fronts charted from actual observations

along the axis. This accounts for the fact that the velocity measured along the line at right angles to the line of fire is abnormally low. The equation of the wave-front is

$$[x - a(1 - e^{-bt})]^2 + y^2 = c^2 t^2, \quad . \quad . \quad . \quad (10.8)$$

which is a circle whose centre at time t is displaced from the muzzle by a distance $a(1 - e^{-bt})$. The experiments showed that even for guns of 10 in. and 12 in. calibre, audible at distances of some ten miles, the velocity 1000 feet from the muzzle differs from the normal by less than one part in a million. From these experiments it would seem that the abnormal velocities near the muzzle of the gun are not due merely to the intensity of the wave.

Using the experiments quoted and reducing the results to dry air

* D. C. Miller, *Sound Waves, their Shape and Speed.*

at standard temperature and pressure, Miller finds for the mean of three sets of observations for distance 6·19 km. the value

$$c = 331\cdot36 \pm 0\cdot08 \text{ metres/sec.}$$

Taking account of the fact that air is not a perfect gas we have

$$c = \sqrt{\frac{\gamma p}{\rho}}\,\phi,$$

where ϕ is a correction factor calculated from the equation of state.

If 1·4029 is taken as the mean experimental value * of γ, then for ϕ calculated from Berthelot's equation of state ($\phi = 0\cdot999251$), $c = 331\cdot384$ metres/sec., while for ϕ calculated from van der Waals' equation ($\phi = 0\cdot998930$) $c = 331\cdot331$ metres/sec. The mean value of these is

$$c = 331\cdot36 \pm 0\cdot05 \text{ metres/sec.}$$

The results by different methods are summarized as follows:

(a) *Gun-fire.*

Esclangon,	330·9 metres/sec.
Angerer and Ladenburg,	330·8 ,,
Miller,	331·36 ,,

(b) *Stationary waves from high-frequency sources.*

Hebb,	331·41 metres/sec.
Pierce, Reid† and Grabau,‡	331·68 ,,

(c) *Stationary waves in tubes.*

Thiessen,§	331·92 metres/sec.
Grüneisen and Merkel,‖	331·57 ,,
Partington and Shilling, ¶	331·4 ,,

9. Velocity of Sound in Gases at Low Temperatures and Pressures.

The measurement of stationary waves of audio-frequency in tubes has been modified and applied to the determination of the velocity of sound in helium at low temperatures and pressures by Keesom and van Itterbeek.** Some of the results obtained are shown in the following table.

Abs. Temp.	Pressure in Atmospheres.	Measured Velocity metres/sec.	Correction for Tube metres/sec.
4·247	0·9121	103·94	+ ·03
4·245	0·3981	114·88	+ ·06
4·245	0·1966	118·31	+ ·09
4·245	0·0736	120·17	+ ·16
3·870	0·6515	102·14	+ ·03
3·875	0·0669	115·12	+ ·15

* Determinations by Lummer and Pringsheim, Shields, Partington and Howe, Brinkworth and Johnston.   † *Phys. Rev.*, Vol. 35, p. 814 (1930).
‡ *Journ. Amer. Soc. Acoust.*, Vol. 5, p.1 (1933).
§ *Ann. d. Physik*, Vol. 25, p. 506 (1908).   ‖ *Ann d. Physik*, Vol. 66, p. 344 (1921).
¶ *Phil. Mag.*, Vol. 6, p. 920 (1928).   ** *Rev. d'Acoustique*, Vol. 2, p. 81 (1933).

10. Sound-ranging in Air.

A knowledge of the velocity of sound in the open air and its variation with atmospheric conditions has an important application in the location of sources of sound. The possibility of locating enemy guns by noting the times of arrival of the report at various points had been discussed in Austria before 1914 and with the outbreak of war it became of vital importance. The first test carried out by the Allies took place near Paris under the direction of Nordmann and Bull. Two guns fired three rounds each and were located to twenty metres for line and thirty metres for range. The microphones were of the carbon-granule type fitted with gramophone horns and were connected to string galvanometers. These experiments demonstrated the practical possibility of the method but revealed serious defects in the type of microphone. These were more sensitive to the shell wave caused by the passage of the projectile through the air than to the sound of the discharge. They were sensitive also to sounds of speech and rifle fire. This difficulty was removed by the invention of the Tucker hot-wire microphone (§ 12, p. 303). This arrangement was much more sensitive to long waves than to short ones. The microphone was in consequence much less sensitive to rifle shots and to the shell wave, which consists of rapid oscillations of pressure of no great amplitude, but responded to hardly audible gun fire. The theory of the method is as follows:

Let M_1, M_2 be two microphones, and let the time interval of reception at the two stations be t'. Then the source of sound must lie on a hyperbola of which M_1 and M_2 are the foci and ct' is the difference of the focal distances. Similarly, if t'' is the time interval for M_2 and a third microphone M_3 the source must lie on a hyperbola of which M_2, M_3 are the foci and ct'' is the difference of the focal distances. The intersection of these two hyperbolas determines the position of the source. The actual procedure is greatly simplified by the fact that the distance to the source is great compared with the distance between the microphones, so that in the neighbourhood of the source the hyperbola may, without much error, be identified with its asymptote. Since the sound rays from the source, owing to its distance, will be approximately parallel, we may proceed as follows. Let M_1, M_2 (fig. 10.12) be two microphones and let M_1M_2 be bisected at A. Let AC be the direction of the source. Draw M_1D parallel to AC and M_2D perpendicular to M_1D. Then

$$M_1D = ct' = M_1M_2 \cos a'$$

$$\therefore \cos a' = \frac{ct'}{a'},$$

where a' is the distance between the microphones. This defines the direction of the line AC on which the source lies. For a second pair of microphones we have

$$\cos a'' = \frac{ct''}{a''},$$

and the intersection of these two straight lines gives us the position of the source.

In actual practice six microphones were used, each giving an electrical record of the receipt of the sound by the movement of its own galvanometer element. Each galvanometer element deflected a spot of light, the six spots being recorded on a moving sensitive film on which hundredths of a second were impressed photographically.

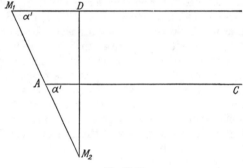

Fig. 10.12

The uniformity of rotation of the drum was secured by a phonic wheel device. The microphones were equally spaced on a circular arc of radius 20–30 " sound seconds " (6 to 10 kilometres). The distance apart of the microphones was 4–5 sound seconds. Theoretically three microphones were sufficient, but the additional ones were made necessary by the exposure of the lines to enemy fire. The location on the map was facilitated by the use of strings and a plotting board. The board had five scales, one corresponding to the point of bisection for each pair of microphones, and the scales were graduated in hundredths of a second. The location could be carried out either by the direct method, in which the enemy gun was located on the map, or by the differential method, in which the position of the enemy gun was compared with that of the shell-burst from the gun directed by the sound-ranging section.

Meteorological data were specially supplied and could be checked by comparing the known position of a bomb discharge with the calculated position obtained from the microphone records. Accidental errors due to defective knowledge of weather conditions were about seven times as great in range as in line. In average weather and for the type of base most used they amounted to 30–40 metres of range. The probable error of one observation on a 4½-second base of radius 25 seconds was about 20 metres at 4 kilometres, and about 80 metres at 12 kilometres along a bisector of the arc.

11. Velocity of Sound in Liquids.

The velocity of sound in liquids is, of course, given by the expression already found on p. 56, namely, $c = \sqrt{(K/\rho)}$. In this case K is the bulk modulus, and as a rule liquids are so nearly incompressible that it is unnecessary to distinguish between the isothermal and adiabatic values.

If we take the case of water, the compressibility is about ·00005 per atmosphere;

$$\therefore K = \frac{76 \times 13\cdot6 \times 981}{\cdot00005} = 2\cdot03 \times 10^{10} \text{ dynes/cm.}^2,$$

$$\therefore c = \sqrt{(2\cdot03 \times 10^{10})} = 1\cdot42 \times 10^5 \text{ cm./sec.} = 1420 \text{ metres/sec.}$$

. If great accuracy is required, however, account must be taken of the difference between the isothermal and adiabatic volume elasticities; we then have $c = \sqrt{(\gamma K/\rho)}$.

For water at 8° C., $\gamma = 1\cdot001$, and the velocity is modified by only one part in 2000. For ethyl ether at 18° C., $\gamma = 1\cdot32$, and the factor is very important. In the case of sea-water γ is sufficiently large to be important if great accuracy is desired; at a temperature of 30° C., $\gamma = 1\cdot0207$.

Accurate measurements of the velocity of sound in liquids enable us to calculate the adiabatic compressibility. The isothermal compressibility can be determined from static measurements, and these two quantities enable us to calculate the ratio of the specific heats for a liquid. This in turn when taken with the measured specific heat at constant pressure enables us to calculate the specific heat of the liquid at constant volume, which is otherwise very difficult to determine.

12. Long-distance Experiments in Water.

The earliest determination was made by Colladon and Sturm (1827) over a distance of about 14 kilometres in the Lake of Geneva. A bell was struck under water and a flash produced above water simultaneously from one boat while the observer in the other boat measured the lapse of time between the instant at which the flash was seen and the instant at which the sound was received by a horn immersed in water. The time was observed to about ⅕ second. As the time interval was 9·4 seconds this gave an accuracy of about 2 per cent. The value obtained was 1440 metres/sec.

Since these experiments of Colladon and Sturm numerous other determinations have been made in sea-water by Threlfall and Adair,* Marti † and others. Next to the velocity of sound in air the velocity in sea-water is by far the most important. Upon a knowledge of the accurate value of this quantity depends the whole practice of echo-sounding and the radio-acoustic method of fixing the positions of ships at sea.

One of the most complete investigations is that due to A. B. Wood, Browne and Cochrane ‡ carried out at Dover under the joint direction of the Director of Torpedoes and Mining and the Director of Research of the British Admiralty. Account was taken of temperature and salinity and the effect of these on the velocity was estimated. Four microphone receivers were laid on the sea bed at intervals of about 4 miles, the positions being determined by an accurate survey. The time intervals of the passage of the explosive wave between the various pairs of hydrophones were obtained by means of a six-stringed Ein-thoven galvanometer recording photographically. A fifth string was operated by a chronometer ticking half-seconds, while the sixth string could be used to record a wireless signal marking the instant of firing the charge. The charge was fired as nearly as possible in the line defined by the microphones. Three results were obtained and are included in the table given below. By comparison of these results obtained at Dover and a similar determination at Shandon (Gare Loch) where the salinity is low (28 parts per 1000 as compared with 35 parts per 1000 at Dover) the effect of salinity is estimated at between 3 and 4 ft. per sec. per 0·1 per cent increase in salinity. The temperature coefficient is estimated at 10·9 ft. per sec. per degree centigrade. Contrary to the results obtained by Threlfall and Adair, these experimenters observed no certain difference in the velocity with the size of charge used, although this varied from a few grains of mercury fulminate to a 300-lb. depth-charge. In the case of the experiments of Threlfall and Adair, however, the velocity was measured much closer to the source of the explosion.

Similar experiments have been carried out by Stephenson § near New York and by Eckhardt ‖ in Californian waters. Stephenson as a result of measurements made between 0° C. and 20° C. gives 2·8 metres/sec. per degree centigrade as the temperature coefficient. This corresponds to 9·1 ft./sec. as against 10·9 ft./sec. obtained by Wood, Browne and Cochrane.

A very complete survey of the existing data was published by Service,¶ comparing the tables published by Heck and Service for

* *Proc. Roy. Soc.*, Vol. 45, p. 450 (1889).   † *Comptes Rendus*, Vol. 169, p. 281 (1919).
‡ *Proc. Roy. Soc.*, A, Vol. 103, p. 284 (1923).   § *Phys. Rev.*, Vol. 21, p. 181 (1923).
‖ *Trans. Roy. Soc. Canada*, Vol. 21, p. 83 (1927).
¶ *Journ. Frankl. Inst.*, Vol. 206, p. 779 (1928).

the American Government * with the British Admiralty † tables, and applying the data in these tables to some of the best experimental determinations. His conclusions are as follows:

(1) Speed increases with temperature by approximately 0·2 per cent per degree centigrade.

(2) Speed at a given depth increases with the depth by about 0·2 per cent per 100 fathoms.

(3) Speed increases very slowly with salinity, the total increase from 31 parts per 1000 to 37 parts per 1000 being only about 0·7 per cent or roughly 0·1 per cent for each 0·1 per cent increase of salinity. He gives the following table:

TABLE VI

Comparison of the Results of Precise Measurements of the Speed of Sound in Sea-Water with the Corresponding Values in the Tables of Heck and Service and of the British Admiralty, respectively.

All measurements were made in comparatively shallow water.

Experimenter	Tempera-ture in deg. cent.	Salinity parts per 1000	Measured Speed metres/sec.	Speed Heck & Service met./sec.	Speed British Ad-miralty metres/sec.
Stephenson	− 0·3	33·5	1453	1449	1442·2
Marti	15	32·3	1504·15	1503	1500·9
Wood, Browne, Cochrane	6	35	1474·0	1474	1472·0
Wood, Browne, Cochrane	7	35	1477·3	1478	1476·1
Wood, Browne, Cochrane	16·95	35	1510·4	1514	1510·4
Eckhardt	13	33·5	1492·3	1498	1495·5

13. Velocity of Sound in Liquids in Tubes.

The objections which can be raised to a determination of the velocity of sound in gases contained in tubes acquire increased importance in the case of liquids. The pressures developed are very much greater and the yielding of the walls at the pressure antinodes may have a marked effect on the results obtained. Where a stationary-wave method is used the tube is forced into a vibration of which the displacement antinodes coincide with the displacement nodes of the vibration in the fluid, and the nodes and antinodes for the tube can be detected by a stethoscope if the vibrations have audio-frequency. The effect of the yielding of the tube is to lower the calculated velocity of sound, as appears from the early experiments of Wertheim and others. This result was predicted by Helmholtz and the magnitude

* U.S. Coast and Geodetic Survey Special Publication, No. 108 (1924).
† Hydrographic Department (1927).

of the effect was calculated by Lamb,* who found an expression of the form

$$c_0 = c\sqrt{1 + \frac{2Ka}{hE}}, \quad \ldots \ldots \quad (10.9)$$

where c_0 is the true velocity of sound in the liquid, c is the velocity in the liquid in the tube of radius a and thickness h, while K is the bulk modulus of the liquid and E the Young's modulus of the material of the tube.

Direct experiments on the velocity of sound in liquids contained in a U-tube were made by Jonescu † and by Cisman.‡ In these experiments a wave started near one end of a U-tube had its arrival at the two ends optically recorded. A wave was then started from a point near the other end and its arrival at both ends optically recorded. The reciprocal observations eliminated errors due to lag in the recording mechanism.

14. Stationary Waves in Liquids in Tubes.

The earlier workers followed Kundt's procedure modified to suit the case of liquids, the arrangement of a powder in the tube marking the positions of the nodes and antinodes in the stationary waves. Experiments by Dörsing § gave the velocity of sound in a number of liquids to an estimated accuracy of 1 per cent. In calculating these values Dörsing used a correction for the tube due to Korteweg.‖ This method was improved by Busse ¶ and applied to fifteen organic liquids; the same correction formula was applied but possible errors were minimized by the use of much thicker tubes.

The case of air-free distilled water was studied in some detail by Pooler ** using the stationary waves in a vertical steel tube, the source of the vibrations being a diaphragm maintained electromagnetically. The reaction of the vibrating liquid column on the diaphragm was reduced to a minimum by arranging the height of the column for resonance.

The correction formulæ of Korteweg, Lamb and Gronwall †† were tried and the two former discarded in favour of the last named. After trying four different diaphragms and three different tubes, Pooler arrived at the value $c_0 = 1485{\cdot}4 \pm 2{\cdot}3$ metres/sec. as the velocity of sound in air-free distilled water at 25° C.

Since the adiabatic bulk modulus K is related to the velocity c_0

* *Proc. Manchester Phil. Soc.*, Vol. 42, No. 9 (1898).
† *Journ. de Phys.*, Vol. 5, p. 377 (1924).   ‡ *Journ. de Phys.*, Vol. 7, p. 347 (1926).
§ *Ann. d. Physik*, Vol. 25, p. 227 (1908).   ‖ *Wied. Ann.*, Vol. 5, p. 525 (1878). ·
¶ *Ann. d. Physik*, Vol. 75, p. 657 (1924).   ** *Phys. Rev.*, Vol. 35, p. 832 (1930).
†† *Phys. Rev.*, Vol. 30, p. 71 (1927).

and to the density ρ_0 by the relation $K = \rho_0 c_0{}^2$ we can calculate K and hence the compressibility C. For 25° C. we find that

$$K = 2 \cdot 2000 \times 10^{10} \text{ dynes/cm.}^2,$$
$$C = 4 \cdot 5455 \times 10^{-11} \text{ cm.}^2/\text{dyne.}$$

The experiments were extended to the case of water at different temperatures up to about 70° C., and the accompanying graph (fig. 10.13) shows the variation of velocity, bulk modulus and compressibility throughout this range.

Experiments on salt solutions indicated an increase in velocity of 1 metre/sec. per 0·1 per cent salinity, so that a solution as strong as sea water would give 1520 metres/sec. at 25°, a value which agrees quite well with the long-range experiments of § 12, p. 267.

15. Supersonic Waves in Liquids.

Just as with gases, so with liquids, the discovery of the piezo - electric properties of quartz opened up an entirely new range of wave-lengths. The stationary-wave method was applied by Boyle and others to a determination of the velocity of supersonic waves in water. A quartz oscillator was used to produce a horizontal train of waves which was reflected from a vertical plate. The resulting stationary waves produced dust figures which could be measured. In a paper published in 1925 Boyle and Taylor * obtained results which suggested a slight increase of velocity with frequency. The increase, however, was so small as to be just on the limits of experimental error and in a further paper † a more careful series of experiments with frequencies ranging from 45,000 to 570,000 indicated that both for water and

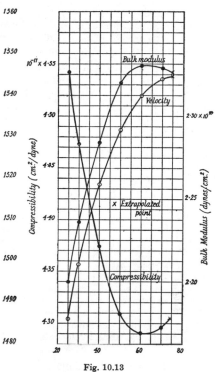

Fig. 10.13

---

* *Trans. Roy. Soc. Canada*, Vol. 19, p. 197 (1925).
† *Trans. Roy. Soc. Canada*, Vol. 21, p. 79 (1927).

for castor oil the velocity is independent of frequency. The actual values found for the velocity in water varied between $1·480 \times 10^5$ cm./sec. and $1·495 \times 10^5$ cm./sec., the measurements being made at $18·5°$ C.

A high-precision instrument known as the supersonic interferometer has been developed, by which the wave-length for liquids of which only a small quantity is available may be determined with great accuracy. The instrument is described in a paper by Hubbard and Loomis * and the principle is that employed by Pierce in his experiments on the velocity of sound in gases. The reflected waves react on the piezo-quartz source, and the variation of one of the quantities in the electrical circuit of the quartz or its associated circuit is measured and goes through a cycle of values as the reflecting surface is moved through half a wave-length. The instrument is shown in fig. 10.14.

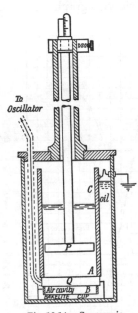

To Oscillator

Fig. 10.14.—Supersonic interferometer

Q is the quartz plate with electrodes on its two faces. The dimensions of the plate are large compared with the wave-length in the liquid. The electrode B is connected to the oscillating system, while the electrode A, the cell C and the piston P are all earthed. The piston P is moved by a micrometer screw, the piston rod being of invar so as to eliminate the effect of an uneven distribution of temperature when determinations at temperatures other than atmospheric are being made. The results were shown to be independent of the materials or dimensions of the cell and the necessity for troublesome corrections was thus avoided.

Measurements were made in mercury and in sodium chloride solutions at various temperatures, with the following results:

Mercury

Temperature $20·0°$ C.; $\lambda/2 = 0·16582$ cm.
Frequency $= 437,600$ cycles/sec.
$c = 1451·3$ metres/sec.

* *Phil. Mag.*, Vol. 5, p. 1177 (1928).

Sodium Chloride Solutions

Temperature °C		·99 per cent NaCl metres/sec.	2·49 per cent NaCl metres/sec.	4·81 per cent NaCl ' metres/sec.
10	..	1460	1483	
20	..	1492	1515	1542
30	..	1517	1538	1565
40	..	1538	1556	1583

14·52 per cent NaCl			25.35 per cent NaCl	
Temperature		metres/sec.	Temperature	metres/sec.
13·8	..	1644.1	8·25 ..	1780·2
17·6	..	1650·9	15·8 ..	1786·0
22·0	..	1658·5	22·05 ..	1789·3
26·7	..	1665·6	31·8 ..	1792·9
29·2	..	1669·4	31·95 ..	1792·9

The values obtained are considered to have sufficient accuracy to justify their use in calculating accurate values of the compressibility of the liquids tested; with this in view a series of experiments was made on organic liquids by Freyer, Hubbard and Andrews.* For this purpose the design of the interferometer was elaborated, although the principle was not modified. Settings of the piston could be made to 0·002 mm. The experiments cover a wide range of organic liquids and the results for the compressibilities are compared with the values obtained by direct measurement by other investigators.

Improvements in design with resulting gain in accuracy have been introduced by Randall † and by Quirk.‡ Randall has made measurements with his interferometer on supersonic velocities in solutions of sugar and in pure distilled air-free water at temperatures between 0° C. and 86° C. The values are used to calculate compressibilities, and in the case of distilled water these are compared with the results of direct measurement. An attempt was also made to determine the compressibilities of solid particles in suspension by comparing the velocity in the pure liquid with that in the suspension. The results obtained were inconclusive, but indicated that the method is a possible one.

The interferometer method has been adapted to measurements of velocity in liquids at very low temperatures by van Itterbeek and Keesom.§ Measurements in liquid oxygen and hydrogen have been made by Pitt and Jackson,‖ with the following results:

* Journ. Amer. Chem. Soc., Vol. 51, p. 759 (1929).
† Bur. of Standards Journ. of Res., Vol. 8, p. 79 (1932).
‡ Rev. Sci. Inst., Vol. 6, p. 6 (1935).
§ Proc. Acad. Sci. Amsterdam, Vol. 33, p. 440 (1930); Vol. 34, pp. 204, 996 (1931).
‖ Canadian Journ. Res., Vol. 12, p. 686 (1935).

Substance			Temp. (Kelvin Scale)	Velocity
Oxygen (gas)	..	..	0°	315·6 metres/sec.
Oxygen (gas)	..	..	−182·9	177·6
Oxygen (liquid)		..	−182·9	912
Hydrogen (gas)		..	−252·9	357
Hydrogen (liquid)		..	−252·7	1127

In the case of the oxygen there was a little superficial boiling only, but in the case of the hydrogen there was some boiling throughout the liquid.

Klein and Hershberger * adapted the interferometer for use with Rochelle salt crystals and with magnetostrictive rods as well as with quartz crystals, and extended its use to measurements on very small quantities of liquids. Their method is analogous to the measurement of refractive index by the shift of the interference fringes due to the insertion of a layer of transparent material whose thickness is known. If less than about 100 c.c. of liquid are available the ordinary method is open to three disadvantages: (1) measurements must be made near the source where nodal planes are less sharply located, (2) accuracy is reduced owing to the fact that only a comparatively small number of internodal distances can be measured, (3) it may be undesirable that the liquid should come into contact with the reflector and the container.

A small bakelite cell with parallel walls is filled with an oil previously investigated and immersed in the same oil between the source and the reflector. A series of nodal planes is then located. The cell is now removed, cleaned, filled with the liquid to be tested, and replaced. The nodal planes are, of course, shifted and the shift is determined for eight or ten.

If $\mu = c_1/c_0$, where c_0 is the velocity of the waves in the oil and c_1 that in the liquid, then the substitution of the liquid for the oil introduces an effective change of path as measured in oil of $(\mu - 1)d/\mu$, and this is Δx, the measured shift of the nodal planes. That is,

$$\mu = \frac{d}{d - \Delta x}.$$

For turpentine the following observations are given. Velocity in oil = 1·5 × 10^5 cm./sec. Thickness of layer of turpentine = 1 in. Shift of nodal planes = −0·115 in.

Then
$$\mu = \frac{1}{1·115} = 0·897,$$

$$c_1 = 0·897 \times 1·5 \times 10^5 \text{ cm./sec.}$$
$$= 1·34 \times 10^5 \text{ cm./sec.}$$

The temperature was 21° C.

* *Phys. Rev.*, Vol. 6, p. 760 (1931).

Meantime an entirely different method of measuring wave-length has been developed from a suggestion of Brillouin.* According to Brillouin, the periodic variations in density of a liquid through which supersonic waves were passing should give it a "structure" which could be revealed by a light diffraction pattern. The suggestion was taken up by Debye and Sears.†

A quartz plate with silvered (electrode) faces is immersed in a glass trough of rectangular cross-section filled with the liquid in which the supersonic waves are propagated. At right angles to the trough a slit and lens are arranged so that plane waves of monochromatic light are sent through the liquid approximately at right angles to the

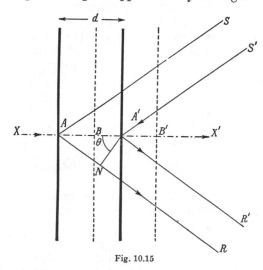

Fig. 10.15

direction of propagation of the supersonic waves. After passage across the supersonic waves the light beam forms not a single image of the slit but a central image flanked by a series of diffracted images.

The complete theory presents many difficulties and has been worked out mainly by Raman and Nagendra Nath,‡ but, as in the case of the diffraction of X-rays in crystals, it can be simplified by treating the phenomenon as due to reflection at a series of parallel planes represented by the loci of maximum compression. In the simplest case the diffraction pattern shows a central undiffracted maximum with two first-order diffraction maxima.

The path difference between successive reflected wave-fronts (fig. 10.15) is $2AN = 2d \sin\theta$, where d is the separation of the compression

* *Ann. de Physique*, Vol. 17, p. 88 (1922).

† *Proc. Nat. Acad. Sciences*, Vol. 18, p. 409 (1932).

‡ *Proc. Ind. Acad. Sci.*, Vol. (A) 2, pp. 406 and 413 (1935); Vol. (A) 3, pp. 75, 119, and 495 (1936).

maxima and θ is the angle between the sound rays and the normal to the light rays. If θ gives the direction of the first diffracted maximum then

$$\sin\theta = \pm\frac{\lambda}{2l}, \quad \ldots \ldots \quad (10.10)$$

where λ is the wave-length of the light and l is the wave-length of the sound. The fact that the layers are progressive does not affect the phenomenon, provided that their separation remains constant.

The diagram of course exaggerates the size of θ, which is of the order of a few degrees even when l is very small indeed, i.e. for very high frequencies. The fact that the phenomenon is really not so simple as this theory would suggest is made clear by the fact that diffraction maxima are observed for many higher orders. These additional maxima, however, seem to be due to multiple passages of the light from side to side of the trough containing the liquid.* The differences in the intensities of the maxima are discussed by Raman and Nagendra Nath,† also by Extermann and Wannier ‡ and by Extermann.§ The theory has been verified experimentally by Parthasarathy,‖ who has also applied the method to the determination of the velocity of supersonic waves in a large number of organic liquids ¶ at frequencies up to 7×10^6 cycles/sec. No dispersion was discovered up to a frequency of 20×10^6 cycles/sec. for sixteen liquids investigated at this higher frequency.

Debye and Sears applied the method to toluene and carbon tetrachloride, with the following results:

Substance	Frequency	Velocity
Toluene	1.7×10^6	1290 metres/sec.
	16.5×10^6	1310 metres/sec.
Carbon tetrachloride ..	1.7×10^6	920 metres/sec.
	16.5×10^6	1310 metres/sec.

Lucas and Biquard ** have applied the method independently to estimate absorption as well as to measure velocities.

A very interesting and useful extension of this method of observation was described by Bär and Meyer,†† by means of which a much larger body of liquid can be brought under observation. Here the light comes not from a single illuminated slit but from a series of pin-

---

* Bär, *Helv. Phys. Acta*, Vol. 8, p. 591 (1935).
† *Proc. Ind. Acad. Sci.*, Vol. 2, p. 406 (1935).
‡ *Helv. Phys. Acta*, Vol 9, p. 520 (1936).   § *Nature*, Vol. 138, p. 843 (1936).
‖ *Proc. Ind. Acad. Sci.*, Vol. 3, pp. 442, 594 (1936); Vol. 4, p. 555 (1937).
¶ *Proc. Ind. Acad. Sci.*, Vols. 2, 3, 4 (1935-7).
** *Comptes Rendus*, Vol. 194, p. 2132 (1932); Vol. 195, p. 121 (1932); Vol. 196, p. 257 (1933); Vol. 197, p. 309 (1933); *Journ. Phys. Radium*, Vol. 3, p. 464 (1932).
†† *Phys. Zeits.*, Vol. 34, p. 393 (1933).

holes regularly distributed over an opaque screen. The light is transmitted through the liquid in a direction at right angles to the direction of the sound *rays* and therefore parallel to the wave-fronts and, in the case of reflection or refraction of the sound waves, at right angles to the plane of reflection or refraction. The direction of the transmitted light is therefore perpendicular to the sound rays and parallel to the wave-fronts both before and after reflection, refraction or diffraction as the case may be. Each pinhole gives its own set of diffracted pinhole images. The separation of these images gives the wave-length of the sound waves; the intensity of the pattern and the number of diffraction spectra visible is a measure of the intensity of the sound waves and, perhaps most important of all, the line joining the diffraction images gives the direction of the sound rays. The sound waves may be diffracted by a grating immersed in the liquid and the direction of the diffracted pencils determined from the distribution of the images in the resulting diffraction pattern of the light. By this means the wave-length of the sound waves can be calculated by two independent methods, and good agreement was obtained. Refraction of ultrasonic waves at the surface of separation of water and various other liquids was observed by Bär * using this method. Among other results he obtained the following values for the supersonic velocities at a frequency of $7 \cdot 5 \times 10^6$ and a temperature of $20°$ C.

Benzene	..	..	.. 1310 metres/sec.
Toluene	..	..	.. 1297 metres/sec.
Carbon tetrachloride		..	926 metres/sec.
Xylene	..	..	.. 1345 metres/sec.

The experimental arrangements were further improved by Bez-Bardili.† He first of all measured the supersonic wave-length in xylene for the various modes of vibration of the piezo-quartz and the corresponding values of the frequency. The velocity of the supersonic waves in xylene was calculated from these values as follows:

Frequency	Wave-length in mm.	Velocity in metres/sec.
$1 \cdot 89 \times 10^6$	$0 \cdot 713$	1350
$5 \cdot 23 \times 10^6$	$0 \cdot 255$	1330
$8 \cdot 52 \times 10^6$	$0 \cdot 160$	1360
$11 \cdot 95 \times 10^6$	$0 \cdot 110$	1320
$18 \cdot 0 \ \times 10^6$	$0 \cdot 0732$	1320
	Mean value at $20°$ C.	1336

Supersonic beams were then allowed to fall on the surface of separation of xylene and glycerine and of xylene and water. Fig. 10.16 is a sketch from a photograph. The incident beam (A) comes from the top left-hand corner. Its intensity is indicated by the fact that five dif-

---

* *Helv. Phys. Acta*, Vol. 6, p. 570 (1933). † *Phys. Zeits.*, Vol. 36, p. 20 (1935).

fraction images are clearly shown; and its direction is indicated by the linear distribution of these images. The reflected and refracted beams (B and C) are clearly shown. Only three diffracted images of each pinhole appear. The separation of these images is greater in xylene than in glycerine; hence the wave-length and therefore the velocity in xylene is less than in glycerine. The ratio of the wave-lengths, which is also the ratio of the velocities and the refractive index, is given (1) by the ratio of the sines of the angles of incidence and refraction, (2) by

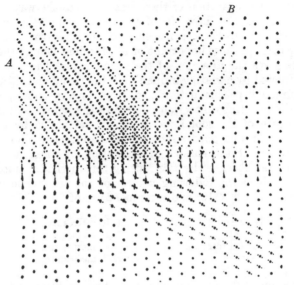

Fig. 10.16

the ratio of the wave-lengths calculated from the separation of the diffracted images. The following results were obtained.

Liquids	Frequency	From Refraction Angles		From Diffraction Effect	
		Refr. Ind.	Vel. in metres/sec.	Refr. Ind.	Vel. in metres/sec.
Xylene/Glycerine	5.23×10^6	0·705	1895	0·702	1900
	8.52×10^6	0·703	1900	0·699	1910
Xylene/Water	5.23×10^6	0·893	1495	0·890	1500

Fig. 10.17 shows the diffraction of a supersonic beam (A), the undiffracted beam (B), the first- and second-order transmitted maxima (E, F) and the first- and second-order reflected maxima (C, D) of the sound beam being clearly outlined by the diffraction pattern of the transmitted light.

Alternatively, of course, instead of observing simultaneously the effect of a series of beams traversing the trough at different points, the trough can be moved at right angles to the light beam and successive observations made. This method is used by Wyss,* whose apparatus is shown in fig. 10.18 (p. 278).

The trough C containing the liquid under experiment is moved by a screw S of pitch 1 mm. along a graduated slide, and this slide can be rotated on a turntable so as to be set at any angle to the transmitted light. The light is condensed by a lens L_1 on to five parallel slits B about 2 mm. apart, so that five separate diffraction patterns are produced in each position of the trough. The trough itself is of brass and the sides of plate glass. The light diffraction pattern is formed in the focal plane of the lens L_2. The quartz Q is held in position by a spring, and stationary waves are produced in the liquid in the trough by reflection from the plate-glass reflector R.

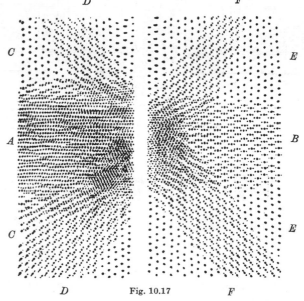

Fig. 10.17

The velocities were calculated both from observation of the stationary wave pattern and by observation of the light diffraction pattern, with the following results:

Liquid	Stationary Wave Pattern Wave-Length	Velocity	Light Diffraction Wave-Length	Velocity
Benzene	0·2032 mm.	1219 metres/sec.	0·208	1250 metres/sec.
Xylene	0·2037 mm.	1222 metres/sec.	0·214	1286 metres/sec.

These values are lower than the values cited earlier and the differences are only partially explained by the different temperatures at which the observations were made.

The supersonic sound field has been made visible both for progres-

* *Helv. Phys. Acta*, Vol. 7, p. 406 (1934).

sive waves and for stationary waves by Hiedemann in conjunction with others,* both by using stationary waves and by viewing progressive waves stroboscopically. The waves have been photographed, and the variation of velocity with distance from the source is revealed in the longer wave-length of the progressive waves near the quartz surface † (fig. 10.19). Many other applications of the method will be found in the papers already referred to.

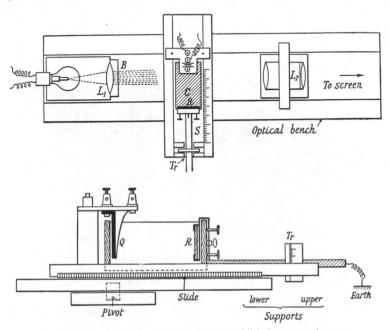

Fig. 10.18.—Apparatus for observing diffraction of light by supersonic waves

16. Position-finding by Submarine Sound Signals.

An accurate knowledge of the velocity of sound in sea-water and its variation with temperature and salinity enables submarine sound signals to be used in the determination of the position of a ship at sea. The methods in use ‡ may be classified as (a) use of synchronous signals, (b) radio-acoustic sound-ranging, (c) echo-sounding and other methods already discussed.

(a) Synchronous signals are largely used by commercial shipping. The method consists in sending out simultaneous signals travelling with different speeds from a known station and measuring the time

* See papers in *Zeits. f. Phys.* (1934).
† *Reports on Progress in Physics*, Vol. 2, p. 168 (1935).
‡ Hubbard, *Journ. Amer. Soc. Acoust.*, Vol. 4, p. 138 (1932).

interval between the receipt of the two signals. The two signals may be selected from (1) air-borne sounds, (2) water-borne sounds, (3) light or wireless. The most reliable combination is water-borne sound and wireless. Experiments * carried out by the United States Hydrographic Department in 1911 showed the reliability of submarine signalling and resulted in the establishment on the Fire Island Lightship, off New York Harbour, of a synchronized signal station emitting submarine bell-sounds and wireless dots. A ship fitted with receiving tanks on both sides of the bow could pick up the bell at a distance of over 8 miles, and by setting the ship's course so as to receive signals of equal strength on the two sides could fix the bearing of the bell

Fig. 10.19.—Progressive waves produced by supersonic radiation in liquids

with considerable accuracy. Determination of the time interval between the receipt of the wireless signal and that of the submarine sound gives the distance from the lightship, so that the position of the ship is completely determined.

(b) Radio-acoustic sound-ranging is based on exactly the same principles as ordinary sound-ranging.

A development of this method was used by A. B. Wood and Browne † in the course of experiments carried out for the British Admiralty. A station was established consisting of four hydrophones laid on the sea bed on a 12-mile base line outside the Goodwin Sands and connected by a cable to a recording string galvanometer at St. Margaret's Bay near Dover. One string of the galvanometer records the arrival of a wireless signal and four others are connected one to each of the hydrophones and so record the arrival of the submarine sound at

---

* *Phil. Mag.*, Vol. 36, p. 7 (1918).   † *Proc. Phys. Soc.*, Vol. 35, p. 183 (1923).

successive hydrophones. The spots of light from the strings are focused on to bromide paper, and the record is crossed by time signals marking tenths and hundredths of a second. In this way the time intervals between the receipt of the wireless signal and the arrival of the submarine sound at each hydrophone are easily read off with an accuracy of $\pm 0 \cdot 01$ second (± 50 ft. in range) and estimated with an accuracy of $0 \cdot 001$ second (± 5 ft. in range).

If the time intervals for the four hydrophones are t_1, t_2, t_3, t_4, then the position of the source lies on a circle of radius ct_1 with the first hydrophone as centre and also on a circle of radius ct_2 with the sound hydrophone as centre. These two circles will intersect in two points, and through one of these will pass a circle of radius ct_3 with the third hydrophone as centre. This fixes the position of the source, the fourth hydrophone being available for confirmation or in the event of failure of one of the others. The source of the sounds is a ship exploding a charge of 9 oz. of guncotton in the water and transmitting simultaneously the wireless signal. The explosion can be detected by hydrophones at a distance of 40 miles. The whole time involved in making and signalling to the ship a " fix " of her position is about seven minutes. A more or less automatic variation of this method is used to fix the position of a surveying vessel in thick weather. A small T.N.T. bomb is exploded at the ship and the instant of the explosion is recorded. The explosive wave travels to a series of three hydrophones at shore positions, where the signal is picked up and transmitted through cables to wireless stations. Each of these stations responds automatically to the hydrophone signal by a radio signal which is received by the ship and recorded. A " fix " can thus be obtained up to a distance of 200 miles. These methods are equally accurate and reliable by day and by night, at all seasons of the year and under all weather conditions.

17. Experimental Determination of Velocity of Sound in Rods.

The first attempt to measure the velocity of sound in solids was a series of long-distance experiments made in 1808 by Biot. At one end of an iron water pipe about 950 metres in length a bell was mounted and struck. At the other end of the pipe two sounds were heard— one conveyed by the air and the other by the wall of the pipe. The velocity was measured by timing the receipt of the two sounds.

The velocity of sound in a solid rod may be at once deduced if the length of the rod and its natural frequency of longitudinal vibration are known. This information was obtained with respect to a number of rods by Pierce in the course of his experiments on magnetostriction oscillators as standards of frequency (see § 8, p. 323). In particular, observations were made on rods of the alloys stoic metal (36 per cent nickel, 64 per cent iron) and nichrome. It was found that the product of the frequency and the length is constant to the degree of accuracy with which the length is measured. This constant when doubled gives the velocity of the vibrations in the rod. The results obtained were:

Material	Diameter	Temperature	Velocity
Stoic metal	0·79 cm.	20° C.	4160 ± 2 metres/sec.
Nichrome	0·96 cm.	23° C.	4981 metres/sec.

From the calculated value of the velocity and the measured value of the density it is possible to calculate Young's modulus q for the material from the relation $c = \sqrt{q/\rho}$. In the paper which has already been referred to Pierce gives the results for iron, nickel, nickel-iron of different percentages and chrome-iron of different percentages and many other alloys. The results for a few of these are shown below:

Material	Velocity Metres/sec.	ρ gm./cm.^{3}	$q \times 10^{-11}$ dyne/cm.^{2}	Temp. coeff. of elasticity $\times 10^6$
Iron	5074	7·688	19·79	−354
Nickel	4937	8·803	21·46	−276
Nichrome	4981	8·269	20·52	−226
Stainless steel	5430	7·720	22·76	−282

In some cases alloys show a minimum value for the velocity at a particular composition (e.g. nickel-iron for 40 per cent of nickel).

The relation $c = \sqrt{q/\rho}$ is in any case only an approximate one. Rayleigh * called attention to the fact that the vibrations are attended with thermal effects, one result of which is to increase the effective value of q beyond that obtained from the statical method. A more exact treatment giving good agreement even at supersonic frequencies has been developed by Giebe and Blechschmidt.† Rayleigh also ‡ estimated the correction required for the lateral motion of the parts of the rod not situated in the axis. Quimby § determined the correction for internal friction, which he found to be small.

18. Experimental Determination of Velocity of Sound in Plates.

The velocity of waves in a plate was determined for supersonic waves by A. B. Wood and Smith‖ using a method depending on Chladni sand patterns. A horizontal sheet of the material is sprinkled with sand and touched at a suitable point by a nickel rod excited by magnetostriction. With a suitable choice of the point of excitation, the nodal lines are found to be parallel to the edge of the plate and are formed by the direct transverse waves crossing those reflected from the edge. The velocity of the transverse waves is deduced from the

---

* *Theory of Sound*, Vol. 1, § 151.   † *Ann. d. Phys.* Vol. 18, pp. 417, 458 (1933).
‡ *Loc. cit.*, § 157.   § *Phys. Rev.*, Vol. 25, p. 558 (1925).
‖ *Proc. Phys. Soc.*, Vol. 47, p. 149 (1935).

distance between the nodal lines and the known frequency of vibration, and the velocity of the longitudinal waves is deduced from that of the transverse waves through a relationship established by Lamb.*

From the relationship

$$c = \frac{(1 + k^2 K^2)^{\frac{1}{4}}}{kK} c_t,$$

where c is the velocity of longitudinal waves, c_t the velocity of flexural waves, $k = 2\pi/\lambda$, and K is the radius of gyration of the cross-section, the relationship

$$c = \frac{c_t}{kK} = c_t \frac{\lambda \sqrt{3}}{\pi t}$$

where t is the thickness, is obtained, when kK is small. The following are some of the values obtained:

Sheet Material	Velocity Transverse Waves cm./sec.	Velocity Longitudinal Waves cm./sec.
Brass	$17\cdot4 \times 10^3$	$3\cdot82 \times 10^5$
Iron	$47\cdot5 \times 10^3$	$5\cdot46 \times 10^5$
Aluminium ..	$42\cdot0 \times 10^3$	$6\cdot05 \times 10^5$
Ebonite ..	$26\cdot2 \times 10^3$	$1\cdot73 \times 10^5$
Celluloid ..	$21\cdot5 \times 10^3$	$1\cdot79 \times 10^5$

The velocities of longitudinal waves in a rod, a plate and an infinite solid respectively are in the ratio

$$1 : \sqrt{\left(\frac{1\cdot}{1 - \sigma^2}\right)} : \sqrt{\left(\frac{1 - \sigma}{(1 + \sigma)(1 - 2\sigma)}\right)},$$

where σ is Poisson's ratio.

19. Velocity of Supersonic Waves in Solids.

The supersonic interferometer was applied by Klein and Herschberger † to the determination of the velocity in solids. The positions of the nodal and antinodal planes in oil are first accurately located. A plane parallel slab is then immersed in the sound beam without change of frequency or temperature. The positions of the nodal and antinodal planes are shifted and this shift is accurately measured.

Then if $\mu = \dfrac{\text{Velocity of sound in solid}}{\text{Velocity of sound in liquid}}$,

d is the actual thickness of slab immersed, and Δx the shift of planes, $\Delta x = (\mu - 1)d/\mu$,

or $$\mu = \frac{d}{d - \Delta x}.$$

* *Dynamical Theory of Sound*, p. 123.   † *Phys. Rev.*, Vol. 6, p. 760 (1931).

In an actual experiment $d = 0.412$ in., $\Delta x = 0.161$ in., $\mu = (0.412/0.251)$ $= 1.64$.

Velocity in oil $= 1.50 \times 10^5$ cm./sec. (known),

$\therefore$ Velocity in solid (bakelite) $= 1.64 \times 1.50 \times 10^5$
$= 2.46 \times 10^5$ cm./sec.

Where the product of velocity and density for the solid is very different from that for the liquid, reflection is copious and the method is difficult to apply. In this case the degree of transmission or reflection

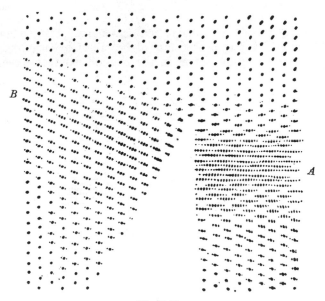

Fig. 10.20

is measured with a beam of variable frequency and hence of variable wave-length, and advantage is taken of the fact that the ratio of the transmitted intensity and the incident intensity is a maximum when the thickness of the slab is an integral number of half wave-lengths (see § 8, p. 206). Bez-Bardili * has applied the method of Bär and Meyer † to the transmission of supersonic waves through solids, and has traced the beam of waves transmitted by a prism immersed in xylene. Fig. 10.20 shows the transmission of a beam of ultrasonic waves by a prism of aluminium. The directions and relative intensities of the incident wave (A) and refracted wave (B) are clearly shown by the light diffraction pattern. By measurement of the angles Bez-Bardili

---

* *Phys. Zeits.*, Vol. 36, p. 20 (1935); *Z. f. Phys.*, Vol. 96, p. 761 (1935).
† *Phys. Zeits.*, Vol. 34, p. 393 (1933).

found these values for the velocity of supersonic waves in solids.

Material	Frequency	Refractive Index	Supersonic Velocity at 20° C. metres/sec.	Vel. for Audio-frequencies metres/sec.
Aluminium	5.23×10^6	0·227	5880 ⎫	
	8.52×10^6	0·217	6150 ⎬	5000
	18.00×10^6	0·211	6330 ⎭	
Copper	5.23×10^6	0·307	4350 ⎫	3600
	8.52×10^6	0·310	4310 ⎭	
Iron	8.52×10^6	0·246	5430	5100
Nickel	11.95×10^6	0·180	7420	4900
Glass	11.95×10^6	0·332	4020	5000

Fig. 10.21 shows the transmission through a plate (A incident beam, B reflected beam, C transmitted beam). Obviously, since the velocity of the supersonic waves in the material is greater than that

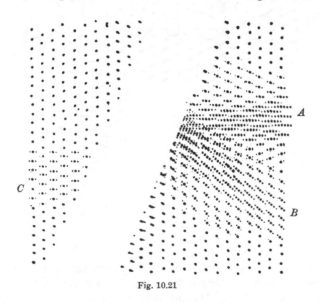

Fig. 10.21

in the xylene in which the plate is immersed, it is possible by rotating the plate to find the position of total reflection and to determine the velocity of the waves in the solid from the refractive index calculated as in the case of Wollaston's method for light.

A very beautiful and interesting extension of the method has been used by Schaefer and Bergmann.* In these experiments a transparent solid, e.g. a cube of glass, is made to transmit simultaneously three sets of supersonic waves of the same period parallel to the three

* See various papers in *Sitz.-Ber. Berl. Akad.*, 1934, 1935, 1936, and also Bergmann, *Ultrasonics*, pp. 164-186.

directions of the edges of the cube. This forms a three-dimensional grating, and when light is transmitted the resulting diffraction pattern is very well defined. It consists (fig. 10.22) of two concentric circles each made up of a number of sharp individual interference points. The theory has been given by Ludloff.* According to this theory the inner circle is formed by diffraction of the light by an elastic space grating generated by the longitudinal waves, while the outer circle is similarly related to the transverse or shear waves for which the velocity is given by $c_t = \sqrt{n/\rho}$, where n is the rigidity modulus.

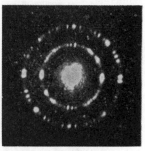

Fig. 10.22

Let λ be the wave-length of light, λ_l' the wave-length of longitudinal elastic waves, λ_t' the wave-length of transverse elastic waves, r_l, r_t the radii of the two circles, d the distance from cube to screen.

Then
$$r_l = \frac{\lambda d}{\lambda_l'}, \quad r_t = \frac{\lambda d}{\lambda_t'}.$$

If c_l, c_t are the velocities of the waves, we have

$$c_l = f\lambda_l' = \frac{f\lambda d}{r_l},$$

$$c_t = f\lambda_t' = \frac{f\lambda d}{r_t}.$$

But (p. 74)
$$c_l = \sqrt{\frac{q}{\rho} \cdot \frac{1 - \sigma}{(1 + \sigma)(1 - 2\sigma)}},$$

and
$$c_t = \sqrt{\frac{n}{\rho}},$$

where n is the rigidity modulus, and Poisson's ratio $\sigma = (q - 2n)/2n$ (from elastic theory).

That is, the elastic constants q, n, σ and also the bulk modulus K are all determined by one set of simultaneous observations.

The method, of course, can be applied to the case of an anisotropic solid. Here the resulting diffraction patterns are more complicated, but they can be interpreted in terms of the theory of Ludloff (loc. cit.). The patterns for quartz (upper series) and calcspar (lower series) are

* *Sitz.-Ber. Berl. Akad.*, p. 248 (1936).

shown in fig. 10.23. The direction of transmission of the light is parallel
to the optic axis and the two electric axes for the quartz, with analogous
directions for the calcspar. Bergmann (loc. cit.) gives the following

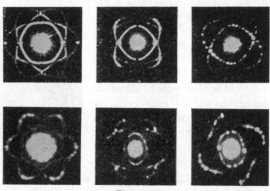

Fig. 10.23

table of the results for the nine elastic constants for barytes compared
with the measurements of Voigt.

Table VII

Comparison of Elastic Constants determined from Interference
Curves for Barytes with Values measured by Voigt

c_{ik}	Measured from Interference Curves	Measured by Voigt
c_{11}	$9 \cdot 0 \times 10^6$	$9 \cdot 0 \times 10^6$
c_{22}	$7 \cdot 96$	$8 \cdot 0$
c_{33}	$10 \cdot 58$	$10 \cdot 7$
c_{44}	$1 \cdot 19$	$1 \cdot 2$
c_{55}	$2 \cdot 85$	$2 \cdot 9$
c_{66}	$2 \cdot 60$	$2 \cdot 8$
c_{12}	$4 \cdot 86$	$4 \cdot 6$
c_{13}	$2 \cdot 74$	$2 \cdot 7$
c_{23}	$2 \cdot 95$	$2 \cdot 7$

It will be seen that the agreement is good, and when it is remembered
that the measurements from the diffraction patterns are made from
three photographs, while Voigt's results depend on some 15,000 measurements on various samples, the possibilities of the newer method are
sufficiently obvious.

CHAPTER XI

Intensity of Sound

1. Kinetic Energy of Plane Progressive Sine Waves.

Taking the equation to the wave as

$$\xi = a \sin(\omega t - kx)$$

we have for the velocity of the layer at a distance x from the origin and at time t the expression

$$v = \dot{\xi} = \omega a \cos(\omega t - kx).$$

The kinetic energy dT of this layer per unit area is $\frac{1}{2}\rho_0 dx \cdot \dot{\xi}^2$. The kinetic energy of a tube of length λ is therefore given by

$$T_\lambda = \tfrac{1}{2}\rho_0 \int_0^\lambda v^2 dx$$

$$= \tfrac{1}{2}\rho_0 \int_0^\lambda \omega^2 a^2 \cos^2(\omega t - kx)\, dx$$

$$= \tfrac{1}{2}\rho_0 \omega^2 a^2 \int_0^\lambda \frac{1 + \cos 2(\omega t - kx)}{2}\, dx.$$

But

$$\int_0^\lambda \cos 2(\omega t - kx)\, dx = 0$$

$$\therefore\ T_\lambda = \frac{\omega^2 a^2 \rho_0}{2} \cdot \frac{\lambda}{2} = \tfrac{1}{4}\omega^2 a^2 \rho_0 \lambda. \quad \cdot \quad \cdot \quad \cdot \quad (11.1)$$

Since the volume involved is λ, the mass is $\rho_0 \lambda$; and the maximum velocity $\hat{V}$ is ωa. Hence

$$T_\lambda = \tfrac{1}{2}(\tfrac{1}{2}\rho_0 \lambda \hat{V}^2), \quad \cdot \quad \cdot \quad \cdot \quad \cdot \quad \cdot \quad (11.2)$$

that is, half the kinetic energy of the whole mass moving with the maximum particle-velocity.

Since $\omega = 2\pi/T = 2\pi c/\lambda = kc$, we have, from (11.1),

$$T_\lambda = \tfrac{1}{4}\rho_0 \lambda k^2 a^2 c^2 = \frac{\pi^2 \rho_0 a^2 c^2}{\lambda}; \quad . \quad . \quad . \quad . \quad (11.3)$$

$\therefore$ mean kinetic energy per unit volume

$$= \frac{T_\lambda}{\lambda} = \frac{\pi^2 a^2 \rho_0 c^2}{\lambda^2} = \tfrac{1}{4}\rho_0 \, \hat{V}^2. \quad . \quad . \quad . \quad (11.4)$$

2. Potential Energy of Plane Progressive Sine Waves.

It has been stated (p. 20) that the energy of progressive waves is equally divided between the kinetic and potential forms, but we can easily obtain directly an expression for the potential energy which verifies this relation.

Since $K = p/s$, the excess of pressure $p = Ks = \gamma P_0 s$, where P_0 is the static pressure. The potential energy of a layer of the medium is the work done in bringing it adiabatically to normal pressure. On compression unit volume becomes $(1 - s)$.

Calling the potential energy U per unit volume, we have

$$U = \int_0^s p \, ds$$

$$= \int_0^s Ks \, ds$$

$$= \tfrac{1}{2}Ks^2 \text{ or } \tfrac{1}{2}\gamma P_0 s^2; \quad . \quad . \quad . \quad . \quad . \quad (11.5)$$

but
$$c^2 = \frac{\gamma P_0}{\rho_0},$$

$$\therefore U = \tfrac{1}{2}\rho_0 c^2 s^2. \quad . \quad . \quad . \quad . \quad . \quad . \quad (11.6)$$

If we consider the layer to have unit cross section perpendicular to the direction of propagation and thickness dx, the potential energy of a tube of the medium of length λ is given by

$$U_\lambda = \tfrac{1}{2}\rho_0 c^2 \int_0^\lambda s^2 \, dx$$

But $s = -\dfrac{\partial \xi}{\partial x} = ka \cos(\omega t - kx)$

$$\therefore U_\lambda = \tfrac{1}{2}\rho_0 c^2 \int_0^\lambda k^2 a^2 \cos^2(\omega t - kx) \, dx$$

$$= \frac{k^2 \lambda a^2 \rho_0 c^2}{4} = \frac{\pi^2 a^2 \rho_0 c^2}{\lambda} = T_\lambda. \quad . \quad (11.7)$$

$\therefore$ Energy in length λ, $E_\lambda = T_\lambda + U_\lambda$

$$= \frac{2\pi^2 a^2 \rho_0 c^2}{\lambda}$$

$$= \frac{\omega^2 a^2 \lambda \rho_0}{2}. \quad \cdots \cdots \cdots \quad (11.8)$$

$\therefore$ Mean energy-density $E = \frac{1}{2}\rho_0 \hat{V}^2$. $\cdots \cdots \cdots \cdots$ (11.9)

3. Total Energy of Plane Progressive Sine Waves.

This may be calculated directly by considering the work done by a piston of unit cross-sectional area in generating the waves.

Let $\xi = a\sin(\omega t - kx)$, and let the position of the piston be $x = 0$.

The excess of pressure on the piston $= Ks = -\gamma P_0 (\partial\xi/\partial x)_{x=0}$

$$= \gamma P_0 ka\cos\omega t.$$

The displacement $d\xi$ of the piston during time dt

$$= \left(\frac{\partial\xi}{\partial t}\right)_{x=0} dt = \omega a\cos\omega t\, dt.$$

Then dE, the work done in an element of displacement

$$= Ksd\xi = \gamma P_0 k\omega a^2 \cos^2\omega t\, dt.$$

The work done per period is therefore given by

$$E_\lambda = \gamma P_0 k\omega a^2 \int_0^T \cos^2\omega t\, dt$$

$$= \frac{1}{2}\gamma P_0 k\omega a^2 T.$$

Putting $\qquad \gamma P_0 = c^2\rho_0$, we have

$$E_\lambda = \frac{2\pi^2 \rho_0 c^2 a^2}{\lambda} = T_\lambda + U_\lambda; \quad \cdots \quad (11.10)$$

hence the intensity I, or the energy flux per unit area normal to direction of propagation, is $\dfrac{E_\lambda}{T} = \dfrac{2\pi^2 a^2 \rho_0 c^3}{\lambda^2}$. $\quad \cdots \cdots$ (11.11)

We also note that $\qquad I = cE$.

That all the work done by the piston in one period should afterwards be contained in one wave-length of the medium may seem to be obvious, but it is not always true. It is a consequence of the fact that in the propagation of sound waves there is no dispersion, all wave-lengths travelling with the same speed. In the propagation of waves where dispersion is a factor there is a distinction between the wave velocity for a particular wave-length and the group velocity, and it is this latter velocity that determines the velocity with which the energy is propagated.

It is important to notice that the equipartition of energy between the kinetic and potential forms is only true when $\dot{\xi} = cs$, and this is true only for plane waves or for diverging waves considered at some distance from the source.

Since, for adiabatic changes, $\dfrac{\partial p}{\partial \rho} = \dfrac{\gamma P_0}{\rho} = c^2$, where p is the excess pressure, we have approximately

$$p = c^2(\rho - \rho_0).$$

But

$$v = cs = c\left(\frac{\rho - \rho_0}{\rho_0}\right),$$

$$\therefore\ p = c\rho_0 v,$$

or

$$v = \frac{p}{c\rho_0}. \qquad \qquad (11.12)$$

We may denote $c\rho_0$ by R and call it the *characteristic impedance* of the medium (pp. 104, 148). We then have a formal analogy with Ohm's law, in which v is analogous to current, p to electromotive force, and R to resistance.

We have already seen that the mean energy-density may be written in the form

$$E = \tfrac{1}{2}\rho_0 \hat{V}^2,$$

where $\hat{V}$ is the amplitude of the particle-velocity v.

Since the mean power transmitted across unit area is the energy transmitted per unit area per second, we have

Sound intensity I = Sound energy flux = $\tfrac{1}{2}\rho_0 \hat{V}^2 c$

$$= \tfrac{1}{2}R\hat{V}^2. \qquad \qquad (11.13)$$

If for $\hat{V}$ the maximum particle-velocity we substitute V the root mean square value, then $V = \hat{V}/\sqrt{2}$, and $I = RV^2 = P^2/R$, from (11.12), where P is the R.M.S. pressure amplitude.

4. Transmission of Power by Plane Waves.

From the expression just obtained we see that the power transmitted varies directly as the square of the pressure amplitude if the medium is the same or has the same characteristic impedance, and that for different media it varies inversely as the characteristic impedance for the same pressure amplitude.

For air at 20° C. we have $c_{20°} = 34,300$ cm./sec., $\rho_{20°} = 1 \cdot 2 \times 10^{-3}$ gm./c.c., $R_a = 41 \cdot 2$.

For water, $c = 147,000$ cm./sec., $\rho = 1$, $R_w = 147,000$.

Therefore in order to convey the same power in these two media the pressure amplitudes will be in the ratio

$$\frac{P_w}{P_a} = \sqrt{\left(\frac{R_w}{R_a}\right)} = \sqrt{\left(\frac{147,000}{41 \cdot 2}\right)} = 60.$$

Since $I = P^2/R$ ergs per sec. per cm.^{2}, for air

$$I = \frac{P^2}{R} \times \frac{10^6}{10^7} \text{ microwatts/cm.}^2$$

$$= \frac{P^2}{412} \text{ microwatts/cm.}^2$$

5. Cavitation in Sound Waves.

In the study of stationary ultrasonic waves it has been noticed that if the intensity is large the planes defining the pressure antinodes are marked by the separation of streams of bubbles. These are due to the escape of dissolved gases at the instant of low pressure. It is obvious that a limit may be set to the energy which can be transmitted by longitudinal waves in a fluid when the pressure amplitude is equal to the equilibrium static pressure. Any greater pressure amplitude than this would involve at the instant of the minimum a negative pressure. Attention has been drawn to this point by Boyle.*

If P is the R.M.S. pressure amplitude, $P = \sqrt{(RI)}$. If P_0 is the static pressure,

$$P_0 \geqq P\sqrt{2} \text{ or } \sqrt{(2RI)},$$

$$\therefore I \leqq \frac{P_0^2}{2R}.$$

That is, if I_m is the maximum value for power transmission,

$$I_m = \frac{P_0^2}{2R};$$

I_m depends only on the static pressure and on the properties of the medium and not at all on the frequency.

* *Proc.* and *Trans. Roy. Soc. Canada*, Vol. 16, p. 157 (1922).

For air at standard pressure and temperature 20° C. we have $R = 41 \cdot 2$, $P_0 \doteq 10^6$ dynes/cm.^{2}

$$\therefore \ I_m = \frac{10^{12}}{82 \cdot 4} = 1 \cdot 2 \times 10^{10} \ \text{erg. sec./cm.}^2 = 1 \cdot 2 \ \text{kilowatts/cm.}^2$$

Now
$$\dot{V} = \omega a = 2\pi f a$$

and
$$\dot{V} = \frac{\dot{P}}{R} = \frac{P_0}{R}.$$

$$\therefore \ \text{maximum} \ fa = \frac{1}{2\pi} \frac{P_0}{R} = 3 \cdot 86 \times 10^3.$$

From this we see that for audible frequencies the amplitudes required to give a cavitation breakdown in transmission are impossibly large.

	Frequency	Amplitude
Lowest audible tone	26	148 cm.
Highest audible tone	26,000	0·15 cm.

The case of transmission of sound in sea-water is of special interest.

Here we have
$$R = 1 \cdot 50 \times 10^5 \ \text{(about)},$$
$$P_0 = P_a + \rho g d,$$

where P_a is the atmospheric pressure $= 10^6$ dynes/cm.^{2}, d the depth below surface, and ρ the density $= 1 \cdot 02$ gm./c.c.

Inserting these figures in our expression we find the following results:

d (metres)	P_0(dyne/sq. cm.)	I_m(watt/sq. cm.)
0	$1 \cdot 0 \times 10^6$	0·33
10	$(1 \cdot 0 + 1 \cdot 00) \times 10^6$	1·33
100	$(1 \cdot 0 + 10 \cdot 0) \times 10^6$	40·3

The corresponding amplitudes are given as before by the expression

$$\text{maximum} \ fa = \frac{P_0}{2\pi R}.$$

d (metres)	fa	f	a (cm.)
0	1·03	26	·039
		26,000	·000039
10	2.06	26	·079
		26,000	·000079
100	11·3	26	·44
		26,000	·00044

These figures suggest that waves in water might in practice be limited by this factor. In a later paper * Boyle and Taylor introduce a correction for the vapour pressure of the liquid in order to account for the fact that cavitation sets in at a lower value of P_0 than the formula suggests. This gives

$$fa = \frac{P_0 - P_v}{2\pi R}$$

where P_v is the vapour pressure of the liquid.

6. Energy of Spherical Simple Harmonic Waves.

Let us assume that the diverging waves come from a pulsating sphere of radius r_0 and are given by the second term of equation 2.37,

$$\phi = \frac{A'}{r} f(ct - r) \quad \ldots \ldots \quad (11.14)$$

where $f(ct - r)$ has the value $\cos k(ct - r)$, so that

$$\phi = \frac{A'}{r} \cos k(ct - r) = \frac{A'}{r} \cos(\omega t - kr). \quad . \quad (11.15)$$

Then

$$v = \dot{\xi} = -\frac{\partial \phi}{\partial r} = -\frac{A'k}{r} \sin(\omega t - kr) + \frac{A'}{r^2} \cos(\omega t - kr). \quad (11.16)$$

The total flux of fluid through the surface of a sphere of radius r is therefore

$$4\pi r^2 v = -4\pi k A' r \sin(\omega t - kr) + 4\pi A' \cos(\omega t - kr). \quad . \quad (11.17)$$

Now at the surface of the sphere let the particle-velocity be $v_{r=r_0} = v_0 \cos \omega t$. Then the total flux of the fluid at the surface of the sphere is

$$4\pi r_0^2 v_0 \cos \omega t = A \cos \omega t,$$

where we write A for $4\pi r_0^2 v_0$. This must also be the value of the previous expression for $4\pi r^2 v$ when we put $r = r_0 \doteqdot 0$.

$$\therefore A \cos \omega t = 4\pi A' \cos \omega t,$$

$$\therefore A = 4\pi A'.$$

Now A is the maximum flux of fluid at the source. This quantity is called the *strength* of the source and we may now insert it in the value for ϕ and obtain

$$\phi = \frac{A}{4\pi r} \cos(\omega t - kr). \quad \ldots \ldots \quad (11.18)$$

* *Phys. Rev.*, Vol. 27, p. 518 (1926).

This of course applies only to a *small* source, i.e. one whose dimensions are small compared with the wave-length.

Then $v = -\dfrac{\partial \phi}{\partial r} = -\dfrac{Ak}{4\pi r} \sin(\omega t - kr) + \dfrac{A}{4\pi r^2} \cos(\omega t - kr).$ (11.19)

Also (p. 60) $\qquad p = \rho\phi = -\dfrac{\rho\omega A}{4\pi r} \sin(\omega t - kr).$ . . . (11.20)

We therefore have

$$pv = +\frac{\rho\omega k A^2}{16\pi^2 r^2} \sin^2(\omega t - kr) - \frac{\rho\omega A^2}{16\pi^2 r^3} \frac{\sin 2(\omega t - kr)}{2}$$

$$= \frac{\rho\omega k A^2}{32\pi^2 r^2} [1 - \cos 2(\omega t - kr) - \frac{1}{kr} \sin 2(\omega t - kr)].$$

Therefore the rate of working, $4\pi r^2 pv$

$$= \rho\omega k A^2/8\pi \, [1 - \cos 2(\omega t - kr) - 1/kr \, \sin 2(\omega t - kr)],$$

so that the work done per period is

$$\frac{\rho\omega k A^2}{8\pi} \int_0^T [1 - \cos 2(\omega t - kr) - \frac{1}{kr} \sin 2(\omega t - kr)] dt$$

$$= \frac{\rho\omega k T A^2}{8\pi} = \frac{\rho k A^2}{4}. \quad . \quad . \quad . \quad (11.21)$$

But the intensity at the surface of a sphere of radius r large compared with λ is given by the work done per square centimetre per second,

$$\therefore I = \frac{\rho k A^2}{4T \cdot 4\pi r^2} = \frac{A^2 \rho c}{8\lambda^2 r^2}. \quad . \quad . \quad . \quad (11.22)$$

Now $K = c^2\rho$, and $s = v/c$,

$$\therefore \tfrac{1}{2}Ks^2 = \tfrac{1}{2}\rho v^2$$

and if $\hat{S}$ is the maximum value of condensation,

$$\tfrac{1}{2}K\hat{S}^2 = \tfrac{1}{2}\rho\hat{V}^2 = E, \text{ the energy-density,}$$

where $\hat{V}$, as before, is the amplitude of the particle-velocity. But when r is large, only the first term in the expression for v is effective:

$$\therefore \hat{V} = -\frac{Ak}{4\pi r} \quad . \quad . \quad . \quad . \quad . \quad (11.23)$$

and $\qquad E = \dfrac{\rho A^2 k^2}{32\pi^2 r^2} = \dfrac{\rho A^2}{8\lambda^2 r^2},$ . . . (11.24)

so that $\qquad Ec = I,$ by (11.22).

Also
$$\hat{P} = K\hat{S}$$

$$\therefore E = \frac{(K\hat{S})^2}{2K} = \frac{\hat{P}^2}{2K}, \quad \ldots \ldots \quad (11.25)$$

$$\therefore I = \frac{1}{2}\frac{\hat{P}^2}{\rho c} = \frac{1}{2}\frac{\hat{P}^2}{R} = \frac{\hat{P}^2}{R}, \quad \ldots \quad (11.26)$$

as before, where R is the characteristic impedance.

For a sphere of radius r *not* large compared with λ we have

Energy-density (kinetic) $= \frac{1}{2}\rho V^2 = \frac{\rho A^2 k^2}{64\pi^2 r^2}\left(1 + \frac{1}{k^2 r^2}\right)$, from 11.16.

Energy-density (potential) $= \frac{1}{2}KS^2 = \frac{\rho A^2 k^2}{64\pi^2 r^2}$,

since
$$K = c^2\rho \quad \text{and} \quad s = \phi/c^2.$$

$$\therefore E = \frac{1}{2}\rho V^2 + \frac{1}{2}KS^2 = \frac{\rho A^2 k^2}{32\pi^2 r^2}\left(1 + \frac{1}{2k^2 r^2}\right).$$

But
$$I = \frac{A^2 \rho c}{8\lambda^2 r^2}, \text{ from 11.22,}$$

$$= \frac{\rho A^2 k^2 c}{32\pi^2 r^2}.$$

$$\therefore E = \frac{I}{c}\left[1 + \frac{1}{2k^2 r^2}\right] \quad \ldots \ldots \quad (11.27)$$

instead of $E = I/c$. The abnormally large energy-density at small distances was referred to in § 11, p. 69.

7. Measurement of Intensity.

The intensity of a sound wave is defined (p. 289) as the average rate of flow of energy per unit area normal to the direction of propagation. It is thus the power transmission per unit area (I), and for plane waves is the mean energy-density multiplied by the velocity of sound (cE). Its measurement in absolute units presents considerable difficulties, and it is only recently that these have been overcome. The methods adopted depend for the most part on the measurement at a point in the medium of some characteristic of the wave (e.g. velocity amplitude or pressure amplitude). This at once presents the difficulty that the introduction of a measuring instrument alters the very characteristics which it is intended to measure. These will only be unaffected if the instrument is small compared with the wave-length of the sound in question. If it is large the pressure fluctuations will be doubled. This difficulty is met in an ingenious way by S. Ballantine,* whose receiver

* *Phys. Rev.*, Vol. 32, p. 988 (1928).

is mounted as part of a solid sphere at the point most remote from the source of sound. Rayleigh's treatment of the diffraction due to a sphere * enables us to calculate the exact ratio of the intensities in front of and behind the sphere. Attempts have also been made to reduce the size of the recording instruments, and condenser micro-phones have been designed by Hall † and Sacerdote ‡ to measure pressure variations without disturbance of the sound field. That of Sacerdote has a diaphragm of aluminium only 0·8 cm. in diameter and about 10^{-3} cm. in thickness. It responds to supersonic frequencies up to about 60,000 cycles/second.

Another difficulty is due to the very small magnitude of the quantity to be measured. The power radiated as sound from an orchestra in a fortissimo passage may rise to 70 watts, whereas in the softest passages it may fall to the power of human speech or less, i.e. to the order of 10 microwatts. The threshold value for intensity is about 10^{-10} micro-watts/sq. cm., while the intensity of the sound due to a full orchestra may rise to about 1 microwatt/sq. cm., a difference in level of 100 decibels (p. 465).

8. Rayleigh's Method of Measuring the Intensity of the Just Audible Sound.

This method is indirect and depends on the measurement of the energy used by the source and of the distance at which the sound is just audible. The experiment was carried out § on a still day with a whistle of frequency 2730 as source. The whistle was placed at the centre of a lawn and was blown with air at a pressure of $9\frac{1}{2}$ cm. of water, using a volume of 196 c.c. of air per sec. The average distance of audibility was 820 metres. The energy expended per second $= 9\frac{1}{2} \times 981 \times 196 = 1·8 \times 10^6$ erg/sec. This energy flows out across a hemi-sphere of radius 820 metres.

$$\therefore \; I = \frac{1·8 \times 10^6}{2\pi(82{,}000)^2} = 4·26 \times 10^{-5} \text{ erg per cm.}^2/\text{sec.}$$

$$= 4·26 \times 10^{-6} \text{ microwatts/cm.}^2$$

Then
$$\hat{V} = \sqrt{\frac{2I}{R}} = 1·44 \times 10^{-3} \text{ cm./sec.},$$

$$\hat{S} = \frac{\hat{V}}{c} = 4·2 \times 10^{-8},$$

$$a = \frac{\hat{V}}{2\pi f} = 8·4 \times 10^{-8} \text{ cm.},$$

and
$$P = \sqrt{RI} = 4·2 \times 10^{-2} \text{ dyne/cm.}^2,$$
where P is the R.M.S. pressure amplitude.

---

* *Phil. Trans.*, A, Vol. 203, p. 87 (1904).   † *Journ. Amer. Soc. Acoust.* Vol. 4, p. 83 (1932).
‡ *Alta Frequenza*, Vol. 2, p. 516 (1933).   § *Proc. Roy. Soc.*, Vol. 26, p. 248 (1877).

It is of course obvious that, small as these values are, they are all upper limits. The calculation depends on the assumption that all the energy put into the whistle is radiated as sound. This is obviously not the case, and, as we shall see later, the values for these quantities obtained by more accurate methods are even smaller than those given by Rayleigh, in spite of the fact that his value for the amplitude is comparable with the diameter of a molecule and his value for the R.M.S. pressure amplitude about one twenty-millionth of an atmosphere.

9. Optical Measurement of Density Amplitude.

This method is a direct one, and the only serious limitation to its use is its lack of sensitiveness. The relationship between refractive index and density may be expressed by the equation

$$\frac{\mu - 1}{\rho} = \frac{\mu_0 - 1}{\rho_0},$$

where μ, μ_0 are the refractive indices corresponding to the densities ρ, ρ_0. If the air in a path of length l changes its refractive index from μ_0 to μ, the equivalent change in path is $(\mu - \mu_0)l$.

But
$$\mu - \mu_0 = (\mu_0 - 1)\frac{\rho - \rho_0}{\rho_0}.$$

Therefore if ϵ is the fringe shift produced in an interferometer,

$$\epsilon\lambda = (\mu - \mu_0)l = l(\mu_0 - 1)\frac{d\rho}{\rho_0}.$$

Now $\hat{P}_0 = A\rho^\gamma$, where A is a constant and P_0 is the total pressure;

$$\therefore \frac{dp}{P_0} = \gamma\frac{d\rho}{\rho_0}.$$

$$\therefore \epsilon = \frac{l}{\lambda}(\mu_0 - 1)\frac{dp}{\gamma P_0}.$$

If $\hat{P}$ is the pressure amplitude in the wave then we may write

$$\hat{P} = dp = \frac{\gamma P_0 \epsilon \lambda}{(\mu_0 - 1)l}$$

If the accuracy of the arrangement is such that a shift of $\frac{1}{40}$ of a fringe width may be measured, we may put $\gamma = 1\cdot4$, $P_0 = 10^6$ dynes/cm.^{2}, $\lambda = 6 \times 10^{-5}$ cm., $\mu_0 - 1 = 3 \times 10^{-4}$, $l = 10$ cm., $\epsilon = \frac{1}{40}$, and calculation gives $\hat{P} = 7 \times 10^2$ dynes/cm.^{2}

This corresponds to a very loud sound. The method was first used

by Töpler and Boltzmann * to determine the pressure amplitude in
a sounding organ pipe, the arrangement of the apparatus being shown
in fig. 11.1.   One beam passes through the pipe and one through the air
outside.   The movement of the interference fringes was slowed down
by a stroboscopic method of observation.   The same principle was used
by Raps,† the moving fringes being photographed on a revolving
cylinder and the interferometer being calibrated by a statical com-

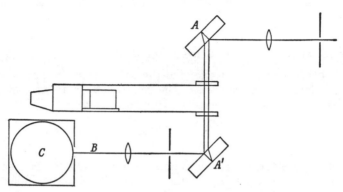

*   Fig. 11.1.—Optical interference method for organ-pipe

pression of the air in the pipe.   The great advantage of this method is
that it involves no interference with the motion of the air transmitting
the waves.

10. Measurement of the Static Pressure due to Sound Waves.

This method was first applied to sound waves in air by Altberg.‡
The disc of a torsion pendulum was arranged so as to close a hole in a
surface exposed to the waves.   The torsion head was then rotated so
as to bring the disc once more into the plane of the surface.

Let k be the coefficient of torsion of the wire, r the length of arm
of the disc, P_0 the static pressure, S the area of the disc, θ the angle
of twist, γ the ratio of specific heats.   Then

$$P_0 = \frac{k\theta}{Sr}.$$

Also if E is the energy-density of incident waves and these are
totally reflected, the energy-density in front of the vane is $2E$ and
$P_0 = E(1 + \gamma)$, from § 7, p. 154.

Further, $I = cE = \dfrac{cP_0}{1 + \gamma}.$ . . . . .   (11.28)

---

* *Ann. d. Physik*, Vol. 141, p. 321 (1870).   † *Ann. d. Physik*, Vol. 34, p. 131 (1910).
‡ *Ann. d. Physik*, Vol. 11, p. 405 (1903).

Altberg worked with a sound giving $P_0 = 2\cdot4 \times 10^{-1}$ dyne/cm.²

The method has been extensively used for the measurement of the intensity of supersonic waves both in gases and in liquids. Abello[*] used a mica vane 1·5 cm. square suspended by a quartz fibre 15 cm. long and 0·002 cm. in diameter. The angle of torsion was of the order of 50°. Assuming the arm r, the length of which is not given, to be 5 cm. and taking θ to be 1 radian, we can calculate I. We have

$$k = \frac{\pi n a^4}{2l}.$$

For quartz $\qquad\qquad n = 3 \times 10^{11}$ dynes/cm.²,

$$\therefore\ k = 3\cdot14 \times 10^{-2}.$$

Then $\qquad\qquad I = \dfrac{ck\theta}{Sr(1 + \gamma)}$ . . . . . . (11.29)

$$= 39 \text{ ergs per sec. per cm.}^2$$

$$= 3\cdot9 \text{ microwatts/cm.}^2,$$

and $\qquad\qquad P = \sqrt{RI} = 40\cdot1$ dynes/cm.²

This would represent a very loud sound if the same power were transmitted at audible frequency.

A similar arrangement is in use for measuring the intensity of supersonic waves in liquids. In this case we have $\gamma = 1$, $P = 2E$, and

$$I = \frac{cP}{2} = \frac{ck\theta}{2Sr}.$$ . . . . . (11.30)

The method has been applied by Boyle, Lehmann and Reid,[†] using two different types of torsion pendulum.

One of these consists of two solid lead discs, 1–2 cm. in diameter and 1–2 mm. in thickness, fixed to the end of the torsion wire as in fig. 11.2, the plane of one being vertical and that of the other horizontal. The ultrasonic beam is directed on to the vertical disc, and a correction applied for the pressure on the edge of the horizontal disc. In the second type a single vane is used, consisting of a hollow capsule formed of mica discs fixed to opposite sides of a

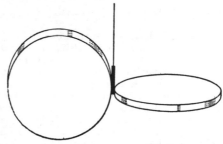

Fig. 11.2.—Torsion pendulum

thin brass or aluminium ring. The vane is adjusted to have a mean density of about unity, and it is attached by its edge to the suspending wire, which is fixed above and below and subjected to a tension which can be varied. The arrangements were used mainly for comparative measurements. Since $S = \pi a^2$ and $r = a$, $I = ck\theta/2\pi a^3$.

These workers applied the method to the survey of the distribution of energy in a high-frequency diffraction beam. The theoretical formula for the distribution of energy between the central and subsidiary maxima can be tested and measurements can be made much closer to the source, relatively to wave-length, than is possible in the case of beams of light. Thus, working at a frequency of 135,000 in water, we have

$$\lambda = \frac{1 \cdot 5 \times 10^5}{1 \cdot 35 \times 10^5} = 1 \cdot 11 \text{ cm.}$$

If the beam is examined at a distance of 200 cm. from the source, the corresponding distance for sodium light would be

$$\frac{200 \times 5 \cdot 89 \times 10^{-5}}{1 \cdot 11} = 0 \cdot 01 \text{ cm.}$$

It was found that the approximation to the theoretical distribution becomes more close as the distance from the source increases.

Sörensen * describes a form of torsion balance used for vertical beams of supersonic waves and measuring directly in gm. wt./cm.^{2}

11. Direct Measurement of Displacement Amplitude of Air Vibrations.

It might seem that in view of the excessively small value of the displacement amplitude in a sound wave all attempts at direct measurement would be likely to be fruitless. With very loud sounds, however, the amplitude is of the order of $\frac{1}{10}$ mm. and in a high-power microscope this is easily measured.

The method has been applied by Carrière † to the motion of the air in a Kundt's tube set in vibration by a telephone diaphragm which is operated by an alternating current at 50 cycles/sec. Dust is blown into the tube by bellows and the tube is viewed at right angles to the beam of light. Observations are made at an antinode and each dust particle in the image of the filament shows up in the field of the microscope by scattered light. When the tube is sounding each particle appears as a short line of light parallel to the axis of the tube. Particles of various sizes were used and it was found that the length of the observed line of light increases as the size of the particle diminishes, until a limiting value is reached. This is assumed to be the amplitude of the air. The measurement is made by rotating in the eye-piece a glass plate with two parallel lines ruled at a known distance apart until the two lines just enclose the path of a particle. This method was applied to various problems, including that of the variation of amplitude with the distance from the wall of the tube. The results, seen in fig. 11.3, cor-

* *Ann. Phys. Lpz.*, Vol. 26, p. 121 (1936).   † *J. de Physique*, Vol. 10, p. 198 (1929).

roborate those of Richardson,* and show that the amplitude is a maximum
at a short distance from the wall of the tube.

This method has been used by Andrade and Parker † for purposes
of absolute measurement. The particles used are smoke particles of
magnesium oxide and their average radius as determined by their
Brownian movement is 3×10^{-5} mm. The vibrations in the tube are
maintained at resonance by a diaphragm operated by a valve amplifier.
The motion of the diaphragm is sinusoidal; the frequency and power
are easily controlled and altered and the frequency and amplitude
are kept constant over long intervals. The particles are observed

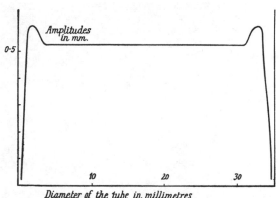

Fig. 11.3

by scattered light, and when convection is excluded by careful temperature control they show as bright spots with the sound field off and
as bright lines with the sound field on (fig. 11.4, p. 302). No difference
between large and small particles is observed, and this supports the
conclusion independently arrived at that all the particles are small
enough to take part fully in the motion of the air.

The pressure amplitude at a point outside the tube at distance r
along the axis of the tube measured from the open end may be taken ‡
as

$$\hat{P} = \frac{\rho \omega^2 a^2}{2r} \xi_0, \quad \cdot \quad \cdot \quad \cdot \quad \cdot \quad \cdot \quad (11.31)$$

where r is the distance, a is the radius of the tube, and ξ_0 is the amplitude at the open end. Here it is assumed that the open end is flush

---

* *Proc. Phys. Soc.*, Vol. 40, p. 206 (1927–8); Vol. 42, p. 1 (1929).

† *Proc. Roy. Soc.*, Vol. 159, p. 507 (1937).

‡ See Crandall, *Vibrating Systems and Sound*, § 42; Davis, *Modern Acoustics*, p. 61.

with an infinite baffle. The root mean square pressure amplitude is
thus

$$P = \frac{\rho \omega^2 a^2}{2r\sqrt{2}} \, \xi_0, \quad \cdot \quad \cdot \quad \cdot \quad \cdot \quad \cdot \quad (11.32)$$

and the average rate of energy flux, from equation 11.26, is given by

$$I = \frac{\rho a^4 \omega^4}{8cr^2} \, \xi_0{}^2, \quad \cdot \quad \cdot \quad \cdot \quad \cdot \quad \cdot \quad (11.33)$$

where c is the velocity of sound.

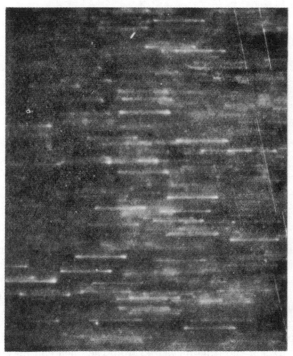

Fig. 11.4.—Motion of smoke particles in a Kundt's tube

The tube was placed high up in one building with the end of the
tube flush with the wall, and an observer was placed in another building with his ear on the axis of the tube. The sound was then adjusted
to the threshold of audibility and the following results were obtained:

f	ξ_0	P	I
410 cycles/sec.	1.9×10^{-4} cm.	1.2×10^{-3} dyne/cm.^{2}	3.4×10^{-8} erg/cm.^{2}/sec.
646	6×10^{-5}	0.94×10^{-3}	2.1×10^{-8}

12. The Hot-wire Microphone.

This device was first applied by Tucker to the reception of the sound waves from gunfire and was used in the sound-ranging sets to which reference has already been made (§ 10, p. 263). In these its purpose was the detection and recording of the wave, not measurement, but it is obviously possible to base a method of measurement upon it. Richards * experimented with a hot-wire grid attached to the prong of a vibrating tuning-fork. When the fork is in vibration the grid is in effect exposed to an oscillating air current whose velocity amplitude depends on the displacement amplitude of the fork. A drop in the resistance of the hot wire results, and by comparing this drop with that produced by steady air currents of various velocities he found that the drop for the oscillating grid is the same as that for a steady current of air of velocity equal to the maximum velocity, relative to the air, of the oscillating grid. Thus if a grid is calibrated in air-streams of varying velocities v, then when the air surrounding the grid is in oscillation with an amplitude a we can find this amplitude from the relation $v = 2\pi fa$ and the calibration curve.

The velocities involved in ordinary sound waves in the open are much too small to be measured by this device, but Richardson † has applied it to the vibrations of air in an organ pipe.

The sensitiveness of the device can be enormously increased by associating it with a resonator, but this, of course, introduces the difficulty that the sensitiveness varies with the frequency. The instrument is described by Tucker and Paris ‡ and is useful up to frequencies of 512. It is simply constructed and easily manipulated and requires only a Wheatstone bridge arrangement. When used with an amplifying valve it can detect and render audible tones which are inaudible to the unaided ear.

The microphone consists essentially of three parts: (1) a platinum wire grid mounted in a circular mica plate in the neck of a Helmholtz resonator; (2) a " holder " which includes the neck of a resonator, the contact pieces and the terminals; (3) the container, which acts as resonator. The grid consists of fine Wollaston wire. This wire is made with a platinum core and silver sheath. It is first drawn out to the necessary degree of fineness, after which it is placed in position and the silver sheath dissolved away. It is mounted on a glass rod bridging a circular aperture in

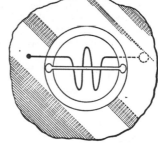

Fig. 11.5

a mica disc (fig. 11.5). The mica disc is placed between two annular discs of silver foil, one end of the wire being soldered to each disc. The diameter of the

---

* *Phil. Mag.*, Vol. 45, p. 925 (1923).   † *Proc. Roy. Soc.*, A, Vol. 112, p. 523 (1926).
‡ *Phil. Trans.*, A, Vol. 221, p. 390 (1921).

wire is about 0·0006 cm. and it is worked with a current of about 30 milliamps. just below red heat.

The manner in which the holder is made up is shown in fig. 11.6. The cylindrical neck A, made of brass, is soldered into the centre of the circular plate E_1 made of the same material. E_1 is provided with the terminal T_1. The mica plate M carrying the grid is clamped between E_1 and the lower ring E_2, which is also of brass and carries the terminal T_2, at the side of the holder. Beneath E_2 is a rubber ring R_1, and this rests on a bed of ebonite P, to which also the plate E_1 is fixed by the screws S. The ebonite bed P is square, and is bolted at the corners to the square brass plate B which forms one end of the container. To ensure an airtight joint a square plate of thin rubber R_2 is inserted between the holder and the container.

When the plate E_1 is screwed down on to the ebonite bed, so that the mica plate with its silver foil electrodes is firmly held between E_1 and E_2, a current can be passed through the grid by connecting a battery to the terminals T_1 and T_2.

The container is cylindrical in shape and its frequency is given (equation 4.5, p. 105) by the formula

$$f = \frac{c}{2\pi} \sqrt{\frac{S}{l'V_0}},$$

where c is the velocity of sound, S the area of cross-section of the aperture, l' the effective length of the neck, and V_0 the volume of the container.

The change in the resistance of the grid may be analysed into two parts: (1) an oscillatory change, (2) a steady change. The first of these requires amplification, but the second may be measured by a simple Wheatstone bridge arrangement, two arms of the bridge having resistances of about 100 ohms, the third carrying the grid, and the fourth having a resistance of about 350 ohms, which is the resistance of the grid when carrying its working current. The steady change of resistance is proportional to the sound intensity.

The instrument must be used for comparative measurements for sounds of the same frequency, and has been applied by Tucker and Paris to the investigation of (1) the distribution of sound intensity in a room, (2) the directional effect due to a trumpet, and (3) the diffraction due to a circular disc.

The sensitiveness of the instrument may be further increased and the variation of sensitiveness with pitch diminished by applying an idea originally suggested by Boys * in connexion with the Rayleigh disc. This involves using two resonators and putting the detector into a small neck connecting the two. The application to the hot-wire microphone was suggested by Callendar in 1918, and early experiments were carried out independently by Tucker. The theory of the arrangement has been developed by Paris.† The doubly-resonating microphone may consist, as in fig.11.7, of a resonator of the stopped pipe variety and a resonator of the Helmholtz type. The natural frequencies of the double resonator are shown to be the roots of the following equation in f:

$$\tan \frac{\pi f}{2f_0} = -\frac{2\pi\sigma}{cC} f \left(1 - \frac{f_1^2}{f^2}\right), \quad \cdots \cdots \quad (11.34)$$

where f_0 is the frequency of the pipe, f_1 the frequency of the Helmholtz resonator, C the conductivity of the neck of the resonator, c the velocity of sound in air and σ the area of cross-section of the pipe.

The best arrangement was found to be that in which the resonance curve

---

* *Nature*, Vol. 42, p. 604 (1890).   † *Proc. Roy. Soc.*, A, Vol. 101, p. 391 (1922).

gives two equal peaks (corresponding to the two values of f) with a small dip between them.

Tucker and Paris used the arrangement to pick up sounds of low intensity from distant sirens, and found that quite inaudible signals could be picked out even from a confused mass of other noises.*

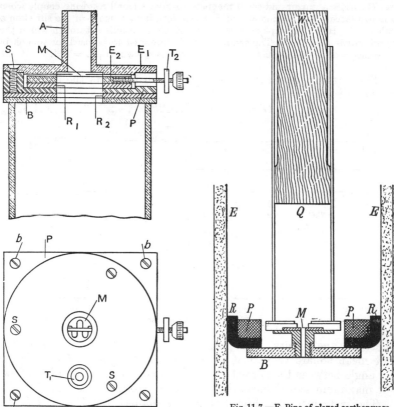

Fig. 11.6.—Tucker selective hot-wire microphone

Fig. 11.7.—E, Pipe of glazed earthenware 120 cm. long. P, Plunger 2·5 cm. thick, 14 cm. in diameter. B, Brass disc. M, Grid. Q, Helmholtz resonator. W, Wooden plunger. R, Rubber washer.

13. Measurement of Air Velocity by the Rayleigh Disc.

This device, which is due to Lord Rayleigh, was first described by him in a paper communicated to the Cambridge Philosophical Society † in 1880. It is based on the principle that a light disc tends to set itself at right angles to an air-stream, no matter whether this air-stream is direct or alternating, and that the deflection of the disc may

---

* See also *Science Progress*, Vol. 20, p. 70 (1925–6).
† See also *Phil. Mag.*, Vol. 14, p. 186 (1882).

be used to measure either the steady velocity in the first case or the mean square velocity in the second case.

The original apparatus was as shown in fig. 11.8. A is a brass tube closed at one end by a glass plate B behind which is a slit C backed by a lamp. The disc D carries a mirror and small magnets to give a small restoring couple when D is displaced. E is a window and F a lens forming an image of the slit C on a scale at G. H is a light paper screen, adjustable in position, through which the sound waves may pass. The arrangement is intended to be used for sounds in resonance with the air in the tube, i.e. for sounds for which $\lambda/2 = CH$.

The formula, obtained by König,* which connects the couple and the velocity, is

$$G = (4/3)\rho r^3 V^2 \sin 2\theta, \quad \ldots \ldots \quad (11.35)$$

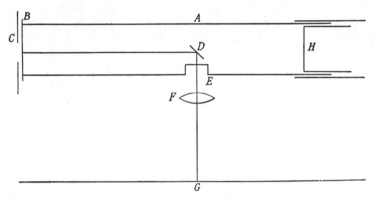

Fig. 11.8.—Rayleigh disc

where ρ is the density of the gas, V the velocity of gas if steady or the root mean square velocity if alternating, r the radius of the disc, θ the angle between the normal to the disc and the direction of gas flow. For maximum sensitiveness the disc must be set so that $\theta = 45°$.

The instrument has been studied by Mallett and Dutton,† C. H. Skinner,‡ and Barnes and West.§ The last-named workers used discs calibrated by (a) continuous air-stream, (b) low-frequency alternating streams, (c) measurements of constants of suspending fibre and disc. They concluded that measurement of velocities down to the order of 0·1 cm./sec. could be effected to an accuracy of 2 per cent. This velocity, however, corresponds to a fairly intense sound wave.|| Sivian¶ has shown that in certain cases increased sensitiveness may be obtained by using resonance between the sound to be measured and the free vibration of the suspended disc.

* *Wied. Ann.*, Vol. 43, p. 43 (1891).   † *J. I. E. E.*, Vol. 63, p. 502 (1925).
‡ *Phys. Rev.*, Vol. 27, p. 346 (1926).   § *J. I. E. E.*, Vol. 65, p. 871 (1927).
|| See also Devik and Dahl, *Journ. Amer. Soc. Acoust.*, Vol. 10, p. 50 (1938).
¶ *Bell Telephone Laboratories*, B. 302 (April, 1928).

More recently the behaviour of the disc has been treated theoretically by King,* and its adaptation to the measurement of particle velocity in water has been studied by A. B. Wood.† Corrections which are negligible in air assume greater importance in the case of water, owing to the greater fluid inertia. In particular, the tendency of the disc to follow the motion of the fluid must be taken into account. If u is the velocity amplitude of the disc and $\beta = u/V$, then the quantity v^2 in the expression for G is replaced by $V^2(1 - \beta)^2$. If M is the mass of the disc, m that of the water displaced and m_ω the water load, then

$$\beta = \frac{u}{V} = \frac{m + m_\omega}{M + m_\omega},$$

or

$$1 - \beta = \frac{M - m}{M + m_\omega}.$$

For a disc broadside on to the flow ‡ the fluid load is $\frac{8}{3}r^3\rho$, and if the disc is at $45°$ this becomes $\frac{4}{3}r^3\rho$.

We therefore have

$$1 - \beta = \frac{M - m}{M + \frac{4}{3}r^3\rho}.$$

The intensity is given by $I = c\rho V^2$, and for $\theta = 45°$ this becomes

$$I = \frac{3}{4}\frac{cG}{r^3(1 - \beta)^2}. \quad \cdots \quad (11.36)$$

In this expression all the quantities are measurable and the formula agrees well with experimental observations. A. B. Wood shows that for a mica disc 1 cm. in diameter, 0·002 cm. in thickness and weighing 5×10^{-3} gm. the factor $1/(1 - \beta)^2$ is 1·08 in air and 2500 in water.

It will readily be seen that the Rayleigh disc can also be adapted for use with a double resonator (see the previous section); the method has all the advantages and disadvantages of the double-resonator method when used with the hot wire.

14. Measurement by Calibrated Microphone.

The Rayleigh disc is the instrument mainly used at the National Physical Laboratory for the absolute measurement of sound intensity. Its indications, which measure velocity, are then compared with those of a microphone responding to pressure, and the values of the air velocity converted to pressures by using the known relation of the two quantities in the wave. Microphones, usually of the condenser type (see section 9, p. 513), are then maintained as laboratory

---

* *Proc. Roy. Soc.*, Vol. 153, p. 17 (1935).   † *Proc. Phys. Soc.*, Vol. 47, p. 779 (1935).
‡ Lamb, *Hydrodynamics*, 3rd ed., pp. 131, 138 (Cambr. Univ. Press, 1906).

standards, against which other microphones can be calibrated by comparison under appropriate conditions. The discs are of glass, about 1 cm. in diameter and silvered on one side. They are suspended by fine quartz fibres, the elastic constants of which are carefully determined previously.

For the determination of the field sensitiveness, i.e. the ratio of the response of the microphone to the sound pressure in a progressive wave, the experiments are conducted in a heavily lagged room with a loud-speaker as source. Observations are made at various points, first with the Rayleigh disc and then with the microphone, the deflection of the disc being measured by the reflection of a beam of light. This method is satisfactory from frequencies of about 10,000 down to about 300. Below 300, reflections from the walls become a disturbing influence, no matter how well lagged the walls may be.

The pressure sensitiveness, i.e. the ratio of the response of the microphone to the sound pressure actuating the diaphragm, is determined from measurements with stationary waves. The microphone diaphragm closes one end of the pipe, at the other end of which the loud-speaker is placed. The Rayleigh disc is inside the pipe and the position of the microphone is altered until the disc is at a velocity antinode. The velocity is calculated and from its value the pressure at the microphone is deduced. This method covers the range from 3500 cycles/sec. or more down to 62·5.

A difficulty already mentioned on p. 295 occurs in the calibration of microphones for free field conditions, namely, the uncertainty due to reflection from the microphone itself. This distorts the field and increases the local magnitude of the oscillatory pressure. The difficulty has been overcome by the Post Office Engineering Department * by the use of a probe-tube of small diameter leading from a condenser microphone. The open end is almost non-reactive and is presented for pressure calibration to the closed end of a much wider resonance tube 7 feet long with a Rayleigh disc at the middle. Various resonance frequencies are used between 80 and 6400 cycles/sec. The probe-tube may then be used to explore without distortion any acoustic field, such as that due to a loud-speaker before or after a microphone is inserted. Maguire and King,† using a similar method, point out that if the microphone is first calibrated in the resonance tube and then in free field conditions, this gives a second determination of the correction for reflection for various frequencies.

The calibration of a microphone can also be carried out by means of a thermophone, an instrument which has been perfected in the Bell Telephone Laboratories. The fact that sounds can be produced by passing through a bolometer alternating currents superimposed on a

---

* P.O. Elec. Eng. J., Vol. 26, p. 260 (1934); West, Nature, Vol. 142, p. 29 (1938).
† Nature, Vol. 141, p. 1016 (1938).

steady direct current was pointed out by F. Braun * in 1898. These experiments of Braun were extended by Weinberg † and the principle was applied to the thermophone by de Lange.‡ The theory of the thermophone as a precision source of sound has been developed by Arnold and Crandall § and Wente ‖.

When an alternating current is passed through a thin conductor, the latter is subject to a periodic variation in temperature which follows the variations of the current. This periodic variation of temperature is the source of temperature waves in the surrounding medium, the amplitude of which falls off so rapidly that the heating effect is practically confined to the immediate neighbourhood of the conductor. The resulting expansion and contraction of the medium

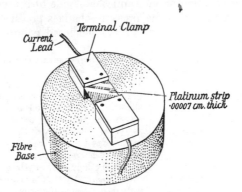

Fig. 11.9.—Simple thermophone

gives rise to pressure variations which are transmitted as sound waves. It is necessary that the conductor should be thin, so that its heat capacity may be small and its temperature may rapidly follow the temperature changes produced by the current variation. A simple form of the instrument is shown in fig. 11.9. The instrument may be operated either with a pure alternating current or with an alternating current superimposed on a direct current.

In the first case the heating effect is proportional to $RI^2 \sin^2 pt$, where $p = 2\pi f$ and f is the frequency of the alternating current. Since

$$RI^2 \sin^2 pt = \frac{RI^2}{2}(1 - \cos 2pt),$$

the acoustic frequency is double the frequency of the current.

* *Ann. d. Physik*, Vol. 65, p. 358 (1898).   † *Elektrot. Zeit.*, Vol. 28, p. 944 (1907).
‡ *Proc. Roy. Soc.*, A, Vol. 91, p. 239 (1915).   § *Phys. Rev.*, Vol. 10, p. 22 (1917).
‖ *Phys. Rev.*, Vol. 19, p. 333 (1922).

If, on the other hand, we superimpose an alternating current $I \sin pt$ on a steady current I_0, the heating effect is proportional to

$$R(I_0 + I \sin pt)^2 = RI_0^2 + 2RI_0I \sin pt + RI^2 \sin^2 pt$$
$$= R\left(I_0^2 + \frac{I^2}{2}\right) + 2RI_0I \sin pt - \frac{RI^2}{2} \cos 2pt.$$

It is clear from this that the double frequency term can be made negligible by a suitable choice of I_0 and I, but the arrangement is less efficient when used in this way.

The thermophone may be used as a source of sound either free or in a cavity. In the latter case it may conveniently be used for standardizing the condenser microphone, and this is one of its most important uses. If the cavity is small the pressure changes produced at the strip are quickly communicated to the whole enclosed volume.

Platinum seems on the whole to be the best metal for the strip, but gold foil may be obtained thinner and is very efficient. Its heat capacity, however, varies considerably for different samples, and it should be tested against platinum. Where the instrument is used in a cavity it is an advantage to fill the cavity with hydrogen, as Wente has shown that the dimensions of the cavity must be small compared with the wave-length of the sound, and the wave-length is longer in hydrogen than in any other gas. Another advantage is that the diffusivity of hydrogen is low. The formulæ developed by Wente (loc. cit.) were checked by standardizing against a condenser microphone four thermophones of different types and dimensions.

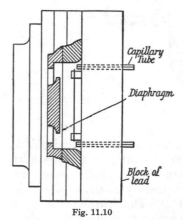

Capillary Tube

Diaphragm

Block of lead

Fig. 11.10

To use the thermophone for calibration a block of lead about 1·5 in. thick is placed against the face of the microphone so as to form a cylindrical enclosure in front of the diaphragm as in fig. 11.10. All crevices are sealed so that the only openings to the cavity are two capillary tubes several inches long and of bore about 0·01 cm., through which hydrogen can be slowly passed. Two strips of gold foil are mounted symmetrically inside this enclosure, the ends being clamped between small brass blocks. The supports are arranged in such a way that a current can be passed through the two strips in series. The thermophone formula enables the pressure amplitude to be calculated and the voltage amplitude is measured.

For frequencies below 62·5 a pistonphone (fig. 11.11) is used. A small piston driven by a motor or by the moving coil of a loud-speaker unit works into a small cavity of which one side is closed by the diaphragm of the microphone. The amplitude of the piston is recorded optically, and from this the pressure amplitude in the cavity is calculated and the corresponding voltage amplitude observed. This method covers the frequency range from 400 to 10 cycles per second.

In the paper quoted the pistonphone was used for frequencies from 10 to 200 cycles/sec. and the thermophone from 60 to 12,000. The

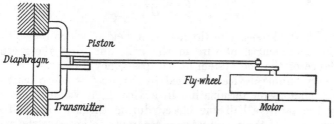

Fig. 11.11

polarizing voltage on the microphone was 200 and the mean value of the sensitiveness about 0·35 millivolt per dyne per square centimetre.

15. Measurement of Intensity by Various Methods.

A very sensitive instrument which can be used in a null method was devised by Gerlach * and Schottky † (see p. 518). It consists of a light metallic ribbon suspended in a strong magnetic field. The ribbon is sufficiently light for it to follow freely the movements of the air up to a frequency of about 4000, and by its motion in the magnetic field it induces an alternating current which can be amplified and measured. When it is used as a null instrument the forces exerted by the oscillatory pressure in the air are balanced by sending through the ribbon an alternating current of such amplitude, frequency and phase that it is brought to rest. This involves very sensitive arrangements for the detection of the motion of the ribbon, but as the electro-dynamic forces acting on the ribbon can be calculated, the instrument can be used for absolute measurement.

A similar null method has been applied by Meyer ‡ to the condenser microphone.

A somewhat similar principle has been applied to the moving-coil receiver by F. D. Smith §. If a coil, movable in a strong magnetic field, is rigidly attached to a surface on which sound waves impinge, the motion of the surface and attached coil gives rise to an alternating current in the coil, which can be measured by a sensitive vibration galvanometer connected to the coil through a tuned-circuit multi-stage amplifier. An alternating E.M.F. of the same frequency is then applied

* *Phys. Zeits.*, Vol. 25, p. 675 (1924).   † *Phys. Zeits.*, Vol. 25, p. 672 (1924).
‡ *Zeit. f. tech. Physik*, Vol. 7, p. 609 (1926).
§ *Proc. Phys. Soc.*, Vol. 41, p. 487 (1928–9).

to the coil and its magnitude adjusted until the same indication is obtained on the vibration galvanometer. It can then be shown that the mechanical force amplitude F is related to the E.M.F. amplitude E by the simple relationship

$$F = \frac{EZ}{Hl},$$

where H is the intensity of the magnetic field in which the coil moves, l is the total length of wire in the coil, and Z is the mechanical impedance of the coil system at the frequency used.

A very simple device was used by Kundt,[*] which consisted of a delicate manometer terminating in a very light valve which opened during the positive half and closed during the negative half of the pressure cycle of the sound wave. Attempts to improve the accuracy of this instrument and adapt it for accurate use have been made by Eisenhour and Tyzzer,[†] Ribbentrop,[‡] Marty,[§] and Lehmann.[||]

Attempts have also been made to determine intensity by measuring the differences in temperature produced in the compressions and rarefactions of a system of progressive or stationary waves. Neuscheler used a strip-resistance thermometer [¶] and recorded temperature changes of 0·13° C. Friese and Waetzmann [**] have made measurements on stationary waves with a frequency of 800 and obtained satisfactory agreement. It seems improbable, however, that the method can be made sufficiently sensitive to compete with the other methods now in common use.

The phonodeik (p. 342) and the reverberation chamber (p. 551) can also be adapted for measurements of intensity.

16. Power of Sources of Sound.

The measurement of the intensity of a sound at any point leads to a calculation of the power of the source, and the results are of special interest in their bearing on speech and music. A great deal of work on the power generated in speech has emanated from the Bell Telephone Laboratories.[††] Measurements have been made of average power and of peak power, and the distribution of power over the range of frequencies used in speech has also been measured. For speech the average power is about ten microwatts. If the energy is measured over intervals as small as $\frac{1}{8}$ second, some 2 per cent of these intervals will show a peak power of the order of 1000 microwatts. For ordinary

[*] *Ann. d. Physik*, Vol. 134, p. 568 (1868).   [†] *J. Frankl. Inst.*, Vol. 208, p. 397 (1929).
[‡] *Zeit. f. tech. Physik*, Vol. 13, p. 396 (1932).   [§] *Ann. de Physique*, Vol. 1, p. 622 (1934).
[||] *Zeit. f. tech. Physik*, Vol. 18, p. 309 (1937).   [¶] *Ann. d. Physik*, Vol. 34, p. 131 (1911).
[**] *Zeits. f. Phys.*, Vol. 29, p. 110 (1924); Vol. 31, p. 50 (1925); Vol. 34, p. 131 (1925).
[††] A very full account of this work will be found in Fletcher, *Speech and Hearing* (D. Van Nostrand Co., 1929).

speech most of the power is found to lie in components whose frequency is between 250 and 1000 cycles per second for male voices and between 500 and 1500 cycles per second for female voices. Very little energy is associated with frequencies below 125 cycles/sec., even in the male voice. Consonants carry very little power and are associated with very high frequencies, particularly the sounds *that*, *thin*, *vat*, *for*, *sit* and *zip*. Although carrying little power these components are very important for intelligibility.

The peak power of various musical instruments has been determined by Sivian, Dunn and White * and is shown in the following table.

Instrument	Peak Power (Watts)	Instrument	Peak Power (Watts)
Full orchestra	.. 70	Bass saxophone	.. 0·3
Large bass drum	.. 25	Bass tuba ..	.. 0·2
Pipe organ ..	.. 13	Double bass	.. 0·16
Snare drum ..	.. 12	Piccolo	.. 0·08
Cymbals	.. 10	Flute	.. 0·06
Trombone	.. 6	Clarinet	.. 0·05
Piano	.. 0·4	French horn	.. 0·05
Trumpet	.. 0·3	Triangle	.. 0·05

A violin played at the lowest level used with an audience shows a peak power of only $3·8 \times 10^{-6}$ watt, so that the power of the full orchestra is about twenty million times greater. For the singing voice the peak power on the higher notes of the range is about 1 watt both for men and for women. They radiate nearly equal power on notes an octave apart—about 100 microwatts at about 130 and 260 cycles per second respectively; and about 100,000 microwatts at about 390 and 780 cycles per second respectively.

* *Jour. Amer. Soc. Acoust.*, Vol. 2, p. 330 (1931).

CHAPTER XII

Pitch and Frequency

1. Pitch.

Pitch is defined as that subjective quality of a sound which determines its position in the musical scale. It may be expressed as the frequency of that pure tone which is judged by the average normal ear to occupy the same position in a musical scale as the sound. It is determined mainly by frequency, but even in the case of pure tones the correlation is not exact and the pitch is modified to some extent by the intensity (see section 4, p. 471). The ear is sensitive over a considerable frequency range. The lowest frequencies used in music are those of the double bass and the bass tuba, which lie between 60 and 80 cycles/sec., while the highest tones occur as partials (section 2, p. 334) and lie in the neighbourhood of 10,000 to 15,000 cycles/sec. Tones of male speech embrace a range of from 120 to 8000 cycles/sec., those of female speech from 200 to 10,000 cycles/sec.

When a note is sounded certain other notes can be picked out by the ear as simply related to it in pitch. The most obvious of these is the octave, and frequency determinations show that two notes forming together the musical interval of the octave invariably have frequencies in the ratio 2 : 1. Again, two notes forming the interval of the fifth always have frequencies in the ratio 3 : 2.

These facts were discovered quite early in the history of acoustics. Pythagoras (572–497 B.C.) knew that if two strings of the same material and stretched with the same tension are made to sound a simple musical interval, the lengths of the strings are in a simple numerical ratio. In Waller's life of Hooke (1635–1703) we find that in July 1681 Dr. Hooke showed (at the Royal Society) " a way of making musical sounds by the striking of the teeth of several brass wheels proportionally cut as to their numbers, and turned very fast round, in which it was observable that the equal or proportional strokes of the teeth, that is, 2 : 1, 4 : 3, &c., made the musical notes ". The same device was later used by Savart and is generally known as Savart's Wheel. Helmholtz * employed a double siren, each revolving disc having four rings of holes, the numbers being respectively 8, 10, 12, 18 and 9, 12, 15, 16. An arrangement of keys enables the rings to be used singly or in com-

---

* *Sensations of Tone*, English trans., 3rd ed., p. 162 (Longmans, 1895).

bination, and taken in pairs they are found to give all the familiar musical intervals.

We thus conclude that musical intervals are those between notes which for some reason the ear recognizes as simply related, and in every case the notes forming these intervals have a fixed and simple frequency ratio. If proceeding up the scale by octaves we are proceeding by equal increments of pitch, and if in so doing we are picking out a series of notes whose frequencies form a geometrical progression with 2 as the common ratio, then it seems reasonable to measure pitch on a logarithmic scale, taking the octave as the fundamental unit and subdividing this into any required number of small parts.

This procedure is implicit in the usual addition of musical intervals of pitch, in which we multiply the frequency ratios instead of adding. Thus the fourth $(4/3)$ + the fifth $(3/2)$ = the octave $(4/3 \times 3/2 = 2/1)$. The same idea is embodied in the notation used for the musical scale.

Thus the note near the middle of the bass clef has a frequency of about 128 cycles/sec. and is denoted by c in the notation of Helmholtz, which is still widely used in musical acoustics. The other notes at octave intervals are $C_1 = 32$, $C = 64$, $c = 128$, $c' = 256$ (middle C of the piano), $c'' = 512$, &c. These frequencies are the physicist's selection and are chosen for convenience. In actual practice the musical standard has varied enormously but in 1939 was fixed by international agreement. Under this agreement the note a' (the second space up in the treble clef) is to have a frequency of 440. This makes c 132 instead of 128 as above.

The logarithmic measurement of pitch is made even more reasonable when we consider the results of experiments on the least appreciable increment of pitch (section 4, p. 469). Experiments on this point have been made by Knudsen and others. Two pure tones are sounded alternately and the frequency of one of them is gradually raised from unison to a point where a difference in pitch is just perceptible. It is found that if f is the frequency and Δf the smallest perceptible change in frequency, then whereas for large or small values of f the fraction $\Delta f/f$ varies from ·003 to 0·1, for values of f from 500 to 4000 $\Delta f/f$ is a constant and has the value ·003. The constancy of this ratio over the range of frequencies in most common use again suggests a logarithmic scale of measurement for pitch.

The scale may be constructed thus. Let I be an interval measured in logarithmic units. Let f_1, f_2 be the frequencies of the two notes forming the interval. Then

$$ I = k \log_{10} \frac{f_1}{f_2}. \qquad \ldots \ldots \quad (12.1) $$

where k is a constant to be chosen.

If I_1 is the interval of the octave then

$$I_1 = k \log_{10} 2,$$

and k must be chosen so as to give a reasonable number of units.

Three values for k have been suggested.

If we put $k = 1000$, $I_1 = 1000 \times 0\cdot3010 = 301$. The unit thus defined is the *savart*, so called after the French physicist of that name (Savart, 1791–1841). This unit has the advantage of rendering the calculations very simple.

Again, we may put $k = 1200/\log_{10} 2$. This gives $I_1 = 1200$ and the unit so defined was adopted by Ellis, the English translator of Helmholtz's *Sensations of Tone*. The advantage of this unit, which is called the *cent*, is that the octave in the modern tempered diatonic scale is divided into twelve equal semitones and each of these consequently comprises 100 cents.

Recently it has been suggested that we should adopt for k the value $100/\log_{10} 2$. This makes $I_1 = 100$, and the resulting unit is the *centi-octave*. This unit corresponds to a frequency ratio given by

$$1 = \frac{100}{\log 2} \log \frac{f + \Delta f}{f},$$

$$\therefore \ \log \frac{f + \Delta f}{f} = \cdot0030,$$

$$\frac{f + \Delta f}{f} = 1\cdot007,$$

$$\therefore \ \frac{\Delta f}{f} = \cdot007.$$

This unit is therefore rather more than double the smallest perceptible increment of frequency under the best experimental conditions, but is of the same order as the smallest perceptible increment in ordinary circumstances.

These scales of pitch are physical scales like the phon scale for loudness (p. 464). For a scale of pitch based directly on pitch sensations see § 4, p. 471.

2. Determination of Frequency by the Siren.

The earliest determination of frequency was made by Mersenne (1588–1648).[*] He set up a long cord held horizontal by a stretching weight and timed the vibrations by eye, using his pulse. He found that if the length was halved, the tension being kept the same, the

---

[*] *Harmonie Universelle*, 1636.

" frequenzia " was doubled. By shortening the cord till the sound was audible and using the musical intervals he had a basis for frequency measurement, and he determined the frequency of an organ-pipe by comparison with a stretched brass wire.

Approximate determinations of frequency are easily carried out in the laboratory by means of the siren. The use of a series of puffs of air to give rise to a tone seems to have been due to John Robison, who describes the arrangement in an article on Temperament of the Musical Scale in the *Encyclopædia Britannica*, 3rd edition, Vol. 2 of Supplement, 1801. He says that when the puffs came at a certain rate " the sound *g* in alt was most smoothly uttered, equal in sweetness to a clear female voice ". When they came more slowly " the sound was more mellow than any man's voice at the same pitch ". The arrangement was improved by Baron Charles Cagniard de la Tour (1777–1859) in 1819. It owes its name to his discovery that it could sing under water. In its present form it was developed by Seebeck (1805–1849).* The siren of Cagniard de la Tour consisted merely of a rotating disc with a circle of perforations rotated steadily in front of a jet delivering air. The perforations rendered the jet intermittent and gave a note whose frequency was known if the number of perforations in the circle and the rate of rotation of the disc were known. This simple arrangement was modified by Seebeck, who replaced the jet by a series of perforations on the top of the wind chest exactly corresponding to the perforations of the disc. This greatly strengthens the sound produced, as puffs of air emerge simultaneously from all the perforations of the disc when the two rows of holes correspond. In addition to this the perforations are slanted in opposite directions, so that the disc is driven forward by the air blast and its speed of rotation can be slightly modified by varying the pressure of the wind in the driving bellows. An automatic revolution counter is attached recording in tens and hundreds.

Ideally the process is very simple. The wind pressure is increased until the siren gives a note practically in unison with that of the sound whose frequency is to be measured. As the ear is not a very accurate judge of unison in some cases, it is well to listen for the beats. The counter is then read and, after 10 seconds or so, read again. If t is the time elapsed in seconds, p the number of perforations in the revolving disc, q the number of revolutions noted by reading the counter, and a the total number of beats counted, then the frequency is given by

$$f = \frac{pq \pm a}{t}. \qquad \ldots \ldots (12.2)$$

* *Pogg. Ann.*, Vol. 35, p. 417 (1841).

3. Stroboscopic Determination of Frequency.

This method is applicable in certain cases only, but may be illustrated in the case of a tuning-fork. The tuning-fork prongs carry two diaphragms, which overlap and are both slotted, so that when the prongs are at rest the slots are in line and light may pass through both. The light which passes through is allowed to fall on a rotating disc which carries a series of concentric rings, the annular spaces between the rings being filled with equidistant black triangles as indicated in fig. 12.1. The number of triangles is different for each ring. If, when the fork is set in vibration and the disc is rotated, any ring of triangles appears stationary, then probably for that ring each triangle succeeds its neighbour between two flashes of the light. If f is the

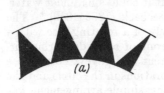

(a)

frequency of the illumination, r the number of revolutions of the disc per second, m the number of triangles in the stationary ring, then $f = mr$.

The pattern for this ring may also be stationary for $f = mr/2$, $f = mr/3, \ldots$. In these cases the wheel will have rotated the width of two, three, ... triangles in the intervals between successive flashes of light. The pattern will be steady but doubled (as in fig. 12.1, b)

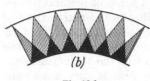

(b)

Fig. 12.1

if $f = 2mr$; and steady but trebled for $f = 3mr$. Any ambiguities involved can be eliminated by gradually increasing the speed of rotation of the disc.

If the adjustment is inexact the pattern in the ring will appear to revolve slowly. Thus if f is approximately equal to mr the pattern will revolve with the wheel for $f < mr$ and against the wheel for $f > mr$. If the pattern moves round through the distance between two triangles a times per second, $f = mr \pm a$.

This method can be applied to determine the frequency of an electrically-maintained tuning-fork.

4. Determination of Frequency by the Tonometer.

The first tonometer was made by Scheibler (1777–1837) in 1834 and consisted of a series of tuning-forks spread over an exact octave and ascending by equal increments of frequency from the lowest to the highest. Each fork produced the same number of beats per second with its neighbours on each side. If there are $p + 1$ forks to the octave and if the number of beats when neighbouring forks are sounded is q per second,

$$f + pq = 2f,$$
$$\therefore f = pq.$$

Scheibler chose $q = 4$, $p = 64$, so that $f = 256$, $2f = 512$.

Any source of sound within the range of the tonometer can have its frequency determined without ambiguity by counting its rate of beating with the two forks nearest to it in pitch. The tonometer is extremely troublesome to adjust but when once made it is very accurate and very constant.

König (1832–1901) produced a more elaborate series using 154 forks covering the frequency range from 16 to 21,845·3 cycles/sec. The forks were provided with adjustable resonators and with sliding weights, by the use of which the frequencies could be varied within certain limits. Appunn * produced a less costly and troublesome, but less accurate instrument consisting of a series of tuned reeds mounted on a windchest. Two such reeds, however, act like a coupled system, and the frequency of a reed varies according as it is sounded with its neighbour just above or just below. These tonometers are described by Ellis.†

5. Comparison of a Tuning-fork with a Seconds Pendulum.

The first attempt at an accurate comparison of a tuning-fork with a seconds pendulum was carried out by Rayleigh ‡ on a fork of frequency about 128 cycles/sec. An electrically-maintained fork of frequency about 32 is employed to drive (a) a phonic wheel with four armatures, (b) an auxiliary fork of frequency about 128.

The interrupted current from the driving fork is led to an electromagnet between the prongs of the auxiliary fork, which has a frequency about four times as great. Its forced vibration has therefore a frequency *exactly* four times that of the driving fork, i.e. about 128. Since there are four armatures on the phonic wheel the frequency of the wheel will be exactly one-quarter that of the driving fork, and if an illuminated bead on a seconds pendulum is viewed through a slit in the phonic wheel eight positions of the bead will be seen. If the phonic wheel has a frequency of exactly 8 cycles/sec. these positions will be stationary, but if the ratio is not exact the positions will appear to move slowly either forwards or backwards. If one position succeeds

---

* *Ann. d. Physik*, Vol. 64, p. 409 (1898).
† Helmholtz, *Sensations of Tone*, 3rd English edition, p. 443.
‡ *Phil. Trans.*, Vol. 174, p. 316 (1883).

another a times per second, then the wheel gains or loses one complete vibration on the pendulum a times per second. Hence

$$\text{Frequency of wheel} = 8 \pm a.$$
$$\therefore \text{ Frequency of driving fork} = 4(8 \pm a).$$
$$\therefore \text{ Frequency of driven fork} = 16(8 \pm a).$$

If now the driven fork is made to beat with the fork of frequency about 128, which is to have its frequency accurately determined, and if the beats on being counted have a frequency b per second, then the required frequency is $16(8 \pm a) \pm b$.

6. Standards of Frequency.

The accurate determination of frequency is a very important measurement in many different connexions. Fundamentally it involves the comparison of the frequency of occurrence of some physical phenomenon like the vibration of a tuning-fork with the frequency of occurrence of the revolution of the earth in space. The mean solar day, in terms of which all measurements of time are expressed, is in effect a practical unit the determination of which is made in terms of the sidereal day. Measurements of time are subject to special difficulties, owing to the difficulty of giving the unit a concrete embodiment in a standard. Standards of mass and length will preserve their identity over long periods, but this is not true of most standards of time if great accuracy is required. A controlled seconds clock is our most practical working standard of time or frequency.

7. Electrically-maintained Tuning-forks.

These are now indispensable as standards of frequency and for many other purposes. The principle is the conversion of electrical energy into the mechanical energy necessary to overcome the frictional resistances and into the energy radiated as sound.

The earliest method will be clear by reference to fig. 12.2. When the spring makes contact with the screw the electric circuit is completed and the prongs are attracted inwards. This breaks contact, the electromagnet ceases to act, and the prongs spring outwards again. It is important to notice that it is only the action of self-induction that enables the vibrations to be maintained. If the strength of the current were a function of the displacement of the prongs only and not of their direction of motion, then the work done by the electromagnetic forces on the fork during the inward motion of the prongs would be exactly equal to the work done by the fork against these forces on the outward motion, and no balance of energy would be available to overcome frictional losses.

Owing to self-induction, however, the rise of the current in the electromagnet is delayed at make (i.e. in the outward journey of the prongs) and prolonged at break (i.e. on the inward journey of the prongs) so that more work is done on the fork than by the fork, and the balance represents energy available for maintenance of the vibrations. This balance of energy is increased where the fork is fixed horizontally and the spring contact is replaced by a wire dipping into a mercury cup. In this case, owing to surface tension, contact with the mercury is delayed on the outward journey of the prong till the wire penetrates the surface film of the mercury, and the break is delayed on the inward journey owing to the adherence of mercury to the wire.

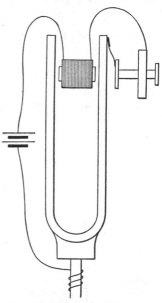

It is obvious that an electrically-maintained fork offers possibilities for use as a frequency standard, but if it is to meet modern requirements in this respect it must be designed with the utmost care. Dadourian * has brought out some of the important points in design. He emphasises the importance of massive mounting, and shows that a change in the constants of the electrical circuit affects the period. Increases in the length of the gaps between the contact springs and contact points increase the period, and the period may vary considerably with the amplitude. The effect of temperature change may be expressed as a temperature coefficient of frequency, and this varies from 1.04×10^{-4} at $-25°$ C. to

Fig. 12.2.—Diagram of electrically driven tuning-fork

1.43×10^{-4} at $56°$ C. for a steel fork. Dadourian was of the opinion that a well-designed fork can give a frequency constant to one part in 50,000. A fork of this type for low frequencies of about 25 to 50 cycles/sec. has been designed by A. B. Wood and Ford † and is used to control the phonic wheel in their phonic chronometer.

In a recent paper Moon ‡ describes an experimental method of comparing the frequency of a fork of frequency about 100 with a pendulum, the two making simultaneous optical records on a revolving drum. The amplitude of the fork is also recorded. The pendulum is of invar with chromium-plated steel knife-edge supported on a sapphire

* *Phys. Rev.*, Vol. 13, p. 337 (1919).   † *Journ. Sci. Inst.*, Vol. 1, p. 161 (1924).
‡ *Bur. of Standards Journ. of Res.*, Vol. 4, p. 213 (1930).

plane. The accuracy claimed for the comparison is about four parts in 1,000,000 and is limited by the precision of the individual vibrations of the fork and the pendulum.

For high frequencies, even down to 100 cycles/sec., a different type of maintenance is preferable. The arrangement in fig. 12.3 was designed by Eccles.*

V is a triode valve whose filament F is heated by the battery FB. The anode A is connected through the anode battery AB and the coil AC to one terminal of the filament. The grid G is connected to the filament through the coil GC. The tuning-fork T is permanently magnetized by an auxiliary magnet on whose pole-pieces the coils AC and GC are wound, the poles of the fork being indicated by N and S. Consider the moment in the vibration when the two prongs are moving away from the respective coils. The motion of the pole S will raise the

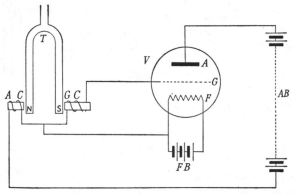

Fig. 12.3

potential of the grid and increase the anode current. This current completes its circuit through the coil AC, producing a magnetization which repels the pole N and assists the vibration. It is essential that the relative directions of winding of the two coils should be as shown.

A very accurate valve-controlled standard fork has been constructed by Dye.† Its frequency is determined by a specially designed phonic wheel. By the use of the new nickel steel known as " elinvar " the temperature coefficient of frequency is greatly reduced and the constancy of the standard correspondingly increased. The fork may be used to operate a " multivibrator ". This is an instrument designed by Abraham and Bloch ‡ to give an alternating current very rich in harmonics. With a standard fork of frequency about 1000 it is possible to use the harmonics as a series of standard frequencies, all known with the same accuracy as that of the standard fork. These harmonics

* *Proc. Phys. Soc.*, Vol. 31, p. 269 (1919).   † *Proc. Roy. Soc.*, A, Vol. 103, p. 240 (1923).
‡ *Comptes Rendus*, Vol. 168, p. 1105 (1919).

carry us well above the range of audible sound and by combination with a second multivibrator standard frequencies up to 1.5×10^6 cycles/sec. may be obtained.

Further improvements in the balancing of the prongs and the clamping of the fork are described in a paper by Dye and Essen.* Precautions are given for maintaining the constancy of the valve voltage, and if the air gap and the enclosure are kept at constant temperature and pressure the accuracy claimed is one part in a million.

8. Magnetostriction Oscillator.

In the paper already referred to on p. 224, Pierce suggested the use of a rod maintained in longitudinal vibration by magnetostriction as a standard of frequency. With a rod of nichrome the frequency was shown to be independent of the valve voltages and characteristics and to have a temperature coefficient $\dfrac{1}{f}\dfrac{\partial f}{\partial \theta}$ of only -1.07×10^{-4}.

In order to obtain high frequencies a " beaded " rod was used, giving a frequency of 295,480 cycles per second. An improved oscillator has been described in a subsequent paper by Pierce and Atherton Noyes.†

9. Quartz Oscillators.

Reference has already been made to the quartz oscillator as a source of high-frequency sound waves (p. 220). It is now also the most valuable precision standard for the determination of high frequencies, and the basis of the stabilization of frequency for radio broadcasting stations. The method is based on the work of Cady ‡ and was further developed by Pierce;§ a detailed discussion is given by Dye ‖ and by K. S. van Dyke.¶ Marrison ** has used the oscillator as the basis of his electrical clock, which is probably the most accurate in existence.

Its usefulness as a standard is due to the fact that if the resonator with its electrodes is connected in parallel with the condenser of an oscillatory circuit tuned approximately to the resonance frequency of the quartz, the effective capacity and resistance of the resonator change sharply at resonance frequency.

The experimental arrangement is shown in fig. 12.4, which is taken from Dye's paper. A current-measuring instrument is inserted in series with the inductance

---

* *Proc. Roy. Soc.*, A, Vol. 143, p. 285 (1934).
† *Journ. Amer. Soc. Acoust.*, Vol. 9, p. 185 (1938).
‡ *Proc. I. R. E.*, Vol. 10, p. 83 (1933).
§ *Proc. Amer. Acad. Arts and Sci.*, Vol. 59, p. 81 (1923).
‖ *Proc. Phys. Soc.*, Vol. 38, p. 399 (1926).   ¶ *Proc. I. R. E.*, Vol. 16, p. 742 (1928).
** *Proc. Nat. Acad. Sci.*, Vol. 16, p. 496 (1930).

of the oscillating circuit and is found to show a very sharp minimum at the resonance frequency. The natural frequency of the quartz oscillator, which is ordinarily very high, may be reduced by loading it with steel.

The oscillator may be used to maintain oscillations of its own frequency by an arrangement used by Pierce and shown in fig. 9.9. The inductance may be used to couple the oscillator to another circuit. Pierce, however, found that in practice the beats with another circuit were usually so loud and clear that no coupling other than static effects was required.

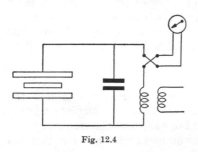

Fig. 12.4

The natural frequency of the quartz is determined by comparison with a valve-maintained tuning-fork and the frequency of this fork is in turn determined by comparison with a standard clock, using a phonodeik (p. 342). The frequency of the fork is checked by comparison of the valve-maintained fork with the oscillations induced by the rotation of an iron-toothed wheel near the poles of a telephone receiver, the rate of rotation of the wheel being independently determined.

By means of the single frequency of the quartz and its various harmonics a calibration of a series of wave-meters was made with an accuracy estimated at 0·1 per cent over the whole range.

10. Doppler's Principle.

For all kinds of waves the apparent frequency depends on the motion of the source and of the observer and may depend on the motion of the medium. The phenomenon is familiar in the case of a passing train or motor-car. If a train passes through a station with the locomotive whistling, an observer standing on the platform notices that just as the train passes the pitch of the whistle appears to drop more or less suddenly. In the case of a car in motion there is generally a hum of recognizable pitch. Here again an observer on the road notices a sudden drop in pitch as the car passes. Similarly, if a source of sound is fixed in position and an observer approaches and passes it, the apparent pitch drops at the instant of passage. The phenomenon is due to the fact that during approach of source and observer the apparent pitch of a source of sound is higher than its true pitch and during separation lower than its true pitch.

Doppler (1803–1853) * applied the principle to explain the colour of stars, the colour being attributed to relative velocity of the star and the earth in the line of sight. If the two were approaching the apparent frequency would be increased and the apparent wave-length diminished so that the star would appear blue, while if the two were separating the star would appear red. This application was unsound in principle and would involve a relative velocity very much greater than that actually found; but the spectroscope shows a displacement of spectral

* *Abh. d. Böhm. Ges. d. Wiss.*, Vol. 2, p. 467 (1842).

lines which is attributed to this cause, and a measurement of this shift enables us to calculate the relative velocity in the line of sight in terms of the velocity of light.

The discovery of the principle seems to have been made independently by J. Scott Russell (1808–1882),* by Fizeau (1819–1896) † and possibly by Babinet.

The simplest case is that in which the velocities are in the line joining the source and observer.

Let c be the velocity of sound, u_s the velocity of the source, u_o the velocity of the observer, f the true frequency of the source, W the velocity of the medium.

Let S (fig. 12.5) be the initial position of the source and S′ its

Fig. 12.5.—Doppler's principle

position one second later. Then if $SA = c + W$ and $SS' = u_s$, the waves emitted by the source in one second occupy the distance $S'A = c + W - u_s$.

Similarly, let O be the position of the observer at a given instant and O′ his position a second later. Let $OB = c + W$ and $OO' = u_o$. Then the waves received by the observer in one second are contained in the distance $O'B = c + W - u_o$.

But f waves are contained in the distance $c + W - u_s$,

$$\therefore \text{ Apparent frequency } f' = f \times \frac{c + W - u_o}{c + W - u_s}. \quad (12.3)$$

(1) *Motion of Medium.*

If $u_o = u_s$, the apparent frequency is always the same as the true frequency and the velocity of the medium is without effect. For all other cases the velocity of the medium is added to the numerator and denominator and the apparent frequency is modified.

(2) *Motion of Source.*

Here we may measure the velocity relative to the medium, in which case we have

$$f' = f \times \frac{c - u_o}{c - u_s}. \quad \quad \quad \quad (12.4)$$

---

* *Brit. Ass. Report, Trans. of Sections*, p. 37 (1846).
† *Ann. de Chim. et de Phys.*, Vol. 19, p. 211 (1870).

As u_s increases from zero f' becomes greater until $u_s = c$. In this case all the waves travel with the source and reach the observer together, so that $f' = \infty$. If $u_s > c$ then f' becomes progressively less as u_s increases but is now negative in sign. This means that the waves emitted are being received in the reverse order, the source having outstripped the waves it has emitted. If u_s is negative, i.e. the source is receding, then f' diminishes gradually to zero as u_s tends to infinity.

(3) *Motion of Observer.*

As u_o increases to c, f' diminishes to zero. For $u_o > c$, f' increases again but is negative. The velocity of the observer being now greater than that of the waves, he overtakes them in the reverse order. If u_o is negative, i.e. if the observer is approaching the source, then f' increases as u_o increases and without limit.

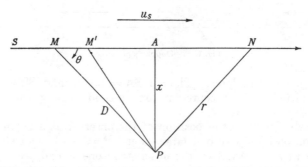

Fig. 12.6.—Doppler's principle; relative velocity not in line joining source and observer

It is worth while noting that for the same relative velocity we get different results according as the source or observer is in motion relative to the medium. Thus for a relative velocity of approach u we have for an observer in motion and a source at rest

$$f_1' = f \times \frac{c - u}{c}. \quad \ldots \quad \ldots \quad (12.5)$$

while for a source in motion and an observer at rest we have

$$f_2' = f \times \frac{c}{c + u}.$$

That is, $$\frac{f_1'}{f_2'} = \frac{c^2 - u^2}{c^2} = 1 - \frac{u^2}{c^2} \quad \ldots \quad \ldots \quad (12.6)$$

If the relative velocity is not in the line joining source and observer the result is not so simple. The change in pitch is more gradual. The difference will be understood if we assume the source of sound to be travelling in a straight line SA (fig. 12.6) which does not pass through the position P of the observer. Let the source pass from M to M' in time δt and let the interval between the arrival at P of the sounds emitted by the source while at M and at M' respectively be $\delta\tau$. Then

$$\delta\tau = \delta t - \frac{MP - M'P}{c}$$

$$= \delta t - \frac{MM' \cos\theta}{c}$$

$$= \delta t - \frac{u_s \cos\theta\,\delta t}{c}$$

$$= \delta t \left(1 - \frac{u_s \cos\theta}{c}\right),$$

$$\therefore f' \doteqdot f\left(1 + \frac{u_s \cos\theta}{c}\right),$$

if u_s is small compared with c.

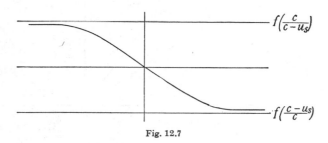

Fig. 12.7

Similarly, as the source recedes we have

$$f' \doteqdot f\left(1 - \frac{u_s \cos\theta}{c}\right)$$

or in general $$f' \doteqdot f\left(1 \pm \frac{u_s \cos\theta}{c}\right). \quad \ldots \ldots \quad (12.7)$$

If $\theta = 0$, $\cos\theta = 1$ and

$$f' = f\left(1 \pm \frac{u_s}{c}\right),$$

which may happen either when the source is moving in a line passing through P, which is the case of $x = 0$, or when the source is very distant, either approaching or receding.

If $x \neq 0$ then the apparent frequency changes from $fc/(c - u_s)$ to $f(c - u_s)/c$ as shown in fig. 12.7, the change being more or less abrupt according as x is small or large. When the source is at A we have

$\theta = \pi/2$ and $\cos \theta = 0$. Then $f' = f$, and the apparent frequency is the true frequency.

11. Air Waves generated by Projectiles.

A rapidly moving projectile acts as a source of sound, the frequency of which depends on its velocity. Dufour relates that in 1868 old soldiers told him how different the sound of an approaching cannon ball was from the sound of a receding one. As it approached it whistled, as it receded it gave a sound of much lower pitch. When they heard this sound they could say " It is not for us—it is for others ". The speed of the projectiles of those days was always less than the speed of sound.

In the case of a shell there are in general three sounds, (1) the report due to firing, (2) a whistling during the course of the motion, (3) the burst.

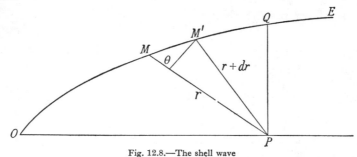

Fig. 12.8.—The shell wave

Let O (fig. 12.8) be the point of firing, OQE the trajectory and E the point at which the shell bursts. If the velocity of the shell is less than the velocity of sound and if all the air waves generated travel with the normal velocity of sound (which is true except within a few metres of the gun) the phenomenon is fairly simple.

As before we have

$$\delta\tau = \delta t \left(1 - \frac{u_s}{c} \cos \theta\right).$$

Since $u_s < c$, $\delta\tau$ is always positive, so the observer at P hears the whistling preceded by the report and followed by the burst.

For modern guns, at least in the early part of the trajectory of the shell, however, the matter is not so simple. For this case $u_s > c$ and $\delta\tau$ is not necessarily positive. For $c = u_s \cos \theta$, we have an arc of the trajectory for which $\delta\tau = 0$, and the waves generated at successive points arrive simultaneously at P. This is the phenomenon which the French call *onde du choc*. It is an intense and sharp sound, which might be confused by the uninitiated with the report or the burst.

This sound is the first to be heard if we suppose that $\delta\tau$ is negative along the arc OM and positive along the arc ME, as is ordinarily the case.

If we take as zero of time the instant when the shell wave reaches P and denote the path OM by σ and the radius vector of a point Q by ρ, then the time of arrival at P of a wave from Q is given by

$$\tau = \int_\sigma^s \frac{ds}{u_s} + \left(\frac{\rho}{c} - \frac{r}{c}\right).$$

But

$$\frac{\rho - r}{c} = \int_r^\rho \frac{dr}{c} = -\int_\sigma^s \frac{ds \cos\theta}{c}.$$

$$\therefore \ \tau = \int_\sigma^s \left(\frac{1}{u_s} - \frac{\cos\theta}{c}\right) ds.$$

For all points on the trajectory beyond M we have ds positive, and since $\cos\theta$ is decreasing the bracket is also positive, so that τ is positive.

For all points on the trajectory earlier than M, ds is negative, and since $\cos\theta$ is increasing the bracket is also negative, so that τ is positive. Hence the shell wave is the first sound to arrive at P.

The time of the arrival of the report at P is given by

$$\tau_1 = \int_0^\sigma \left(\frac{\cos\theta}{c} - \frac{1}{u_s}\right) ds$$

and the time of arrival of the burst by

$$\tau_2 = \int_\sigma^s \left(\frac{1}{u_s} - \frac{\cos\theta}{c}\right) ds,$$

where s is the arc OE. That is, the report may arrive at P before or after the shell-burst. If the whistling is heard from the earlier part of the trajectory it is heard from the various points in the inverse order of their traversal by the projectile.

In the case of a projectile travelling in a straight line with constant velocity the phenomenon is greatly simplified.

Let a (fig. 12.9) be the position of the projectile at any instant. Mark positions b, d, e, on the trajectory at distances behind it of u_s, $2u_s$, $3u_s$ ft. With these points as centres describe a series of spheres of radii c, $2c$, $3c$. The envelope of these spheres is a cone of semi-angle $a = \sin^{-1}c/u_s$. Each element of the cone moves normal to its own plane, so that an observer at P hears the shell wave from a point M such that $\cos\theta = \sin a = c/u_s$. That is,

$$c - u_s \cos\theta = 0.$$

Thus we see that for the case $u_s > c$ the first sound to be heard is the shell wave, and it is followed by the whistling. The former is liable to confusion with the report due to the firing of the gun, but differs from it in consisting of rapid alternations of small intensity extremely disagreeable to the ear but producing very little effect on any mechanism of large inertia. The report affects the ear much less. Theoretically the whistling is double, proceeding from the parts of the trajectory before and after the origin of the shell wave. The whistling from the early part of the trajectory finishes with the sound of the report, and that from the later part with the sound of the burst, but the order of arrival of these two sounds depends on the position of the observer.

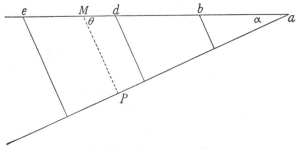

Fig. 12.9.—Waves from a shell

It has been suggested by Bouasse that thunder may be due to the arrival of a series of " shock " waves. The lightning may play the part of a projectile of infinite speed, in which case the foot of each normal dropped from the observer to the path of the lightning would give the source of one " shock " wave.

12. Experimental Investigation of Doppler's Principle.

To most observant people to-day Doppler's principle is a fact of common experience, but high-speed sources of sound are now much more frequently met with than was the case a century ago. When first stated the principle was strongly contested and experimental demonstration was called for.

The first experiments were carried out by Buijs Ballot * on a single-track railway between Utrecht and Maarsen. A trumpet was carried on the locomotive and three others were used by groups posted at the side of the track. The trumpets were sounded alternately on the locomotive and at the side of the track, and the apparent change of pitch was observed both for a moving source and for a moving observer by musicians whose estimate of small intervals of pitch was

* *Pogg. Ann.*, Vol. 66, p. 321 (1845).

considered to be reliable. Fourteen observers took part, and the estimated changes of pitch were in accord with the predictions of theory. Similar experiments were carried out with greater numerical precision by Vogel in 1876.

Mach * devised a laboratory experiment to illustrate the principle. A wooden rod about 2 metres long is made to turn about a horizontal axis through its centre. At one end is attached a whistle blown by air admitted through the axle and carried down a tube in the interior of the wooden rod. To an observer in the plane of rotation the velocity of the whistle varies between $\pm 2\pi r m$, where r is the half-length of the rod and m is the number of revolutions per second. If $m = 1$ then $2rm$ is approximately 6 metres/sec. Nothing is gained by making m too large, as the time interval between successive notes is then too small for easy recognition of pitch. It follows that r must be large. For $m = 3$ we have the ratio of the two apparent frequencies given by

$$\frac{f_1}{f_2} \doteqdot \frac{340 + 18}{340 - 18} \doteqdot 1\cdot 11$$

which is approximately the interval of a tone.

König operated with two tuning-forks of frequency approximately 512, but giving about four beats per second. He verified the fact that when one of the forks was moved or when the observer moved relatively to the forks the number of beats per second varied by the amount required by the principle. Humby,† using two telephone diaphragms maintained in vibration by the same oscillating circuit, showed the effect of beats by the action of a sensitive flame when one of the diaphragms was moved. Here again the number of beats per second is in accord with the theory of Doppler's principle.

---

* *Pogg. Ann.*, Vol. 112, p. 66 (1881).   † *Proc. Phys. Soc.*, Vol. 39, p. 435 (1927).

CHAPTER XIII

Analysis of Sounds

1. Quality.

It used to be possible to classify all sounds roughly as either " notes " or " noises ". The recently accepted definition of a noise as " a sound which is not desired by the recipient " puts this classification out of date, but as it is convenient for some purposes to retain the old meaning of the word noise as an antithesis to note, we shall do so in this chapter.

Sounds, then, may be roughly classified as being either " notes " or " noises ". The division between the two classes is by no means sharp, and its exact location is to some extent a matter of personal taste. Leaving this borderland territory out of account, however, we shall find that many sounds have a smooth, regular, and pleasing character with an assignable pitch which marks them as musical notes, while others have a rough, irregular, unpleasant character and no assignable pitch and are unhesitatingly classed as noises.

There is, however, a further complication. Very many musical notes have noises associated with them, and many noises have the more or less definite pitch which we are accustomed to associate with a note. An ordinary piece of firewood when dropped on the hearth gives a sound which might hastily be dismissed as a noise. Yet the sound has a quite definite pitch, which may be recognized if a number of pieces are dropped in succession. Especially is this true if the pieces have previously been adjusted in length, breadth, or thickness to give a recognizable succession in pitch. The xylophone is an instrument in which the notes are sounds of this type, produced by the transverse vibrations of bars.

Conversely, musical notes carry associated noises. We all recognize the scraping noise associated with the notes produced by the unskilled violinist. Probably few of us are aware of the amount of noise associated with the expert production of music. If, while listening to a really skilled performance we concentrate our attention on the noise of the piano action and of the fingers of the pianist on the keys, or the scrape of the violinist, or even the breathing of the singer, we shall be surprised at the amount of noise which ordinarily escapes our notice simply because we are deliberately attending to the notes and not to the noises.

The classification of sounds can be carried a step further by subdividing the class "notes". Notes have three characteristics. Two
of these, pitch and loudness, we have already discussed. There remains
the third characteristic—quality or tone, known in French as *timbre*
and in German as *Klangfarbe*. This is the characteristic which enables
us to distinguish between two notes of the same pitch and loudness
produced on two different types of musical instrument, e.g. the violin
and the piano. It even enables us to distinguish between two notes
of the same pitch and loudness produced on two instruments of the
same type, e.g. two voices. This characteristic is associated with the
fact that in general musical notes are complex. When the ear has its
attention directed to the musical note which it receives, it does not
merely hear that one musical tone which dominates the sensation
when received uncritically and determines the pitch of the note; it
becomes aware also of a whole series of musical tones of higher pitch.

It may be that Aristotle had this analysis in mind when propounding some
of his problems. In Book XIX, Problem 8, we find: "Why does the low note
contain the sound of the high note? It is like an obtuse angle, whereas the high
note is like an acute angle." Again, in Problem 13, we read: "Why is it that
in the octave the concord of the upper note exists in the lower but not vice versa?"
Mersenne refers to the work of Aristotle in his book *Harmonie Universelle* (1636).
In a section headed "To determine why a vibrating string gives several sounds
simultaneously" (p. 208), he says: "But it must be remarked that Aristotle
did not know that the struck string gives at least five different sounds simultaneously, of which the first is the natural sound of the string, serving as fundamental to the others and to which alone attention is paid in singing; all the
more because the others are so weak that only the best ears can hear them easily.
It is necessary to choose a deep silence in order to hear them, although this will
no longer be necessary when the ear has become accustomed. As for myself,
I have no difficulty: I have no doubt that anyone can hear them who gives the
necessary attention. Now these sounds follow the ratio of the numbers 1, 2, 3, 4, 5,
because four sounds are heard different from the fundamental, of which the
first is the octave above, the second is the twelfth, the third is the fifteenth, and
the fourth the major seventeenth."
It seems worth while to reproduce this passage, which appears to be the
earliest clear exposition of the phenomenon subsequently elaborated at such
length by Helmholtz. The association of these harmonics with quality is clearly
implied in Mersenne's query in the same section whether "the sound of each
string is the more harmonious and agreeable as it causes to be heard a greater
number of different sounds simultaneously".

Sauveur (1653–1716) in 1701 applied the term *harmonics* to these
higher tones which accompany the lower tone or *fundamental*. He also
gave the first satisfactory explanation of the origin of these tones in
the case of the vibrating string by showing that the string actually
vibrates as a whole and in segments at one and the same time. Each of
the harmonics corresponds to the vibration of the string in segments
or parts: hence the use of the term *partial* as equivalent to the term
harmonic in this case.

In a bell these constituent tones or overtones are very obvious, but a little care and attention will reveal their presence in the notes of the piano, violin, and almost all other musical instruments. We may perhaps clarify this further distinction by continuing to use the term " note " for all musical sounds which are complex and the term " tone " for musical sounds which are simple and unanalysable and for the constituent simple musical sounds into which the " note " can be analysed. The number and relative intensity of the constituent tones determine the quality of the note. Simple tones differ only in pitch and loudness and are identical in quality.

It was at one time thought that pitch was simply related to frequency, loudness to intensity and quality to overtone structure. Fletcher * has shown that these relationships are not in fact so simple. The pitch of a musical note depends not only on the frequency of the fundamental tone but also on the overtone structure of the note. The loudness depends not only on the intensity but also on the frequency and the overtone structure. The quality depends not only on the overtone structure but also on the frequency and the intensity.

2. Partial Tones and Harmonics.

The vibration of an elastic system in parts can be illustrated by means of a rubber cord. If a long rubber cord which is fixed at one end is held at the other end and the hand moved gently up and down, with a little manipulation it is easy to hit the right frequency and make the cord vibrate as a whole, the centre having the greatest amplitude. If the frequency of the motion of the hand is doubled the cord splits up into two vibrating segments, each occupying half its length and separated by a relatively stationary point or node at the centre. If the frequency of the motion is made three times the original frequency, then the cord splits into three vibrating segments separated by two nodes. With patience and skill this process can be pushed much further and we find that the vibrating cord has a whole series of possible modes of vibration, each with its appropriate frequency, and that these frequencies are approximately in the ratio $1 : 2 : 3 : 4 : \ldots$

We may parallel this experiment in the region of audible sound by replacing the rubber cord with a thin wire stretched between two bridges and tuned to a frequency of 128. If now red paper riders are placed one-quarter and three-quarters of the length from either end and a white rider is placed at the midpoint, and we take a sounding tuning-fork of frequency 256 and place its shaft on the wire where it crosses the bridge of the monochord, the two red riders will be thrown and the white one will remain in position. The fork has imposed on the wire a frequency double that of its vibration as a whole and it has split up into two segments separated by a node at the centre.

* Journ. Amer. Soc. Acoust., Vol. 6, p. 59 (1935).

Three segments are given by a fork of frequency 384, and four by a fork of frequency 512. The tones given out by the string, or any sounding body, when vibrating in parts are called *partial tones*. They may be in the simple frequency ratio $1 : 2 : 3 : \ldots$, as is approximately true in the case of the wire, and they are then said to be *harmonic*, or they may be in no such simple relation, as in the case of the bell or the tuning-fork, and are then said to be *inharmonic*. Strictly harmonic partials are hardly ever found, but approximately harmonic partials are common. In the case of the siren there are no partial tones in the strict sense, since there are no parts to vibrate, but there is a series of harmonics.

This fact makes clear a distinction between a partial tone and a harmonic which French writers on acoustics have frequently insisted upon. A harmonic is always a simple tone; a partial is not simple and may carry its own series of harmonics. The case in which the partials and harmonics are identical is a limiting case to which in practice we approximate more or less closely. In the *Glossary of Acoustical Terms and Definitions* published by the British Standards Institution (March, 1936) this distinction is obliterated. According to it, a partial is simply a pure tone component of a sound. An overtone is a partial having a frequency higher than that of the fundamental. A harmonic is a partial having a frequency which is an integral multiple of that of the fundamental. It is noted that in physics and electrical engineering the nth harmonic implies a frequency equal to n times the fundamental frequency, whereas in music it implies a frequency equal to $(n + 1)$ times the fundamental frequency.

3. Analysis by Ear.

Reference has already been made to the possibility of analysing by ear the composite tones of musical instruments. Some observers seem to find analysis easier than others, but almost all observers improve with practice. When a mass of sound from an orchestra falls on the ear it is comparatively easy to shut the eyes and listen at will to the first violins or the 'cellos or the drums, or any single group of instruments. In listening to a vocal quartet we can follow any individual voice. Now the vibration of the air in the ear passage is composite; somehow the ear must be separating out the several constituents. This is a very remarkable power. If various systems of waves were passing across the surface of the sea, one system due to the wind, another to a passing steamer, and a third perhaps to a yacht, it would be quite impossible for the eye by observing one point on the surface through a tube to determine what systems were present. Yet, as Helmholtz points out, this is analogous to the task which the ear habitually performs with success. But the analysis with which we are at present concerned goes a step further. The examples just considered deal with sounds from different sources, and until comparatively recently there are few records of observers who appreciated separately the series of partial tones constituting a musical note and coming from the same source. Every observer appreciates these synthetically as quality, but they are not perceived analytically as separate constituents.

The capacity to hear partial tones is not necessarily associated with a musically-trained ear; it depends more on a faculty of attention than upon musical training. If, in the case of a stretched wire, tuned as before to a frequency of 128, we pluck it near one end, we are conscious at first of hearing only one tone—the fundamental tone of the wire with a frequency of 128. If while the wire is still sounding we follow the procedure suggested by Sauveur and touch the mid-point lightly with a feather or the corner of a handkerchief, the vibrations corresponding to the fundamental (which require a place of maximum motion at the mid-point) are damped out and the octave sings out with great distinctness. The effect of the damping is not to produce a new tone but to remove the tone on which attention was concentrated and leave the mind free to attend to the next tone of the series. In the same way, if the wire is damped at a point one-third of its length from one end, the twelfth with a frequency of 384 sings out unmistakably. This is the lowest tone which has a node at the point touched. The double octave and higher tones can be easily demonstrated in the same way. This damping process, however, is not the most conclusive demonstration. After eliciting the octave as a partial by damping, we may use it as a guide to what to listen for, and if we now pluck the string in the ordinary way the octave will be easily heard in the complex sound without damping the fundamental at all. The same is true of the twelfth, which is even more easily heard. Indeed, when the experiment has been repeated once or twice the existence of the partial tones will be so obvious that it seems amazing that they could ever have been missed. Helmholtz * after long practice was able in the case of a thin string to hear the series of partials up to the sixteenth.

A similar experiment may be carried out with the piano, which gives a good series of partials. Sound any note on the piano as a guide to the ear, and when the sound has ceased strike the note an octave below strongly, and the tone an octave above it will be distinctly heard. Again, sound g′ as a guide to the ear, and then sound c strongly; g′ will be heard as one of its partials. After a little practice, especially in the case of the trained ear which knows what to listen for, the guide will be unnecessary and the experimenter will be launched on the career of unaided analysis by ear.

Upper partials on most wind instruments and in the human voice are at first more difficult to hear than those on stringed instruments.

* *Sensations of Tone*, 3rd English ed., p. 50.

The case of the human voice is probably the most difficult. Yet here Rameau (1685–1764) * succeeded without any adventitious aids. Helmholtz † suggests the following experiment. " Get a powerful bass voice to sing e♭ to the vowel o in sore (more like aw in saw than o in so), gently touch b♭ a twelfth above, which is the third partial of the e♭, and let its sound die away while you are listening to it attentively. The note b♭ will appear really not to die away but to keep on sounding even when the string is damped by removing the finger from the key, because the ear unconsciously passes from the tone of the piano to the partial tone of the same pitch produced by the singer and takes the latter for a continuation of the former."

In order that the physical significance of this analytical capacity of the ear may be appreciated it is necessary first of all to consider the theorem known as Fourier's theorem.

4. Fourier's Theorem ‡.

In 1822 J. B. Fourier (1768–1830) published his *Analytical Theory of Heat*, and in the course of it stated an important mathematical theorem now known by his name. It may, for our present purpose, be expressed as follows: Any continuous single-valued periodic function whatever can be expressed as a summation of simple harmonic terms, having frequencies which are multiples of that of the given function. This means that any periodic curve, however complicated, may be built up from a series of sine curves of appropriate amplitudes and relative phases having the periods $T/1, T/2, T/3, \ldots$. This is a very remarkable theorem. It seems incredible that a vibration represented for instance by the straight-line graph in the upper half of fig. 13.1 can be built up out of or analysed into a series of smooth sine curves: yet such is the case, and the result of the analysis is perfectly definite. Given the graph corresponding to any periodic vibration, however complicated, the constituent simple harmonic vibrations may be found, together with the amplitude and relative phase of each.

Analytically Fourier's theorem may be put in the form:

$$x = a_0 + a_1 \cos \omega t + a_2 \cos 2\omega t + \ldots + a_r \cos r\omega t + \ldots$$
$$+ b_1 \sin \omega t + b_2 \sin 2\varphi t + \ldots + b_r \sin r\omega t + \ldots.$$

If we integrate both sides of this equation with respect to t from $t = 0$ to $t = T$, the integrals of all the sine and cosine terms are equal to zero and we are left with

$$\int_0^T x\,dt = a_0 T.$$

$$\therefore a_0 = \frac{1}{T} \int_0^T x\,dt = \text{mean value of } x.$$

* *Nouveau Système de Musique Théorique* (Paris, 1726).   † Loc. cit., p. 51.
‡ For a full treatment see Carslaw, *Fourier's Series and Integrals* (Macmillan, 1906).

Again, if we multiply both sides by $\cos r\omega t\, dt$, and integrate between 0 and T, the integrals of all the terms on the right-hand side are equal to zero, except $\int_0^T a_r \cos^2 r\omega t\, dt$, and we have

$$\int_0^T x \cos r\omega t\, dt = a_r \int_0^T \frac{1 - \cos 2r\omega t}{2}\, dt$$

$$= \frac{a_r T}{2}.$$

$$\therefore\ a_r = \frac{2}{T} \int_0^T x \cos r\omega t\, dt.$$

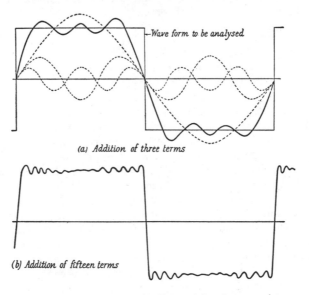

(a) Addition of three terms

(b) Addition of fifteen terms

Fig. 13.1.—Analysis of a straight-line graph into the appropriate series of sine curves

Similarly, if we multiply by $\sin r\omega t\, dt$ and integrate from 0 to T we have

$$b_r = \frac{2}{T} \int_0^T x \sin r\omega t\, dt.$$

If we apply the theorem to the straight-line graph in fig. 13.1 we see that

$$x = +a \text{ from } t = 0 \text{ to } t = T/2,$$

$$x = -a \text{ from } t = T/2 \text{ to } t = T.$$

Hence $\quad a_0 = \dfrac{1}{T}\displaystyle\int_0^T x\,dt$

$$= \frac{1}{T}\int_0^{T/2} a\,dt - \frac{1}{T}\int_{T/2}^T a\,dt$$

$$= \frac{a}{T}\frac{T}{2} - \frac{a}{T}\frac{T}{2} = 0.$$

$$a_r = \frac{2}{T}\int_0^T x\cos r\omega t\,dt$$

$$= \frac{2}{T}\int_0^{T/2} a\cos\frac{2\pi rt}{T}\,dt + \frac{2}{T}\int_{T/2}^T\left(-a\cos\frac{2\pi rt}{T}\right)dt$$

$$= \frac{a}{\pi r}(2\sin\pi r - \sin 2\pi r)$$

$$= 0 \text{ for all values of } r.$$

$$b_r = \frac{2}{T}\int_0^T x\sin\frac{2\pi rt}{T}\,dt$$

$$= \frac{2}{T}\int_0^{T/2} a\sin\frac{2\pi rt}{T}\,dt + \frac{2}{T}\int_{T/2}^T\left(-a\sin\frac{2\pi rt}{T}\right)dt$$

$$= \frac{a}{\pi r}(1 + \cos 2\pi r - 2\cos\pi r).$$

For all integral values of r this gives

$$b_r = \frac{a}{\pi r}(2 - 2\cos\pi r).$$

For r even, $\qquad b_r = 0:$

For r odd, $\qquad b_r = \dfrac{4a}{\pi r},$

$$\therefore\; x = \frac{4a}{\pi}\left(\sin\omega t + \tfrac{1}{3}\sin 3\omega t + \tfrac{1}{5}\sin 5\omega t + \ldots\right).$$

The larger the number of terms taken, the more nearly does the graph approach the straight-line form, but only by taking the infinite series is the correspondence made exact. This will be seen from fig. 13.1.

In most actual cases the periodic curve is too complicated for the amplitudes of the respective components to be calculated without immense labour, and machines have therefore been devised which perform mechanically the integrations required. The graph to be analysed is drawn to the required scale and then placed on the base of the instrument. The pointer is run along the graph and the relative amplitudes of the first few terms of the series can be read off directly.

5. Ohm's Law.

The importance of the harmonic analysis of a complex vibration was first made clear by G. S. Ohm (1787–1854). Obviously there are a great many possible methods of analysing a complex vibration. The analysis by Fourier's series is only one of these possible methods. It derives its importance from the fact that it corresponds to the analysis of the complex note actually made by the human ear. Ohm * asserted that vibrations which are strictly simple harmonic are unanalysable and are perceived by the ear as simple tones, but that all other forms of periodic vibration can be analysed by the ear and each harmonic constituent separately perceived, if of sufficient intensity. The results of this analysis are not as a rule consciously registered; that is, in listening to a musical note we do not ordinarily notice its complex nature, but a proper direction of our attention enables us to do so. Thus the ear is a practical Fourier analyser, and harmonic analysis in the case of musical notes derives its importance from this fact.

A simple tone, then, always corresponds to a simple harmonic vibration and can be represented by the graph

$$x = a \sin (2\pi ft - \epsilon).$$

It can be varied in only two ways: (1) a may be altered and with it the loudness of the tone; (2) f may be varied and with it the pitch of the tone.

The form of the curve can be altered by compounding it with other curves whose periods are $T/2$, $T/3$, $T/4$, ...

If we select the first of these periods we can assume that we are dealing with two vibrations given respectively by

$$x = a_1 \sin \frac{2\pi t}{T}, \quad x = a_2 \sin \frac{4\pi t}{T}.$$

These represent two simple tones, the second of which is the octave of the first. If we plot for each the value of x lying between $t = 0$ and $t = T$, the result is as shown by the dotted curves in fig. 13.2. If for each value of the abscissa we add the corresponding ordinates and join the resulting points we get the continuous curve shown in the figure. This is a curve representing a note no longer simple. It has the same pitch as the tone given by

$$x = a_1 \sin \frac{2\pi t}{T},$$

* *Pogg. Ann.*, Vol. 59, p. 513 (1843); Vol. 62, p. 1 (1844).

but it has a different loudness and a different quality. If instead
we had compounded

$$x = a_1 \sin\frac{2\pi t}{T}, \quad x = a_3 \sin\frac{6\pi t}{T},$$

we should again have had a note of the same pitch but of different
loudness and quality.

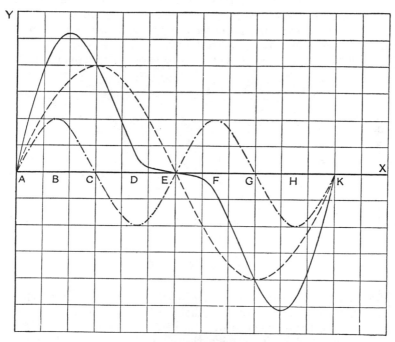

Fig. 13.2.—Composition of displacement curves

The dotted curve represents displacements due to a note and its octave. The continuous
curve represents the resultant displacements when the two are compounded

So far we have neglected the terms represented by ϵ, i.e. the relative
phases. Variation of these terms would alter the appearance of the
composite curve, but we shall see that there is reason to doubt whether
such an alteration always modifies the quality of the note which the
curve represents. The matter is considered further in section 14,
p. 364.

6. Graphical Analysis.

This method consists essentially in obtaining a graph representing
the displacement-time relation for the air vibration, and in submitting

this to analysis either by mathematical or by mechanical methods. It is, of course, difficult to obtain the required graph unless we are satisfied that the movement of a membrane or diaphragm upon which the sound waves impinges faithfully follows the movement of the air.

One of the earliest attempts to record the movement of the air in this way was made by Scott * using his " phonautograph ". To a flexible diaphragm closing the receiving horn was attached a pointer which traced on a smoked surface. In this way a curve was obtained which more or less reproduced the to-and-fro motion of the air in contact with the diaphragm. Later the phonograph was used for the same purpose. The early phonograph produced on a rotating cylinder of wax a furrow of varying depth, the tracing point moving in to or

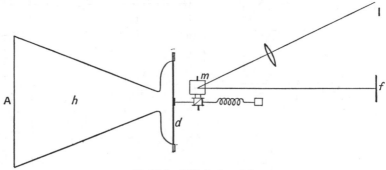

Fig. 13.3.—Miller's phonodeik

out from the wax with the motion of the diaphragm on which the sound impinged. One end of a long light lever was then made to retrace the furrow on the cylinder or disc, while the other end traced a curve on a smoked drum. By placing the pivot of the lever close to the point moving over the record, considerable magnification was obtained, and a curve which roughly corresponded to the motion of the original tracing point—and therefore of the diaphragm of the recording mechanism—was produced. This method is obviously open to very serious disadvantages. The indentation of the tracing point on the wax will follow the movement of the air very imperfectly, as the resistance of the wax will vary with the depth of the indentation, and the finer details of the air movements are likely to be blurred and obscured.

A great advance in this method of analysis was marked by the design of the phonodeik by D. C. Miller.† Its mechanism will be understood by reference to fig. 13.3.

* *Cosmos*, Vol. 14, p. 314 (1859); *Comptes Rendus*, Vol. 53, p. 108 (1861).
† *The Science of Musical Sounds* (Macmillan, 1916).

The horn A collects the sound and concentrates it on the very fine glass diaphragm d of thickness about ·0076 cm. To the centre of this diaphragm is fixed a very fine wire, which passes once round the vertical steel staff and is held taut by a light spring. To the staff is fixed a very small mirror m about 1 mm. square. The varying pressure in the sound wave causes vibration of the diaphragm, and this vibration in turn pulls and releases the attached wire, so causing rotation of the steel staff and mirror. A beam of light from a fixed source I is reflected from the mirror on to a vertical film f, where it is focused. The rotation of the staff will thus produce a horizontal oscillation of the image of the source, and if the film is made to move vertically the spot of light will trace on it a curve which reproduces the motion of the diaphragm, and therefore, presumably, of the air in the horn. The speed of the film is about 40 ft. per second, and the magnification is about 40,000, so that an amplitude of $\frac{1}{10}$ mm. in the diaphragm would produce an amplitude of 4 m. in the resulting curve.

By means of this instrument Miller has obtained curves corresponding to the human voice and various musical instruments, and some of these are shown in fig. 13.4 (p. 344).

The difficulty about this instrument, as about all instruments devised for analysing sounds, is to be sure that the response of the instrument is uniform over the whole frequency range, so that the various components preserve their relative intensity. The diaphragm, for instance, will have a series of natural frequencies corresponding to different partial tones. Clearly, any component tone having a frequency coinciding with that of one of these partials will produce a disproportionate response in the instrument, and will appear in the ultimate analysis with its intensity greatly exaggerated. The horn is open to the same objection, as is also the air cavity at the end of the horn in which the diaphragm is housed.

The only effective method of checking the response of the phonodeik is to produce a series of pure tones of the same intensity, distributed over the whole frequency range, and measure the response in each case. At the time when the phonodeik was first used there was no simple method available for producing pure tones of known intensity, and Miller had a series of organ pipes specially designed by an expert to give equal loudness of tone. With this series he calibrated the phonodeik, and used this calibration curve to correct the results of the analysis.

A modification of the phonodeik has been designed and constructed by S. H. Anderson.*

The film record obtained by Miller was enlarged to the required size by projecting it optically on to a sheet of drawing paper and tracing it in pencil. The drawing was then put through the analyser and the analysis recorded.

Instead of recording the movement of a diaphragm on which the sound waves are impinging, we may use this movement to generate

---

* *Journ. Amer. Soc. Acoust.*, Vol. 11, p. 31 (1925).

a variable electric current whose variations follow the pressure variations in the sound wave. Any form of microphone may be used in this transformation, the most faithful reproductions probably being given by the condenser microphone. The resulting current may be amplified

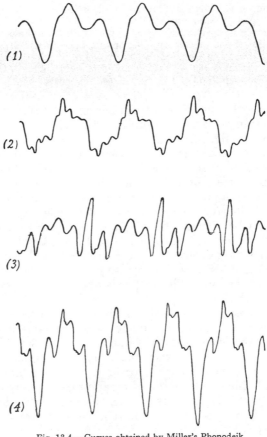

Fig. 13.4.—Curves obtained by Miller's Phonodeik

(1) Flute   (2) Clarinet   (3) Oboe   (4) Saxophone

without distortion, and analysis of this current may be carried out in a variety of ways.

The current may be led to an oscillograph consisting of a suspended magnet carrying a mirror and so arranged that the variations of the current are recorded by the deflection of the magnet. The spot of light is received on a moving film and traces what is in effect the displacement diagram for the air vibrations. This curve is then submitted to analysis by calculation or by a mechanical analyser.*

7. Analysis by Resonators.

It is possible by means of the principle of resonance to demonstrate the existence of partial tones quite independently of the ear. If two sounding bodies are tuned to resonance, then when one is sounded the other responds. Not only so, but if one is tuned to a partial of the other, when this other is sounded so that the partial is present the first will respond. Depress the key corresponding to c′ on the piano and when the note has ceased to sound keep the key depressed and sound (strongly) c an octave below. Release the key corresponding to c and its octave will sing out until the corresponding key is released. The string has been set in vibration by resonance with the partial. The existence of the first four or five partials is easily demonstrated in this way.

Helmholtz † carried out his experiments on the analysis of musical notes largely by means of air cavity resonators. These are made of glass or metal. They have two apertures; the wider one is presented to the source of sound and the narrower one is coated with soft wax and pressed into the ear. The wax moulds itself to the shape of the ear and subsequently fits air-tight. If one ear is plugged and a resonator inserted into the other most tones will be heavily damped, but if the proper tone of the resonator is present as a partial in any mass of tone it sounds in the ear most strongly. With these resonators Helmholtz was able to determine which partials were present in a given note, although no estimate of relative intensity was possible.

The hot-wire microphone described in section 12, p. 303 can be used for experiments of this kind, and has been so used by Tucker. It can be made extremely sensitive and will respond to notes of such feeble intensity as to be inaudible to the normal ear. It also enables us to obtain some idea as to relative intensities.

Instead of air resonators we may use reeds. Hickman ‡ has worked with an arrangement of this kind. A series of tuned reeds is mounted so that the reeds can be driven electromagnetically. Each reed carries a small concave mirror with which light from an illuminated slit can be focused on a screen. These slit images form a series of lines in the order of the reed frequencies. When a current having a complex wave form, such as the speech current from a microphone, is passed through the electromagnet, the reeds and in consequence the slit images on the screen will oscillate. The driving system and the reeds are so designed that the amplitude of oscillation of each image is proportional to the strength of the corresponding harmonic component

---

* Steinberg, *Journ. Amer. Soc. Acoust.*, Vol. 6, p. 16 (1934).
† Loc. cit., p. 43.   ‡ *Journ. Amer. Soc. Acoust.*, Vol. 6, p. 108 (1934).

in the driving current. Hence, by observing or photographing the slit image amplitude, the frequencies and the relative energy of the components of the complex current may be determined.

8. Heterodyne Analysis.

The principle underlying this type of analyser is the formation and measurement of combination tones (p. 478) produced by combining the note to be analysed with a pure tone of variable frequency. Fig. 13.5 shows a functional diagram of the apparatus. The current from the microphone is led to a balanced modulator. To this modulator is applied another wave, in series with the first, produced by an oscillator whose frequency may be varied over a wide range. The output of the modulator then contains a series of combination frequencies formed by the interaction of the incoming frequencies and the output of the oscillator. By a suitable arrangement of the modulator it can be

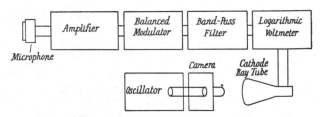

Fig. 13.5.—Functional diagram of the heterodyne analyser

ensured that the only frequencies present will be (1) a band of frequencies formed by the sum of each incoming frequency and the oscillator frequency and (2) a band formed by the difference of each incoming frequency and the oscillator frequency.* This mixture of frequencies is next applied to a narrow band-pass filter and the output of this is measured. Thus if it is desired to analyse a band of frequencies distributed between 0 and 5000 it may be done by using a narrow band-pass filter of frequency 11,000 and an oscillator giving a carrier wave the frequency of which varies from 11,000 to 16,000. In this case every frequency from 0 to 5000 present in the wave to be analysed will form with some frequency of the carrier wave a difference tone whose frequency is 11,000, and this difference tone will therefore be passed by the filter.

A very convenient form of filter is the magnetostriction type.† It consists of a rod of monel metal or some other metal showing the magnetostriction effect, supported at its mid-point and fitted with two coils, one on each end. The coils

---

* Carson, *Proc. I. R. E.*, Vol. 7, p. 187 (1919); Heising, *Proc. I. R. E.*, Vol. 13, p. 291 (1925).

† Hall, *Proc. I. R. E.*, Vol. 21, p. 1328 (1933).

are shielded from one another and supplied with a polarizing current. The rod is set in longitudinal vibration by a current of its own natural frequency passing through one coil and its vibration induces a voltage in the other coil (§ 5, p. 224) The resonance is very sharp and the arrangement acts as a very selective band-pass filter. The arrangement can be fitted with a recording device.*

In the arrangement described by Schuck † and called the " sound prism ", the observer (or performer) can hear a tone and observe its spectrum at the same time. Instead of the carrier frequency being slowly changed, it is rapidly swept through its range a number of times per second. The indications of the measuring device are arranged to produce vertical motion of a spot of light on a screen while the spot is moving horizontally in proportion to the carrier frequency (or to the logarithm of the frequency), so that the spot traces the frequency spectrum on the screen. The tracing of the spectrum is continuously repeated at a rapid rate so that the phenomenon of persistence of vision may enable the eye to see a steady spectrum. Inharmonic as well as harmonic constituent tones may be identified and measured, and the operation of the analysis may be made so rapid that changes in quality may be observed while the note is actually being played.

Freystedt ‡ used a cathode-ray tube as a recording apparatus, which has the advantage of possessing no inertia. The zero position of the spot of light suffers a horizontal deflection proportional to the logarithm of the frequency component whose vertical deflection is being measured. The record is taken on photographic film.

The use of difference tones in analysis seems to have been anticipated by the insects, for it has been shown § that by this means locusts converse. With insects having a tympanic organ there is no peripheral mechanism which can effect the analytical action performed by the cochlea of vertebrates. Yet insects seem to discriminate some quality other than loudness. The tympanic membrane is small, is generally tuned to a very high range of frequencies, and is quite in-sensitive to a pure tone of low frequency. Yet the auditory nerve, limited by the refractory period of the nerve-fibres, responds mainly to low frequencies and gives only a random response to high. Experiment with the locust shows, however, that a " carrier wave " of 8000 cycles/sec. modulated up to 300 cycles/sec. gives a nervous discharge consisting of bursts of activity at the frequency of modula-tion. So it seems that discrimination is effected by means of difference tones of low frequency present, not as Fourier components, but as frequencies of modula-tion or rapid beats hardly noticeable to us except as a " trilling " effect. When such a wave acts on a non-linear system, a component having as frequency the beat-frequency is introduced and can be filtered out, just as in the " rectification " of wireless signals. In the same way a cricket can recognize the stridulation of its mate even when the shrill " carrier wave " has been so reduced by artificial distortion that the note is unrecognized by the human ear.

9. Analysis by Diffraction Grating.

The formation of a sound spectrum by the use of a suitable diffrac-tion grating has been achieved by Meyer.‖ The general arrangement of the apparatus is shown in fig. 13.6.

* Hall, *Journ. Amer. Soc. Acoust.*, Vol. 7, p. 102 (1935);   Macdonald and Schuck, *J. Frankl. Inst.*, Vol. 218, p. 613 (1934);   Freystedt, *Zeit. f. tech. Physik*, Vol. 16, p. 533 (1935).

† *Proc. I. R. E.*, Vol. 22, p. 1295 (1934).   ‡ *Zeit. f. tech. Physik*, Vol. 16, p. 533 (1935).

§ Pumphrey and Rawdon-Smith, *Nature*, Vol. 143, p. 806 (1939).

‖ *Journ. Amer. Soc. Acoust.*, Vol. 7. p. 88 (1935).

The sound to be analysed is received by a microphone, amplified, and passed to a balanced modulator, where it is combined with a carrier frequency of 45,000. The lower sidebands (difference tones) are filtered out and the higher sidebands (summation tones) are transmitted, amplified and finally radiated from a ribbon loud-speaker giving approximately cylindrical waves. The concave grating has a length of three metres, and the grating elements are steel needles, 3·4 mm. in diameter, with their axes about 1 cm. apart. The diffracted spectrum is received on a movable condenser microphone. The theory of the arrangement is very fully discussed and examples of its records are given. It is said to afford possibilities of very rapid analysis.

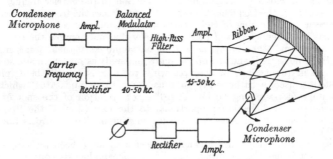

Fig. 13.6.—General arrangement for grating spectroscopy of sound

10. Analysis of Musical Notes.

The results of analyses of the notes given by the commoner musical instruments are given at some length by D. C. Miller.* Fig. 13.4, p. 344, gives typical examples of the kind of trace made by the spot of light on the film and afterwards analysed. The results of some of the analyses are set out graphically in figs. 13.7 and 13.8. Fig. 13.7 gives a comparison

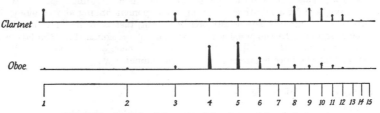

Fig. 13.7.—Analysis of the tones of the oboe and the clarinet

of the analyses for the clarinet and for the oboe, the distance of the dot from the base line in each case being a measure of the physical intensity of the corresponding harmonic. The figure brings out one very surprising result. Until these analyses were published it was always believed that the fundamental tone is by far the most intense and

* *The Science of Musical Sounds; Sound Waves, Their Shape and Speed.*

that the higher harmonics form a series of rapidly diminishing intensity. These analyses make it quite clear that this is by no means the case. The oboe has a relatively insignificant fundamental tone, but has twelve or more partials, the fourth and fifth predominating and carrying between them 66 per cent of the total energy. The clarinet, on the other hand, although the energy carried by its fundamental is rather

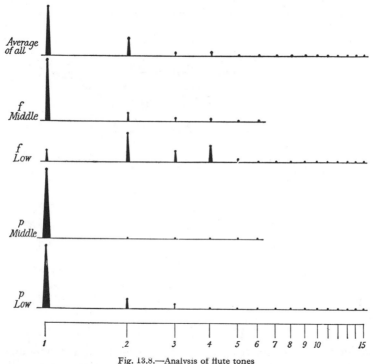

Fig. 13.8.—Analysis of flute tones

greater in proportion, distributes its energy over a longer series of partials, and the eighth, ninth, and tenth carry 18 per cent, 15 per cent, and 18 per cent respectively of the total energy or, together, about 50 per cent. The analysis of flute tones for strong and soft blowing is given in fig. 13.8, and here we see, as we should perhaps expect from the quality of tone, that we are dealing with notes giving much stronger fundamentals and relatively weak partials.

There is, however, not yet sufficient agreement in detail between the results of different observers. This is especially noticeable in the analysis of violin tones. Fig. 13.9 gives a comparison of the sound spectra for the G string as obtained by various observers. The first is the analysis obtained by Miller. The second was obtained by Grützmacher,* using his electrical analyser, and shows strong harmonics of the orders 6 and 8 respectively. The third and fourth analyses were obtained by Backhaus,† with two specially good old violins. The last two spectra are from Grützmacher and apply to the cornet and the horn respectively.

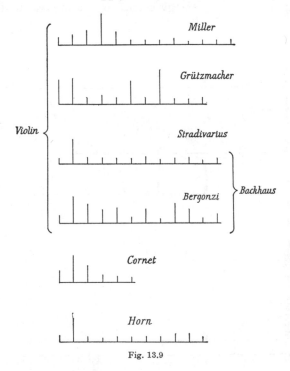

Fig. 13.9

It is quite obvious that the analyses for the violins differ more among themselves than they do from those for the cornet and horn. These discrepancies may be due in part to defects in the experimental methods and in part to the existence of differences which are significant for quality alongside of differences which are relatively unimportant. In any case, against these discrepancies we may place results in which very good agreement is shown. Thus Fletcher,‡ using the electrical analyser of Wegel and Moore, agrees with Miller in attributing to the clarinet three very strong harmonics of the orders 8, 9 and 10 respectively. The results of vowel analysis, to which a great deal of attention has lately been directed, also show a very gratifying measure of agreement.

* El. Nachr. Techn., Vol. 4, p. 533 (1927).   † Zeits. f. tech. Phys., Vol 8, p. 509 (1927).
‡ Phys. Rev., Vol. 23, p. 427 (1924).

11. Analysis of Speech Sounds.

The recording of speech sounds is of special interest, and the records at once reveal the difficulties of analysis. Figs. 13.10 and 13.11 were obtained at the Bell Telephone Laboratories, using the oscillograph method. The speech waves are picked up by a telephone transmitter and converted into electrical waves, great care being taken to design a transmitter in which the electrical waves will reproduce the original sound waves faithfully. These electrical waves are then magnified by a specially designed amplifier and delivered to an oscillograph, where they cause a very small ribbon to vibrate in a way which exactly reproduces the form of the original air waves.

This record is photographed, and an example of it is given in fig. 13.10 for the word "farmers". It will be seen that the first letter *f* is characterized by very high frequencies. After these high frequencies the *a* sound is produced by only 5 complete waves having a fundamental frequency corresponding to approximately 120 cycles per second. The *r* sound is followed by about 20 complete waves having this same fundamental frequency, followed by about 9 complete waves of the *m* sound, also with the same frequency. As the *er* sound is reached, the pitch of the voice is slightly raised to a pitch corresponding to a fundamental frequency of about 130 cycles per second. This is followed by the *s* sound, again characterized by very high frequencies. The wave form of the word "poor" is shown in fig. 13.11.

The most interesting of the speech sounds are probably the vowels, and these, being capable of sustained production, lend themselves more easily to analysis. According to Tyndall, the question of how we distinguish one vowel sound from another when both are sung to a note of the same pitch and of equal intensity was made a prize question by the Academy of St. Petersburg in 1769, and the prize was awarded to Kratzenstein for the successful manner in which he imitated the vowel sounds by mechanical arrangement.

The first important contribution to the whole subject was made by Robert Willis * in a very remarkable paper read to the Cambridge Philosophical Society in 1829. According to Willis each vowel sound is marked by a characteristic frequency. These frequencies are the natural frequencies of the air vibrations in the cavities of the mouth and nose, as set for the pronunciation of the vowels. These vibrations are excited as free vibrations by the more or less periodic puffs of air from the vocal cords. The frequencies need have no simple relation to one another or to the fundamental tone being produced by the voice, and the method of harmonic analysis is not really applicable. This view has since been developed by Hermann and later by

---

* *Trans. Cambr. Phil. Soc.*, Vol. 3, p. 231 (1829).

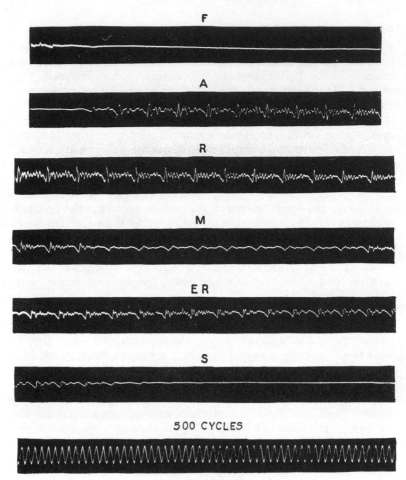

Fig. 18.10.—Wave form of the word " farmers "

Scripture.* It is generally agreed, however, that in at least some cases, and probably in all, a vowel sound is characterized by two frequencies produced as partials of the air in the mouth and nose or by dividing the cavity so as to have two parts each giving its own proper tone.

Helmholtz took a point of view which in theory is very different from that of Willis and yet in practice works out very much the same. He agreed about the existence of characteristic frequencies, and agreed further that these were what give to each vowel its characteristic quality.   The frequencies, as in the theory of Willis, are varied by

* *Researches in Experimental Phonetics* (Carnegie Institute, Washington, 1906).

adjusting the mouth and tongue, but whereas on the theory of Willis the characteristic frequencies are due to the *free* vibrations of the air in the cavities, on the theory of Helmholtz they are due to the *forced* vibration of the air. The frequencies are thus harmonics of the note on which the vowel sound is produced and the method of harmonic analysis is applicable. Helmholtz * collected a great deal of

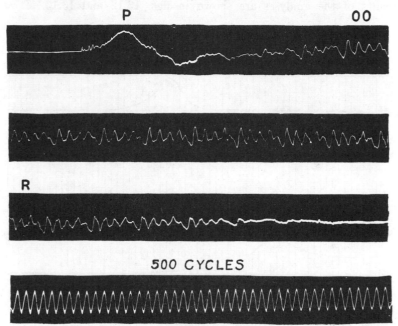

Fig. 13.11.—Wave form of the word " poor "

the earlier material, and by analysing vowel sounds by his resonators and attempting to synthesize them by his harmonic series of tuning-forks he made a valuable contribution to the subject.

Following this view Miller applied his phonodeik to the analysis of the vowel sounds. The vowel sound *a* in the word " father " was sung by various voices to notes of different pitch, and the analysis carried out in each case. It was found that when the vowel was intoned at a frequency of 155, the sixth partial carried 69 per cent of the total energy. When it was intoned at frequency 182, the fifth partial carried 48 per cent of the energy. When it was intoned at frequency 227, the fourth partial contained 65 per cent of the energy. It will be noticed that the actual pitch of the strong partial is nearly the same in the three cases: $6 \times 155 = 930$, $5 \times 182 = 910$, $4 \times 227 = 908$. Miller's observations showed that in all cases this general rule holds

* Loc. cit., pp. 103–9.

and that whatever the frequency of the note on which the vowel sound is produced, the strong partial is the one which comes nearest in pitch to the frequency 910. Extending this investigation to other vowels, Miller arranged them in two series, in one of which they seem to be characterized by loud partials in one particular region of pitch, while in the other they are characterized by two such regions. The results of the analyses are shown in figs. 13.12 and 13.13. If we

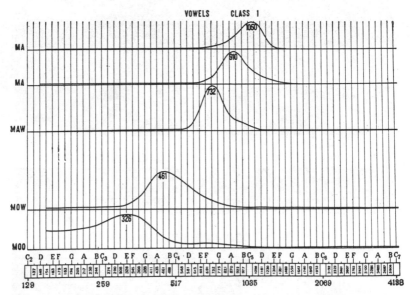

Fig. 13.12.—Characteristic curves for the distribution of the energy in vowels having a single region of resonance

attempt to pronounce one of these series of vowel sounds, we shall find that each series is produced by a progressive movement of the mouth and tongue.

These results were confirmed in three different ways. If, for instance, we take the vowel sound *ow* as in " mow ", we see that it belongs to the series which has one principal region of resonance in the neighbourhood of 461. If we sing this vowel sound on any given note and record it on a gramophone record, then when the record is run at the proper speed the vowel sound will be accurately reproduced. If, however, the record is run too slowly the sound will tend to become *oo*, whereas if the record is run too quickly it will tend to become *aw*. It is claimed that this variation of the characteristic region of resonance when a gramophone record is run at the wrong speed accounts for the extraordinary distortion of speech sounds which results. The experi-

ments not only verified the change in vowel quality but gave a good
numerical check for the frequencies characterizing the four vowels of
this series. This claim has since been challenged.

Another method of check was to obtain phonodeik records of whispered vowel sounds. In this case the voice tones are absent, and the
record consists mainly of small vibrations characteristic of the vowel.
These were counted and confirmed the original observations.

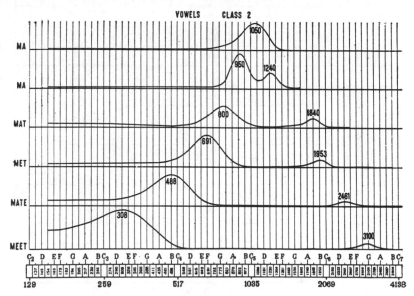

Fig. 13.13.—Characteristic curves for the distribution of energy in vowels having two
regions of resonance

Lastly, the vowel sounds were synthesized using a series of specially-
designed stopped organ pipes such that the loudness of tone could be
adjusted. Synthetic vowel sounds when judged by ear are difficult to
appraise, but in this case they were not merely judged by ear but were
used for the production of a phonodeik record, which was compared
with that of the original sound and found to show a very fair agreement.

Electrical analyses have been carried out by Crandall and Sacia *
using a method described as " photo-mechanical ", and by Wegel and
Moore using a form of electrical analyser.

The general results obtained confirm the work of Miller with the
phonodeik, except that all the vowels seem to be characterized by *two*
resonance regions, the region of higher pitch being much less important in the case of the series to which Miller assigned only one resonance.

* *Phys. Rev.*, Vol. 23, p. 309 (1924).

The acoustic spectra of the vowel sound *e* as in " eat " are shown in fig. 13.14 for four different fundamental pitches, and it is obvious that in each case the partials are strongly reinforced in the neighbourhood of 2000 to 2500.

Very important work has been done in Germany by Stumpf * and

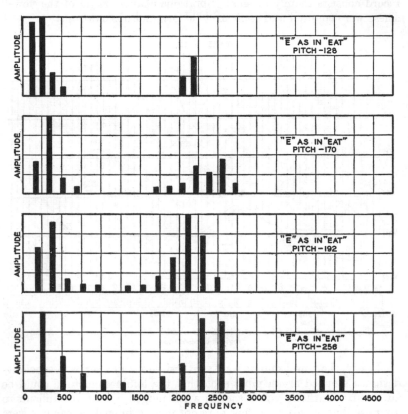

Fig. 13.14.—Electrical analysis of vowel sound *e* as in " eat ", showing marked concentration of energy in the frequency region 2000 to 2500

by Trendelenburg.† Stumpf worked with electric filters and found the regions of frequency in which the various vowel sounds were most sensitive to the suppression of components. He also carried out analyses using harmonic components only, and obtained results which, considering the difference in language, show good agreement with those of American experimenters.

* *Die Sprachlaute* (Berlin, 1926).
† *Wiss. Veröff. a. d. Siemens-Konz.*, Vol. 3/2, p. 43 (1924).

Vowel curves for the vowel sound *i* and the corresponding harmonic analysis by Trendelenburg are shown in figs. 13.15-17. It will be seen that dissimilar as the curves seem to be they all reveal on analysis a strong component frequency in the region of 3000 cycles/sec. This is

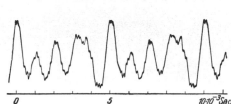

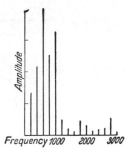

Fig. 13.15.—Vowel i in a man's voice and its line spectrum (fundamental frequency 200)

to be compared with the vowel sound in " meet ", for which Miller gives a strong component at 3100.

A very complete discussion of the whole question is contained in Fletcher, *Speech and Hearing* * and Sir Richard Paget, *Human Speech*;† the latter includes valuable experiments on the artificial synthesis

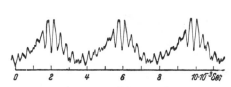

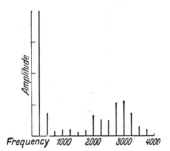

Fig. 13.16.—Vowel i in the lower register of a woman's voice, together with spectrum (fundamental frequency about 250).

of vowel sounds. On Paget's view English and most European and Indian languages are based on whispered speech, and what he calls " phonation ", i.e. the use of the vocal cords to produce a note, is only an auxiliary device to give inflection, melody and emotional quality to speech and song and to increase the audible range. Following out a suggestion of R. S. Lloyd ‡ that every cardinal vowel has two chief characteristic frequencies, one derived from the anterior or oral cavity and one from the posterior or pharyngeal cavity, he demonstrates these regions of pitch by shaping his mouth for the vowel and

* D. Van Nostrand Co., 1929.   † Kegan Paul, 1930.

‡ *Journ. Anat. and Physiol.*, Vol. 31. p. 240 (1897);   *Proc. Roy. Soc. Edin.*, Vol. 22, pp. 97, 219 (1897–9).

blowing air across the front of it from a pair of bellows. He sum-
marizes these for a whispered sentence in staff notation in fig. 13.18.

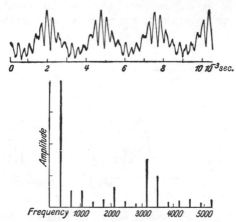

Fig. 13.17.—Vowel i in the upper register of a woman's voice, together
with spectrum (fundamental frequency about 350)

Fig. 13.18.—Pitch of whispered vowels

The modifications of the cavities by the lips and tongue are shown in
fig. 13.19. By using plasticine or cardboard Paget has produced double
resonators (fig. 13.20) in which the proper tone of each is adjusted so as

to give the characteristics for the various vowel sounds. The part of
the vocal cords is played by a reed, and air is blown from this reed
into the double resonator.

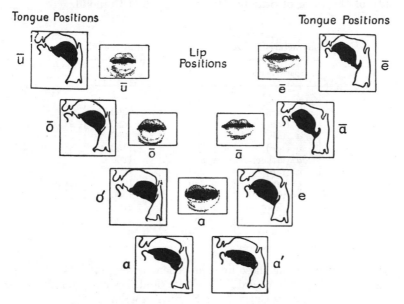

Fig. 13.19.—Tongue and lip positions for enunciation of vowels

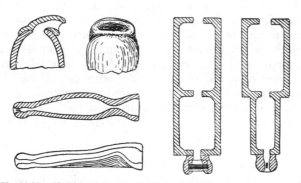

Fig. 13.20.—Sir Richard Paget's models for the production of vowel sounds

The consonantal sounds are more difficult to analyse, but Paget
finds that *k* contains a component of frequency about 3000, *th* has
frequencies between 2500 and 3400, *sh* has frequencies greater than
3000, *f* has frequencies between 5000 and 6000, whereas in the case of
s there are frequencies in excess of 6000. On the other hand, the

strong frequencies in the nasal consonants *m*, *n*, &c., may be below 200.

The following table was constructed by Fletcher after a thorough study of the work of Stumpf, Miller, Paget and Crandall.

TABLE VIII

Characteristic Frequency of the Vowel Sounds

Speech Sound	Low Frequency	High Frequency
u (pool)	400	800
u (put)	475	1000
o (tone)	500	850
a (talk)	600	950
o (ton)	700	1150
a (father)	825	1200
a (tap)	750	1800
e (ten)	550	1900
er (pert)	500	1500
a (tape)	550	2100
i (tip)	450	2200
e (team)	375	2400

Further work along these lines has been carried out by Steinberg,[*] using an oscillograph record; by Obata and Tesima [†] for Japanese vowel sounds; and by Curry [‡] for English vowels.

In a communication to *Nature* [§] Scripture challenges the whole explanation of vowel quality in terms of characteristic frequencies and maintains that the vowel quality attaches to the " profile " of the curve representing the vowel. According to his view this profile is not the sum of a few discrete free vibrations, but an integration of an infinite number of such vibrations differing infinitely little from one another and each subject to specific damping. These vibrations are the partials of one cavity of complicated shape which he maintains cannot be treated as two or more separate cavities. He claims that with a gramophone record of speech, electrical filters and a loud-speaker he has filtered out various regions of frequency as follows: (1) all frequencies above 1350 cycles/sec., (2) all frequencies below 750, (3) all frequencies above 1350 and below 750, (4) all frequencies between 750 and 1350. His contention is that the musical character of the speech changed with every alteration but the specific characters of the vowels remained unchanged. In contradiction of all previous work, he concludes that the character of a sound as vowel does not depend

[*] *Journ. Amer. Soc. Acoust.*, Vol. 6, p. 16 (1939).
[†] *Proc. Imp. Acad. Jap.*, Vol. 10, p. 322 (1934).
[‡] *Proc. Univ. Durham Phil. Soc.*, Vol. 9, p. 153 (1934).
[§] Vol. 129, pp. 275, 965 (1932).

on the presence of any special tones or regions of tone, and that any region of frequency assigned to any particular vowel can be filtered out with no change in the vowel apart from its musical character.

On this view the vowel character depends on the general shape of the " vibration profile "; and any frequencies of any kind may be present provided they give the same general form of profile. Hence, according to Scripture, the imitation of the human voice by the magpie or parrot.

This view receives some support from Bárány.* He quotes experiments with the gramophone † in which considerable variation in record speed produced little change in the character of certain vowel sounds. Adapting for this purpose an experiment used as a lecture demonstration by Tyndall in 1867 when he inhaled hydrogen and then continued his lecture, Bárány filled his lungs with pure hydrogen and tested the articulation for a random collection of consonant/vowel/consonant combinations representing important Swedish speech sounds. If the hydrogen completely fills the resonating cavities the corresponding frequency is four times the normal. The articulation was found to be reduced only to 75 per cent of that with air in the same circumstances.

As a warning against any undue simplification of the problems Scripture's work is extremely useful, but the " formant " theory of vowel character (i.e. the reinforcement of a specific region of pitch) is too well established and too well supported by the most recent work to be seriously shaken.

12. Frequency Range of Speech.

Speech contains almost the whole range of frequencies to which the ear is sensitive, but some regions are more important than others and some carry more of the energy than others. Crandall and Mac-Kenzie ‡ have compared the energy radiated in various frequency bands in speech by analysing the speech waves as impressed on a condenser microphone. They use a tuned circuit transmitting narrow frequency bands, and the separate syllables of connected speech are pronounced sufficiently slowly for a reading to be made for each syllable. One instrument records the total energy and one records that corresponding to the frequency band being tested. The frequency carrying maximum energy is centred on 160 cycles/sec., and 50 per cent of the energy is radiated in frequencies of 350 cycles/sec. or less. This does not necessarily mean, however, that from the point of view of intelligibility low frequencies are the most important. We have

---

* *Journ. Amer. Soc. Acoust.*, Vol. 8, p. 217 (1937).
† Fletcher, *Speech and Hearing*, p. 292; Engelhardt and Gehrcke, *Zeits. f. Psych.*, Vol. 115, p. 1 (1930); Kucharski, *Comptes Rendus*, Vol. 195, p. 979 (1932).
‡ *Phys. Rev.*, Vol. 19, p. 222 (1922).

already quoted Paget's view that intelligibility depends on high frequencies and the low frequencies—the proper tones of the vocal cords —act as a kind of carrier wave upon which the higher frequencies are impressed. This view is borne out by direct experiment. Interpretability or articulation is measured by the dictation of a series of meaningless syllables and by noting the percentage of these correctly interpreted. The speech is received by a microphone, passed through an electrical filter and emitted by a loud-speaker. Fig. 13.21 shows the results in graphical form. The ordinates of the solid curves represent percentage of articulation syllables correctly recorded. The abscissæ represents the "cut-off" frequency of the filter. "Articulation L" gives the results for the low-pass filter, passing all frequencies below

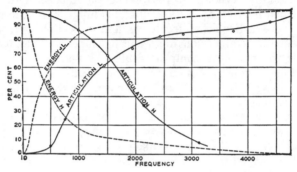

Fig. 13.21.—Effect upon the articulation and energy of speech of eliminating certain frequency regions

the value indicated, while "Articulation H" gives the results for the high-pass filter, passing all frequencies above the value indicated. The dotted curves indicate the percentage of energy passed under corresponding conditions.

It will be seen that although the fundamental cord tones with their first few harmonics carry a large portion of the speech energy, they carry relatively little of the speech articulation. A filter which eliminates all frequencies below 500 cycles/sec. eliminates 60 per cent of the energy in speech but reduces the articulation by only 2 per cent. A system which eliminates frequencies above 1500 cycles/sec. eliminates only 10 per cent of the speech energy but reduces the articulation by 35 per cent.

The two solid curves intersect on the 1550 frequency abscissa and at 65 per cent articulation, showing that the elimination either of all frequencies above 1550 or all frequencies below 1550 reduces the articulation by the same amount, namely to 65 per cent. It is found that mistakes as to the consonantal sounds *th*, *f* and *v* are responsible for nearly 50 per cent of the mistakes of interpretation. The characteristics of these sounds are carried principally by the very high frequencies.

13. Pitch and Quality of Filtered Notes.

It is the fundamental tone of a musical note whose frequency determines the pitch of the note, and this tone is the only constituent of the note which is perceived by the untrained ear. That its physical intensity should be so small compared with that of the other constituent tones which are not heard at all unless by an effort is sufficiently surprising. Still more surprising is the fact discovered by Fletcher * that this tone can be completely suppressed without the apparent pitch of the note being altered. The experiments were carried out by means of a high-quality telephone system designed to secure that the sound coming out of the receiver was in every way a faithful copy of that going into the transmitter. Electrical filters † were introduced into this system so that any components present could be reduced in intensity to values between ·001 and ·0001 of those without the filter. Judgments of pitch and quality were made by three persons familiar with music. The notes were produced at intensities of 10^7 or 10^8 times the minimum audible intensity (some 70 to 80 decibels (p. 465) above threshold audibility). In the case of the vowel *ah* sung at a frequency of 145 cycles/sec. it was found that the elimination of the fundamental and first two harmonics only slightly affected pitch or quality, and even with the elimination of the fundamental and the next six harmonics the pitch still corresponded very definitely with that of a pure tone of frequency 145 cycles/sec. The harmonic analysis of this filtered tone revealed no frequencies below 1000 cycles/sec. Neither the pitch nor the quality of the notes of a rich baritone or contralto voice were found to be appreciably affected by eliminating the fundamental and the first two or three harmonics, but the elimination of high harmonics, even above the fifteenth, produced notable differences of quality. The effect of elimination of high harmonics was less marked for a soprano voice. Elimination of the fundamental and low-order harmonics affected the quality of the principal musical instruments more than it did the quality of sung vowels, but in no case did it produce any change of pitch. The pitch remained constant so long as the filtered sound could be recognized as a musical note. We shall return to this phenomenon in section 8, p. 482.

14. Quality and Phase Differences.

Quality is clearly associated with the existence of partials and with their relative intensity. If the note of a stretched string is produced by plucking it with a soft instrument, such as the finger, and again by

---

* *Speech and Hearing*, p. 248.   † *Phys. Rev.*, Vol. 15, p. 513 (1920).

plucking it with a sharp instrument, such as a plectrum, the resulting quality is notably different. In the first case we may describe the quality as tending to be soft and dull. In the second case it tends to be harsh and brilliant. The sharper discontinuity imposed on the string in the second case means on analysis a longer series of harmonic components of relatively greater intensity. The quality given by a tuning-fork mounted on a resonance box or by a wide-stopped organ pipe is relatively dull and is nearly pure. Good musical quality always involves important harmonics.

The question naturally arises whether quality depends only on the relative intensities of the harmonics, or whether it depends also on their relative phase. Differences in relative phase produce differences in wave form, i.e. differences in the form of the displacement diagram, and it is at least possible that these differences influence the quality.

Helmholtz * satisfied himself that relative phase is without effect on the quality of a note. His method of experiment was to take a series of electrically driven tuning-forks forming together the first few members of the harmonic series. Opposite to the ends of the prongs of each fork is the opening of a tuned resonator, the distance of which from the fork can be varied. The opening of each resonator can be partly closed by an adjustable disc. Relative intensity of the various harmonics can be modified by altering the distance of the resonator from the fork. Partial shading of the opening of the resonator modifies the intensity, but it also slightly mistunes the resonator and alters its phase relative to the fork and therefore to the exciting current. For very slight shading the effect on intensity is small and that on phase considerable. In the hands of a less competent experimenter with a less highly trained ear, the results arrived at would have had much less value.

As it was, R. König † disputed Helmholtz's conclusion. His experiments were made with a wave siren. In this instrument a curved profile was cut on the edge of a wheel. The wheel revolved under a narrow slit placed exactly in the position of a radius of the wheel and the wind was driven through this slit as the wheel rotated and the curve alternately cut off and let pass the stream of air. The theory of the instrument was that if the profile was a sine curve the resulting modification of the air blast would give a simple tone, while if the profile was the curve produced by combining a series of harmonics these would be present in the resulting note in intensities and phases corresponding to the components of the curve. By keeping the intensities constant and varying the phase relations König produced a series of curved profiles which gave variations of quality. The results of these experiments are, however, vitiated by the discovery that the

* Loc. cit., p. 126.   † *Wied. Ann.*, Vol. 12, p. 335 (1881).

notes produced do not correspond to the simple theory of the instrument on which König worked.

The question was attacked later by Lloyd and Agnew * using a telephone operated by a series of harmonically varying electric currents whose frequencies were in the ratio of the whole numbers. They altered the relative phases of the constituent variations and corroborated the view of Helmholtz that variations of phase of the components are without influence on the quality of a complex note.

This conclusion has been challenged by Chapin and Firestone † on grounds both of theory and of experiment. They base their theoretical case on the accepted fact that pure tones supplied to the ear generate in the ear their own series of harmonics—harmonics which become audible when the pure tone is sufficiently intense (section 5, p. 472). If now one of these harmonics is supplied to the ear as a second pure tone it will combine with the harmonic of the first produced in the ear itself, and the intensity of the resultant tone will depend on the relative phase of the two components and will inevitably affect the quality of the combination. This effect on quality was experimentally verified by all observers tested, as was the fact that the loudness depended on the relative phase of the two tones supplied to the ear and might even be less for the two tones combined than for the single fundamental. In considering this result in relation to the evidence already quoted it ought to be noted (1) that this result involves no assumption that the ear is sensitive to phase difference *per se*, and depends upon the fact that pure tones are not heard as pure tones if the loudness exceeds a certain level, and (2) that the loudness level used in these experiments was high, the fundamental (frequency 108) being supplied at an intensity level of 104 decibels and a loudness level of 96 phons (p. 464).

* *Bull. Bur. Stands.*, Vol. 6, p. 255 (1909).
† *Journ. Amer. Soc. Acoust.*, Vol. 5, p. 173 (1934).

CHAPTER XIV

Vibrations of Strings

1. Velocity of Transverse Waves on Stretched Wires or Strings.

For the purposes of this discussion we assume a wire or string to be a body whose length is great compared with its diameter and which is perfectly flexible. From this it follows that the ends of any element are subject to forces of tension directed along the tangent. Of course perfect flexibility is never found in actual cases, but the approximation is sufficiently close to be useful.

Let us assume first that a wave of any given type can be propagated along the wire without change and with velocity c. In this case the wave can be brought to rest in space by moving the wire in the opposite direction with velocity c. If we consider the motion of the element ds (fig. 14.1), the resultant of the two equal tensions applied at its ends is directed towards the centre of curvature of the element and is equal to P, where

$$\frac{P}{ds} = \frac{X}{R},$$

R being the radius of curvature and X the tension. That is,

$$P = \frac{X}{R}\, ds.$$

But this is the force which gives to the element its required acceleration towards the centre of curvature. Hence

$$\frac{X}{R}\, ds = m\, ds\, \frac{c^2}{R},$$

where m is the mass of the string per unit length.

Therefore $\qquad c^2 = \dfrac{X}{m}$, i.e. $c = \sqrt{\dfrac{X}{m}}$, $\quad . \quad . \quad . \quad . \quad$ (14.1)

which gives the velocity of the wave in terms of the tension of the string and of its mass per unit length.

The same result can be derived more rigorously as follows:

Let the tension in the string be X, as in fig. 14.1, and let its mass be m per unit length as before. Let the amplitude of the wave be small, so that α is small. Then the transverse component of the tension at A is $-X \sin \alpha$. Since α is small we can put $\sin \alpha = \tan \alpha = \partial y / \partial x$. The transverse component of the tension at the other end is approximately $X\{(\partial y / \partial x) + (\partial^2 y / \partial x^2)\, \delta x\}$.

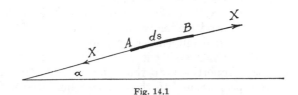

Fig. 14.1

Hence   Resultant transverse force $= X \dfrac{\partial^2 y}{\partial x^2}\, \delta x.$

Mass of element $= m \delta s \doteqdot m \delta x$, so that

$$X \frac{\partial^2 y}{\partial x^2}\, \delta x = m \delta x\, \frac{\partial^2 y}{\partial t^2},$$

or
$$\frac{\partial^2 y}{\partial t^2} = \frac{X}{m}\, \frac{\partial^2 y}{\partial x^2}. \quad \cdots \cdots \quad (14.2)$$

Hence
$$c^2 = \frac{X}{m},$$

i.e.
$$c = \sqrt{\frac{X}{m}}.$$

2. Frequency of Transverse Vibrations of Strings.

The transverse vibrations of stretched strings are one of the most ancient recognized methods of producing musical notes. They were familiar to the Greeks, and the Greek tetrachord played an important part in the development of the musical scale. Pythagoras found that the simple musical intervals are formed by notes for which the vibrating lengths on a given stretched string form simple numerical ratios. According to him the intervals in music are " rather to be judged intellectually through numbers than sensibly through the ear " and " the simpler the ratio of the two parts into which the vibrating string is divided the more perfect is the consonance of the two sounds ". He was the first to use the monochord, a sounding board and box with scale on which a single string was stretched.

No further progress in the study of vibrating strings was made until the time of Galileo (1564–1642), whose results were published in his *Dialoghi delle Nuove Scienze*. He deduced quantitatively the relations between the frequency and the length, diameter, density and tension of the string.

These relationships were independently deduced by the Minorite Friar Marin Mersenne of Paris and were actually published by him in his *Harmonie Universelle* in 1636, two years earlier than Galileo's *Dialogues*. It is quite well known, however, that the publication of Galileo's book was delayed for many years, and it seems fairly certain that his work was carried out earlier. He found that the frequency of vibration of a stretched string is (1) inversely proportional to its length, (2) directly proportional to the square root of the stretching force, (3) inversely proportional to the diameter for wires of the same material. If wires are not of the same material this law becomes (3a) inversely proportional to the square root of the mass per unit length.

These laws are all qualitatively familiar in their application to musical instruments. The scale is produced on the violin, for instance, by altering the vibrating length by stopping with the fingers, and the shorter the length the higher the pitch. The string is tuned by altering the tension by screwing the peg to which the string is attached. To secure a low note without using an unduly long string or an unduly low tension we choose a thick string, or if that is not sufficiently flexible we may load a comparatively thin string by wrapping fine metal wire round it (as in the case of the violin G string). All four violin strings are now made in the wrapped variety, and it is possible to use a steel core. When this is done the wrapping is of lighter metal, in order to increase the diameter.

We can deduce the exact formula for the frequency from the relations $c = f\lambda$ and $c = \sqrt{(X/m)}$. For the simplest mode of vibration the two ends are nodes, so that $\lambda = 2l$;

$$\therefore f = \frac{c}{2l} = \frac{1}{2l}\sqrt{\frac{X}{m}}.$$

If ρ is the density of the material and r the radius of the string,

$$m = \pi r^2 \rho, \ c = \frac{1}{2rl}\sqrt{\frac{X}{\pi \rho}}.$$

We may represent the motion of the string by the general equation

$$\frac{\partial^2 \xi}{\partial t^2} = c^2 \frac{\partial^2 \xi}{\partial x^2}.$$

Assuming further that we are dealing with simple harmonic vibrations only, we may put $\xi = a \cos \omega t$. Substituting this value in the general equation we get

$$\frac{\partial^2 \xi}{\partial x^2} + \frac{\omega^2}{c^2} \xi = 0. \quad \ldots \ldots \quad (14.3)$$

The solution of this is

$$\xi = \left(A \cos \frac{\omega x}{c} + B \sin \frac{\omega x}{c} \right) \cos \omega t. \quad \ldots \quad (14.4)$$

If the string is fixed at $x = 0$ and $x = l$, we have

$$(\xi)_{x=0} = 0 \text{ and } (\xi)_{x=l} = 0 \text{ for all values of } t.$$

$$\therefore \ (\xi)_{x=0} = A \cos \omega t = 0$$

and $\qquad\qquad A = 0.$

Also $\qquad\qquad (\xi)_{x=l} = B \sin \frac{\omega l}{c} \cos \omega t = 0,$

$$\therefore \ \frac{\omega l}{c} = m\pi, \text{ where } m \text{ is any integer,}$$

and $\qquad \xi_m = B_m \sin \frac{m\pi x}{l} \cos \frac{m\pi ct}{l}. \quad \ldots \ldots \quad (14.5)$

For the fundamental mode $m = 1$,

$$\xi_1 = B_1 \sin \frac{\pi x}{l} \cos \frac{\pi ct}{l}.$$

Since ξ_1 repeats its values when $\pi ct/l$ increases by 2π, if T is the corresponding value of t we have

$$\frac{\pi cT}{l} = 2\pi,$$

$$T = \frac{2l}{c},$$

$$f = \frac{c}{2l} = \frac{1}{2l}\sqrt{\frac{X}{m}}. \quad \ldots \ldots \quad (14.6)$$

The easiest way to evoke singly the partial modes of vibration of a stretched string is by resonance. A wire mounted on a monochord is stretched with suitable tension and tuned to give a frequency of 128. If small paper riders are placed on the string all will be thrown off if a fork of frequency 128 is sounded and the shaft rested on the bridge over which the wire passes. If now riders are placed at $\frac{1}{4}l$, $\frac{1}{2}l$, $\frac{3}{4}l$ from one end and a fork of frequency 256 is used, the first and third riders are unseated and the middle one remains in position. The relative intensity of the partial tones actually present when the string is sounded, and hence the quality of the note, depends on the place and mode of excitation.

We have already seen that the possible modes of vibration are given by

$$\xi_m = B_m \sin \frac{m\pi x}{l} \cos \frac{m\pi ct}{l}, \quad \ldots \ldots \quad (14.7)$$

where m has the successive integral values. These modes can exist together. The most general type of vibration will then be given by

$$\xi = \Sigma B_m \sin \frac{m\pi x}{l} \cos \left(\frac{m\pi ct}{l} + \epsilon_m \right). \quad \ldots \quad (14.8)$$

This can be put in the form, first given by Daniel Bernoulli (1700–1782) in 1755,

$$\xi = \Sigma \sin \frac{m\pi x}{l} \left\{ a_m \cos \frac{m\pi ct}{l} + b_m \sin \frac{m\pi ct}{l} \right\}, \quad (14.9)$$

where $\qquad B_m \cos \epsilon_m = a_m, \ -B_m \sin \epsilon_m = b_m.$

The constants a_m and b_m depend on the initial conditions of the vibration and can be calculated by the method already given under Fourier's Theorem (p. 337).

In the initial position of the string the coefficients of b_m are all zero and the coefficients of a_m are all unity. Hence

$$(\xi)_{t=0} = \Sigma a_m \sin \frac{m\pi x}{l}$$

represents the initial distribution of the displacement along the string.

Also $\dot{\xi} = \Sigma \sin \dfrac{m\pi x}{l} \left\{ - \dfrac{a_m m\pi c}{l} \sin \dfrac{m\pi ct}{l} + \dfrac{b_m m\pi c}{l} \cos \dfrac{m\pi ct}{l} \right\}.$

The initial distribution of velocities along the string is therefore given by

$$(\dot{\xi})_{t=0} = \frac{\pi c}{l} \Sigma m b_m \sin \frac{m\pi x}{l}.$$

Using the method indicated under Fourier's theorem we can evaluate the constants from these two equations by multiplying both sides of the corresponding equations for single components by $\sin m\pi x/l$ and integrating from 0 to l. We have

$$\xi_m = a_m \sin \frac{m\pi x}{l},$$

$$\int_0^l \xi_m \sin \frac{m\pi x}{l} \, dx = a_m \int_0^l \sin^2 \frac{m\pi x}{l} \, dx$$

$$= \frac{a_m}{2} \int_0^l \left(1 - \cos \frac{2m\pi x}{l}\right) dx$$

$$= \frac{a_m l}{2}.$$

Therefore

$$a_m = \frac{2}{l} \int_0^l \xi \sin \frac{m\pi x}{l} \, dx. \quad \ldots \quad (14.10)$$

Similarly

$$b_m = \frac{2}{\pi c m} \int_0^l \dot{\xi} \sin \frac{m\pi x}{l} \, dx. \quad \ldots \quad (14.11)$$

3. Progressive Waves on Strings.

Imagine an infinite string in tension to start from rest with an isolated small disturbance of form $f(x)$, which is conveniently taken to be zero except near the origin (fig. 14.2).

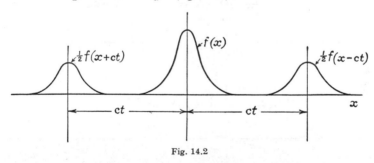

Fig. 14.2

Then, as for a string of finite length, Fourier analysis will give the form of the constituent normal vibrations. In this instance the result is an integral instead of an infinite series, and for $t = 0$ we have

$$f(x) = \frac{1}{\pi} \int_0^\infty dk \int_{-\infty}^{+\infty} f(x') \cos k(x' - x) dx'. \quad . \quad (14.12)$$

The amplitude of the modes comprised in the range k to $k + dk$ is thus

$$\frac{dk}{\pi} \int_{-\infty}^{+\infty} f(x') \cos k(x' - x) dx'. \quad \ldots \quad (14.13)$$

Now the natural period must be such that the time factor is $\cos\omega t$, where $\omega = ck$, and therefore after a time t has elapsed the amplitude is

$$\frac{dk}{\pi}\int_{-\infty}^{+\infty} f(x')\cos kct\,\cos k(x'-x)dx'$$

$$= \frac{dk}{\pi}\int_{-\infty}^{+\infty} \tfrac{1}{2}f(x')[\cos k(x'-x+ct)+\cos k(x'-x-ct)]dx'.$$

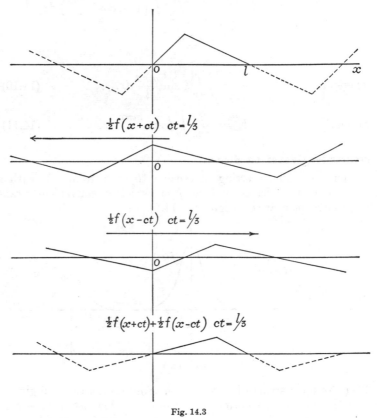

Fig. 14.3

This is evidently the amplitude in the same range k to $(k+dk)$ in the analysis of the function

$$\tfrac{1}{2}f(x-ct)+\tfrac{1}{2}f(x+ct).$$

Thus the analysis appropriate to a set of normal stationary vibrations does yield the result of progressive waves which is also obtained directly from the wave equation (p. 52).

A similar result obviously applies to a semi-infinite string when the initial displacement is given near one end.

If the string is finite, the range within which the appropriate Fourier series must be valid is also limited. If we consider the value of the series outside these limits, it is evident that the sum is periodic and is capable of representing, for all values of x, a function made by repeating the initial shape of the string indefinitely. The connexion with the infinite string is now apparent. The imposition of constraints to fix the ends of a string is equivalent to making the initial disturbance periodic in the length $2l$, for the series $\Sigma a_m \sin(m\pi x/l)$ is unaltered if x is changed to $(x + 2l)$. The train of disturbance may then be divided into two progressive waves, and their recombination will give, in the interval 0 to l, the actual vibrations of the string. The example considered in section 6, p. 377 is shown in fig. 14.3 as it appears by this method.

4. Reflection of Waves on Stretched Strings.

The most important practical case is that of reflection from a fixed end. We may regard the vibration of the string as due to the passage of two waves, a direct wave given by $\xi_1 = F_1(ct - x)$, and a reflected wave given by $\xi_2 = F_2(ct + x)$, where F_1 and F_2 are arbitrary functions. Then

$$\xi = \xi_1 + \xi_2 = F_1(ct - x) + F_2(ct + x).$$

If the string is fixed at the point $x = 0$,

$$(\xi)_{x=0} = 0,$$

$$\therefore F_1(ct) + F_2(ct) = 0$$

$$\therefore F_2(ct + x) = -F_1(ct + x)$$

$$\therefore \xi = F_1(ct - x) - F_1(ct + x). \quad (14.14)$$

Hence for the direct wave at $x = 0$, we have

Displacement $= (\xi_1)_{x=0} = F_1(ct).$

Slope $= \left(\dfrac{\partial \xi_1}{\partial x}\right)_{x=0} = -F_1'(ct).$

Particle-velocity $= \left(\dfrac{\partial \xi_1}{\partial t}\right)_{x=0} = cF_1'(ct).$

For the reflected wave at the same point, since

$$\xi_2 = -F_1(ct + x), \text{ we have}$$

Displacement $= (\xi_2)_{x=0} = -F_1(ct).$

Slope $\qquad = \left(\dfrac{\partial \xi_2}{\partial x}\right)_{x=0} = -F_1{}'(ct).$

Particle-velocity $\quad = \left(\dfrac{\partial \xi_2}{\partial t}\right)_{x=0} = -cF_1{}'(ct).$

$$\therefore \left(\dfrac{\partial \xi_1}{\partial x}\right)_{x=0} = \left(\dfrac{\partial \xi_2}{\partial x}\right)_{x=0}$$

$$\left(\dfrac{\partial \xi_1}{\partial t}\right)_{x=0} = -\left(\dfrac{\partial \xi_2}{\partial t}\right)_{x=0}.$$

At reflection, therefore, the slope of the wave remains the same but the particle-velocity is reversed.

The reflection of waves from the point of attachment of two wires of different linear densities stretched with the same tension provides

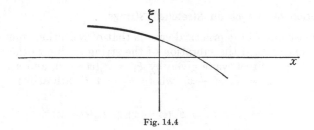

Fig. 14.4

us with an interesting analogy to the partial reflection of light waves at the surface of a transparent medium.

Suppose that a simple harmonic wave proceeding from left to right past the junction of the two wires at $x = 0$ in fig. 14.4 is given by $\xi_0 = a_0 \cos(kx - \omega t)$, where $k = 2\pi/\lambda$, $\omega = 2\pi/T$.

For the reflected wave we have

$$\xi_1 = a_1 \cos(kx + \omega t),$$

and for the wave transmitted in the second wire

$$\xi_2 = a_2 \cos(k'x - \omega t),$$

where $k' = 2\pi/\lambda'$. The waves in the second wire must have the same period but the wave-velocity and therefore the wave-length will be different.

Since the displacement of both wires at the junction must be the same, we have

$$(\xi_0)_{x=0} + (\xi_1)_{x=0} = (\xi_2)_{x=0},$$

$$a_0 \cos(-\omega t) + a_1 \cos(\omega t) = a_2 \cos(-\omega t). \quad . \quad . \quad (14.15)$$

Further, the transverse forces on the two wires must be the same at $x = 0$. Hence

$$T\left(\frac{\partial \xi_0}{\partial x} + \frac{\partial \xi_1}{\partial x}\right)_{x=0} = T\left(\frac{\partial \xi_2}{\partial x}\right)_{x=0}.$$

But

$$\frac{\partial \xi_0}{\partial x} = -ka_0 \sin(kx - \omega t),$$

$$\frac{\partial \xi_1}{\partial x} = -ka_1 \sin(kx + \omega t),$$

$$\frac{\partial \xi_2}{\partial x} = -k'a_2 \sin(k'x - \omega t).$$

$$\therefore \ ka_0 \sin(-\omega t) + ka_1 \sin(\omega t) = k'a_2 \sin(-\omega t). \quad (14.16)$$

Hence by (14.15) $\qquad a_0 + a_1 = a_2,$

and by (14.16) $\qquad k(a_0 - a_1) = k'a_2,$

so that $\qquad \dfrac{a_0 + a_1}{a_0 - a_1} = \dfrac{k}{k'},$

or $\qquad a_1 = a_0 \cdot \dfrac{k - k'}{k + k'}.$

But $\qquad \dfrac{k}{k'} = \dfrac{\lambda'}{\lambda} = \dfrac{c_2}{c_1},$

where c_1, c_2 are the velocities of the waves on the two wires.

$$\therefore \ a_1 = a_0 \frac{k/k' - 1}{k/k' + 1} = a_0 \frac{c_2/c_1 - 1}{c_2/c_1 + 1}$$

$$= a_0 \frac{c_2 - c_1}{c_2 + c_1}.$$

Since the tensions are equal,

$$\frac{c_2}{c_1} = \sqrt{\frac{m_1}{m_2}}.$$

Therefore $\qquad a_1 = a_0 \dfrac{\sqrt{m_1} - \sqrt{m_2}}{\sqrt{m_1} + \sqrt{m_2}}. \quad \ldots \ldots \quad (14.17)$

The coefficient of reflection is

$$R = \frac{a_1}{a_0} = \frac{\sqrt{m_1} - \sqrt{m_2}}{\sqrt{m_1} + \sqrt{m_2}}. \quad \ldots \ldots \quad (14.18)$$

If $m_1 > m_2$, then a_1 and a_0 have the same sign and the displacement is reflected without change of displacement phase.

If $m_1 < m_2$, then a_1 and a_0 have opposite signs and the displacement is reflected with change of phase π.

For the amplitude of the transmitted wave we have

$$a_2 = a_0 + a_1 = a_0(1 + R) = a_0 \cdot \frac{2\sqrt{m_1}}{\sqrt{m_1} + \sqrt{m_2}}. \qquad (14.19)$$

5. Experimental Illustration of Mersenne's Laws.

Mersenne's laws may be illustrated by the use of a sonometer—a rigid frame with one fixed bridge and one movable bridge across which wires can be stretched. The wires are fixed beyond the fixed bridge, and beyond the movable bridge they are attached to scale pans which can be loaded. In order that the tension of the wire between the bridges may be the actual load, there must be as little friction as possible, and this is best secured by using a vertical sonometer.

(1) A suitable tension is applied and the movable bridge is adjusted so as to tune the pitch of the vibrating portion of the wire successively to a series of tuning-forks of known frequencies. If f is now plotted against $1/l$ the result will be a straight line, showing that $f \propto 1/l$.

(2) Three forks fairly close together in pitch are chosen, the adjustable bridge is set to give a convenient length and the load in the scale-pan adjusted so that the vibrating length is tuned to each of the three forks in turn. The weight of the scale-pan must of course be added to the load in each case. It will be found that $f/\sqrt{X}$ is constant, where X is the total stretching force.

(3) Two wires of different section and different material are stretched with the same tension and tuned successively to the same tuning-fork by adjusting the movable bridge. It will be found that

$$l_1\sqrt{m_1} = l_2\sqrt{m_2},$$

where m_1, m_2 are the masses per unit length of the two wires.

An interesting illustration of the frequency formula, although a very inaccurate one, is afforded by Melde's experiment. A long horizontal thread is attached to the prong of a tuning-fork at one end, while the other end passes over a frictionless pulley and carries a scale-pan which can be weighted. The fork, which is electrically maintained, is adjusted so that it gives a horizontal transverse vibration to the end of the thread. The thread thus has a fixed frequency imposed on it and a definite tension. It has a fixed mass per unit length. The only variable is the vibrating length, and the thread accordingly divides by a series of nodes into vibrating lengths of the proper magnitude. As the load is increased by adding weights the vibrating lengths become longer and the number of segments into which the string divides itself becomes smaller. If for each load X giving an exact number of segments the corresponding number of segments p is noted, it will be found that $p^2X =$ const. This result is derived from the formula

$$f = \frac{1}{2l'} \sqrt{\frac{X}{m}}.$$

If in this formula l' denotes the length of a segment, then $l' = l/p$. Hence

$$f = \frac{p}{2l} \sqrt{\frac{X}{m}},$$

$$\therefore p^2X = 4l^2f^2m = \text{const.}$$

6. Plucked Strings.

Strings are set in vibration principally in three ways:

(1) Plucking—as in the harp, mandoline, &c. The string is pulled aside at one point and then released.

(2) Striking—as in the piano. The string is struck by a hammer which rebounds and leaves the string free to vibrate.

(3) Bowing—as in the violin, &c. The string is attacked by a bow which is drawn across it.

Of these methods of initiating the vibrations of a string the first is the simplest to deal with theoretically. Let us consider the various

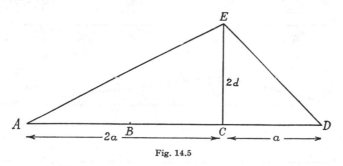

Fig. 14.5

stages of the vibration, first of all by considering them as the result of the propagation of waves along the string reflected at the fixed ends with change of sign for $\partial \xi/\partial t$ (particle-velocity) and no change of sign for $\partial \xi/\partial x$ (slope). We also have the relation $\partial \xi/\partial t = \pm c(\partial \xi/\partial x)$, according as the wave is travelling in the negative or positive direction. Let us take the case (fig. 14.5) when a point $2l/3$ from the end is displaced by an amount $2d$.

We may regard the displacement along AE as due to the super-position of two waves (fig. 14.6), each giving half the total slope, and with particle-velocities equal and opposite, so that they will represent waves travelling in opposite directions. The slope and particle-velocity are given by (1) $d/2a$, $-cd/2a$, (2) $d/2a$, $+cd/2a$.

Similarly, for ED, where the slope is negative, we have two waves

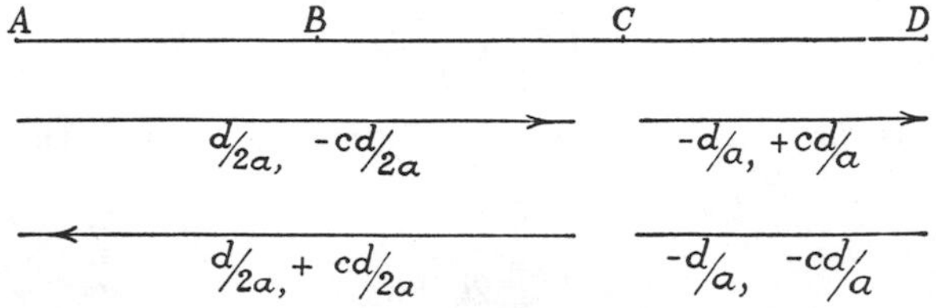

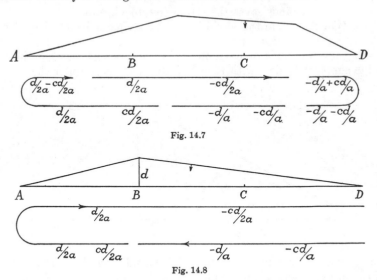

Fig. 14.6

for which slope and particle-velocity are given by (3) $-d/a$, $+cd/a$, (4) $-d/a$, $-cd/a$. Since for (1) and (3) $\dot{\xi}$ and ξ' have opposite signs these will be moving in the positive direction.

Consider the position of the waves after they have travelled along the wire through a distance $a/2$, remembering that the sign of the particle-velocity is changed on reflection from a fixed end.

Fig. 14.7

Fig. 14.8

By superposing the slopes for the two waves effective at each point as in fig. 14.7 we see that the resultant slope is

$$\text{A to mid-point,} \quad \frac{d}{2a} + \frac{d}{2a} = \frac{d}{a}.$$

Mid-point to $\dfrac{5a}{2}$, $\dfrac{d}{2a} - \dfrac{d}{a} = -\dfrac{d}{2a}$.

End portion, $-\dfrac{d}{a} - \dfrac{d}{a} = -\dfrac{2d}{a}$.

By superposing the particle-velocities of the three segments into which the wire is divided by the differences of slope we see that the first and third are at rest and the middle one moving downwards.

Following the waves for another twelfth of the period of vibration we have fig. 14.8. The successive positions may be worked out in the same way and are shown in figs. 14.9–12.

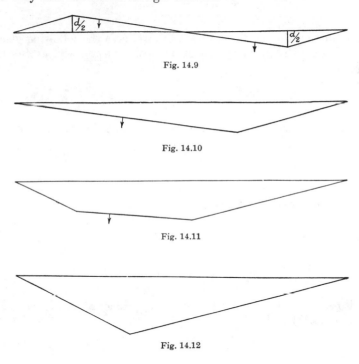

Fig. 14.9

Fig. 14.10

Fig. 14.11

Fig. 14.12

Fig. 14.13 shows that if a parallelogram is constructed with the two portions of the string in its original position as adjacent sides, then all the subsequent positions of the string are given by moving the line PQ backwards and forwards parallel to itself from S to R and back again.

More generally, if any point in the string is displaced so that S_1, $-S_2$ are the slopes for the two portions, then in every subsequent position the string combines in different ways the slopes S_1, $-S_2$

and $\frac{1}{2}(S_1 - S_2)$. The last is the slope of the line which in the particular case considered is represented by PQ.

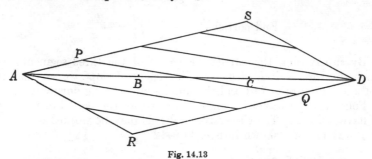

Fig. 14.13

Considering the matter analytically, we have the following general expression for the displacement of any point on the wire at any time (14.9),

$$\xi = \varSigma \sin \frac{m\pi x}{l} \left\{ a_m \cos \frac{m\pi ct}{l} + b_m \sin \frac{m\pi ct}{l} \right\}.$$

The initial distribution of displacement along the string is given by

$$(\xi)_{t=0} = \varSigma a_m \sin \frac{m\pi x}{l}.$$

But if a point on the string distant d from the end is displaced through a distance h, we have

$$\frac{\xi}{x} = \frac{h}{d} \text{ for } 0 < x < d,$$

$$\frac{\xi}{l - x} = \frac{h}{l - d} \text{ for } d < x < l.$$

Also $\dot{\xi} = 0$ at $t = 0$ for all values of x. Hence all the b_m constants are zero (14.11) and

$$\xi = \varSigma \sin \frac{m\pi x}{l} \cdot a_m \cos \frac{m\pi ct}{l}. \quad \cdots \quad (14.20)$$

But (14.10) $a_m = \frac{2}{l} \int_0^l \xi \sin \frac{m\pi x}{l} \, dx$

$$= \frac{2}{l} \left[\int_0^d \frac{hx}{d} \sin \frac{m\pi x}{l} \, dx + \int_d^l \frac{h(l - x)}{l - d} \sin \frac{m\pi x}{l} \, dx \right]$$

$$= \frac{2hl^2}{m^2\pi^2 d(l - d)} \sin \frac{m\pi d}{l}. \quad \cdots \cdots \cdots (14.21)$$

Therefore (1) $a_m = 0$ if $d = \dfrac{l}{m}, \dfrac{2l}{m}, \dfrac{3l}{m}, \ldots$

Hence any partial tone of order m is absent for which the point of plucking divides the string so that the short segment is exactly l/m. This is true for all methods of attack, as was pointed out by Young. No partial can be present if the string is attacked at a point where the partial in question requires a node. Helmholtz attributed the fact that the piano is so designed that the hammers strike the strings at about $\frac{1}{8}$ of the string from one end to an empirical attempt to eliminate the inharmonic 7th and 9th partials.

(2) The amplitudes of the successive partial tones are in the ratio $1/1^2, 1/2^2, 1/3^2, \ldots$, and so form a rapidly diminishing series.

It will be obvious from the foregoing that the quality of the tone given by a plucked string will depend both on the point of plucking and on the instrument used for plucking. If the middle of the string is plucked all the even partials are excluded and the tone is of poor quality, while if the string is plucked near the end the full series of partials is present and the tone is more brilliant. A soft plucking instrument like the finger gives a rounded form to the wire at the point of attack and generates fewer high partials than the hard plectrum of the mandoline.

7. Struck Strings.

The problem of the vibrations excited in strings or wires by striking with a hammer is one of great interest in itself, and also of practical importance owing to its use in the pianoforte. The pianoforte is unique among the commoner musical instruments in that the whole energy to be radiated as sound has to be communicated in the small interval, about $1/500$ of a second, during which the hammer is in contact with the string, whereas in bowed instruments and wind instruments the note is sustained and energy is continuously communicated. In order to secure sufficient loudness the evolution of the piano has been in the direction of more strings (two or three to a single note), more massive strings, and higher tensions. A typical pianoforte action is shown simplified in fig. 14.14, and in this, as in all forms of the action, the hammer is projected against the string and at the instant of impact is free from the system of levers which set it in motion.

From this it would appear that the only variables in the case of a given wire are the point of impact and the velocity of the hammer head. This would mean that for a particular pianoforte the performer can vary the loudness by his " touch ", but not the quality. Most musical critics, however, are agreed that there is much more in " touch " than this analysis would suggest, and it seems possible that vibrations of the hammer itself may depend on the way in which the lever motion is initiated by the performer and that these may in turn react on the quality of the sound produced.

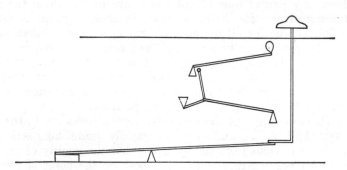

Fig. 14.14—Simplified pianoforte action with key depressed and hammer about to strike the wire

The earliest theoretical treatment is that of Helmholtz,[*] who assumed the force exerted by the hammer on the string to vary sinusoidally during the period of contact and the duration of the contact to be short compared with the period of the fundamental of the string.

8. Bowed Strings.

In the case of the bowed string the analytical treatment of the motion is based on experimental data. The bowed string differs both from the plucked string and from the struck string in the fact that the production of the sound is sustained and the note of the string is continuously under the control of the performer. The string adheres to the bow and moves with it until the tension overcomes the static friction, when it slips past the bow until it once more comes to rest relative to the bow and is drawn aside once more. That it moves exactly with the bow during displacement has been demonstrated by C. V. Raman,[†] by K. C. Kar [‡] and by M. N. Mitra.[§] The energy radiated as sound and used in overcoming frictional losses thus depends on the fact that more work is done on the string by the bow during displacement than is done by the string on the bow during the subsequent slip, and this depends again on the difference between static and dynamic friction. The speed of any point

---

[*] *Sensations of Tone*, 3rd English ed., p. 380.
[†] *Ind. Ass. Cult. Sci. Bull.*, Vol. 11, p. 43 (1914).
[‡] *Phys. Rev.*, Vol. 20, p. 148 (1922).   [§] *Ind. Journ. Phys.*, Vol. 1, p. 311 (1926).

on the string is nearly uniform in both halves of its vibration, so that the displacement diagram consists of two straight lines which for the mid-point on the string have the same slope (see also the next section).

9. Experimental Study of Vibrating Strings.

A method of recording the motion of a point on a vibrating string was devised by Krigar-Menzel and Raps * and, with modifications, has been widely used by subsequent observers.

An image of a brightly illuminated slit is formed in the plane of vibration of the string, the length of the slit being at right angles to the undisturbed position of the string. The string and the image of the slit are then projected on a photographic plate or film moving parallel to the length of the string. If the film and string are at rest the appearance on the negative will be a dark line (the final image of the slit) broken by a bright point. When the film is moved and the string is vibrating this bright point traces what is really the displacement-time graph for the point of the string under observation. The mode of vibration can thus be compared with theory.

The method was applied by Krigar-Menzel and Raps to an examination of the motion of bowed and plucked strings. It was also applied by Kaufmann † to check his own theoretical treatment of the action of the pianoforte. He assumed the hammer to be hard and unyielding and the time of contact to be comparable with the period of vibration of the string. He varied the point of impact and found that the tone is fullest and strongest when the point of impact is between $\frac{1}{7}$ and $\frac{1}{9}$ of the length of the string from one end. The method was used by Klinkert ‡ to study the vibrations of an electrically maintained string.

The motion of a vibrating string was first studied point by point by Helmholtz, using his vibration microscope.§

In this method a grain of starch was placed on the string at the point to be observed and upon it was focused a microscope with a fixed eyepiece but with the objective attached to the prong of a tuning-fork. The fork was arranged so that its direction of vibration was at right angles to that of the point on the string. The motion observed was thus the motion of the point on the string compounded with the simple harmonic motion of the prong of the fork executed in a direction at right angles to it. If the fork had the same frequency of vibration as the string the form of the vibration of the point observed could be elucidated.

The method was applied by Helmholtz ∥ to a study of the bowed string. He describes the motion in terms of fig. 14.15 as follows. The foot d of the ordinate of the highest point moves backwards and forwards

* *Ann. d. Physik*, Vol. 50, p. 44 (1893).   † *Wied. Ann.*, Vol. 54, p. 675 (1895).
‡ *Ann. d. Physik*, Vol. 65, p. 849 (1898).   § *Phil. Mag.*, Vol. 21, p. 393 (1861).
∥ Loc. cit., p. 384.

with a constant velocity on the horizontal line ab while the highest point of the string describes in succession the two parabolic arcs ac_1b and bc_2a, and the string is always stretched in the two lines ac_1 and bc_1 or ac_2 and bc_2. All points on the string pass through their undisplaced positions simultaneously.

More recently a great deal of experimental and theoretical work has been done, notably by W. H. George.* The hammer used in these experiments is a rigid pendulum whose mass and velocity of impact can be varied. The duration of contact and the variation of pressure during contact are studied by including an oscillograph in circuit with the wire and hammer. The vibration of a point on the string is recorded optically by a modification of the method of Krigar-Menzel and Raps, and the resulting curves are analysed by a Mader harmonic analyser. As the partials decay fairly rapidly and with unequal decrements, only the first few vibrations after impact are used. It appears that the pressure between the hammer and the string varies considerably during impact, an instan-

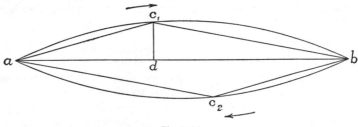

Fig. 14.15

taneous complete separation between hammer and string taking place before the final separation in some cases. The ratio of the mass of the hammer to the whole mass of the string is an important factor. For very light hammers ($m/M = 0.4$ or less, where m is the mass of hammer and M the mass of the string) the energy lost by the hammer increases rapidly with the distance of the point of impact from the end, but soon reaches a maximum which remains constant over the rest of the string. For $m/M = 0.5$ the position for maximum energy communication is at the centre of the string, but heavier hammers give the maximum point near the ends and strengthen the fundamental at the expense of the partials.

10. Longitudinal Vibrations of Strings or Rods.

We have already seen (p. 75) that the velocity of a longitudinal wave along a string or rod is given by $c = \sqrt{q/\rho}$, where q is Young's modulus and ρ the density of the material. When we come to consider the longitudinal vibrations of a rod or string of finite length we see that for a string the problem is similar to that for transverse vibrations. The string must be fixed at both ends, and starting from the general

* *Phil. Mag.*, Vol. 48, p. 34 (1924); Vol. 50, p. 491 (1925); *Proc. Roy. Soc.*, A, Vol. 108, p. 284 (1925); Vol. 114, p. 111 (1927); Vol. 116, p. 115 (1927).

differential equation of the wave motion and expressing the fact that $\xi = 0$ for all values of t at $x = 0$ and $x = l$, we get (14.5, p. 369)

$$\xi_m = B_m \sin\frac{m\pi x}{l} \cos\frac{m\pi ct}{l}.$$

Hence if $m = 1$

$$\xi_1 = B_1 \sin\frac{\pi x}{l} \cos\frac{\pi ct}{l}, \quad \cdot \ \cdot \ \cdot \ \cdot \ \cdot \quad (14.22)$$

and this represents the fundamental mode of vibration.

If T is the period of the vibration,

$$\frac{\pi cT}{l} = 2\pi$$

or

$$T = \frac{2l}{c},$$

so that

$$f = \frac{c}{2l} = \frac{1}{2l}\sqrt{\frac{q}{\rho}}. \quad \cdot \ \cdot \ \cdot \ \cdot \ \cdot \quad (14.23)$$

It may be noted that in this case the frequency is independent of the tension *per se* and depends only on the length and the constants for the material.

That the frequency of the longitudinal vibration is in general much greater than that of the transverse can be seen at once by a comparison. Let the wire in question be subject to a tension X and let the extension produced by this tension be l'. Then if f_t is the frequency of transverse vibration and f_l the frequency of longitudinal vibration, we have

$$f_t = \frac{1}{2l}\sqrt{\frac{X}{m}} = \frac{1}{2l}\sqrt{\frac{X}{S\rho}},$$

where S is the area of cross-section. But

$$\frac{X}{S} = \text{stress} = q \times \text{strain} = q\frac{l'}{l}.$$

$$\therefore f_t = \frac{1}{2l}\sqrt{\frac{ql'}{l\rho}} = f_l\sqrt{\frac{l'}{l}}.$$

$$\therefore \frac{f_t}{f_l} = \sqrt{\frac{l'}{l}}, \quad \cdot \ \cdot \ \cdot \ \cdot \ \cdot \ \cdot \quad (14.24)$$

and f_t only becomes equal to f_l when the wire or rod is stretched to double its length, that is, never.

In the case of a rod one or both ends may be free. If both ends are free the fundamental frequency is the same as if both ends are fixed. If, however, one end is fixed and one is free,

$$\xi = \left(A \cos\frac{\omega x}{c} + B \sin\frac{\omega x}{c}\right) \cos\omega t$$

as before, but this time ξ is zero for all values of t at $x = 0$ and $\partial\xi/\partial x$ is zero for all values of t at $x = l$ (the free end).

The first condition gives $A = 0$.

For the second, $\dfrac{\partial\xi}{\partial x} = \dfrac{\omega B}{c} \cos\dfrac{\omega x}{c} \cos\omega t$,

and $\left(\dfrac{\partial\xi}{\partial x}\right)_{x=l} = \dfrac{\omega B}{c} \cos\dfrac{\omega l}{c} \cos\omega t$ is to be zero for all values of t.

Therefore $\dfrac{\omega l}{c} = (2m - 1)\dfrac{\pi}{2}$

and $$\xi_m = B_m \sin\frac{(2m - 1)\pi x}{2l} \cos\frac{(2m - 1)\pi ct}{2l}. \qquad . \quad (14.25)$$

Obviously for the fundamental

$$T_1 = \frac{4l}{c}, \text{ or } f_1 = \frac{c}{4l},$$

and for the next possible mode of vibration

$$T_2 = \frac{4l}{3c}, \text{ or } f_2 = \frac{3c}{4l} = 3f_1,$$

and so on. That is, the partial tones form the odd members of the harmonic series.

CHAPTER XV

Organ Pipes

1. Æolian Tones.

The sound produced by wind as it whistles through long grass or roars through the trees in the forest is one of the most familiar natural sounds. The utilization of the phenomenon for the production of musical sounds in an " æolian harp " is the subject of occasional vague references in early literature, but according to Richardson * the first systematic account of an instrument of this kind occurs in an early seventeenth-century book by Athanasius Kircher. The early instruments consisted of a number of equal strings tuned to unison on an appropriate sound-box. Later instruments were made with wires of different thicknesses still tuned in unison—an improvement which is justified by the theory subsequently developed.

The tones can be well heard with a simple piece of apparatus due to Lord Rayleigh and shown in fig. 15.1. A is a glass tube drawn out

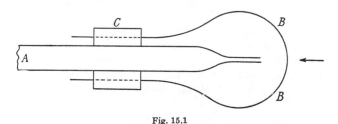

Fig. 15.1

to a bore of 1 mm. or 2 mm. and placed so as to face the air-stream just behind the wire. B is a loop of iron or brass wire about 1 mm. in diameter, attached to the tube by insertion into a cork C. The glass tube can be connected to the ear by a rubber tube, and when held in the crack of a slightly opened door or window the arrangement yields a fairly pure and steady tone.

Some early experiments on these tones were carried out by Young, who showed that the frequency is independent of the part of the wire

* *Proc. Phys. Soc.*, Vol. 36, p. 153 (1923).

on which the air-stream impinges and that at the appropriate wind velocity the string vibrates as a whole, giving its fundamental tone. The first quantitative experiments were carried out by Strouhal.* In these experiments a vertical wire was mounted at a measured distance from the centre of a whirling table with vertical axis. In this way a known velocity could be imparted to the wire and the frequency of the resultant tone could be estimated. Strouhal found that the frequency is independent of the length and of the tension of the wire and can be approximately represented by an expression of the form

$$f = K \frac{V}{D} \quad \ldots \ldots \ldots \quad (15.1)$$

where f is the frequency of the tone, V the velocity of the air, D the diameter of the wire, and K a constant which is about 0·185.

The explanation of the phenomenon and the theoretical justification of this empirical relationship came later.

Rayleigh † refers to the following entry in his notebook. " Bath, Jan., 1884. I find in the baths here that if the spread fingers be drawn pretty quickly through the water (palm foremost was best) they are thrown into transverse vibration and strike one another. This seems like the æolian string. . . . The blade of a flesh brush about 1½ inches broad seemed to vibrate transversely in its own plane when moved through water broadways forward. It is pretty certain that with proper apparatus these vibrations might be developed and observed."

The streaming of water past an obstacle was studied by Mallock,‡ who noticed that in the rear of the obstacle vortices are formed and carried off by the stream. These vortices were independently studied by Bénard.§ He found two parallel rows of alternate and equally spaced vortices, one row forming on each side of the obstacle. Obviously the periodic shedding of these vortices would produce a periodic transverse vibration of the obstacle if it were free to move, and if the obstacle were a wire stretched with the required tension it would be set in resonant vibration. Kármán ‖ showed that only two arrangements of vortices are possible. They may be shed simultaneously in pairs from opposite sides of the obstacle (fig. 15.2) or they may be shed alternately and symmetrically from opposite sides of the obstacle. He showed that the first of these arrangements is unstable and that only the second can persist. Later work by Kármán and Rubach ¶ showed that h/l is constant and independent of D and of V, where h is the distance between the two parallel rows of vortices and l the distance between successive vortices in the same row. It appeared

* *Ann. d. Physik*, Vol. 5, p. 216 (1878). † *Phil. Mag.*, Vol. 29, p. 433 (1915).
‡ *Proc. Roy. Soc.*, Vol. 9, p. 62 (1907); *Proc. Roy. Soc.*, A, Vol. 84, p. 490 (1910).
§ *Comptes Rendus*, Vol. 147, p. 839 (1908) and many subsequent papers.
‖ *Göttingen Nachr.*, 547 (1912). ¶ *Phys. Zeitschr.*, Vol. 13, p. 49 (1912).

also from their work that $l = bD$, where b is constant and >1, and $U = aV$, where a is constant and <1. U is the velocity of the vortices relative to the stationary fluid.

Krüger and Lauth used the results to derive Strouhal's formula

$$f = \frac{V - U}{l},$$

whence

$$\frac{V}{fD} = \frac{Vl}{D(V - U)} = \frac{l}{D}\frac{V}{(V - aV)} = \frac{b}{1 - a}. \quad . \quad (15.2)$$

Using Kármán and Rubach's data for a and b they obtained for this constant the value 5, which compares well with Strouhal's results. Subsequent experimental work with air and with water has been

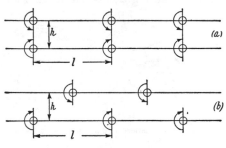

Fig. 15.2

done by Rayleigh,* Relf † and Richardson.‡ These all show that the constant has a value of about 5, the notable departures from this value occurring for very small values of V or of D.

The frequency is found not to be much affected by the viscosity of the fluid. The dimensions of the coefficient of kinematic viscosity ν are L^2T^{-1}. If this quantity is to occur in the expression for the frequency of the æolian tone along with V and D, a consideration of dimensions shows that it must do so in the form of the dimensionless Reynolds number $N = VD/\nu$, so that

$$f = \frac{V}{D}F(N), \quad . \quad . \quad . \quad . \quad . \quad (15.3)$$

so long as the compressibility is not effective, that is, if V is small compared with c.

Rayleigh gives the following formula as agreeing well with

* *Phil. Mag.*, Vol. 29, p. 433 (1915).   † *Phil. Mag.*, Vol. 42, p. 73 (1921).
‡ *Proc. Phys. Soc.*, Vol. 36, p. 153 (1923–4).

observations both for water ($v = 0\cdot0115$ c.g.s.) and air ($v = 0\cdot15$ c.g.s.):

$$f = 0\cdot195\,\frac{V}{D}\Big(1 - \frac{20\cdot1}{N}\Big). \quad \ldots \ldots \quad (15.4)$$

Since in the cases occurring in practice N is usually greater than 500, the second term in the expression is very small, and we have approximately

$$f = 0\cdot2\,\frac{V}{D}. \quad \ldots \ldots \ldots \quad (15.5)$$

Though the effect of the value of N on the frequency is small, its effect on the initiation of the vortices is determinative. When the fluid streams past an obstacle a region of stationary fluid (fig. 15.3) tends to be established in the rear of the obstacle. Shearing forces are developed by the viscosity acting across the layer which separates this

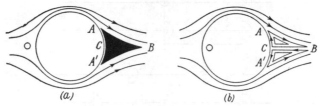

(a)   (b)

Fig. 15.3.—Formation of eddies behind a cylinder

dead fluid from the moving stream, and it is here that the vortices tend to develop. If N falls below about 100 (i.e. for thin wires and low velocities) vortices cease to be formed and the phenomenon disappears.* For air $v = 0\cdot15$ and the critical velocities for wires of various diameters may therefore be found by putting

$$V_c = \frac{15}{D}. \quad \ldots \ldots \ldots \quad (15.6)$$

An interesting experiment for demonstrating the phenomenon was devised by Rayleigh.† A loaded rigid pendulum was arranged with its lower end dipping into water in a large basin. The point of insertion was well away from the centre and the pendulum was arranged so that it could oscillate along a radius. The basin was then made to revolve about a vertical axis carrying the water with it; when the speed of rotation was such that the frequency of vortex shedding coincided with the natural frequency of the pendulum the resonant vibrations of the pendulum became very marked.

* Relf, *Phil. Mag.*, Vol, 42, p. 173 (1921).   † Loc. cit.

2. Edge Tones.

If a jet of moving air is projected into stationary air the conditions for the formation of vortices are again present. If the jet issues from a slit the vortices tend to be shed to the two sides alternately, and the jet itself pursues a sinuous course between them (fig. 15.4). The result is a very feeble indecisive tone called the jet tone, the frequency of which has been determined as

$$f = 0.055\, V/D, \quad \ldots \ldots \quad (15.7)$$

where V is the velocity of efflux and D the width of the slit. This tone is two octaves below the æolian tone for a cylindrical obstacle of diameter D. A similar phenomenon exists for a circular jet, but the vortices are vortex rings shed alternately on the inside and outside of the jet.

Fig. 15.4

The tones obtained in this way are weak, fluctuating and unstable. In 1853, however, both Masson [*] and Sondhauss [†] called attention to the fact that if an edge—a wedge of small angle—is presented to the jet from the slit, the edge being parallel to the length of the slit, then certain frequencies tend to be stabilized and the tone produced is stable and stronger.

The formation of these tones was discussed by a number of investigators and a good deal of experimental work was done. Among the more important contributions are those of Wachsmuth,[‡] Schmidtke,[§] König,[||] Krüger,[¶] Benton,[**] Richardson [††] and Carrière.[‡‡]

By far the most complete experimental investigation of these tones hitherto available is that of Brown[§§] and this is followed by a theoretical discussion by the same author.[¶¶] Earlier explanations invoked the Kármán system of vortices. Brown criticizes the experimental evidence for this, even in the case of slit tones when no edge is present. He suggests alternatively that the fluid stream divides at the edge, half passing up each side. Since the whole phenomenon is found to occur within the sound-sensitive range of the jet, a slight vibration of the apparatus or a sound of the order of the minimum audibility of the human ear will be sufficient to produce a vortex which will pass up one side or other of the wedge. The passage of the vortex along the

[*] *Comptes Rendus*, Vol. 36, p. 257 (1853).
[‡] *Ann. Phys. Lpz.*, Vol. 14, p. 469 (1904).
[||] *Phys. Zeitschr.*, Vol. 13, p. 1053 (1912).
[**] *Proc. Phys. Soc.*, Vol. 38, p. 109 (1926).
[††] *Proc. Phys. Soc.*, Vol. 43, p. 394 (1931).
[§§] *Proc. Phys. Soc.*, Vol. 49, p. 493 (1937).

[†] *Comptes Rendus*, Vol. 36, p. 1004 (1853).
[§] *Ann. Phys. Lpz.*, Vol. 60, p. 715 (1910).
[¶] *Ann. Phys. Lpz.*, Vol. 62, p. 673 (1920); *Phys. Zeitschr.*, Vol. 37, p. 842 (1936).
[‡‡] *Rev. Acoustique*, Vol. 5, p. 138 (1936).
[¶¶] *Proc. Phys. Soc.*, Vol. 49, p. 508 (1937).

side of the edge displaces air, and it is suggested that in flowing back again in the wake of the vortex this air has sufficient momentum to deviate the stream to the opposite side of the wedge. This deviation, if its amplitude is sufficient, may itself be followed by wake disturbance, causing the jet to be deflected once more, and this undulation may occur in portions of the jet which have not yet reached the edge. According to the amplitude of the resulting wake disturbance (depending in turn on the velocity and wedge distance) vortex motion may begin at the first, second or third crest of the following undulations. This gives four vortex stages and corresponding jumps in tone.

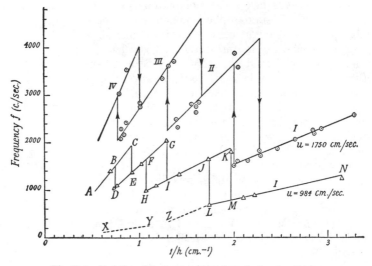

Fig. 15.5.—Variation of frequency with reciprocal of wedge-distance

In the experiments the slit used can be varied in width, and a brass wedge of angle 20°, the height of which from the slit can be carefully adjusted and measured, is presented to the stream. When the distance h from wedge to slit is varied it is found that for all velocities the tone formation occurs in four distinct stages. Fig. 15.5 shows the results obtained. As the wedge is withdrawn from close proximity to the slit no sound is heard until, as in the case of u (air velocity) = 984 cm./sec., a clear bright tone begins at a point defined by the values of f and h indicated by the point N. This diminishes in frequency as h is increased until the point L is reached, when the frequency jumps to the value indicated by J. Further increase in h causes a steady drop in frequency until the point H is reached, when there is another jump to F. The frequency now drops again to the point D, when it jumps once more to B and finally finishes at A, in an irregular and confused noise. If the edge is now made to approach the slit the changes occur in the reverse order but the jumps do not take place at the same values of h. The representative point in the diagram traces the path ACEGIKMN and once more stops abruptly at N. The dotted lines LZ, YX represent the persistence of stage I along with subsequent stages. When h is maintained constant and the velocity varied a similar set of stages is found and the results for a slit of width 0·1 cm. are shown in fig. 15.6. The four possible vortex

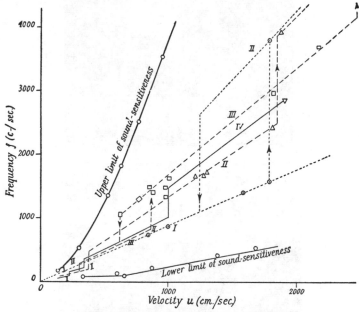

Range of edge-tone production $\nabla\!-h = 1\cdot5\,cm.:\;\text{--}\square\text{--}h = 1\cdot0\,cm.:$
$\cdots\triangle\text{--}h = 0\cdot75\,cm.:\;\text{--}\odot\text{--}h = 0\cdot50\,cm.$

Fig. 15.6

stages are photographed in fig. 15.7. It is found that the frequency may be represented by an expression of the form

$$f = 0\cdot466\,j(u - 40)\left(\frac{1}{h} - 0\cdot07\right) \quad . \quad . \quad . \quad (15.8)$$

where j has the values 1, 2·3, 3·8, 5·4 respectively for stages I, II, III, IV.

3. Vibrating Air Columns.

The vibrations of air columns are the source of sound in the organ and in almost all wind instruments, and the phenomena are also of great theoretical interest. In the theoretical treatment it is usual to make certain assumptions which are justified in all cases of practical importance. These are as follows:

(1) The diameter of the pipe in which the vibrations take place is sufficiently great to justify neglect of viscosity effects.

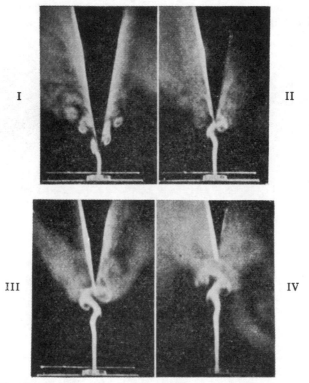

Fig. 15.7.—The four stages in vortex formation producing the same frequency

Stage I, $h = 0.81$ cm.   Stage II, $h = 1.73$ cm.   Stage III, $h = 2.65$ cm.   Stage IV, $h = 3.5$ cm.
$f = 126$ c./sec. $u =$ const. $= 272$ cm./sec.

(2) The diameter is small compared with the length of the pipe and with the wave-length of sound.

(3) The walls of the pipe are rigid.

There are two types of pipe which are of practical importance: the pipe open at both ends, known as the *open pipe*, and the pipe closed at one end, known as the *closed pipe*. The elementary facts about the possible modes of vibration in these cases can easily be arrived at.

In the open pipe there must be a displacement antinode at each end and therefore, in the fundamental mode of vibration, a node in the middle. The wave-length of the corresponding sound, which is four times the distance between a node and the adjacent antinode, must be $2l$, where l is the length of the pipe. The frequency of the fundamental, c/λ, is therefore $c/2l$. In the next possible mode of

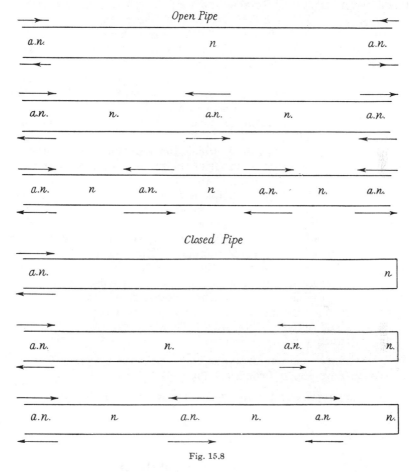

Fig. 15.8

vibration there must be two nodes in the pipe and an antinode at the centre. The wave-length is now l and the frequency c/l. In the next possible mode there are three nodes in the pipe; the wave-length is $2l/3$ and the frequency $3c/2l$. The first three possible modes of vibration are shown in fig. 15.8; the arrows show the direction of the movement of the air. The figure shows the distribution for each mode at the two instants of maximum velocity in each vibration. It will be seen that the fundamental mode of vibration has a frequency $c/2l$ and the other modes frequencies which bear to this the ratios $2:1$ and $3:1$.

If now we turn to the closed pipe we find that it must always have a node at the closed end and an antinode at the open end. In the fundamental mode of vibration the wave-length is therefore $4l$ and the frequency $c/4l$. When there is a second node in the pipe the wavelength is $4l/3$ and the frequency $3c/4l$. When there is a third node in the pipe the wave-length is $4l/5$ and the frequency $5c/4l$. The possible modes are illustrated in fig. 15.8.

In contrast to the open pipe, then, the closed pipe has a fundamental which is an octave lower in pitch, and its partial tones consist of the odd members of the harmonic series only. These facts have an important bearing on the quality of tone given by organ pipes and wind instruments generally.

Another point of view from which the frequency of a vibrating air column may be deduced is that of the travelling pulse of air. The time of vibration of the column of air is the same as the time in which a pulse of air within the pipe completes its cycle of changes. Considering first of all a pipe open at both ends, we start a compression from one end and follow its course. From the farther end it is reflected as a rarefaction, and returning to its point of initiation it is reflected as a compression, and its cycle is complete. The time occupied is $2l/c$, so that the frequency is $c/2l$. In the case of a pipe closed at one end we start a compression from the open end. It is reflected as a compression from the closed end, as a rarefaction from the open end, as a rarefaction again from the closed end and as a compression from the open end, completing its cycle. Thus the time occupied is $4l/c$ and the frequency $c/4l$.

4. Vibration of Air in Cylindrical Pipes.

We may represent the motion of air in the pipe by the general equation

$$\frac{\partial^2 \xi}{\partial t^2} = c^2 \frac{\partial^2 \xi}{\partial x^2}.$$

As in equation 14.4, p. 369, the solution of this is

$$\xi = \left(A \cos\frac{\omega x}{c} + B \sin\frac{\omega x}{c} \right) \cos\omega t.$$

Hence the compression at any point is given by

$$-\frac{\partial \xi}{\partial x} = \frac{\omega}{c} \cos\omega t \left(A \sin\frac{\omega x}{c} - B \cos\frac{\omega x}{c} \right), \qquad . \quad (15.9)$$

and the particle velocity by

$$\frac{\partial \xi}{\partial t} = -\omega \sin \omega t \left(A \cos \frac{\omega x}{c} + B \sin \frac{\omega x}{c}\right). \qquad . \quad (15.10)$$

(a) *Open Pipe.* Let the pipe be open at both ends, i.e. at $x = 0$ and at $x = l$. Then

$$\left(\frac{\partial \xi}{\partial x}\right)_{x=0} = 0 \quad \text{and} \quad \left(\frac{\partial \xi}{\partial x}\right)_{x=l} = 0$$

for all values of t, since there is an antinode with no variations of pressure at these points.

Hence $\qquad -\dfrac{\omega}{c} \cos \omega t \cdot B = 0, \quad \text{i.e. } B = 0,$

and $\qquad \dfrac{\omega}{c} \cos \omega t \left(A \sin \dfrac{\omega l}{c} - B \cos \dfrac{\omega l}{c}\right) = 0.$

$$\therefore \frac{\omega l}{c} = m\pi,$$

where m is any integer. That is,

$$\omega = \frac{m\pi c}{l},$$

and the possible frequencies are found by giving m successive integral values in the expression

$$f_m = \frac{\omega}{2\pi} = \frac{mc}{2l}. \qquad . \quad . \quad . \quad . \quad (15.11)$$

Thus the open pipe has the fundamental frequency $c/2l$ and gives the full series of partials.

The case of a pipe closed at both ends leads to exactly the same conclusion but is of no practical importance, except perhaps in the calibration of microphones by means of the Rayleigh disc.

(b) *Closed Pipe.* In this case let us assume the pipe open at $x = 0$ and closed at $x = l$. From this we deduce as before that $(\partial \xi / \partial x)_{x=0}$ is zero for all values of t, and hence, as before, $B = 0$. Since at the closed end the particle velocity must always be zero, we have also

$$\left(\frac{\partial \xi}{\partial t}\right)_{x=l} = 0 \text{ for all values of } t.$$

Hence $\qquad -\omega \sin \omega t \left(A \cos \dfrac{\omega l}{c} + B \sin \dfrac{\omega l}{c}\right) = 0.$

$$\therefore \frac{\omega l}{c} = \frac{(2m-1)\pi}{2},$$

where m is any integer. That is,

$$\omega = \frac{(2m - 1)\pi c}{2l},$$

and the possible frequencies are obtained by giving m the successive integral values in the expression

$$f_m = \frac{\omega}{2\pi} = \frac{(2m - 1)c}{4l}. \quad . \quad . \quad . \quad (15.12)$$

Here the fundamental tone has the frequency $c/4l$ and the pipe gives only the odd members of the harmonic series as its partials.

5. Vibration of Air in Conical Pipes.

In the case of cylindrical pipes the wave propagation is of the plane wave type and the motion over any cross-section is everywhere parallel to the axis of the pipe. In a conical pipe of small angle this may still be regarded as approximately true, but if the cone has a wide angle the restriction no longer applies and we must think of the waves as divergent and convergent—spherical rather than plane.

We can write the wave equation (2.36, p. 61) in the more convenient form

$$\frac{\partial^2(rs)}{\partial t^2} = c^2 \frac{\partial^2(rs)}{\partial r^2},$$

since s is related to ϕ by the equation $\phi = c^2 s$.

If, as before, we assume a wave of simple harmonic type we may put

$$rs = a \cos\omega t,$$

and the equation becomes

$$\frac{\partial^2(rs)}{\partial r^2} + \frac{\omega^2}{c^2}(rs) = 0.$$

The solution of the equation is, as before,

$$rs = \left(A \cos\frac{\omega r}{c} + B \sin\frac{\omega r}{c}\right) \cos\omega t.$$

There are two cases of special interest.

(a) *Open Cone.* At the vertex $r = 0$, and hence $rs = 0$, unless s is infinite, which cannot be the case. It is therefore immaterial whether the vertex is open or closed. In both cases we have

$$(rs)_{r=0} = 0 \text{ for all values of } t.$$

But
$$(rs)_{r=0} = A \cos\omega t,$$
$$\therefore A = 0.$$

If the wide end is open and is at a distance l from the vertex, where l is measured along the slanting side of the cone, then here s must be zero and we have

$$(rs)_{r=l} = 0 \text{ for all values of } t.$$

Hence
$$B \sin \frac{\omega l}{c} \cos \omega t = 0;$$

$$\therefore \frac{\omega l}{c} = m\pi,$$

where m is any integer. That is, the frequency is

$$f_m = \frac{\omega}{2\pi} = \frac{mc}{2l}. \quad \cdots \cdots \quad (15.13)$$

The fundamental tone, therefore, has the frequency $c/2l$, which is the same as that for the open cylindrical pipe, and the conical pipe gives the full series of harmonic partials.

(b) *Closed Cone.* As in the previous case we have $A = 0$, no matter what the condition at the vertex.

Hence
$$rs = B \sin \frac{\omega r}{c} \cos \omega t$$

and
$$\frac{\partial}{\partial r}(rs) = \frac{\omega B}{c} \cos \frac{\omega r}{c} \cos \omega t,$$

so that
$$r \frac{\partial s}{\partial r} + s = \frac{\omega B}{c} \cos \frac{\omega r}{c} \cos \omega t,$$

$$\therefore \frac{\partial s}{\partial r} = \frac{\omega B}{cr} \cos \frac{\omega r}{c} \cos \omega t - \frac{B}{r^2} \sin \frac{\omega r}{c} \cos \omega t.$$

At the closed end $(r = l)$ we must have $\partial s/\partial r = 0$ for all values of t,

$$\therefore \frac{B}{l^2} \left(\frac{\omega l}{c} \cos \frac{\omega l}{c} - \sin \frac{\omega l}{c} \right) \cos \omega t = 0.$$

$$\therefore \tan \frac{\omega l}{c} = \frac{\omega l}{c}. \quad \cdots \cdots \quad (15.14)$$

The solution of this equation is given by the points of intersection of the graph $y = \tan(\omega l/c)$ with the graph $y = \omega l/c$. These intersections occur approximately (fig. 9.1, p. 215) for values of $\omega l/c$ given by $3\pi/2$, $5\pi/2$, $7\pi/2$, ... More accurately, the solutions are given by

$$\frac{\omega l}{\pi c} = 1 \cdot 43, \ 2 \cdot 46, \ 3 \cdot 47, \ 4 \cdot 48, \ 5 \cdot 48. \ \cdots \quad (15.15)$$

It follows that the frequency of the fundamental is $\omega/2\pi = 1\cdot43c/2l$, and that the partial tones are inharmonic.

The distribution of nodes and antinodes along the pipe is of some interest. Let us suppose the pipe to be sounding its fourth partial. For this case $\omega l/\pi c = 4\cdot48$,

$$\text{i.e. } \omega = \frac{4\cdot48\pi c}{l}. \quad \ldots \ldots \quad (15.16)$$

For the antinodes $s = 0$,

$$\therefore \ rs = 0,$$

$$\therefore \ \frac{\omega r}{c} = K\pi,$$

where K is any integer which does not make $r > l$. That is,

$$\frac{4\cdot48\pi r}{l} = K\pi, \quad \text{or} \quad r = \frac{Kl}{4\cdot48}. \quad \ldots \quad (15.17)$$

The antinodes are therefore equidistant, and their distances from the vertex (measured along the slant side) are obtained by giving to K the successive values 1, 2, 3, 4. The distances so obtained are $0\cdot223l$, $0\cdot447l$, $0\cdot670l$, $0\cdot893l$.

At the nodes we have the condition already presented for the closed end, namely, $\partial s/\partial r = 0$,

$$\therefore \ \frac{\omega r}{c} = \tan\frac{\omega r}{c}.$$

But for the fourth partial we have $\omega = \dfrac{4\cdot48\pi c}{l}$,

$$\therefore \ \frac{\omega r}{c} = \frac{4\cdot48\pi r}{l};$$

and $\omega r/c = \tan(\omega r/c)$ when $\omega r/c$ has the successive values $1\cdot43\pi$, $2\cdot46\pi$, $3\cdot47\pi$, $4\cdot48\pi$, ... The successive nodes are therefore given by

$$\begin{aligned}
&\text{(i)} \quad \frac{4\cdot48\pi r}{l} = 1\cdot43\pi, \\
&\qquad\qquad r = \frac{1\cdot43l}{4\cdot48} = 0\cdot319l. \\
&\text{(ii)} \quad\quad r = \frac{2\cdot46l}{4\cdot48} = 0\cdot549l. \\
&\text{(iii)} \quad\quad r = \frac{3\cdot47l}{4\cdot48} = 0\cdot775l. \\
&\text{(iv)} \quad\quad r = \frac{4\cdot48l}{4\cdot48} = l.
\end{aligned} \right\} \quad \ldots \quad (15.18)$$

The nodes, then, are unequally spaced along the tube.

The difference between the cone and the cylinder may be shown experimentally by taking a cylinder open at both ends, a cylinder closed at one end, and a cone open at the base, all giving 256 cycles per second as fundamental. The cylinder open at both ends and the cone will have approximately the same length; the cylinder closed at one end will have about half this length. All three will reinforce the sound from a 256 fork by resonance. The cone and the cylinder open at both ends will respond to a 512 fork, but not the cylinder closed at one end. All three will respond to a 768 fork.

6. Flue Pipes.

In the flute and in some important types of organ pipe the edge tone plays an important rôle. The design of these instruments was of course empirical, and even when the vibration of the air in the associated pipe was understood the method by which the vibration was initiated remained completely obscure. The structure of a flue pipe is shown in fig. 15.9. The air enters by the foot A into a chamber B through which it is directed by the languid L to a narrow slit C (the flue), and the jet issuing from this impinges on the edge E or passes very near to it. M is the mouth of the pipe; D and E the lower and upper lips. Here, then, we have all the conditions necessary for the production of the edge tone, while the pipe itself is capable of giving the series of partial tones proper to a column of air open at both ends in the case of the open diapason or closed at one end in the case of the

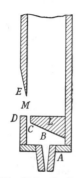

Fig. 15.9.—Section of wooden flue pipe

stopped diapason. In this latter case the upper end of the pipe, which is usually square and made of wood, is closed with a wooden stopper covered with leather and adjustable for tuning. The pitch of the edge tone is determined for a given wind pressure by the "height of the mouth", which must be carefully adjusted. Organ builders have always recognized the importance of this, without knowing why it was important. Clearly, however, we have here a coupled system consisting of the edge tone and the vibrating column. The column is the predominant partner in the combination, and the best result will obviously be secured when the natural frequency of the edge tone coincides with that of the fundamental mode of vibration of the column.

The phenomena characteristic of " overblowing " and " under-blowing ", although somewhat complicated in detail, are susceptible of satisfactory explanation in their main features on this theory and

have been briefly discussed by Brown.* He experimented with an
open diapason organ pipe of rectangular cross-section 4·7 × 5·8 cm.
with a flue of length 4·7 cm. and breadth approximately 0·175 cm.;
the cut-up (see section 10, p. 406) was 1·6 cm. The pipe gave a fundamental tone of 130 cycles/sec. This frequency of 130 cycles/sec. was
found to be higher than that of the pipe when tested as a resonator,
probably because the system is a coupled one. The results are shown
in fig. 15.10.

The author describes the sequence of changes as follows: "The tones emitted
by the pipe correspond exactly with those found by Rayleigh. His account of his
experiments with an open 2-ft. metal pipe in which the pressure was slowly
decreased is reproduced below:

Rayleigh	Diagram
About this point the octave of the normal note is heard, after which the normal note itself disappears.	$i + j$ h
The normal note reappears, the octave continuing.	g
The octave goes	f
and then the normal note,	e
after which there is silence.	ed
Octave comes in again	d
and then the normal note, at a pitch which falls from considerably above to a little below the natural pitch. At the lowest pressures the normal note is unaccompanied by the octave.	cb

"In order to explain the mechanism of the production of this sequence, it
is more convenient to consider what occurs with increasing velocity. In the
pipe used, the construction of the block and lower lip was such that the jet of
air is directed outwards and does not encounter the edge until its velocity is
200 cm./sec. Consequently Stage 1 is unstable and edge tone oscillation commences
at a (Stage 2): when this reaches a frequency of $f = 100$ cycles/sec., oscillation is
set up in the pipe and the edge tone changes suddenly to $f = 126$ cycles/sec. at b,
and this frequency is feebly emitted by the pipe. The combination of the pressure
changes in the pipe, and those in the wake of the vortices entering the pipe (which
according to my theory are the cause of free edge tone production) result in the
frequency of pipe and edge tone rising continually and slowly together to $f =$
136 cycles/sec. at c ($u = 290$ cm./sec.). The pressure changes in the pipe are not
sufficient to affect the edge tone any further and the sound ceases. But it happens
that Stage 3 in the free edge tones at $u = 290$ cm./sec. has a frequency very
close to the octave, and this gives rise, for a short interval, to a very feeble octave
note at d.

"The construction of the block and lip now causes the jet to pass just inside
the edge, and silence ensues, together with absence of edge-tone oscillation, until
the velocity reaches 380 cm./sec. At this velocity a disturbance passing up the
jet and striking the edge would produce a frequency of nearly double the fundamental, and pressure variation of this frequency being reinforced by resonance,
the note is maintained in spite of the fact that the jet does not strike the edge
centrally. If the velocity is increased very slowly, however, the fundamental

* *Nature*, Vol. 141, p. 11 (1938).

is elicited first at *e*. This presumably is due to the fact that the fundamental frequency, $f = 130$ cycles/sec., is *less* than half the octave, $f = 264$ cycles/sec., so that the edge tone reaches double the fundamental of the pipe before reaching equality with the octave. When the octave sounds at *f*, the pipe takes complete control and the frequency remains constant (Stage 2). When the velocity reaches 550 cm./sec. at *h*, the real fundamental of the pipe begins to sound and the jet oscillates as a whole from side to side (Stage 1). The octave note can still be heard but disappears at *i*. The occurrence of Stage 1 at such a high velocity is quite impossible without a resonator."

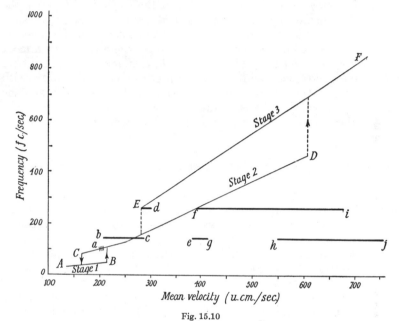

Fig. 15.10

———, free edge tones; ———, organ-pipe tones; ||||, organ-pipe edge tones. Open wood diapason. Fundamental 130 c./sec.; under-blown octave, 264 c./sec.

The phenomenon of underblowing may give rise to trouble from the point of view of the organist when the air blast is admitted gradually instead of suddenly. The pipe begins to speak on a higher partial instead of on the fundamental, and we have the " coughing " bourdon. Organ builders commonly attempt to prevent this phenomenon by the use of what is known as the " beard ". One of the best-known forms of this device is the " rolling bridge ", which is a piece of cylindrical wooden rod fixed horizontally across the mouth of the pipe close to the lower lip and leaving ample space above between the bridge and the upper lip. The effect of the beard is to deviate the air stream, and the result is the same as if the edge were displaced so that it was no longer central. Brown found that with an experimental beard almost touching the air stream this latter was deviated towards the beard and no oscillation was observable, but as it was pulled away first Stage 1 appeared, then Stage 2, and finally Stage 3. Thus Stage 1 can be brought back after the pipe has jumped to Stage 2 or Stage 3 by interposing the beard.

7. Experimental Investigation of Modes of Vibration of Organ Pipes.

There are several ways in which the vibration of the air in an organ pipe may be investigated. One of the earliest of these is the manometric flame devised by König and used to locate the places of maximum pressure change, i.e. the pressure antinodes. The method involves boring a hole in the wall of the pipe where the measurement is to be made. Over this hole, about 1 cm. in diameter, a thin rubber membrane is stretched and held in position by a metal capsule with two apertures. One of these apertures leads to the gas supply and the other to a fine gas jet. The gas supply is turned on and the jet lit. The pipe is then made to sound. If there are changes of pressure at the point in question, the membrane will vibrate and the jet of gas will oscillate with the frequency of the pipe. These oscillations will of course be invisible if the flame is observed directly, but if its image in a revolving mirror is examined it will be found to give a bright band with a serrated edge. A velocity antinode will leave the flame unaffected. If the capsule attachment is placed at the middle of an open pipe, the image shows the serrated edge due to a pressure antinode while the pipe is sounding its fundamental, but if the pipe is overblown so as to give the second partial the image of the flame in the moving mirror is drawn out into a bright band with a smooth edge.

An investigation by this method has the disadvantage that the pipe must be perforated at all the points where it is to be tested. This difficulty is avoided in an application of the hot-wire microphone due to Richardson.* We have already seen that the resistance of a hot wire placed in an oscillating current of air is lowered by the cooling effect, and that the amount of the cooling is the same as if it were placed in a steady current of velocity equal to the maximum velocity of the oscillatory current (p. 303). In this way not only may the nodes and antinodes be located in the pipe, but numerical results for the velocity amplitude from point to point in the pipe may be obtained. Also, the wire causes a minimum of interference with the vibrations of the air in the pipe and can be inserted from the end without requiring any special adaptation of the pipe itself. The result for a stopped pipe is shown in fig. 15.11. There is an abnormal increase in velocity amplitude close to the mouth, due, no doubt, to the vorticity of the motion in the neighbourhood of the slit and edge of the pipe. From the velocity amplitude both displacement amplitude and pressure

---

* *Proc. Roy. Soc.*, A, Vol. 1124, p. 522 (1926).

amplitude can be easily deduced. Richardson obtained 0·0003 atmosphere for this latter quantity at the closed end of the pipe.
The possibility of applying the interferometer method of Töpler

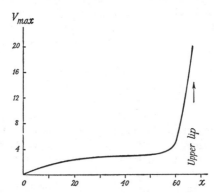

Fig. 15.11.—Displacement amplitude along a stopped organ-pipe

and Boltzmann (section 9, p. 297) or the Rayleigh disc (section 13, p. 305) may be noted, as well as the method employed by Brown of observing smoke-impregnated air stroboscopically (section 11, p. 300).

8. Effect of Temperature on the Frequency of Pipes.

Since the frequency of a vibrating air column depends upon the velocity of sound in it, obviously anything that affects the velocity affects the pitch. If two organ pipes are tuned to unison and sounded together and one is then gently warmed, beats are at once heard. This is due to the rise in pitch of the warmer pipe. We have already seen that the velocity of sound in air increases by about 0·2 per cent per degree centigrade rise in temperature. A rise in temperature of 5° C. will therefore cause an increase in frequency of 1 per cent, which corresponds to about one-twelfth of a tone—a quite perceptible change of pitch. Owing to this variation of pitch with temperature to which all wind instruments are subject, it is necessary to specify a temperature at which the instruments shall give the correct pitch, and this temperature is taken as 60° F. The warming up of a brass instrument with the player's breath may cause quite a perceptible sharpening of pitch, and the rise in temperature of the room during a concert has the same effect.

Blowing an organ pipe with a gas in which the velocity of sound is greater than in air causes a marked change of pitch, and even a small admixture of coal gas or hydrogen can be detected if two pipes tuned to unison are blown one with pure air and the other with air containing the other gas; beats at once reveal the change of pitch.

9. End Correction.

Even in the case of a cylindrical pipe with a clean-cut end the antinode does not coincide with the end of the pipe, and the effective length of the pipe is always greater than its geometrical length (see section 6, p. 253). For a cylindrical pipe the " end correction " is about $0 \cdot 6R$, where R is the radius of the cross-section of the pipe, so that of two pipes of the same geometrical length but different diameters the wider pipe gives the lower note.

The correction is approximately independent of the wave-length of the sound. If this were strictly true the partials for an open pipe would still form an harmonic series. Since it is only approximately true the higher partials are slightly mistuned, and hence are not strongly elicited when the correction is large. This accounts for the relative purity of tone given by wide pipes as compared with the full series of partials given by narrower pipes.

The magnitude of the correction for other than cylindrical ends depends on the degree of openness or " conductivity " of the end. Thus an uncovered hole in a flute is an open end, but the correction will be greater than for the case previously discussed. In the same way the correction for the embouchure of an organ pipe may be two or three times the radius, and the pitch of the pipe will be markedly below that calculated for a pipe of the actual length from embouchure to upper end.

10. Musical Instruments of the Flute Type.

Among the commoner organ stops constructed on the flue system are the Diapason, Viola and Flute. Differences in quality of tone may be secured in a variety of ways.

(1) The pipe may be stopped or open. We have already seen that the open pipe is capable of giving the full harmonic series of partials, whereas the closed pipe gives the odd-numbered harmonics only.

(2) The " cut-up " or height of the mouth in terms of the width of the mouth may be varied. In some cases this is 1 in 4, as with a height of $\frac{1}{2}''$ and a width of $2''$, in some cases it is only 1 in 2, while in wood pipes of flute tone it may be 1 in 1. Low-cut mouths encourage high partials.

(3) The shape of the bevel of the lip of the pipe may be varied. Many minor modifications are possible.

(4) The material of the pipe may be varied. In the discussion of the vibrations of air in organ pipes we have so far assumed that the walls are perfectly rigid and that only the geometrical form of the pipe matters. This is certainly not the case. Miller * constructed three organ pipes of identical dimensions, one of wood, one of thin zinc,

* *Phys. Rev.*, Vol. 35, p. 1417 (1930).

single-walled, and one of the same zinc but double-walled. The first gave a frequency of 192 and the other two gave about 173. By touching the second pipe outside at various points, marked differences in the quality of its tone were produced. The space between the walls in the third pipe was filled with water, and this was gradually run off while the pipe was sounding, with the result that the tone quality changed conspicuously and inharmonic partials were formed.

Walls which are yielding tend to lower pitch and also to absorb energy, so that the sound is less intense than with rigid walls. On the other hand, materials with a high modulus of elasticity tend to have well-marked natural frequencies, with consequent modification of tone quality.

(5) The scale of the pipe, i.e. the ratio of diameter to length, may be varied. Small-scale pipes give more prominent high partials but also, of course, tend more easily to overblow.

(6) The shape and position of the languid (p. 401) may be varied. These modifications are largely empirical, as indeed many of the others are also. Organ-building as an art is some way in advance of organ-building as a science.

The most important orchestral instruments acting on the flue-pipe principle are the flute and the piccolo. The lips project the jet of air which, impinging on the edge of the mouth hole, gives rise to the jet tone and initiates the vibrations in the pipe. The performer has the blowing pressure and the height of the mouth under control, and so can modify the frequency of the jet tone within wide limits. The mouth hole is of course a displacement antinode, as is also the open hole nearest to the mouth hole. The distance between these is approximately half the wave-length of the tone produced, except when a high partial is being elicited by overblowing.

The end corrections for the flute as for the organ pipe are considerable. Thus G. T. Walker * found 0·20″ as the correction for the open end of his flute and 1·80″ for the mouth end, while for a half-inch hole in the flute the correction was 0·60″. The bore of the flute had a diameter of 0·75″, so that the end correction was $(0·20/0·375)R = 0·53R$.

11. Reed Pipes.

A large number of organ stops use pipes with an attached reed. The air first enters the boot g (fig. 15.12, p. 408) and then passes the tongue d into the shallot, from which it passes into the pipe. The tongue is usually a thin strip of brass which in its equilibrium position stands clear of the shallot. It may be a beating reed, in which case it is wider than the aperture in the shallot and completely closes it when pressed against it by the air blast; or it may be a free reed, in which case it is just smaller than the aperture and passes through it

* *Proc. Ind. Ass. for the Cultivation of Science*, Vol. 6, p. 113 (1920–21).

with very slight clearance. The reed can be tuned by adjusting the tuning spring e, which controls the vibrating length. The reed and the pipe together form a coupled system, and the best quality of tone is produced when the reed is tuned to the fundamental frequency of the air in the pipe. The partials of the column of air will also be elicited, but the partials of the tongue, being inharmonic, will not be reinforced by the air column.

We may think of the maintenance of vibrations as follows. The initial entry of air into the boot causes a compression to enter the pipe and closes the reed against the shallot. The compression travels up to the open end of the pipe, where it is reflected as a rarefaction and returns to the reed end. The reed remains closed and the rarefaction returns to the open end, where it is reflected as a compression. When this compression returns to the reed it assists the resilience of the reed, which opens and allows more air to enter, reinforcing the compression. Thus the reed acts as a closed end, and an open cylindrical pipe gives only the odd series of partials in association with a reed. On the other hand, a conical pipe gives the full series of partials (p. 399), because each impulse must be reversed as at an open end on reflection at the reed if infinite compressions are excluded. The clarinet stop has a cylindrical pipe, while the oboe stop is conical with an open conical cap more widely flared.

Fig. 15.12.—Reed pipe

The vibrating length of the metal tongue d is controlled by the tuning spring e

A, beating reed.	a, head of shallot.	e, tuning spring.
B, filled-in shallot.	b, lip of shallot.	f, wedge.
C, open shallot.	c, lip of tube.	g, boot.
D, closed.	d, tongue.	

A large number of orchestral wind instruments use some form of reed. The clarinet, which may be of wood or of metal, has a cane reed and a cylindrical pipe. The oboe has two reeds and a conical pipe.

An entirely different type of reed is that obtained by stretching two rubber bands edge to edge across a hole through which air can be blown. The rubber bands impose a periodic intermittence on the air blast, producing a tone. The voice functions by a mechanism of this type. To emit a sound we stretch the vocal " cords ", leaving only a narrow slit between their free edges. These "cords" are maintained in vibration by the air current, and the resulting sound is modified by the cavities of the mouth and nose. In the brass instruments (horn, trombone, trumpet, &c.) the lips act as a double reed of this kind. The mouthpiece is a hemispherical cup to which the lips are applied, the tension of the lips and the extent of the vibrating portions being modified so as to give the pitch of the note which it is desired to produce. Only notes which occur in the harmonic series of partials for the instrument can be produced. These may be written as

$$C \quad c \quad g \quad c' \quad e' \quad g' \quad (a'\sharp) \quad c'' \quad d'' \quad e'' \quad (f''\sharp) \quad g'' \quad (a''\flat) \quad (a''\sharp) \quad b'' \quad c'''$$
$$1 \quad 2 \quad 3 \quad 4 \quad 5 \quad 6 \quad 7 \quad 8 \quad 9 \quad 10 \quad 11 \quad 12 \quad 13 \quad 14 \quad 15 \quad 16$$

Some of these partials do not belong to the scale, but in practice the performer has considerable control of the note. He can not only correct these partials but modify the other tones so as to produce sharps and flats. The number of partials actually used is not in general large. The flute and clarinet use only three. The trumpet may go as high as the twelfth. In the case of the clarinet and oboe the effective vibrating length of the air column is modified by uncovering holes as in the flute. In the case of the trombone the actual length of vibrating air column is modified by the use of a slide, a long U-shaped crook of which one end can be telescoped over the end of the straight tube attached to the mouthpiece and the other over the end of the straight piece attached to the bell.

The quality of tone depends on the shape of the tube, the scale of the tube, the kind of reed, if any, the material, and a number of other factors, but here again we are largely in the realm of the empirical. Interesting work, however, has lately been done on the relation of the quality of tone of an instrument to the region of pitch in which resonance is strongest. Just as in the production of vowel sounds the characteristic thing is not the reinforcement of a particular order of partial but the reinforcement of whatever partials occur in a certain fixed region of pitch, so each musical instrument is characterized by a tendency to reinforce partials in the neighbourhood of a fixed pitch. The table by Hermann-Goldap on p. 410 gives the results of an analysis of the quality of tone of various wind instruments.[*]

It will be seen that in some cases the intensity of the prominent region of tone or formant is actually greater than that of the fundamental, while in other cases it is less.

The air pressures developed in playing wind instruments have been investigated by Stone,[†] Barton and Laws [‡] and Foord.[§] The

---

[*] See also Richardson, *Acoustics of Orchestral Instruments*, Arnold (1929).

[†] *Elementary Lessons in Sound*, p. 171 (Macmillan, 1879).

[‡] *Phil. Mag.*, Vol. 3, p. 385 (1902).   [§] *Phil. Mag.*, Vol. 27, p. 272 (1914).

pressure was measured while the notes were actually being produced, a water manometer being connected to a small tube held in the mouth of the performer. As might be expected, the pressure developed increases with loudness, and also as a rule with the frequency of the note. For the trombone the pressure varies from 13 cm. of water to 122 cm., for the cornet from 13 cm. to 106 cm. For the clarinet Foord found that the usual relation between blowing pressure and frequency

Instrument	Range of Fundamental Investigated	Range of Tone always Prominent	Intensity of Fundamental / Intensity of Formant
Oboe	f′ to f″	g♯‴ to b♭‴	0 to 0·48
B♭ trumpet ..	b to b′	b♭ to c″	0·13 to 0·30
Horn	c′	b♭′ to c‴	0·57 to 1
Tenor trombone ..	g to a, d′ to f″	b♭′ to d″	0·57 to 0·88
B♭ clarinet * ..	a″ to e″	g‴ to b♭‴	1·32 to 5·0
Flute *	d″ to c♯‴	f‴ to a‴	1·04 to 3·16

does not hold, the blowing pressure being actually less for high notes than for low notes. This he attributed to the fact that the increase in frequency was in this case produced by manipulation of the free length of the vibrating reed by slight pressure with the lip. Foord also remarked that the production of the higher notes is aided by the player imagining that he is singing a high note, from which fact it must be assumed that the form of the cavity of the mouth and throat exert an influence on the production of the derived notes. This suggests that there are really three vibrating systems involved; experiment suggests that this is true for the reed pipes of the organ as well, the form and volume of the boot contributing to the quality of the tone.

* Presumably made of wood.

CHAPTER XVI

Rods, Membranes, and Plates

The theoretical study of the vibrations of the systems considered in this chapter is more difficult than that of simple systems, and developed gradually from the time of the discovery of Hooke's law. Experiments done concurrently have continued to yield interesting phenomena ever since the classical work of Chladni (1756–1827) drew attention to the beautiful sand-figures observed with vibrating rods and plates. This progress is still continuing under the stimulus of new methods.

It is of value first to consider certain well-established theorems which apply to mechanical systems of many degrees of freedom, such as a number of masses elastically connected. These results will also apply, directly or by analogy, to continuous systems, such as those in question, for which the relative movement of the elastically connected parts constitutes the natural manner of vibration.*

1. Systems of More than One Degree of Freedom.

The small oscillations of an undamped system of n degrees of freedom in which the restoring forces are due to internal strain are not usually of simple harmonic type, nor are they necessarily periodic in time. They can, however, be analysed into n " modes " of vibration which are simple harmonic, provided that the elastic forces are of the linear type proportional to the corresponding strains. Any one of these modes can exist independently of the others, and then the displacements of the separate parts from their equilibrium positions retain constant ratios throughout the motion. The displacements may then be expressed by means of a single variable ϕ_m, say, a sinusoidal function of time, once these ratios have been determined. Then as there are n such variables ϕ_m, they also form a complete set of " co-ordinates " whereby the configuration of the system at any instant may be expressed. In general, each ϕ_m will have a different period, the natural period of the system as it vibrates in the mth mode (the exceptions, however, are important). This way of expressing the

---

* These results of general mechanics are systematically presented in standard works such as Lamb, *Higher Mechanics* (C. U. P., 1929).

motion is not confined to natural, or free, vibration, but extends to forced vibration. Any free vibration of the system can be described through a knowledge of the n periods, with the initial values of the quantities ϕ_m.

For example, a light stretched string loaded with two equal masses m at intervals a has two degrees of freedom and the position may in the first instance be described simply by means of the displacements y_1 and y_2 of the two masses.

Then if T denotes the kinetic energy, V the potential energy, and P the tension in the string, we have

$$2T = m\dot{y}_1{}^2 + m\dot{y}_2{}^2,$$

$$V = \frac{P}{a}\left(y_1{}^2 - y_1 y_2 + y_2{}^2\right).$$

If V comprises all the forces, the motion being then free and undamped, the equations of small oscillations are

$$\left.\begin{aligned}\frac{d}{dt}\left(\frac{\partial T}{\partial \dot{y}_1}\right) + \frac{\partial V}{\partial y_1} &= 0,\\[1mm]\frac{d}{dt}\left(\frac{\partial T}{\partial \dot{y}_2}\right) + \frac{\partial V}{\partial y_2} &= 0,\end{aligned}\right\}$$

for in each case $\partial T/\partial \dot{y}$ represents a momentum and $-\partial V/\partial y$ the force tending to change it. These equations give

$$m\ddot{y}_1 + \frac{2P}{a}y_1 - \frac{P}{a}y_2 = 0,$$

$$-\frac{P}{a}y_1 + m\ddot{y}_2 + \frac{2P}{a}y_2 = 0.$$

If y_1 and y_2 are supposed to oscillate with the same angular frequency ω, then

$$\left.\begin{aligned}\left(-m\omega^2 + \frac{2P}{a}\right)y_1 - \frac{P}{a}y_2 &= 0,\\[1mm]-\frac{P}{a}y_1 + \left(-m\omega^2 + \frac{2P}{a}\right)y_2 &= 0,\end{aligned}\right\} \quad . \quad . \quad (16.1)$$

and these equations can only be consistent if

$$\left(-m\omega^2 + \frac{2P}{a}\right)^2 - \frac{P^2}{a^2} = 0,$$

that is,

$$\omega = \sqrt{\frac{P}{ma}} \quad \text{or} \quad \sqrt{\frac{3P}{ma}}.$$

The two natural periods are therefore $2\pi\sqrt{(ma/P)}$ and $2\pi\sqrt{(ma/3P)}$.

To find the corresponding modes of vibration, we observe that

$$\frac{y_1}{y_2} = \frac{-m\omega^2 + (2P/a)}{P/a} = +1 \text{ or } -1,$$

according as ω takes the lower or higher value. The two vibrations are shown in fig. **16.1**. They suggest an analogy with the two lowest modes of vibration of a uniform heavy stretched string.

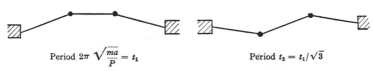

Period $2\pi \sqrt{\dfrac{ma}{P}} = t_1$ Period $t_2 = t_1/\sqrt{3}$

Fig. 16.1

The normal modes, once ascertained, may be used to simplify the equations of motion, to which we now return and write

$$\left.\begin{array}{l} y_1 = q_1 + q_2 \\ y_2 = q_1 - q_2 \end{array}\right\}, \quad \cdots \cdots \quad (16.2)$$

where the ratio of the coefficients of q_1 or q_2 in the two equations is so chosen that when one vanishes, the ratio of y_1 and y_2 is appropriate to a normal mode of vibration. We now have

$$2T = 2m\dot{q}_1{}^2 + 2m\dot{q}_2{}^2,$$

$$V = \frac{P}{a}(q_1{}^2 + 3q_2{}^2).$$

That T and V now appear as sums of squares is a result inherent in the method of choosing the new co-ordinates. The equations of motion in Lagrange's form, which apply to this or any kind of co-ordinate, lead to the result that

$$\left.\begin{array}{l} \ddot{q}_1 + \omega_1{}^2 q_1 = 0, \\ \ddot{q}_2 + \omega_2{}^2 q_2 = 0, \end{array}\right\} \quad \cdots \cdots \quad (16.3)$$

equations which, unlike (16.1), contain only one dependent variable each. Thus q_1 and q_2 are the normal co-ordinates, and have respectively the periods t_1 and t_2.

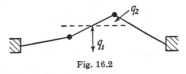

Fig. 16.2

To express any combination of y_1 and y_2 in terms of them, equations (16.2) are to be solved, giving (fig. 16.2)

$q_1 = \frac{1}{2}(y_1 + y_2)$, the mean displacement,

$q_2 = \frac{1}{2}(y_1 - y_2)$, half the difference of the displacements.

The simplest oscillations are those in which only one normal co-ordinate varies, the other remaining zero. The initial conditions $y_1 = Y$, $y_2 = 0$, $\dot{y}_1 = \dot{y}_2 = 0$, do not produce one of these, for then

$$q_1 = q_2 = \tfrac{1}{2}Y \text{ initially,}$$

and the subsequent motion is a superposition of

$$q_1 = \tfrac{1}{2}Y \cos\omega_1 t \text{ and } q_2 = \tfrac{1}{2}Y \cos\omega_2 t,$$

so that

$$y_2 = \tfrac{1}{2}Y(\cos\omega_1 t - \cos\omega_2 t)$$
$$= Y \sin\tfrac{1}{2}(\omega_2 - \omega_1)t \sin\tfrac{1}{2}(\omega_1 + \omega_2)t.$$

The initially undisplaced mass does not remain so, but executes a motion suggesting beats.

If, on the other hand, the initial conditions are $q_1 = Q$, $q_2 = 0$, $\dot{q}_1 = \dot{q}_2 = 0$, the subsequent motion is represented by

$$q_1 = Q \cos\omega_1 t, \ y_1 = y_2 \text{ initially and subsequently.}$$

This simplification suggests that forced oscillations of complex systems may be capable of expression by equations of the type $a(\ddot{q} + \omega^2 q) = F$ for each co-ordinate q, provided that the appropriate quantity F can be ascertained. This is indeed so in the form of " generalized " forces as they appear in the standard theory. The value of F may be obtained from the fact that $\int F dq$ is to represent the work done by the external forces in a displacement of the co-ordinate q. In the system considered, if the forces W_1 and W_2 act on the two masses,

$$\left.\begin{array}{l} F_1 = W_1 + W_2 \\ F_2 = W_1 - W_2 \end{array}\right\}$$

in which the coefficients are the same as for equation (16.2), but now the new quantities are on the left-hand side. Thus no symmetrical combination of forces can excite the second mode ($y_2 = -y_1$) and no antisymmetrical combination can excite the first ($y_1 = y_2$), or in other words, only combinations of forces which do work when the centre of gravity moves will tend to move it.

2. Systems of Many Degrees of Freedom.

When there are n degrees of freedom, n co-ordinates $q_1, q_2, \ldots, q_n$ are required and the kinetic energy T is given by the expression

$$2T = a_{11}\dot{q}_1{}^2 + a_{22}\dot{q}_2{}^2 + \ldots + 2a_{12}\dot{q}_1\dot{q}_2 + \ldots \ ,$$

where the a's are " coefficients of inertia " to which each movable mass contributes according to the movement it experiences when the corresponding co-ordinates vary, in the rather complicated expression

$$a_{rs} = \Sigma m \left\{ \frac{\partial x}{\partial q_r} \cdot \frac{\partial x}{\partial q_s} + \frac{\partial y}{\partial q_r} \cdot \frac{\partial y}{\partial q_s} + \frac{\partial z}{\partial q_r} \cdot \frac{\partial z}{\partial q_s} \right\} = a_{sr}.$$

These coefficients are constants for sufficiently small displacements, and bear to their respective pairs of co-ordinates the same relation as moments and products of inertia do to angular displacements in the theory of rotation.

In discussing small oscillations about a position of stable equilibrium, it is convenient to choose such co-ordinates q as will vanish in that position. Then the potential energy, measured above the equilibrium value, is of the form

$$2V = c_{11} q_1{}^2 + c_{22} q_2{}^2 + \ldots + 2c_{12} q_1 q_2 + \ldots,$$

which ensures the equilibrium conditions $\partial V/\partial q_r = 0$ for all displacements. The c's are constants analogous to coefficients of induction in electrostatics, and might be called coefficients of elasticity.

If q_r varies harmonically, so that

$$q_r = Q_r e^{i\omega t}$$

with the same frequency $\omega/2\pi$ for all the co-ordinates, the equations which correspond to (1) are

$$\sum_{s=1}^{s=n} (-a_{rs}\omega^2 + c_{rs})Q_s = 0, \quad \ldots \ldots \quad (16.4)$$

$$(n \text{ equations})$$

and these are only consistent for values of ω such that

$$\Delta(-\omega^2) \equiv \left| -a_{11}\omega^2 + c_{11}, \; - a_{12}\omega^2 + c_{12}, \; \ldots \right| = 0. \quad (16.5)$$

$$-a_{nn}\omega^2 + c_{nn}$$

This is an equation of the nth degree in ω^2 and it will have in general n distinct roots, values of ω^2 which are all positive if, as we shall suppose, V is an absolute minimum in the equilibrium position.

These values of ω^2 give the natural frequencies of the separate modes of vibration, and also enable the equations to be solved for the amplitudes Q, or rather, as the equations are homogeneous, for the ratios of these amplitudes.

A continuous system does not easily fit into this scheme, in that the actual displacements will generally be expressed as functions of independent co-ordinates, e.g. the transverse displacement of a membrane as a function of co-ordinates taken in the plane of equilibrium. The energy will be in the form of an integral which may involve not only the displacements but their derivatives with respect to the independent co-ordinates. The equations of motion can be derived by applying Lagrange's " variational " equation, and instead of equations (16.4) and (16.5) there are partial differential equations and boundary conditions. The solutions will represent normal functions, that is, amplitudes, just as do the ratios obtained from equation (16.4). The normal functions for a string stretched from $x = 0$ to $x = l$ are $\sin(\pi x/l), \sin(2\pi x/l), \ldots, \sin(r\pi x/l), \ldots$, corresponding to vibration in $1, 2, \ldots, r, \ldots$ segments (see 14.5, p. 369). Continuous systems have an infinite number of normal modes of vibration.

The equations to be solved for amplitude-ratios are the same for any ω as for $-\omega$, so that $e^{i\omega t}$ and $e^{-i\omega t}$ are equally applicable to a mode of frequency $\omega/2\pi$. Then q_r may be written as

$$q_r = A_r e^{i\omega t} + B_r e^{-i\omega t},$$

where B_r/A_r is one constant for all co-ordinates; in real terms this becomes

$$q_r = Q_r \cos(\omega t + a),$$

where the arbitrary phase constant is the same for all co-ordinates. That is, in a normal mode of vibration all constituents oscillate in phase, apart from a possible change of sign which may be regarded as an ambiguity of π. The constants Q_r and a are available to satisfy two conditions, which may be taken either as initial displacement and velocity, or as amplitude and phase of the vibration at a given moment.

In order to express the configuration of the parts of the system exclusively in terms of normal co-ordinates, we take

$$q_r = Q_r(\omega_1)\phi_1 + Q_r(\omega_2)\phi_2 + \ldots + Q_n(\omega_n)\phi_n,$$

for then, if all the quantities ϕ are zero, except ϕ_1, the amplitudes are in the ratios appropriate to the first mode, and so on. We may fix the absolute values of the ϕ's arbitrarily. The values of ϕ are then normal co-ordinates, and as in the simple example already considered, the kinetic energy reduces to a sum of terms in $\dot{\phi}_1{}^2, \dot{\phi}_2{}^2, \ldots$, without $\dot{\phi}_1\dot{\phi}_2, \ldots$.

3. Longitudinal Vibrations of Rods.

Solid rods can vibrate in three different ways, longitudinally, transversely and in torsion. Bending and the allied transverse vibration were successfully investigated by Euler (1707–1783) and Daniel Bernoulli (1700–1782), and Chladni investigated all three types of vibration experimentally.

The study of straight bars will also give qualitatively the important properties of tuning-forks, the vibration of which to some extent resembles such vibrations of a free bar as would in any case have nodes at the middle where the stalk is to be placed, and to some extent those of a bar clamped at one end.

The longitudinal vibrations of a rod bear some resemblance to longitudinal vibrations in air. The displacement ξ is evaluated by equating the mass-acceleration of an element to the corresponding elastic restoring force, and we have seen (section 14, p. 75) that this leads to the equation

$$\frac{\partial^2 \xi}{\partial x^2} = \frac{\rho}{q} \frac{\partial^2 \xi}{\partial t^2}.$$

It is not sufficient to study this equation alone. As with air columns, the conditions which hold at the ends are important and determine the natural frequencies.

The equation as it stands is that of waves propagated with a velocity $\sqrt{(q/\rho)}$, and the quantity q, strictly a modulus of adiabatic elasticity, is given closely enough for most purposes by the ordinary statical Young's modulus. The determination of this velocity and the resulting modulus are referred to in section 17, p. 280.

A rod which is not constrained in any way by the manner in which it is supported will have antinodes at both ends and one or more nodes at intermediate positions. If l is its length, the wave-lengths (in the solid, not in air) are $2l$, $2l/2$, $2l/3$, . . ., and the frequencies $\frac{1}{2l}\sqrt{\frac{q}{\rho}}$ $\times 1, 2, 3, \ldots$, form a complete harmonic series of partial tones. The odd partials alone will be appropriate to a rod of the same length fixed at the middle, for these have a node there in any case.

If both ends are fixed the partials are the same, for it may be noted that

$$\frac{\partial^2}{\partial x^2}\left(\frac{\partial \xi}{\partial x}\right) = \frac{\rho}{q}\frac{\partial^2}{\partial t^2}\left(\frac{\partial \xi}{\partial x}\right),$$

by differentiating the equation already stated. Now $\partial \xi/\partial x$ satisfies the same end-conditions for a free end as does ξ for a fixed, that is, it vanishes. Hence one solution will be obtained by differentiating the other and the frequencies will correspond.

The fundamental frequency of a rod of the same length fixed at one end only is an octave lower, as this is equivalent to a rod of twice the length fixed at the middle.

The general, more complicated vibrations may be considered in terms of the normal ones. This seems more natural than expressing results in terms of progressive waves, as the actual modes of free vibration are stationary waves obtained by superposition of pairs of progressive waves travelling in opposite directions. But though any possible vibration can be so analysed, this does not imply that a single progressive wave cannot be established. A rod will suffer no disturbance of strain or displacement at one end in consequence of a blow at the other until sufficient time has elapsed for the impulsive wave to travel the whole length. It may seem curious that even such a wave can be analysed in terms of stationary vibrations, but this is possible and the result is shown in section 3, p. 371 for a string.*

To determine the normal modes of a rod directly we may proceed with the supposition that ξ depends on x and t in the form $\xi(x)e^{i\omega t}$. Then any permissible solutions of the resulting equation will already represent stationary, not progressive, waves.

Making this substitution we obtain (cf. section 2, p. 367),

$$\xi(x) = \xi_0 \cos\left(\frac{\omega x}{c} - a\right).$$

The proper solution for a rod free at both ends will be such that $\partial\xi/\partial x$ vanishes there, so that

$$\xi(x) = \xi_0 \cos\frac{r\pi x}{l},$$

where l is the length, and r is any integer.

Hence
$$\omega = \frac{r\pi c}{l},$$

and the frequency $= \omega/2\pi = rc/2l$, as already found. By differentiating this normal function, or by applying the condition $\xi = 0$ at the ends, we find for the case of a rod fixed at both ends,

$$\xi(x) = \xi_0 \sin\frac{r\pi x}{l},$$

as given for a stretched string (cf. section 10, p. 384).

---

* Another difficulty is that normal functions fulfilling the boundary or end conditions are used to express initial conditions which may violate them. This is a problem in the convergence of infinite series; if there is an impulsive force at $x = o$, $t = o$, then this will be a point of non-uniform convergence where the members of the series, but not its sum, will be continuous.

The possibility of sound waves in solid rods accounts for some of the transmission of noise in buildings. The velocity of transmission for ordinary solids is very large (Chapter X), and this explains why the natural frequencies of longitudinal vibration for a given length are very much higher than those of an equal air-column. Such natural vibrations may be excited in the laboratory by friction and observed by means of dust, which collects at the nodes (cf. p. 254), or if the material is transparent, by means of the effect of strain on a beam of plane-polarized light passing across the rod.* Polarized light has also been used in this way to detect the passage of a pulse along a rod and so to measure the velocity directly, as in gelatin by Herbolsheimer.†

A more direct method of observation is that of Davis ‡ and of Clark,§ who examined with a microscope bright points on a string excited by continuous rubbing. The vibrations qualitatively resemble transverse ones due to bowing. The properties of longitudinal vibrations of rods apply equally to strings and wires, independently of any permanent tension they may have, except that damping may be appreciable above the elastic limit.

The longitudinal oscillations of a rod of metal such as nickel may be excited by magnetostriction, using a solenoid through which the current from a valve oscillator passes. This is a very convenient method of generating mechanical vibrations of high frequency and also of calibrating other apparatus (p. 224). A quartz rod may be excited in the same way as a quartz plate, by using the piezo-electric effect (see p. 220), and a standard clock designed at the N.P.L. makes use of the longitudinal oscillations of a quartz ring supported at three of its six nodes and oscillating at 100 kilocycles per second.

The compressions in a bar in longitudinal vibration are not purely dilatational. This holds even for the simplest kind of longitudinal compression, such as that of air in a tube, where the resulting shear-component leads to viscosity attenuation. In a bar or rod the shear is less important, but there is an actual lateral motion resulting from the expansion which always accompanies longitudinal compression. There is a corresponding contribution to kinetic energy, leading to a small diminution of the wave velocity. This diminution is proportional to ω^2 and does not greatly complicate the phenomena of the lower modes of vibration. It is, moreover, usually quite small if the bar is sufficiently long in comparison with its width. In the longitudinal vibrations along a plate the lateral component can only occur in the direction normal to the plate, and in an extended

---

* Biot, *Physique*, Vol. 2, p. 15 (1828); Mach, *Ann. d. Physik*, Vol. 146, p. 316 (1872).
† *Zeits. f. Phys.*, Vol. 3, p. 182 (1920).   ‡ *Proc. Amer. Acad.*, Vol. 41, p. 691 (1906).
§ *Phys. Rev.*, Vol. 7, p. 561 (1916).

solid it is wholly suppressed. The effect of this restriction on the velocity is considerable (p. 282), but it is due to the change in the relevant elastic modulus, not to the small correction to the kinetic energy.

The lateral or radial motion may, however, be important at high frequencies, and may become markedly dependent on frequency, so that anomalies result. Experiments have shown that the calculated correction holds for quite high frequencies, and that ultimately there are changes in wave-propagation resembling those of anomalous dispersion in optics. This is to be expected in view of the complexity of the true frequency-equation.*

4. Transverse Vibrations of Bars.

The transverse vibration of bars differs from the longitudinal in several respects. The restoring forces are due to bending and therefore involve the same modulus of elasticity, Young's modulus, but the equations of motion are quite different. The series of partials is no longer harmonic. Furthermore, a permanent tension radically alters the vibration. We shall consider only the case in which there is no permanent tension.

Ignoring for the moment the end conditions, we may obtain the wave equation from two principles of bending. It is supposed that when a bar bends, each longitudinal filament changes in length, except those lying on a " neutral surface " near the middle of any cross-section. This leads to the formula for the bending moment exerted across any section as

$$G = qSk^2 \frac{\partial^2 y}{\partial x^2},$$

where q is Young's modulus, S the area of cross-section supposed uniform, k the radius of gyration of the cross-section about the axis in which the neutral surface cuts it, and y the lateral displacement at the position x. The x-axis is the undisplaced position of the rod. In a bar originally straight the bending moment varies as the local curvature; in a slightly curved bar the change of curvature would play the same part, so that initial curvature due to the weight of a bar can be ignored if it is fairly small.

The forces which act across any section of the bar may always be represented by a single force and a couple. The single force may be supposed, in absence of permanent tension, to act in the plane of the cross-section as a shearing force F. F and G, the bending couple, are not independent of one another, and at any element where no

---

* See Love, *Mathematical Theory of Elasticity* (Cambr. Univ. Press, 1920).

external force is being applied to the bar the equation of moments acting on an element, of length δx, shows that

$$F = -\frac{\partial G}{\partial x},$$

provided that there is no angular acceleration (fig. 16.3).

The resultant lateral force on such an element is given by $(\partial F/\partial x)\delta x$ or $-(\partial^2 G/\partial x^2)\,\delta x$. Hence the equation of lateral motion becomes

$$\rho S \frac{\partial^2 y}{\partial t^2}\,\delta x = -qSk^2 \frac{\partial^4 y}{\partial x^4}\,\delta x,$$

or

$$\frac{\partial^4 y}{\partial x^4} + \frac{1}{c^2 k^2} \cdot \frac{\partial^2 y}{\partial t^2} = 0, \quad \ldots \ldots \quad (16.6)$$

where $c^2 = q/\rho$, and c is the velocity of longitudinal waves.

This is not the simplest type of wave-equation, but it is evident without solution that a change of scale in which x, k and t alter in the same ratio will leave the equation unchanged. Exactly similar bars or tuning-forks have their fundamental free period proportional to the linear dimensions, and the same holds for any specified mode. The width of the bar or fork parallel to the neutral surface, however, does not affect the period. That period and linear dimensions are pro-portional is a general result for vibrating systems of this kind, and may be established by the method of dimensions.

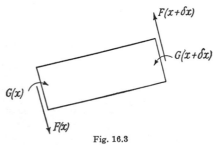

Fig. 16.3

There are several possible combinations of end-conditions. Either end may be free, clamped, or supported on a knife-edge. The corresponding conditions are

(i) Free: G vanishes; hence $\dfrac{\partial^2 y}{\partial x^2} = 0$.

  F vanishes; hence $\dfrac{\partial^3 y}{\partial x^3} = 0$.

(ii) Clamped: y and $\dfrac{\partial y}{\partial x}$ vanish.

(iii) Supported: G vanishes; hence $\dfrac{\partial^2 y}{\partial x^2} = 0$,

  y vanishes.

The substitution of $e^{i\omega t}y(x)$ in (16.6) gives the equation

$$\frac{\partial^4 y}{\partial x^4} - \frac{\omega^2}{c^2 k^2} y = 0.$$

The complete solution containing four arbitrary constants may be put in the form

$$y(x) = A\cos bx + B\sin bx + C\cosh bx + D\sinh bx,$$

where $b = \sqrt{(\omega/ck)}$ and ω is yet undetermined. If the bar is clamped at one end $(x = 0)$ and free at the other $(x = l)$,

$$y(0) = 0,$$

$$\left(\frac{\partial y}{\partial x}\right)_0 = 0,$$

whereas at $x = l$ the second and third derivatives vanish. These conditions require that

$$A + C = 0$$

$$B + D = 0,$$

$$-A\cos bl - B\sin bl + C\cosh bl + D\sinh bl = 0,$$

$$A\sin bl - B\cos bl + C\sinh bl + D\cosh bl = 0,$$

or

$$A(\cos bl + \cosh bl) + B(\sin bl + \sinh bl) = 0,$$

$$A(\sin bl - \sinh bl) - B(\cos bl + \cosh bl) = 0,$$

and these equations can only be compatible if

$$\cos bl \cosh bl + 1 = 0.$$

The values of bl for which this is true occur quite close to zeros of $\cos bl$ and therefore differ slightly from odd multiples of $\pi/2$.

The corresponding equation for a bar free at both ends or clamped at both ends is

$$\cos bl \cosh bl - 1 = 0.$$

The roots of this equation are approximately the same as those of the previous one, omitting the first, as the table shows.

Values of bl for Lower Partials of a Bar

clamped-free bar	1·875	4·694	7·855	10·996	14·137	&c.
free-free bar		4·730	7·853	10·996	14·137	

Inserting these values of b in the solution for y we get the normal functions of the problem. In any one mode the frequency is $\omega/2\pi = ckb^2/2\pi$. The fundamental frequency is $ck(1\cdot875)^2/2\pi l^2$ for a clamped-free bar, as compared with $c/4l$ for longitudinal vibrations of a rod fixed at one end. The transverse vibrations have a lower frequency in the ratio $2\cdot24(k/l)$, and k is usually very much less than l.

A measurement of the frequency of flexural vibrations of a bar of known dimensions may be used to determine c, as an alternative to the use of longitudinal vibrations. This method has been employed to determine Young's modulus for the material, e.g. by Davies and James,* Grime,† and Grime and Eaton.‡

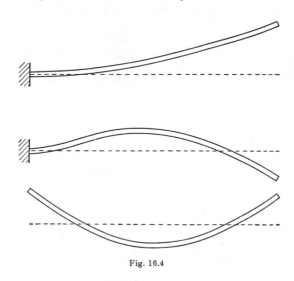

Fig. 16.4

The interval between the first two partials of a clamped-free bar is large, as the frequencies are proportional to the squares of the numbers in the table. It amounts to $2\cdot65$ octaves or 2 octaves $+$ 195 savarts (p. 316). (A perfect fifth is approximately 176 and a minor sixth 204 in these units.)

The normal functions of the fundamental and the next partial are shown in fig. 16.4, with the fundamental of a free-free bar.

The frequencies of the higher partials are approximately proportional to the squares of the odd integers and they therefore do not form a harmonic series.

* *Phil. Mag.*, Vol. 18, pp. 1023, 1053 (1934).   † *Ibid.*, Vol. 20, p. 304 (1935).
‡ *Ibid.*, Vol. 23, p. 96 (1937).

5. Tuning-forks and Reeds.

If a tuning-fork is strongly bowed it may be possible to hear a partial tone which is nearer to the fundamental than that described. It is a general fact that higher harmonics of a tone are introduced if the restoring forces depart from linearity. A term in y^3 instead of y makes a correction to the fundamental pitch depending upon amplitude, and introduces the 12th of the fundamental as an additional partial. In the sound of a tuning-fork both effects have been noticed, and there is a slight rise of pitch as the sound dies away. A strongly bowed fork will give the octave, no doubt because of the asymmetry of this method of excitation and to the asymmetry inherent in the design of forks, which probably leads to terms in the restoring force proportional to y^2. Thus in general any proper mode of vibration can become the " fundamental " of a harmonic series of tones.

The two prongs of a tuning-fork are analogous to the two masses in the problem used as an example of two degrees of freedom, for the stalk and its support, to which both prongs are attached, are in practice imperfectly rigid and provide a mechanical coupling. The asymmetrical mode of vibration which involves a deflecting strain of the support is usually much more quickly damped than the symmetrical mode which does not, so that the beats caused when only one prong is struck are usually inaudible unless special precautions are taken.

The tuning-fork, whether bowed or electrically maintained, gives a note which is practically a pure tone, for the other tones are weak and quickly damped. It is a most important and convenient standard of frequency or time-base (section 7, p. 320). The frequency of a steel fork can be calculated approximately from the formula

$$f = \frac{(1\cdot875)^2}{2\pi}\frac{ck}{l^2},$$

for if the section is rectangular and of thickness h,

$$k = \frac{h}{2\sqrt{3}},\ c = 5\cdot43 \times 10^5 \text{ cm./sec., so that}$$

$$f = 8\cdot8 \times 10^4 \frac{h}{l^2} \text{ cm./sec.,}$$

where l is the length of one prong. For a U-shaped fork the actual value is about $\frac{2}{3}$ of this.

The prong of a tuning-fork, because it has a small width, and for reasons given in section 11, p. 69, does not radiate sound efficiently into the surrounding air. Experimentally the rate of radiation can be increased by diminishing the circulation of air from the front of the prong to the back, and so increasing the pressure changes set up. A sheet of cardboard held close to the prong in a plane normal to the direction of vibration does this and also partly separates the two components of the "double source" (section 6, p. 200) that the prong represents. A noticeable increase in loudness results.

Use is often made of a sound-box tuned to the note of the fork that is mounted on it, and this enhances the already great predominance of the fundamental tone. With this arrangement or whenever the stem is not rigidly clamped, it is no longer accurate enough to compare a fork with a clamped-free bar. The vibration is communicated to the box by vertical motion of the stem, as without such motion the vibrating fork would be vertically unbalanced. Indeed, a loosely held fork may be regarded as a form of free-free bar, though the nodes are much closer to the stem than this might suggest. Further, it is found that with a resonance-box of double frequency the octave may be strongly elicited, probably because of the centrifugal forces involved in motion which is concave to the box.

A fork held loosely against a metal plate will show sub-harmonics due to intermittent contact and jumping.

The Tinsley standard tuning-fork consists of a pair of clamped straight bars, with adjustable masses near the ends. The vibrations are electromagnetically maintained, and the resulting frequency differs slightly from the true resonance frequency. It also depends slightly on amplitude, but the fork may be run at an amplitude for which the frequency is a minimum and therefore least sensitive to changes.

Steel forks have an important temperature correction, with a coefficient of the order 10^{-4} per degree (section 7, p. 321), the pitch falling about $\cdot 05$ savart or $\frac{1}{500}$ semitone for a rise of one degree. Young's modulus for steel has a temperature coefficient of $-2 \cdot 4 \times 10^{-4}$, and the linear expansion has a coefficient of the order 10^{-5}. The former is much the more important. The latter term does not lower the frequency, since the dimensional relation previously mentioned presumes a constant density; allowing for both effects of expansion, the frequency varies as the square root of the linear dimensions. The calculated temperature coefficient of frequency agrees with that measured. The modern "elinvar" standard forks give only about a tenth of the effect.

Bars and reeds find many applications in musical instruments, e.g. in the harmonium and the mouth-organ, which employ reeds excited by an air-stream. In the xylophone, free-free bars supported at the nodes are struck with hammers, different sizes providing the variety of pitch. The celesta also employs metal plates, but has a keyboard. The triangle is a bent bar struck with a straight one, and this manner of excitation produces a jangle of partial tones. In the musical-box there are metal reeds plucked with metal prongs.

Bars and reeds may be tuned by loading, as in the Tinsley fork, or by paring, as in the reeds of a harmonium. Pitch is lowered by removing material near the clamp, and raised by removing it near the free end.

In deriving the simple equation for the transverse vibrations it is assumed that rotary motion of the elements may be neglected. If this factor is included the equation becomes

$$\frac{\partial^4 y}{\partial x^4} + \frac{1}{c^2 k^2} \frac{\partial^2 y}{\partial t^2} - \frac{1}{c^2} \frac{\partial^4 y}{\partial x^2 \partial t^2} = 0.$$

The new term will be negligible so long as k, the radius of gyration of the cross-section, is small enough, but will be increasingly important as the wave-length diminishes. Rayleigh * shows that the frequency is to be corrected in the ratio

$$1 - \left(1 + \frac{m}{2}\right) \frac{mk^2}{l^2}$$

for partials of moderate order, where m is the appropriate number in the table of values of bl (p. 422).

6. Torsional Oscillations of Rods.

When a rod of circular section is twisted, the torque at any cross-section at a distance x from the end is equal to $T(\partial\theta/\partial x)$, where T is the torsional constant $(\pi n/2)a^4$, n is the modulus of rigidity, and a the radius.

The resultant torque on an element in angular motion is $T(\partial^2\theta/\partial x^2)\delta x$ and if ρ is the density the equation of angular acceleration is

$$\frac{\pi n a^4}{2} \frac{\partial^2 \theta}{\partial x^2} \, \delta x = \rho(\pi a^2 \delta x) \frac{a^2}{2} \frac{\partial^2 \theta}{\partial t^2},$$

so that

$$\frac{\partial^2 \theta}{\partial x^2} - \frac{\rho}{n} \frac{\partial^2 \theta}{\partial t^2} = 0,$$

and this is the familiar equation of wave motion with velocity $b = \sqrt{(n/\rho)}$.

Since †

$$n = \frac{q}{2(1 + \sigma)},$$

where q is Young's modulus, σ Poisson's ratio, the ratio of this velocity to that of longitudinal waves c is given by the equation

$$\frac{b}{c} = \frac{1}{\sqrt{2(1 + \sigma)}},$$

* *Sound*, Vol. I, § 186.   † *Properties of Matter*, Champion and Davy, p. 52.

which lies between $1/\sqrt{2}$ and $1/\sqrt{3}$. This is also the ratio of frequencies for the same rod, vibrating in corresponding modes of torsional and longitudinal vibration.

More detailed examination shows that other types of torsional wave are possible, in which the torsional strain, instead of being uniform over any one section, varies as a function of the radius; but all the possible types have the same velocity of propagation.

7. Orthogonal Property of Normal Functions.

It is a part of the general theory of small oscillations that the kinetic and potential energies are expressed as homogeneous quadratic functions of the velocities or displacements, which reduce in normal co-ordinates to sums of squares. This simplification is connected with the "orthogonal" property of the normal functions, for it implies that there are no "mutual" terms in the array of co-efficients of inertia and of elasticity. This property follows for a system of many degrees of freedom from equations (16.4), p. 415, in which ω is to be given a value ω_m which will make them consistent. The values of ϕ_s may be given an extra suffix m to denote that they refer to the mth mode of vibration. The rth equation is now multiplied by Q_{rl}, where l refers to another mode, the lth. On adding all n equations we have

$$-\omega_m{}^2 A_{lm} + C_{lm} = 0,$$

where

$$A_{lm} = \sum_{r=1}^{n} \sum_{s=1}^{n} a_{rs} Q_{rl} Q_{sm},$$

A_{lm} being the coefficient of inertia for the normal co-ordinates ϕ_l and ϕ_m, and

$$C_{lm} = \sum_{r=1}^{n} \sum_{s=1}^{n} c_{rs} Q_{rl} Q_{sm},$$

C_{lm} being the coefficient of elasticity for the normal co-ordinates ϕ_l and ϕ_m.

In the same way it follows that

$$-\omega_l{}^2 A_{lm} + C_{lm} = 0,$$

and hence, if $(\omega_l/2\pi)$ and $(\omega_m/2\pi)$ are different natural frequencies of the system,

$$A_{lm} = C_{lm} = 0.$$

This is the orthogonal property.

The quantities A_{mm} and C_{mm} which do not vanish are very important, since they represent "inertia" and "elasticity" of the mode m and jointly determine the natural frequency $\omega_m/2\pi$. The double suffix is now unnecessary and we may write

$$-\omega_m{}^2 A_m + C_m = 0. \quad \ldots \ldots \quad (16.7)$$

This equation may be established otherwise by using the substitution

$$q_r = \sum_{m=1}^{n} Q_{rm}\phi_m, \quad \ldots \ldots \quad (16.8)$$

which expresses the relation between the different sets of co-ordinates. With this and the orthogonal property, we have

$$2T = \Sigma\Sigma\, a_{rs}\dot{q}_r\dot{q}_s$$
$$= \sum_{m=1}^{n} A_m\dot{\phi}_m{}^2,$$
$$2V = \sum_{m=1}^{n} C_m\phi_m{}^2,$$

whence it appears that (16.7) is a form of the energy equation.

We have here the essentials for calculating the natural frequency of any mode of vibration, provided that the ratios of the amplitudes of oscillation (normal functions) are known, by calculating the appropriate inertias and elasticities.

The orthogonal property applies equally to continuous systems. We now have a continuous co-ordinate q and an amplitude Q_m which is a continuous function of the same variable or variables x. Then

$$q(x) = Q_1(x)\phi_1 + Q_2(x)\phi_2 + \ldots,$$
$$2T = \int\rho\dot{q}^2 dx$$
$$= \dot{\phi}_1{}^2\int\rho Q_1{}^2 dx + \ldots,$$

because, for the same reasons as in n degrees of freedom, the integrals like $\int\rho Q_m Q_l dx$ vanish. So, in the case of a uniform string of length l, $\int_0^l \sin(r\pi/l)\sin(s\pi/l)\,dx$ vanishes unless $r = s$.

This leads naturally to a search for the coefficients such as $A_1 = \int\rho Q_1{}^2 dx$ and the elastic terms for which

$$2V = C_1\phi_1{}^2$$

in the first mode. Then the energy equation

$$T + V = \text{constant},$$

or $(-\omega_1{}^2 A_1 + C_1)\phi_1{}^2 = \text{constant}$, in the first mode, cannot be fulfilled unless the coefficient of $\phi_1{}^2$ is zero, and the natural frequency follows at once from $\omega_1 = \sqrt{(C_1/A_1)}$.

This procedure may be used to obtain, by means of a further important theorem, a very good estimate of a natural frequency with nothing better than an approximate form of the normal function. The value of this lies in the fact that it may be easy to guess a good enough approximate form even when the accurate function is very difficult to calculate.

8. Stationary Property of Normal Modes.

Suppose that a system of n or of infinitely many degrees of freedom is so constrained that only one degree is left, and that the type of vibration is then varied in an arbitrary manner, but so as to preserve its simple harmonic character and frequency $\omega/2\pi$. For example, a stretched string might be supposed to become perfectly inflexible and to be hinged at one point, thus vibrating in two straight segments. In general, the type of vibration will not be one of the normal types of the unconstrained system, and so

$$2T = \sum_m A_m \dot{\phi}_m{}^2,$$
$$2V = \sum_m C_m \phi_m{}^2.$$

The frequency will be given by the equation

$$\omega^2 = \frac{C_1\phi_1{}^2 + C_2\phi_2{}^2 + \cdots}{A_1\phi_1{}^2 + A_2\phi_2{}^2 + \cdots}$$

As the squares and also the C's and A's are essentially positive, this shows that ω^2 is stationary when all the normal co-ordinates vanish but one, and the type of vibration is one of those natural to the unconstrained system.

Further, if that type is the fundamental, variation from it can only make ω^2 larger than $C_1/A_1(=\omega_1{}^2)$, so that ω is a minimum at the fundamental value ω_1. It appears also that any small departure from normal type causes only a small difference of the second order in the frequency, and that an estimate of the fundamental frequency made by using an approximate normal function will always be an over-estimate.

9. Vibrations of a Circular Membrane.

These principles may be applied to calculate approximately the fundamental of a uniform stretched circular membrane with no damping. As an approximate normal function we may use that which is correct for a uniform static pressure, namely,

$$\xi = \xi_1 \left(1 - \frac{r^2}{a^2}\right),$$

where ξ is the displacement at radius r, ξ_1 the displacement at the centre, and a is the radius of the membrane. The kinetic energy will be

$$2T = \int_0^a \rho \dot{\xi}_1{}^2 (1 - r^2/a^2)^2 \,.\, 2\pi r \, dr,$$

where ρ is the surface density, and this is equal to $\frac{1}{3}\pi \rho a^2 \dot{\xi}_1{}^2$.

Now $2T \doteqdot A_1 \dot{\xi}_1{}^2$, since other terms are assumed small,

$$\therefore\ A_1 = \tfrac{1}{3}\pi \rho a^2 = \tfrac{1}{3} \times \text{mass of membrane}.$$

For a static pressure P

$$\xi_1 = \frac{a^2 P}{4\tau} = \frac{\text{total force}}{4\pi\tau},$$

where τ is the tension of the membrane, and hence if V is the work done against tension,

$$2V = P \int_0^a \xi_1 (1 - r^2/a^2) 2\pi r \, dr$$
$$= 2\pi\tau \xi_1{}^2.$$

Then if $\qquad\quad 2V \doteqdot C_1 \xi_1{}^2,$

we have $\qquad\quad C_1 = 2\pi\tau = \tfrac{1}{2} \times$ stiffness constant * at centre,

$$\omega_1{}^2 = \frac{C_1}{A_1} = \frac{6\tau}{\rho a^2},$$

and the fundamental frequency is

$$\frac{\omega_1}{2\pi} = \frac{2 \cdot 450}{2\pi a} \sqrt{\frac{\tau}{\rho}}.$$

This will be a slightly overestimated value.

Another example of the use of approximate normal functions occurs in the case of lateral vibrations of a bar, where the effect of rotary inertia may be calculated by assuming the normal functions obtained without it to be accurate enough. This example and many others are given in Rayleigh's *Theory of Sound*.

10. Higher Modes of Vibration of a Membrane.

The equation of motion may be obtained by observing that the force restoring an element of a stretched membrane to its position of equilibrium is determined by the total curvature. Consider a rectangular element whose edges are parallel to the axes of x and y. Then after displacement there are forces $\tau \, \delta y$ normal to the y edges and they act at inclinations $\partial \xi(x)/\partial x$ and $\partial \xi(x + \delta x)/\partial x$, so that the resultant is $\tau(\partial^2 \xi/\partial x^2) \, \delta x \, \delta y$ normal to the surface. The tension on the other edges

* I.e. the constant giving ξ_1 in terms of the pressure.

results in a force $\tau(\partial^2\xi/\partial y^2)\,\delta x\,\delta y$. The equation of motion is therefore

$$\rho\,\frac{\partial^2\xi}{\partial t^2} - \tau\nabla^2\xi = 0,$$

where $\nabla^2\xi$ denotes $\partial^2\xi/\partial x^2 + \partial^2\xi/\partial y^2$.

Then as $\sqrt{(\tau/\rho)}$ is a velocity c, the equation may be written in the form

$$\nabla^2\xi - \frac{1}{c^2}\frac{\partial^2\xi}{\partial t^2} = 0,$$

an equation of wave motion which has the following particular solutions:

(a) $\qquad\xi = f(ct - lx - my),$

where $l^2 + m^2 = 1$. No fixed boundary will allow of this.

(b) $\qquad\xi = \xi_0 e^{i\omega t}\sin\dfrac{l\omega}{c}\,x\,\sin\dfrac{m\omega}{c}\,y.$

With the boundary condition $\xi = 0$ it will obviously be desirable to choose co-ordinates in which this condition takes a simple form. For a rectangular membrane Cartesian co-ordinates are suitable, and solution (b) will apply with axes along two edges provided that

$$\frac{a l\omega}{c} = r\pi,$$

$$\frac{b m\omega}{c} = s\pi,$$

so that $\qquad\xi = \xi_0 e^{i\omega t}\sin\dfrac{r\pi x}{a}\,\sin\dfrac{s\pi y}{b},$

where a and b are the lengths of the sides of the rectangle parallel to the x- and y-axes, and r and s are integers. Then

$$\omega^2 = c^2\pi^2\left(\frac{r^2}{a^2} + \frac{s^2}{b^2}\right).$$

In this type of vibration there are $(r - 1)$ nodal lines parallel to the y-axis and $(s - 1)$ nodal lines parallel to the x-axis, and every pair of values of r and s will yield a new normal function with the appropriate value of ω in the formula. It requires only an application of Fourier's theorem to show that by superposing solutions of this type, any initial configuration of the rectangular membrane may be represented. The subsequent motion will be complicated, each mode following its own period. The frequency equation shows that these do not form a harmonic series, and the motion will generally not be periodic.

If the membrane is square, $a = b$, and ω is the same for the combination r, s as for s, r. This is an exception to the rule so far assumed in this chapter that different normal modes have different periods, and it leads to important consequences. One of these is that the two characteristic modes which are obtained by inserting the values of r and s may be combined in different ways without altering the frequency, and the nodal lines change accordingly. A similar " degeneracy " occurs if a/b is any rational number.

Equal Natural Periods.

In the ordinary case equation (16.4), p. 415, can be solved for the amplitudes Q, given any one of them, when a root $(-\omega_m{}^2)$ has been obtained for the determinantal equation $\Delta(-\omega^2) = 0$, and the ratios are given by

$$\frac{Q_1}{a_{r1}} = \frac{Q_2}{a_{r2}} = \frac{Q_3}{a_{r3}}, \quad \ldots \ldots \quad (16.9)$$

where a_{rs} is the co-factor in Δ of the constituent in the rth row and the sth column. Moreover, any row r will give the same result:

$$\frac{Q_k}{Q_l} = \frac{a_{rk}}{a_{rl}} = \frac{a_{sk}}{a_{sl}} \quad \ldots \ldots \quad (16.10)$$

or $a_{rk}a_{sl} = a_{rl}a_{sk}.$

By differentiation of Δ with respect to $(-\omega^2)$ we have

$$\frac{d\Delta(-\omega^2)}{d(-\omega^2)} = \underset{r\ s}{\Sigma\Sigma}\, a_{rs}a_{rs} = \frac{1}{a_{kk}} \underset{r\ s}{\Sigma\Sigma}\, a_{rs}a_{rs}a_{kk},$$

where a_{kk} is one of the minors $a_{11}, \ldots, a_{nn}$.

If then Δ vanishes for $\omega = \omega_m$,

$$\Delta'(-\omega_m{}^2) = \frac{1}{a_{kk}} \underset{r\ s}{\Sigma\Sigma}\, a_{rs}a_{rk}a_{sk}, \text{ from (16.10)},$$

$$= \frac{A_m}{a_{kk}},$$

since the a's refer to the mth normal mode; this expression will be used later. For the moment we need only observe that if all the a's vanish for some value ω_m of ω, then this will be a zero of $\Delta'(-\omega^2)$ and therefore a double zero of $\Delta(-\omega^2)$. The ratios of amplitudes can no longer be calculated from (16.9), and instead of one amplitude we now require two amplitudes to be specified before the rest are determined. This is what might be expected physically from the superposition of two modes of vibration having the same period. In such a case the application of a well-known geometrical theorem shows that the nodal lines of the combined mode will pass through the intersections of those of the separate modes. Fig. 16.5 shows this for a square membrane with two nodal diameters or, alternatively, a nodal ring. These are formed by the combination

$$\xi = A \sin\frac{3\pi x}{a} \sin\frac{\pi y}{a} + B \sin\frac{\pi x}{a} \sin\frac{3\pi y}{a},$$

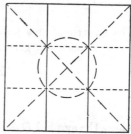

A and B being given different pairs of values.

(i) $A = -B$ gives two diagonals.

(ii) $A = B$ gives the nodal ring, which is not quite circular. Intermediate forms are obtained with different ratios of B and A. Even this is not exhaustive, for the two constituents are not necessarily in phase.

Fig. 16.5.—Nodal lines for square membrane

If the second constituent is in advance by an amount ϵ, the amplitude is given by

$$\sqrt{\left\{\left(A \sin\frac{3\pi x}{a} \sin\frac{\pi y}{a} + B \cos\epsilon \sin\frac{\pi x}{a} \sin\frac{3\pi y}{a}\right)^2 \right.}$$
$$\left. + \left(B \sin\epsilon \sin\frac{\pi x}{a} \sin\frac{3xy}{a}\right)^2\right\}$$

$$= \sqrt{\left\{A^2 \sin^2\frac{3\pi x}{a} \sin^2\frac{\pi y}{a}\right.}$$
$$\left. + 2AB \sin\frac{3\pi x}{a} \sin\frac{\pi x}{a} \sin\frac{3\pi y}{a} \sin\frac{\pi y}{a} \cos\epsilon + B^2\sin^2\frac{\pi x}{a} \sin^2\frac{3\pi y}{a}\right\}.$$

This cannot vanish for real values of the variables unless $\cos\epsilon = \pm 1$. As in experiments the nodal figures are usually observed by creating a node somewhere, this condition is automatically ensured.

11. Forced Vibrations.

A physically important result for the forced vibrations of a complex system has been alluded to (p. 414). It is that the amplitude of oscillation of any co-ordinate is a superposition of the contributions from all the normal modes of vibration, vibrating with the period of the impressed forces, if we neglect transients. These amplitudes in turn are found by applying the ordinary rules for forced vibrations, using the generalized forces; that is, each normal co-ordinate requires the corresponding type of force. The generalized forces, which comprise the total effectiveness of the actual forces in producing vibration in the mode in question, are obtained by the rule inverse to equation

(16.8). Thus if $F_r e^{i\omega t}$ is the force of type r, the generalized force $\Phi_m e^{i\omega t}$ for the mth mode of vibration is given by the rule

$$\Phi_m = \sum_{r=1}^{n} F_r Q_{rs}.$$

The equations now to be solved are those of (16.4), p. 415, with the forces F inserted, giving

$$\sum_s (a_{rs} D^2 + c_{rs}) q_s = F_r e^{i\omega t} \quad \ldots \quad (16.11)$$
$$\ldots \ldots$$
$$(n \text{ equations})$$

where the symbol D denotes d/dt.

For the moment ignoring transients of the motion, as is usual in calculating impedances, we simply replace D^2 by $(-\omega^2)$ and solve the equations, obtaining

$$q_s = \sum_{r=1}^{n} \frac{a_{rs}(-\omega^2)}{\Delta(-\omega^2)} F_r e^{i\omega t}. \quad \ldots \quad (16.12)$$

This equation as it stands contains no obvious reference to normal modes and may indeed offer an easier way to the complete result. $a_{rs}(-\omega^2)$ and $\Delta(-\omega^2)$ are so labelled to indicate that they refer to a particular frequency, and of course if this should happen to coincide with a natural frequency, $\Delta(-\omega^2)$ would vanish and the solution would break down. This is the case of resonance.

The use of the method in the form applicable to continuous systems may be shown by the example of a circular membrane vibrating under the influence of a uniform oscillatory pressure $P e^{i\omega t}$ applied to the upper surface. This problem bears some relation to that of a diaphragm used to detect sound waves. The equation of motion is

$$\rho \frac{\partial^2 \xi}{\partial t^2} - \tau \nabla^2 \xi = -P e^{i\omega t}.$$

Neglecting transients, we write

$$\xi = \xi_0 e^{i\omega t},$$

and then

$$\omega^2 \xi_0 + \frac{\tau}{\rho} \nabla^2 \xi_0 = \frac{P}{\rho}$$

or in polar co-ordinates (r, θ) with $\tau/\rho = c^2$, $k = \omega/c$, we have

$$\frac{\partial^2 \xi_0}{\partial r^2} + \frac{1}{r} \frac{\partial \xi_0}{\partial r} + \frac{1}{r^2} \frac{\partial^2 \xi_0}{\partial \theta^2} + k^2 \xi_0 - \frac{P}{\tau} = 0. \qquad (16.13)$$

If we assume a solution of the type $\xi_0 = R(r)e^{in\theta}$, this gives as the form of vibration

$$R - \frac{Pe^{-in\theta}}{\tau k^2} = J_n(kr),$$

where $J_n(x)$ is the nth-order Bessel function of x.*

Since there may be an infinite series of such terms we have finally

$$\xi_0 = \frac{P}{\tau k^2} + \sum_{n=1}^{\infty} A_n e^{in\theta} J_n(kr),$$

where each A_n is an arbitrary constant.

To satisfy the condition $\xi_0 = 0$ at the boundary $r = a$, we have

$$0 = \frac{P}{\tau k^2} + f(\theta),$$

where $f(\theta)$ is a periodic function of θ: but evidently from this equation itself

$$f(\theta) = \text{constant} = A_0 J_0(ka),$$

and finally

$$\xi_0 = \frac{P}{\tau k^2}\left[1 - \frac{J_0(kr)}{J_0(ka)}\right].$$

Thus we have arrived at the amplitude in forced vibration without recourse to the normal functions, for any frequency where no resonance occurs. Evidently from the result, resonance will occur when $J_0(ka) = 0$, but, as we shall see, this is not exhaustive. With $P = 0$ the motion is free, and equation (16.13) is satisfied † by $J_n(kr)$, provided that at the boundary

$$J_n(ka) = 0,$$

and with this restriction on k, the solution will be of the form

$$\xi = J_n(k_m r)\cos n(\theta - \theta_0)\cos(\omega t + a).$$

For any of these solutions there are n nodal diameters. Each value of n is accompanied by a series of values of k corresponding to $0, 1, 2, \ldots n$ nodal circles.

In the simplest case with no nodal diameters the condition $J_0(ka) = 0$ has the roots ‡

$$k_1 a = 2\cdot4048,$$
$$k_2 a = 5\cdot5201,$$
$$k_3 a = 8\cdot6537, \text{ &c.}$$

---

* Gray, Mathews, and MacRobert, *A Treatise on Bessel Functions* (Macmillan, 1922).

† This solution is not exhaustive if the initial conditions require infinities at the origin, in which case Bessel functions of the "second kind" are necessary.

‡ See Jahnke and Emde's *Tables of Functions* (Teubner, Leipzig, 1933), where there are graphs which assist in visualizing these forms.

A similar series will be found for $J_1(ka) = 0$, with one nodal diameter. Arranging these in order, and expressing all of the frequencies in the form $\beta(c/2\pi a)$, we have the following series of values of β:

Nodal Diameters	Nodal Circles	β	Interval with 2nd Partial	Nearest Harmonic Interval
0	0	2·405	202 savarts	204 = minor 6th
1	0	3·832		
2	0	5·135	127 ,,	125 = 4th
0	1	5·520	159 ,,	
3	0	6·379	221 ,,	222 = major 6th
1	1	7·016	263 ,,	
4	0	7·586	297 ,,	301 = octave
2	1	8·417	342 ,,	

The table shows that the four tones having only nodal diameters form, as Rayleigh showed, approximately the chord of the $\frac{6}{4}$, for the second and third of them are respectively a fourth and a major sixth above the first. Taken as a whole the series is inharmonic, and this explains the unmusical quality of most drums. The tympani (kettledrums) are struck with soft hammers at a place half-way between the centre and the edge of the skin. This has been found to depress the inharmonic partials. The note to which the instrument is tuned is further emphasized by the resonance of the cavity. Tuning is effected by varying the tension and hence c.

It is possible to form some idea of the behaviour of membranes in free vibration at high frequencies by using an approximation for $J_n(kr)$ in the form $\cos(kr - \pi/4 - n\pi/2)$. Evidently $J_n(ka)$ will pass through successive zeros each time ka increases by π, one nodal circle being added each time. The same increment of frequency with n increased by 2 will leave the number of circles unchanged: in fact, nodal circles are twice as effective in raising the frequency as are nodal diameters, an effect which shows itself at the lower frequencies in the table already given.

12. Forced Vibrations in Terms of Normal Functions.

It is not always convenient to study forced vibrations by directly solving equation (16.11), p. 434. Equations (16.12), however, can be developed in partial fractions, as Δ is a polynomial of degree n in $(-\omega^2)$, and

$$\frac{a_{rs}(-\omega^2)}{\Delta(-\omega^2)} \equiv \sum_{m=1}^{n} \frac{a_{rs}(-\omega_m^2)}{\Delta'(-\omega_m^2)} \frac{1}{\omega_m^2 - \omega^2}.$$

If there is only one force, F_r

$$q_s = \sum_{m=1}^{n} \frac{a_{rs}(-\omega_m^2)}{\Delta'(-\omega_m^2)} \frac{1}{\omega_m^2 - \omega^2} F_r e^{i\omega t},$$

and using an expression obtained on p. 432 for $\Delta'(-\omega_m^2)$, we have

$$q_s = \sum_{m=1}^{n} \frac{a_{kk}(-\omega_m^2)\, a_{rs}(-\omega_m^2)}{A_m} \frac{F_r e^{i\omega t}}{\omega_m^2 - \omega^2}.$$

and since

$$a_{kk}\, a_{rs} = a_{kr}\, a_{ks},$$

$$q_s = \sum_{m=1}^{n} \frac{Q_{rm} Q_{sm}}{A_m} \frac{F_r e^{i\omega t}}{\omega_m^2 - \omega^2}.$$

This equation readily shows how the amplitude is affected by varying ω, for it becomes large whenever ω approaches a resonance frequency ω_m. Also, the effect at s of a harmonic force applied at r, for a given mode m, is inversely proportional to the inertia coefficient in that mode and directly proportional to the product of the amplitudes at r and at s. Thus no motion in a particular mode can be observed if either s is at a node ($Q_{sm} = 0$) or F is applied at a node ($Q_{rm} = 0$). The determining factors are thus: (i) the proximity of the frequency to a natural frequency of the system, (ii) the proximity of its point of application to a node of the type of vibration it is desired to observe, (iii) the proximity of the point of observation to a node of the type of vibration.

These principles have innumerable applications in acoustics; (ii), (iii) are not confined to forces varying harmonically, and (ii) then is a statement of Young's law (p. 380).

Further, if there are several forces F_r with the same frequency the separate contributions must be added, and since $\Sigma F_r Q_{rm} = \Phi_m$, the force of normal type,

$$q_s = \sum_m \frac{Q_{sm}}{A_m} \frac{\Phi_m e^{i\omega t}}{\omega_m^2 - \omega^2},$$

and finally, since

$$q_s = \sum_m Q_{sm} \phi_m,$$

$$\phi_m = \frac{1}{A_m} \frac{\Phi_m e^{i\omega t}}{\omega_m^2 - \omega^2}.$$

This result may be obtained directly by considering each equation separately in normal form, and is another example of the independence of normal modes. It would give directly, for example, the amplitude of transverse vibrations of a string acted on by a harmonic force varying along the length sinusoidally. Such a force is of the same type as the corresponding mode of oscillation. In cases where the force is not of normal type, it will have components in some or all of the normal types, and these components determine the effectiveness of the force in exciting their respective types of vibration.

13. Transients in Forced Vibration.

There is available a fairly simple method for calculating the complete solution of the equations of motion, including the transient part, when the system starts from rest. This is convenient, for it may be used to study both forced vibration and free vibration. For example, an impulse may be given and the forces then vanish. Alternatively, a constant force may be applied suddenly and allowed to remain, and the resulting motion about the new position of equilibrium will be the same as the oscillation about the original position on release from the displaced position.

For a simple system of natural frequency $\omega/2\pi$ the equation is

$$\frac{d^2y}{dt^2} + \omega^2 y = f(t),$$

where $f(t)$ is a function of the time equal to the applied force divided by the mass. Then (cf. p. 79)

$$y = \frac{1}{D^2 + \omega^2} f(t)$$

$$= \frac{1}{2i\omega} \left(\frac{1}{D - i\omega} - \frac{1}{D + i\omega}\right) e^{i\omega t} e^{-i\omega t} f(t)$$

$$= \frac{e^{i\omega t}}{2i\omega} \int_0^t e^{-i\omega t'} f(t') dt' - \frac{e^{-i\omega t}}{2i\omega} \int_0^t e^{i\omega t'} f(t') dt'$$

or

$$y = \frac{1}{\omega} \int_0^t \sin\omega(t - t') f(t') dt'.$$

This solution is complete for the case $y = 0$, $dy/dt = 0$ at $t = 0$. If these are not the actual initial conditions, then the terms

$$y_0 \cos \omega t + \frac{u_0}{\omega} \sin \omega t,$$

where u_0 is the initial velocity, must be added. This solution has the advantage that it still applies even if $\omega = \omega_m$ and resonance occurs, so that no " steady state " exists.

The same formula would apply to the mth component of a complex vibration, working in normal co-ordinates and normal forces, with $\omega = \omega_m$. In any other system of co-ordinates we have (cf. equation 16.12, p. 434)

$$q_s = \sum_{r=1}^n \frac{a_{rs}(D^2)}{\Delta(D^2)} F_r e^{\cdot \omega t}, \quad \ldots \quad (16.14)$$

where the symbol D denotes $\partial/\partial t$. If we again use partial fractions for the expression a/Δ, it can be shown that, if $q_s = \dot{q}_s = 0$ at zero time, and if for simplicity we consider only one force F_r,

$$q_s = \sum_{m=1}^{n} \frac{Q_{rm}Q_{sm}}{A_m\omega_m} \int_0^t \sin \omega_m(t - t')F_r(t')dt'. \qquad (16.15)$$

Some important results follow at once, for if we make $F_r(t')$ merely a constant, we have the effect already described, equivalent to release from a displaced position of equilibrium under the action of a force F_r. Then

$$q_s = \sum_m \frac{Q_{rm}Q_{sm}}{A_m\omega_m^2} F_r(1 - \cos \omega_m t)$$

and the oscillatory part is what interests us. If there are several forces the result in normal co-ordinates is

$$\phi_m = \frac{\Phi_m}{A_m\omega_m^2} (1 - \cos\omega_m t).$$

Hence the vibrations in different modes tend to converge as $1/\omega_m^2$. But if the force is impulsive, and we write

$$\int_0^t F(t')dt' = \text{constant} = P$$

(provided that t refers to an instant after the impulse is over and $\omega_m t$ is small), the subsequent motion is given by

$$\phi_m = \frac{P_m}{A_m\omega_m} \sin \omega_m t$$

and the partial tones converge on the whole as $1/\omega_m$, except where in any case the normal impulse P_m is small or happens to vanish.

This difference in the strength of the higher partials explains differences in quality between the notes emitted by an object which is plucked in the one case and struck in the other. A deflected tuning-fork gives on release an all but pure note, but when struck with a hard object the shriller partials are revealed. A soft hammer, again, depresses them, because then the area of contact is larger and P_m converges more quickly. The same applies to a piano string, where the normal impulses are obtained by Fourier analysis of the pressure-distribution of the hammer along the interval of length of the string.

14. Experiments with Vibrating Membranes.

Early experiments with stretched paper membranes, using organ pipes as sources of sound and a sprinkling of sand to indicate nodal lines (where it collects), verified that resonance occurs in the expected manner, and is accompanied by the sudden appearance of the appropriate nodal lines and circles. A wide variety of frequencies can be obtained by varying the tension, superficial density and size of the membrane.

Theoretically, in the absence of damping a variation of pitch should be accompanied by a continuous transition from one system of nodal lines to another, the actual pattern depending upon the place of application of the forces or the manner of their variation over the surface in vibration. With a perfectly uniform pressure only the symmetrical class of vibrations with no nodal diameters should be seen, and as the frequency is varied, nodal circles should shrink towards the centre and make their appearance one at a time at the circumference of the membrane each time a frequency of resonance is passed. In practice the amplitude may be too small except at resonance to show the effects clearly. Damping, too, is always present, and this may destroy the phase-relations that are necessary to make the intermediate nodal lines sharp. Further, at high frequencies, the separate modes become close together in frequency and their resonances, blunted by damping, become indistinct.

Besides those of stretched membranes used in methods of sound-detection, the vibrations of this class include also those of soap-films, ripples on water arising from surface tension, and the " crispations " formed when a vessel containing liquid is set into vibration. Some interesting experiments with soap-films have been carried out with a Hartmann air-jet generator, which gives an air-jet impinging on an obstacle at a speed above that of sound.* In this way an output of about 100 watts can be obtained at 10,000 cycles per second, or 5 watts at 40,000. At the lower frequencies in this range, a soap-film responds below a critical thickness.† A circular film shows a granular appearance; a rectangular one breaks up first into striations and then into granulations. Hartmann and Mathes conclude that the natural state of vibration of a liquid film is that which would be formed by three sets of transverse stationary waves at 120° to one another.

15. Damping of Oscillations.

We have already considered how in a simple system the effect of damping is to make the amplitude finite at resonance, and to diminish the sharpness of resonance (section 4, p. 83). In complex systems the simplicity of the theory becomes obscured, and modes of vibration which are independent in the absence of damping may lose their independence when damping is present. Only in special cases, as for example when the force of resistance acting on each mass is proportional to its momentum, do the equations reduce to a form analogous

---

* *Engineering*, Vol. 142, p. 491 (1936).

† Hartmann and Mathes, *Phil. Mag.*, Vol. 22, p. 883 (1936).

to that for the simple harmonic oscillator. In this special case, the free normal modes remain independent and the normal co-ordinates execute damped oscillations all with the same damping coefficient. In any case, however, the displacement in the steady state with given forces is of the form

$$q_s = \frac{a_{rs}(i\omega)}{\Delta(i\omega)}\, F_r e^{i\omega t},$$

where the r, s constituent of Δ is now of the form $-\omega^2 a_{rs} + i\omega b_{rs} + c_{rs}$,

or
$$\dot{q}_s = \frac{F_r e^{i\omega t}}{Z_{rs}},$$

where
$$Z_{rs} = \frac{\Delta(i\omega)}{i\omega a_{rs}(i\omega)}$$

is of the nature of a mechanical impedance. Evidently this result can be applied even when the analysis in terms of normal modes cannot. Z_{rs} is either a " driving-point impedance ", if $r = s$, or a " transfer impedance ", if $r \neq s$.

For the complete solution of the problem, including transients, we may follow the method of partial fractions, but these will not now fall in convenient pairs as in the absence of damping. The general case is most simply treated by Heaviside's method, in which the effect of a variable force is analysed in terms of that of a constant force suddenly applied. Supposing that unit force at r suddenly applied at time τ produces a displacement at time t denoted by $q_{sr}(t, \tau)$, then a variable force produces a contribution $F_r(0)q_{sr}(t, 0)$, due to its initial value, and a contribution, due to subsequent changes, comprised in the integral $\int_0^t F_r{}'(\tau)q_{sr}(t, \tau)\,dt$. In these expressions it may readily be shown by the method of partial fractions that

$$q_{sr}(t, \tau) = \sum_{m=1}^{2n} \frac{a_{rs}(i\omega_m)}{i\omega_m \Delta'(i\omega_m)} \left\{ e^{i\omega_m(t-\tau)} - 1 \right\},$$

and it may also be shown that

$$\sum_{m=1}^{2n} \frac{a_{rs}(i\omega_m)}{i\omega_m \Delta'(i\omega_m)} = \frac{-a_{rs}(0)}{\Delta(0)},$$

so that
$$q_{sr}(t, \tau) = \sum_{m=1}^{2n} \frac{a_{rs}(i\omega_m)e^{i\omega_m(t-\tau)}}{i\omega_m \Delta'(i\omega_m)} + \frac{a_{rs}(0)}{\Delta(0)}.$$

The equivalent expression in the absence of damping is obtained from

(16.15) on integrating by parts,* for then it will contain $F_r'(t)$ instead of $F_r(t)$.

The detailed examination of these results forms a subject in itself, and we may leave it with a brief illustration of the continuous case. We have already considered a membrane vibrating without damping. By suitable simplifying assumptions it is possible to calculate how its behaviour will be affected by radiation resistance and internal damping, for if these forces are comprised in the term $-F(\partial \xi/\partial t)$, this will make the equation of free vibration

$$\rho \frac{\partial^2 \xi}{\partial t^2} + F \frac{\partial \xi}{\partial t} - \tau \nabla^2 \xi = 0,$$

and in the case of circular symmetry, if $\xi = \xi_0 e^{\lambda t}$,

$$\frac{\partial^2 \xi_0}{\partial r^2} + \frac{1}{r} \frac{\partial \xi_0}{\partial r} + k^2 \xi_0 = 0,$$

where now

$$\rho \lambda^2 + \lambda F + \tau k^2 = 0,$$

instead of the previous relation

$$-\rho \omega^2 + \tau k^2 = 0.$$

The solution of the equation of motion will be

$$\xi_0 = A J_0(kr)$$

as before, where k takes such values as to make $J_0(ka)$ vanish. But now λ is complex: writing $a = F/2\rho$, $\omega_0^2 = \tau k^2/\rho$, we have

$$\lambda = -a \pm i\sqrt{\omega_0^2 - a^2},$$

and if a is small enough it is convenient to write

$$\omega^2 = \omega_0^2 - a^2$$

and ω will then be real.

Finally, the complete solution will be

$$\begin{aligned}
\xi = {}& A_1 J_0(k_1 r) e^{-at} \cos(\omega_1 t - \beta_1) \\
& + A_2 J_0(k_2 r) e^{-at} \cos(\omega_2 t - \beta_2) \\
& + \cdots,
\end{aligned}$$

where the constants necessary to ensure the fulfilment of initial conditions are present and suffixes denote that they refer to the corresponding modes already specified by $k_1 a = 2 \cdot 405$, $k_2 a = 5 \cdot 520$, $\ldots$. This, then, is one of the special cases in which the normal modes

---

* A short but reasoned exposition of Heaviside's method is given in Bateman, *Partial Differential Equations of Mathematical Physics*.

retain their independence and are altered only by the inclusion of a constant of damping, α, the same for all modes.

In presence of a uniform oscillatory pressure $-Pe^{i\omega t}$, the solution already found in the absence of damping will still hold with the new value of k^2,

$$k^2 = \frac{\rho\omega^2 - i\omega F}{\tau},$$

in the form

$$\xi(r) = \frac{P}{\tau k^2}\left[1 - \frac{J_0(kr)}{J_0(ka)}\right]e^{i\omega t}; \quad \cdot \quad \cdot \quad \cdot \quad (16.16)$$

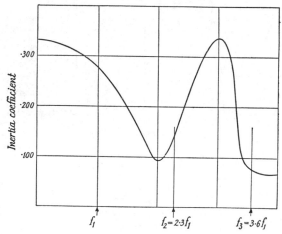

Fig. 16.6.—Inertia coefficient in terms of total mass for circular membrane

but now k is complex, so that ξ includes both in-phase and quadrature components. The complex impedance Z is now

$$Z(r) = \frac{\text{Pressure}}{\dot{\xi}} = \frac{\tau k^2}{-i\omega\left[1 - \frac{J_0(kr)}{J_0(ka)}\right]};$$

at low frequencies this reduces to

$$Z = \frac{F + i\left(\rho\omega - \frac{4\tau}{a^2\omega}\right)}{1 - r^2/a^2},$$

and evidently the three terms in order are analogous to electrical resistance, inductive reactance and capacitative reactance.

We have seen already how the inertia coefficient may be calculated for the whole membrane when the normal function is known, and that for very low frequencies this approaches one-third of the total mass. Now as ω varies, the damped membrane will assume the form given in equation (16.16), and the appropriate inertia coefficient has been calculated by Wegel for a particular value of F (see fig. 16.6). Evidently the inertia of the membrane has minima near the frequencies of natural undamped vibration.

This procedure can also be used to obtain the variation of elastic and resistance coefficients. A rather more interesting development is

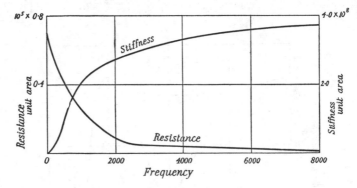

Fig. 16.7.—Reactions in air film

to study the effect of the proximity of a damping plate behind the membrane. This example may be worked at low frequencies by replacing the membrane with the "equivalent piston", a rigid plate having the area of the damping plate, a mass equal to one-third that of the membrane and a stiffness constant equal to half that at the centre of the membrane. The result is shown * in fig. 16.7.

16. Derivation of Normal Functions: Methods of Approximation.

(i) Methods of deriving normal functions are of some importance, and one of the simplest approximate methods is based on the stationary property of normal modes. We have already invoked this to show that the equilibrium shape of a membrane under static pressure must give an approximately correct natural frequency of vibration in the fundamental mode. With this frequency f_1 in the form $f_1 = \beta c/2\pi a$ we obtained $\beta = 2.450$, and the accurate value was $\beta_1 = 2.4048$.

Suppose that a function $u_6(x)$ is chosen as an approximation to an unknown fundamental normal function $u(x)$ and whilst satisfying the boundary conditions depends in exact form on some parameter θ. Then the method we have already used for the fundamental of a membrane will give a value f of the frequency which approximates to

* This and other matter is taken from Crandall, *Theory of Vibrating Systems and Sound.*

f_1 but exceeds it. As θ varies, $u_\theta(x)$ will at some value reach optimum agreement with $u(x)$, denoted by a minimum value of f. This minimum will be the desired approximation. Fig. 16.8 shows this for the membrane with

$$u_\theta(r) = \frac{\cos(\theta r/a) - \cos\theta}{1 - \cos\theta}.$$

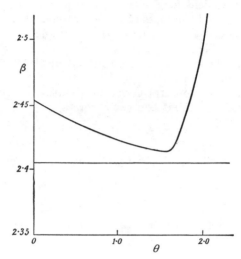

Fig. 16.8.—Fundamental of a membrane

The equation of free vibrations is

$$\tau\nabla^2 u + \omega^2\rho u = 0$$

where

$$\xi = ue^{i\omega t},$$

and the energies are calculated according to

$$T = \pi\rho\dot{\xi}_1^2 \int_0^a u_\theta^2 r \, dr,$$

$$V = \pi\tau\xi_1^2 \int_0^a (\nabla^2 u_\theta)u_\theta r \, dr.$$

For such a function the minimum of f occurs at the value $\theta = 1.56$, and then $\beta = 2.413$, which is scarcely distinguishable from the true value 2.4048. The previous approximation corresponds to $\theta = 0$.

This method is not equally applicable to higher modes of vibration.

(ii) If the displacements of a system are known, the forces can be calculated in the static case by using the coefficients c_{rs}. The inverse process of finding what displacements will result from given forces is that of solving the simultaneous equations for the displacements, and in the general case corresponds to the rather difficult problem of calculating capacities in electrostatics.

The result for n degrees of freedom will be of the form

$$y_r = \Sigma k_{rs} f_s,$$

in which it is convenient for the present purpose to use f_s, the ratio of the actual force F and the mass of the body upon which it acts. Each k constant represents the product of the mass and a compliance.

In vibration problems the static forces may be replaced by a system of kinetic reactions and the corresponding displacements are then regarded as produced by them.

Then if $2\pi/\omega$ is the natural period of vibration in which this state of affairs is possible without additional forces,

$$f_r = \omega^2 y_r,$$

and the natural modes are those for which

$$\frac{1}{\omega^2} f_r = \sum_s k_{rs} f_s.$$

Then the values of $1/\omega^2$ which make this possible are the roots of the determinantal equation

$$\begin{vmatrix} k_{11} - x, & k_{12}, \; \ldots \ldots \\ k_{21}, & k_{22} - x \\ & & \ddots \\ & & & k_{nn} - x \end{vmatrix} = 0$$

and the same values of ω will result as were obtained in the other way.

In normal co-ordinates the results are more simply expressed,

as

$$\frac{1}{\omega^2} \psi_m = K_m \psi_m$$

or

$$\frac{1}{\omega^2} = K_m = \frac{A_m}{C_m} = \frac{1}{\omega_m{}^2},$$

where A and C are the inertial and elastic coefficients previously used.

Consider any superposition of normal accelerations, say

$$a_1\psi_1 + a_2\psi_2 + \ldots .$$

The corresponding displacements in normal co-ordinates will be

$$a_1 K_1 \psi_1 + a_2 K_2 \psi_2 + \ldots$$

and by the previous equation this is equal to

$$\frac{a_1}{\omega_1{}^2}\psi_1 + \frac{a_2}{\omega_2{}^2}\psi_2 + \ldots .$$

Now let these displacements be chosen as a new system of forces. The new displacements will be

$$\frac{a_1}{(\omega_1{}^2)^2}\psi_1 + \frac{a_2}{(\omega_2{}^2)^2}\psi_2 + \ldots .$$

Evidently, since ω_1 is the lowest frequency of the system, the indefinite repetition of this process must result in the emergence of the first term as the only important constituent, and ultimately at each repetition the amplitude will appear with a value $1/\omega_1{}^2$ times that of the previous one. Thus both the normal function and the frequency of the fundamental are found. Moreover, it is not necessary that the calculation should be done in normal co-ordinates.

A very simple illustration may be given with the problem of the two equal masses attached at equal intervals to a light string. In this problem, writing k for ma/P, where P is the tension, we have

$$y_1 = \tfrac{2}{3}kf_1 + \tfrac{1}{3}kf_2,$$
$$y_2 = \tfrac{1}{3}kf_1 + \tfrac{2}{3}kf_2.$$

We start with a static " force " f_1 alone, giving displacements

$$y_1 = \tfrac{2}{3}kf_1,$$
$$y_2 = \tfrac{1}{3}kf_1$$

as in fig. 16.9 (a).

Next consider the result of applying forces $\tfrac{2}{3}kf_1$ and $\tfrac{1}{3}kf_1$; by direct substitution we have

$$y_1' = \frac{5}{9}k^2f_1,$$

$$y_2' = \frac{4}{9}k^2f_1$$

as in fig. 16.9 (b).

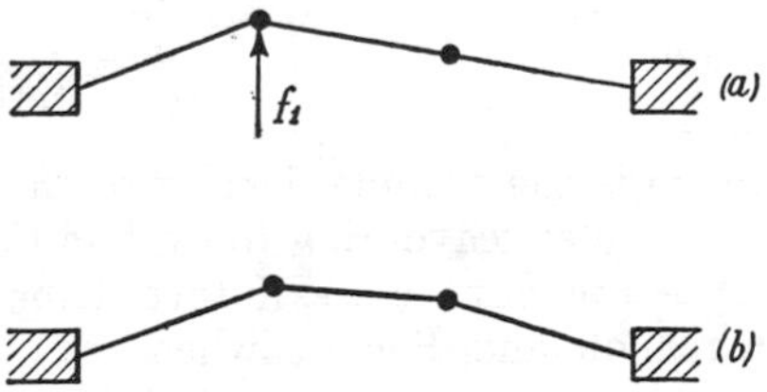

Fig. 16.9

Yet another substitution gives $(14/27)k^3f_1$ and $(13/27)k^3f_1$, and it is evident that the type of displacement is rapidly approaching the equality characteristic of the fundamental normal mode, and that the ratio of successive amplitudes is approaching k, whence we infer that

$$\frac{1}{\omega_1{}^2} = k \text{ and } \omega_1 = \sqrt{\frac{P}{ma}}$$

as found earlier by the direct method (section 1, p. 412).

17. Vibrations of Plates.

It is noticeable that the objects in this class, which may be widened to include objects which are not flat, more often emit " noises " than " notes ". They are generally described as " metallic " noises and are rather unmusical, though by no means devoid of pitch. Even the notes of bells and cymbals, though used in the orchestra, are called by no accident " kitchen music ".

In order to study the motion of a thin uniform flat plate we need an expression of its energy of bending. The potential energy per unit area at a place where the principal radii of curvature are ρ_1 and ρ_2 is

$$V = \frac{qh^3}{3(1 - \sigma^2)} \left\{ \frac{1}{\rho_1{}^2} + \frac{1}{\rho_2{}^2} + \frac{2\sigma}{\rho_1\rho_2} \right\},$$

as may be found by integrating the work required to produce this curvature, allowing for the effect expressed in Poisson's ratio σ; q is Young's modulus and h the thickness. It is sufficient for the moment to notice that the formula gives the known value of the " anticlastic " curvature of a blade when one principal curvature is fixed and V is allowed to assume its minimum value. The result is the familiar saddle-back shape which a bent blade assumes. This effect acts as a mechanical coupling of perpendicular directions of bending, and greatly complicates the theory of the motion. The derivation of the appropriate equation and boundary conditions is lengthy.* The equation of motion is

$$\nabla^4\xi + \frac{1}{c^4}\frac{\partial^2\xi}{\partial t^2} = 0,$$

where

$$c^4 = \frac{qh^2}{3\rho(1 - \sigma^2)}$$

and ρ is the volume density of the material. This equation, towards which in endeavouring to explain Chladni's experiments Mlle. Germain made the first successful contribution in 1815, was completed by Kirchhoff and Poisson when they rectified the boundary conditions.

---

* See Rayleigh, *Theory of Sound*, Vol. I, §§ 214, 215.

It is in contrast to the equation of a stretched membrane; the comparison may be made for a rectangular plate fixed at the edges. It is natural to try a solution of the form

$$\sin \frac{m\pi x}{a} \sin \frac{n\pi y}{b},$$

and this results in the frequency equation

$$\omega = c^2 \pi^2 \left(\frac{m^2}{a^2} + \frac{n^2}{b^2} \right),$$

and for comparison we may repeat the membrane formula

$$\omega = c\pi \sqrt{\frac{m^2}{a^2} + \frac{n^2}{b^2}}$$

(though of course c has quite a different value). For a given m and n both periods vary as the linear dimensions.

18. Experiments with Vibrating Plates.

In his early experiments, which preceded and provoked theoretical discussion, Chladni used circular and square brass plates free at the edges and supported at the centre. They are set in vibration with a bow, and the figures which Chladni observed are shown by sprinkling a little sand on the plate; this collects along the nodal lines and forms a symmetrical pattern. The pattern may be varied by bowing at different points and by damping the motion at some other point on the edge with the finger. A nodal line meets the edge where the damping is applied. The kind of result obtained is that of fig. 16.10. The phase of vibration changes over on crossing a nodal line.

The vibrations of a square plate free at the edges are not so simple as those of a fixed plate. It is not difficult to form a picture of the results by assuming that $\sigma = 0$, when the plate will be subdivided like a free bar with nodal lines parallel to one side. Then by superposing the two modes with perpendicular nodal lines in various ratios we have one set of nodal curves just as for a membrane. The true modes for a free plate, which will be slightly different, have been calculated by a method of approximation developed by Ritz *, and Pavlik † has compared the experimental periods satisfactorily with theory. The modes have nodal lines approximately parallel to the edges, or else are derived from combinations of such modes.

It seems that under the conditions of experiment ideal simplicity is not reached; departure from perfect uniformity and symmetry causes complications in the result. Vibrations produced by bowing,

---

* *Ann. d. Physik*, Vol. 28, p. 737 (1909).   † *Ann. d. Physik*, Vol. 27.6, p. 532 (1936).

though at least mainly determined by natural modes of vibration, are in the strict sense not free. It is found that when finally a plate of this kind is left to vibrate freely, the nodal diameters may show a tendency to rotate. This might result from the mutual action of two progressive waves proceeding in opposite senses of rotation with slightly different velocity. A slight asymmetry of the plate would resolve the " degenerate " mode of vibration into two definite modes with slightly different periods, and these by their beats might give an alternation of nodal lines, but there would be no distinct nodal lines in intermediate positions.

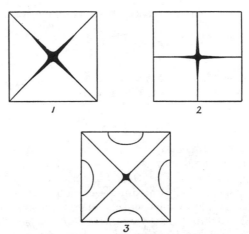

Fig. 16.10.—Sand patterns obtained with Chladni's plate

The vibrations of plates and membranes have been studied experimentally over a wide range of frequencies. Colwell * has used a valve generator and applied vibrations up to 10 kilocycles per second by a rod attached to the diaphragm of an electrodynamic loud-speaker, above those frequencies by a magnetostrictive rod. The nodal figures were observed

(i) up to 500 cycles with paper membranes of diameter 10 in.
(ii) up to 15 kc. with thin brass plates,
(iii) up to 50 kc. with glass discs of diameter 1 in.

It is verified in the case of a square plate that the theoretical " degeneracy " occurs. The figures are very complex.

Waller † has also investigated these phenomena with the aid of solid CO_2, which can be used as a means of excitation by touching the plate with a piece. All Chladni's original figures have been reproduced. These are often made more complex by the presence of a mode having only nodal diameters, as well as the principal mode under observation. No doubt the proximity of two frequencies, assisted by damping, is the cause of this confusion. It is concluded that the vibrations of ideal plates and membranes would conform to the theoretical type.

* *Journ. Amer. Soc. Acoust.*, Vol. 7, p. 288 (1936).
† *Proc. Phys. Soc.*, Vol. 50, p. 70 (1938).

Schünemann * has used a different method of observation on a circular plate with free edges. This is made into one plate of a condenser. It is excited by a magnetostrictive rod applied eccentrically. From analysis of the electrical oscillations it is concluded that the phase does not change abruptly on crossing a nodal line. At resonance, however, the sharpness of transition greatly increases. As the frequency is displaced from resonance, the lines spread out and the waves become progressive.

A. B. Wood † has shown by experiments on small free steel discs of appreciable thickness that the velocity of sound may be determined by this means in a substance available only in small quantities.

Important applications of vibrating plates are the piezo-electric quartz oscillator and the telephone diaphragm.

Colwell and Hill ‡ have shown that flexural piezo-electric vibrations of a quartz plate excited in an electric field give the same Chladni figures as vibrations excited directly at the same frequency by contact with a magnetostrictive rod.

The importance of diaphragms has led to the development of various methods of detecting their amplitude of vibration. A diaphragm as used in a telephone with a permanent magnetic field is under tension and is therefore intermediate between a clamped plate and a stretched membrane, though its stiffness makes it more like a plate. It may be of iron and cause changes in a magnetic circuit, or it may compress carbon granules, or carry a small coil which moves in a magnetic field (p. 511). In the condenser microphone the diaphragm forms one plate of a condenser. All of these arrangements convert the vibrations into electrical signals, and, except for the carbon microphone, may be used the other way to radiate sound when electrically excited. The electrodynamic principle is that now chiefly used for loud-speakers having a flabby conical diaphragm more or less free at the edge.

The vibration of diaphragms coupled to sound-boxes and horns is of course fundamental in acoustic gramophones. Corrugated and conical diaphragms have a much lower natural frequency than flat ones of the same size, and both have been applied in sound-boxes and loud-speakers. The development of diaphragm apparatus for accurate linear reproduction of sounds is not a matter of the diaphragm alone, but of the whole system of which it forms part. A damping-plate will affect the response profoundly, and the complexity of the effects may best be minimized by description in terms of impedance, as illustrated for the closely related case of the stretched membrane. The experimental side may be investigated by an appropriate electrical method, but there are also mechanical methods which, though affecting the behaviour to some extent by the attachment of other apparatus, are of some importance.

* *Ann. d. Physik*, Vol. 24.6, p. 507 (1935).   † *Proc. Phys. Soc.*, Vol. 47, p. 794 (1935).
‡ *J. App. Phys.*, Vol. 8, p. 68 (1937).

The manometric capsule may be mentioned as one of the earlier means of observation (section 7, p. 404).

With the aid of an optical lever Kennelly and Taylor * have accurately measured amplitudes of the order 10^{-5} cm. This can be done either with a mirror directly attached at the edge of a diaphragm where there is angular motion, or else by operating a separate mirror from a small post at the centre of the diaphragm. In this way the surface is explored.

Partridge † has developed a method, originally devised by Bragg, in which the intermittent chattering contact of a small pendulum on the diaphragm is used. By moving the suspension until the pressure is just too great to prevent the pendulum from being thrown off, the maximum acceleration is measured. Amplitudes of the order of 10^{-6} cm. may be measured and the method is accurate if the vibration is applied at the centre of percussion of a compound pendulum. An electrical contact indicates when chattering ceases.

A delicate optical method is the observation of fringes formed between the diaphragm and an optical flat: this enables amplitudes of $\cdot 5 \times 10^{-6}$ cm. to be measured.‡

19. Plates of Considerable Thickness.

The formulæ as usually considered apply to plates of negligible thickness, and neglect rotary inertia and shearing motion. The bending effect for the analogous case of a thin blade varies as $12G/h^3$, where G is the bending moment and h the thickness. The shear angle will vary as F/h, where F is the shearing force. The curvature resulting from the shear will vary as

$$\frac{1}{h}\frac{\partial F}{\partial x} = -\frac{1}{h}\frac{\partial^2 G}{\partial x^2}.$$

If, as is always the case, the modulus of rigidity is rather less than $q/2$, then the latter contribution becomes important (with $G = G\cos 2\pi x/\lambda$) when

$$\frac{8\pi^2}{\lambda^2 h} \doteqdot \frac{12}{h^3},$$

that is, when the wave-length λ ceases to be sufficiently large in comparison with the thickness. The rotary inertia also begins to be important at high frequencies.

We have alluded also to anomalies in longitudinal vibration. These seem to be special cases of a general rule that the simple theories no longer apply to a rod or plate that either departs from the geometrical ideal to any considerable degree or vibrates in segments that no longer have the special rod-like or plate-like quality. Thus it is

---

* *Proc. Amer. Phil. Soc.*, Vol. 96 (1915).   † *Phil. Mag.*, Vol. 20, p. 953 (1935).

‡ Thomas and Warren, *Phil. Mag.*, Vol. 5, p. 1125 (1928).

not surprising that at high frequencies the predicted behaviour of plates does not occur. In particular Waller * has shown with a circular plate that the number of nodal diameters, in the frequency range examined, which for raising the frequency are equivalent to one nodal circle, increases from two to five in going from modes with more circles to modes with more diameters. The theory would indicate that two diameters are always equivalent to one circle in raising the natural frequency of a thin plate, just as for a membrane.

Similarly, when a plate becomes thick we reach a body which is neither specially plate-like nor specially rod-like, and there will be a tendency for longitudinal shear to replace flexure. These shearing vibrations follow a motion whose equation is similar to that for a membrane, with a value of c depending on the modulus of rigidity.

If we express the frequency for a thin disc of radius a as

$$f = \frac{Ach}{a^2},$$

which varies directly as the thickness h, then A is a constant depending on the shape and the mode of vibration but not on the dimensions. For thicker plates Field † finds

$$f = \frac{A'c}{a}(1 - e^{-kh/a})$$

for the modes examined (one with 2 diameters, the other with one circle). This reduces to the simpler form if h is small, and A', k are factors of A.

20. Bells.

The vibrations of bells are very complex in character and they present features not included in those of flat plates. Early attempts to account for their tones in terms of flexural vibrations of annular sections were only partly successful, as the flexure in axial planes is also important.

The dimensional relation that each frequency varies inversely as the linear dimensions should, of course, hold for bells of similar shape and material. This does hold for thin cylinders, such as are used in the glockenspiel, in the form of Fenkner's formula ‡ for the pitch,

$$f \propto \frac{h}{a^2},$$

---

* *Proc. Phys. Soc.*, Vol. 50, p. 70 (1938).   † *Nature*, Vol. 137, p. 153 (1936).
‡ *Wied. Ann.*, Vol. 8, p. 185 (1879).

where h is the thickness and a the radius. As this formula contains no reference to length, it shows that the type of motion is approximately two-dimensional.

The nodal systems of bells do resemble those of a free circular plate to the extent that there are nodal radii or meridians from the support and also nodal circles of latitude. The lowest tone has four nodal meridians and corresponds to flexure of the type shown in fig. 16.11.

In a bell this type of flexure is accompanied by circumferential motion, as the material offers great resistance to longitudinal compression, and it is easily seen that A is a node for the tangential motion, whereas B is a node for radial motion. The nodes of one type coincide with the antinodes of the other. The tangential motion is employed when wine-glasses are made to sing by means of the wetted finger rubbed round the rim, and the radial motion may be demonstrated by ripples on the surface of water poured into the glass.

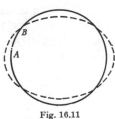

Fig. 16.11

The special qualities of a bell are connected with its actual shape, and with its having a thickened rim or sound-bow near to the open end, where impact occurs. Bells are tuned after casting by turning out metal, and a skilfully-made bell will have an approximately harmonic series of partials. In bells examined by Rayleigh it was possible to trace the nodal circles by tapping, for a mode will fail to be produced by a blow aimed at any of its nodal lines. The meridians are more difficult, as for a perfectly symmetrical bell their position would be indeterminate. In actual bells there is sufficient asymmetry to produce the associated beats between two modes with determinate nodal lines, and when such beats are not elicited it follows that the blow has been applied at a node of one of these.

It appears from Rayleigh's results that the important partials in order of pitch have usually the nodal lines indicated in the Table. The approximate pitch is also given for a particular case.

	Meridians	Circles	Pitch
(i)	4		g
(ii)	4	1	g'
(iii)	6		a'
(iv)	6	1	d''
(v)	8		$f''\sharp$

In the list the lower octave (i) is the " hum note " which tends to persist after the others but is less prominent at impact. The pitch appears to be given nominally as the octave below (v) in the list, in this example $f'\sharp$, but this is always close to (ii), so that (ii) may be the real nominal pitch. The nomenclature is derived as a rule from the "strike note" which at first dominates the sound emitted, and is difficult to account for, in that it does not seem to be a member of the list of partials at all. It is not elicited by resonance like the other tones and may be a subjective effect, as it is noticeable only when the sound is loudest. According to A. T. Jones,[*] who has applied several tests, it is not a difference tone. Jones also agreed with Rayleigh's conclusion that the strike note is usually determined, apart from the octave in which it lies, by (v), since in those bells most carefully examined it does not exactly coincide with (ii).

Curtiss and Giannini have made many detailed observations on the notes of bells, both large and small. In one of these [†] they studied a set of church bells in Philadelphia, and measured as many as 20 partials of an f' bell (345·3 c./sec.) with frequencies between 130 and 1125; the prominent partials were themselves composite. The hum note comprised tones of 150 and 187 c./sec. and the strike note 330, 345, and 365 c./sec. The acoustic output of the bell as registered with a noise-meter did not vary smoothly with time after the moment of impact, but had no fewer than 5 peaks due to the emergence of successive partials. Further, they find [‡] that each of the fundamental tones has its natural harmonics. The third partial is judged to be unmusical because of undesirable combination tones, and the quality is improved by damping it out artificially. On various grounds these authors put forward the view that small bells with electrical amplification are preferable to large ones for use in a carillon.[§]

21. Flexural Waves.

It has been stated that progressive waves and normal vibrations are alternative constituents of the most general kind of vibrations of solid bodies. In some cases one in particular is more natural than the other. This is very obvious in the case of a longitudinal impulse in the earlier stages of its propagation along a bar. In the same way the idea of progressive waves applies to transverse flexural oscillations. In the equation

$$\frac{\partial^4 y}{\partial x^4} + \frac{1}{c^2 k^2}\frac{\partial^2 y}{\partial t^2} = 0$$

we now adopt the trial solution $\cos\omega(t - x/V)$ where V is the wave-velocity. This gives

$$\frac{\omega^4}{V^4} - \frac{\omega^2}{c^2 k^2} = 0,$$

$$V = \sqrt{\omega c k},$$

[*] Journ. Amer. Soc. Acoust., Vol. 8, p. 99 (1937).
[†] Journ. Amer. Soc. Acoust., Vol. 5, p. 159 (1933).
[‡] Rev. Sci. Inst., Vol. 6, p. 293 (1935).
[§] Journ. Amer. Soc. Acoust., Vol. 5, p. 159 (1934).

so that the wave velocity depends on the frequency. The phenomena of " group " propagation result. A localized disturbance will spread out and the maximum disturbance will be a resultant of all the elementary sinusoidal constituents. It will not travel with the wave velocity of its most prominent constituent, but with the " group velocity " U, where

$$U = V - \lambda \frac{\partial V}{\partial \lambda},$$
$$= 2V,$$

λ being the wave-length. Thus both U and V vary inversely as the square root of the wave-length. A concentrated disturbance at one

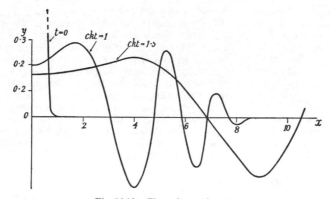

Fig. 16.12.—Flexural wave in a bar

end of a bar will spread out in the manner indicated in fig. 16.12. The ideal case of an infinitely intense displacement of zero width is capable of exact solution in the form *

$$y = \tfrac{1}{2}(\pi ckt)^{-\frac{1}{2}} \sin\left(\frac{\pi}{4} + \frac{x^2}{4ckt}\right).$$

In a similar way flexural waves can exist in plates, and a localized disturbance will spread out, again with the appropriate group velocity if there is a well-marked group of waves.

* Havelock, *The Propagation of Disturbances in Dispersive Media* (Cambridge, 1914).

CHAPTER XVII

The Ear and Hearing

1. Structure of the Ear.

As a matter of convenience it is usual to regard the ear as divided into three parts as shown in fig. 17.1. Of these the outer ear comprises the visible part—the *pinna*—and the passage leading down to the drum-skin or *tympanum*. The middle ear consists of the small chamber containing the chain of small bones which communicate the motion of the tympanum to the inner ear. The inner ear consists of the *cochlea* and the *semicircular canals*.

Outer Ear.

The pinna now plays little, if any, part in the process of hearing. In animals it is movable and can be used to collect sound and to locate the direction of its source. Man has now almost completely lost this capacity for moving the pinna. It may play some slight part in shielding the ear from sounds from behind, thus making easier the discrimination between sounds coming from behind and sounds coming from in front, and the more obtrusive the ears are the better will they serve this purpose, but in actual practice the discrimination is nearly always made by turning the head so as to present one ear to the source of sound and leave the other shielded by the head.

Leading down from the pinna is a passage about $2\frac{1}{2}$ cm. in length which is terminated by the tympanic membrane or drum-skin. It is the variation of pressure in this cavity that stimulates the membrane and ultimately gives rise to the sensation of sound. The passage is protected against insects by hairs and by a waxy secretion.

The drum-skin is a very thin and delicate membrane which is slightly conical and has a muscle for tightening it. The contraction of this muscle is usually, but not always, involuntary, and tends to suppress loud low-frequency sounds.*

Middle Ear.

The middle ear is the cavity which contains the chain of bones or ossicles which acts as a system of levers to communicate the motion

---

* Békésy, *Elek. Nachr. Techn.*, Vol. 12, p. 71 (1935).

of the tympanum to the *fenestra ovalis*. From their shape these bones are known as the *malleus* or hammer (attached to the tympanic membrane), the *incus* or anvil, and the *stapes* or stirrup. The footplate of the *stapes* closes an aperture into the inner ear known as the *fenestra ovalis* and is held in position by an annular ligament. The effect of the chain of bones is to reduce the amplitude of motion of the air and apply it to a smaller area of fluid. It thus does something to match the impedances.

It is obvious that for the tympanic membrane to function at its best the pressure on its opposite sides must be the same, i.e. the pressure

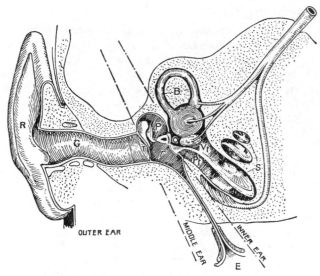

Fig. 17.1.—Diagrammatic section through the right ear

R, pinna; G, auditory meatus; T, tympanum; P, chain of bones; O, oval window; S, cochlea; Vt, scala vestibuli; Pt, scala tympani; B, semicircular canals; E, eustachian tube; r, round window.

in the middle ear must be atmospheric. This condition is secured by the connexion of the middle ear to the back of the throat through a passage known as the *Eustachian tube*. This tube opens every time the act of swallowing is performed and pressure is thus adjusted. An airman in rapid descent is conscious of temporary deafness and a painful sensation in the ears which is eased by rapid swallowing. Similar temporary deafness is occasionally produced in the act of blowing the nose when air happens inadvertently to be blown up the Eustachian tube into the middle ear. The act of swallowing restores normal hearing. The Eustachian tube also serves the purpose of drainage, but may give bacterial infections from the throat and nose access to the middle ear.

Inner Ear.

The inner ear consists essentially of a bony cavity containing the semicircular canals and a spirally wound passage, called the *cochlea*, from its resemblance to a snail-shell. The semicircular canals are not concerned with hearing. The cochlea is filled with fluid and if unwound would show a tapering passage partially divided longitudinally by a bony shelf shown in the transverse section of the passage as in fig. 17.2. The longitudinal division of the passage is completed by two membranes, the *membrane of Reissner* and the *basilar membrane*. The upper passage so formed—known as the *scala vestibuli*—leads up from

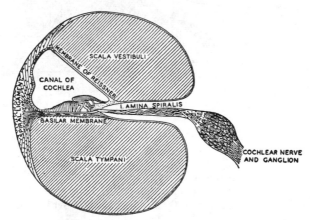

Fig. 17.2.—Cochlea in transverse section

the *fenestra ovalis* to the apex of the cochlea, where it connects with the lower passage or *scala tympani* through a tiny hole, the *helicotrema*. The scala tympani terminates in the *fenestra rotunda* or round window. As the fluid in the ear is nearly incompressible it would be impossible to impart vibrations to it if the bony cavity had only one opening. The windows are so arranged that the membrane covering the round window gives outwards when that attached to the stapes is driven inwards at the oval window.

The basilar membrane tapers the reverse way to the cochlea as a whole; it is narrowest at the base of the cochlea and widens towards the apex. It is strengthened by transverse fibres and there is evidence that it is more tightly stretched transversely at its narrower end. It carries the organ of Corti (fig. 17.3), which contains the nerve terminals in the form of small hair cells. The minute hairs attached to these extend into the fluid in the passage between the basilar membrane and the membrane of Reissner. Lying over these hair cells is another loose soft membrane, called the *tectorial membrane,* fixed at one end to the bony shelf. When the vibrations are excited in the scala vestibuli by the motion of the oval window these vibrations can easily pass through the membrane of Reissner and the basilar membrane to the scala tympani, producing relative motion of the hair cells and the tectorial membrane and giving rise to the sensation of sound. The three membranes (Reissner, tectorial and basilar) vibrate in phase.*

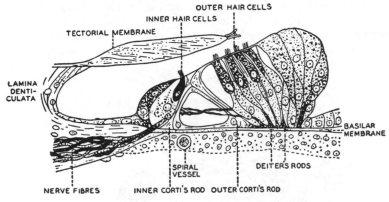

Fig. 17.3.—Corti's organ

Some idea of the dimensions of the cochlea may be formed from those of the basilar membrane, whose total length is about 31 mm. and whose breadth varies from 0·16 mm. near the oval window to 0·52 mm. near the apex.

2. Sensitiveness of the Ear to Intensity.

If a pure tone of given frequency is produced at a very low level of intensity it is inaudible. As the intensity is gradually increased a threshold value is reached at which it just becomes audible (the *threshold of audibility*).

The earliest experiments on the threshold of audibility were made by Töpler and Boltzmann in 1870. The pressure amplitude at the end of an organ pipe when sounding was measured by the optical interference method already described (section 9, p. 297) and the amplitude at the maximum distance of audibility was calculated from this. The determination was incidental to the course of their work and no claim to great accuracy can be made. Converting their result to intensity, we find that at a frequency of 181 the minimum audible intensity is $8·3 \times 10^{-5}$ ergs/cm.^{2} per sec. The first experiment of Rayleigh in 1877 has already been described (section 8, p. 296). Using a frequency of 2730 he found as the upper limit of the quantity in

* Békésy, *Elek. Nachr. Techn.*, Vol. 12, p. 71 (1935).

question 4×10^{-5} ergs/cm.^{2} per sec., or 4×10^{-12} watt/cm.^{2} The problem was subsequently studied by numerous experimenters and a good critical comparison of their results was made by Swan.* All the results indicate a very considerable variation of the sensitiveness of the ear with frequency, the sensitiveness being greatest in the neighbourhood of 3000 cycles/sec., which was the highest frequency used.

A considerable amount of recent work has been done on the subject by Fletcher and Wegel,† Sivian and White,‡ and Fletcher and Munson.§ The experiments of Sivian and White were made on a group of young people with generally excellent hearing and favoured by freedom from fatigue and noise.

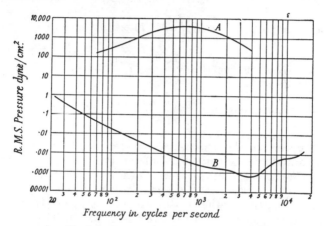

Fig. 17.4.—Limits of audibility for normal ears

A, Threshold of feeling (after Wegel)
B, Threshold of audibility (after Fletcher and Munson)

They measured the intensity of the " free field " of the progressive wave before the insertion of the head of the observer and at a frequency of 1000 cycles/sec. found the minimum value of this to be $1·9 \times 10^{-16}$ watt/cm.^{2}, which corresponds to an R.M.S. pressure amplitude of about ·00028 dyne/cm.^{2} The minimum value of the audible field occurred for a frequency of about 3500 and corresponded to a pressure amplitude of about ·000079 dyne/cm.^{2} The accepted standard for purposes of definition is an intensity of 10^{-16} watt/cm.^{2} or an R.M.S. pressure amplitude of ·000204 dyne/cm.^{2} at a frequency of 1000 cycles/sec.   The results of Fletcher and Munson are shown in curve B, fig. 17.4.

The threshold varies for different ears—even for ears which may

---

* *Proc. Amer. Acad. Arts and Sciences*, Vol. 58, p. 425 (1923).

† *Proc. Nat. Acad. Sci.*, Vol. 8, p. 5 (1922).

‡ *Journ. Amer. Soc. Acoust.*, Vol. 4, p. 288 (1932).   § *Ibid.*, Vol. 5, p. 82 (1933).

be fairly regarded as normal—but there is sufficient agreement to justify the calculation of an average value for each frequency, and it is from these values that the curve B is drawn.

It is interesting to calculate the various quantities for the minimum audible sound wave at the frequency to which the ear is most sensitive. We may take the frequency as 3500 and the R.M.S. pressure amplitude as 8×10^{-5} dyne/cm.^{2}

Intensity $I = \dfrac{P^2}{R} = \dfrac{(8 \times 10^{-5})^2}{41 \cdot 2} = 1 \cdot 55 \times 10^{-10}$ ergs per cm.^{2}/sec.

$$= 1 \cdot 55 \times 10^{-11} \text{ microwatt/cm.}^2$$

Velocity amplitude $\hat{V} = \sqrt{\dfrac{2I}{R}} = 2 \cdot 74 \times 10^{-6}$ cm./sec.

Maximum condensation $\hat{S} = \dfrac{\hat{V}}{c} = 8 \cdot 07 \times 10^{-11}$.

Displacement amplitude $a = \dfrac{\hat{V}}{2\pi f} = 1 \cdot 25 \times 10^{-10}$ cm.

The problem has been attacked differently by Wilska,[*] who attempted to measure the amplitude of the tympanic membrane itself. His results are shown in fig. 17.5, which shows to what incredibly small amplitudes the ear-drum will respond. In fact, Sivian and White (loc. cit.) have calculated that the pressure due to thermal noise in the air is, between the frequencies of 1000 cycles/sec. and 6000 cycles/sec., of the same order of magnitude as the pressure sensitiveness of very sensitive ears. This means that any further increase of sensitiveness would be useless in these cases.

If the intensity of any pure tone is raised above the threshold of audibility it increases in loudness until a value is reached at which the character of the sensation seems to change and become one of pain. This value is the *threshold of feeling* for that frequency. It has been investigated by Wegel [†] and is represented in fig. 17.4 by the curve A. The intercept on any frequency ordinate lying between the curves A and B represents the range of intensities which correspond to audible sounds for that particular frequency. This range again obviously varies with frequency. Thus for a frequency of 1000 the ratio of the extreme pressure amplitudes is about $10^7 : 1$. The ratio of the extreme intensities is therefore about $10^{14} : 1$. It says a great deal for the mechanism of the ear that it is able to cope with such an enormous range of intensities. On the other hand, at a frequency of 80 the ratio of the

[*] *Skand. Arch. f. Physiol.*, Vol. 72, p. 161 (1935).

[†] *Ann. Otol., Rhinol., und Laryngol.*, Vol. 41, p. 740 (1932).

extreme pressure amplitudes is only about 10^4, and that of the extreme intensities about 10^8.

If the curves A and B of fig. 17.4 are conjecturally continued until they will enclose an area every point in which defines an audible pure tone. If we start with any given frequency and infinitesimal intensity and gradually raise the intensity while keeping the frequency the same, the tone remains inaudible until the threshold value of the

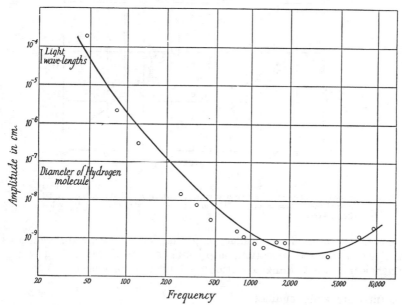

Fig. 17.5.—The circles show the amplitude of vibration of the eardrum at threshold, as determined by Wilska. The curve represents the calculated amplitude of the air molecules in a sound-wave at threshold pressure. Where the ear is most sensitive, the amplitude of vibration of the eardrum is less than the diameter of a hydrogen molecule.

intensity is reached. Thus all points outside the area correspond to pure tones which are inaudible.

Békésy * has investigated the threshold of audibility for very low frequencies. Some kind of auditory sensation is established for frequencies down to two or three cycles per second. Between 3 cycles/sec. and 50 cycles/sec. there is some evidence that the processes involved are quantal in nature. This is shown in the accompanying curve (fig. 17.6). The step at frequency 18 cycles/sec. is the most marked; it is about this frequency that the tonal character of the sensation begins to make its appearance, and this character is established at a frequency of about 25 cycles/sec. It is, of course, impossible for the intensity

* *Ann. d. Physik*, Vol. 26, p. 554 (1936).

required for audibility at these low frequencies to be imposed on the ear without aural harmonics (section 5, p. 472) being generated, and it is difficult to assess the effect which these may have. Békésy also

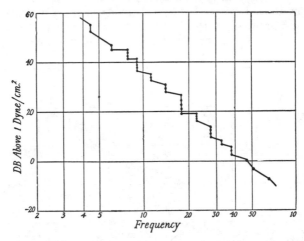

Fig. 17.6.—The minimum audible pressures for low frequencies. This threshold curve shows the step-like character which may indicate the quantal nature of the process involved. The most prominent step occurs at 18 cycles. (After Békésy).

experimented on the threshold of feeling, and here he differentiates between a tactual sensation, a pricking sensation (at very low frequencies) and a tickling sensation (at higher frequencies).

3. Intensity and Loudness.

For the measurement of loudness it is necessary to have a standard tone and a standard scale. By decision of the International Electrotechnical Commission (Paris, 1937) a pure tone of frequency 1000 has been chosen as a standard and the scale is defined as follows:

" The standard tone shall be a plane sinusoidal sound wave coming from a position directly in front of the observer and having a frequency of 1000 cycles per second. The listening shall be done with both ears, the standard tone and the sound under measurement being heard alternately. The intensity level of the standard tone shall be measured in the free progressive wave. The reference level shall be taken to be that corresponding to an R.M.S. sound pressure of 0·0002 dyne per sq. cm. (being the threshold value for the standard frequency). When, under the above conditions, the intensity level of the standard tone is n decibels above the stated reference intensity the sound under measurement is said to have an equivalent loudness of n phons."— Definition 2017, *British Standards Institution.*

The experimental realization of the definition of equivalent loudness requires the resources of a standardizing laboratory, but approximate methods of measurement have been devised for ordinary use, and some of these are described later. The results of experiments on the equivalent loudness of pure tones are given in fig. 17.7. The curves represent frequencies varying from 30 to 10,000, and for each frequency equivalent loudness as defined above is plotted against sensation level. Sensation level is defined as follows: if I_0 is the intensity corresponding to the threshold of audibility for a given frequency and I is the intensity of any pure tone of the same frequency, the sensation level of

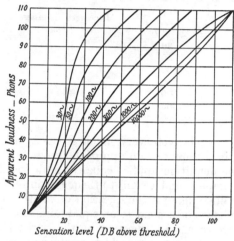

Fig. 17.7.—Relation between sensation level (intensity above threshold) and apparent loudness for various frequencies

this tone in decibels is $10 \log_{10} I/I_0$. The curve corresponding to the standard tone is, by definition, a straight line passing through the points 10, 10; 20, 20; ... The figure shows that for an equivalent loudness of 50 phons, for instance, the sensation levels for various frequencies are as follows:

Frequency.	Sensation Level.
30	18
50	23
100	29
200	36
500	44
1000	50
10,000	53

Thus, for the commonly occurring frequencies of 500–10,000, covering a range of about $4\frac{1}{2}$ octaves, equivalent loudness in phons is very nearly given by the sensation level, and since the three curves lie fairly close to one another this is true not only for the particular value of 50 phons to which this comparison refers but to all values of equivalent loudness up to 110. For all frequencies less than 500 the equivalent loudness in phons is considerably greater than the sensation level in decibels.

There is another aspect of this discrepancy between sensation level and equivalent loudness. If the sensation level of all frequencies is raised by the same amount the relative loudness of the various tones will be profoundly modified. Thus fig. 17.7 shows that if the sensation level of all frequencies is raised from 30 db. to 40 db. the change in loudness for the various frequencies will be as follows:

Frequency.	Increased Loudness in Phons.
30	15
50	21
100	20
200	17
500	13
1000	10
10,000	10

Thus low notes are relatively very much strengthened, a fact which may be noticed in listening to an approaching band.

Obviously the definition applies equally to all continuous sounds, no matter how complex, and assigns to them a definite place on a scale. This scale of loudness ignores the question of whether equal intervals on the scale of phons correspond to an equal number of loudness steps. Some light is thrown on this question by the work of Knudsen, who measured the change in intensity which corresponds to a just perceptible change in loudness.* He used as his source a valve-operated telephone giving a range of frequencies from 30 to 20,000. The intensity could be carried from the threshold of hearing to the threshold of feeling, and precautions were taken to keep the tones pure.

The connexion between the intensity of a sensation and that of the corresponding physical stimulus was first investigated by Weber for weights, and his conclusion, known as Weber's law, was that the increase in the stimulus necessary to produce the minimum perceptible increase in the resulting sensation is proportional to the pre-existing stimulus. Thus if W is a weight producing a sense of pressure and ΔW is the increase in weight which gives a just perceptible increase Δs of the pressure sensation, then

$$k \frac{\Delta W}{W} = \Delta s$$

where k is a constant.

* Phys. Rev., Vol. 21, p. 84 (1923).

Fechner took the relation in this form and, assuming that ΔW and Δs are true differentials, he integrated the equation and obtained the relation

$$s = k \log W.$$

This is known as the Weber-Fechner law and is more or less applicable to all sensations.

The sensation of light, like the sensation of sound, does not follow the Weber-Fechner relation exactly. Nutting has modified it in the case of light into an expression of the form

$$\frac{\Delta I}{I} = P_m + (1 - P_m)\left(\frac{I_0}{I}\right)^n,$$

which covers satisfactorily both low and high intensities. I is the intensity of the light, ΔI the minimum perceptible increase in intensity, I_0 the threshold intensity, P_m the limiting value of $\Delta I/I$ for large values of I, and n an arbitary number depending on the frequency of the light.

Knudsen has shown that his results for sound can be expressed by an equation of the same form,

$$\frac{\Delta I}{I} = F + (1 - F)\left(\frac{I_0}{I}\right)^n.$$

For a frequency of 1000, $n = 1\cdot05$, while for a frequency of 200, $n = 1\cdot63$.

Experiments by Riesz * are in general agreement with the above. For all values of the intensity for which I is greater than the value given by the equation

$$10 \log I/I_0 = 60$$

the differential sensitiveness is found to be practically constant, and for various frequencies $\Delta I/I$ lies between $0\cdot05$ and $0\cdot15$.

Results from the Bell Telephone Laboratories are set out in fig. 17.8. It will be seen that over a range of frequency from 60 to 10,000 the minimum perceptible change in intensity is a nearly constant fraction of the intensity for a sensation level of 60 db., while the same is nearly true for a sensation level of 40 db., and therefore for all sensation levels between these. For lower sensation levels the fractional increase of intensity required to produce a perceptible change in loudness is larger over the middle of the frequency range and increases to a very marked extent for low and high frequencies. For a sensation level of 60 db. and a frequency of 1000 an increase of intensity of $0\cdot05$ is just perceptible under the best conditions. This corresponds to a

* *Phys. Rev.*, Vol. 31, p. 867 (1928).

change in sensation level of 0·2 db. At this frequency and under the best conditions about 370 distinct steps in loudness are perceptible.

The phon scale of loudness is, as we have noted, on a purely physical basis. It places all noises in the order of their loudness, but the ratio of the numbers representing two noises on the phon scale may not convey any very accurate idea of the ratio of the strength of the sensations. Indeed, it might very reasonably be doubted whether in this matter the phrase "ratio of the strength of the sensations" has any meaning.

Work to test this and if possible to lay the foundations for a purely psychological scale of loudness has been done by Fletcher and Munson,* Geiger and Firestone,† and Fletcher.‡ The crux of the matter may be

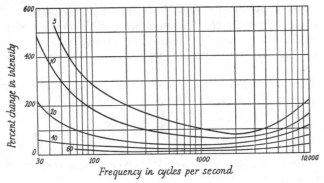

Fig. 17.8.—Showing minimum perceptible change in intensity by the human ear. Numbers on the curves indicate the sensation level of the test tone in decibels above threshold

said to lie in the validity of judgments of "twice as loud". In Fletcher's experiments these judgments were tested in three ways: (1) directly, by adjusting one sound until it is twice as loud as another of the same pitch, the pressure amplitude of both being determined; (2) indirectly, by adjusting one sound until when heard by one ear only it appears equally loud with another of the same frequency heard by both ears simultaneously; the first sound is then assumed to be twice as loud as the second; (3) indirectly, by balancing a 1000-cycle tone against a pure tone of widely different frequency until they sound equally loud. A second 1000-cycle tone is then balanced against the two combined. It is assumed that this 1000-cycle tone is twice as loud as the first. The curves obtained by plotting subjective loudness measured in these ways against pressure amplitudes agree so closely as to leave little doubt that this kind of scale is feasible, and for some purposes it may have advantages, but the phon scale is perfectly definite, and

* *Journ. Amer. Soc. Acoust.*, Vol. 5, p. 25 (1933).
† *Ibid.*, Vol. 5. p. 35 (1933).   ‡ *Journ. Frankl. Inst.*, Vol. 220, p. 405 (1935).

its divergences from a true sensation scale are shared by our temperature scales, which are very rarely criticized on this ground.

4. Sensitiveness of the Ear to Pitch.

It was quite early recognized that just as the eye is sensitive only
over a definite range of wave-lengths for electromagnetic waves, so
the ear is sensitive only over a limited range of sound wave-lengths
or frequencies.

König made a series of experiments· with numerous sources of
sound, as a result of which he concluded that the lowest audible frequency is 16 cycles/sec. In the course of his work on the upper frequency limit he discovered the fact, now so well established, that the
highest audible frequency varies greatly with age. At the age of forty-
one he could hear a tone of frequency 23,000 cycles/sec. Sixteen years
later this upper limit had dropped to 20,480 cycles/sec., and after
another ten years to 18,432 cycles/sec.

Early experiments on both limits yielded rather discrepant results.
These discrepancies were only in part due to the variations characteristic of individual ears. A glance at fig. 17.4 shows that an attempt
to discover the frequency limits for audibility has no meaning unless
it is conducted at a specified intensity level. Thus if the R.M.S. pressure
amplitude is 0·001 dyne per sq. cm. the lower frequency cut-off is
at 400 cycles per sec. At an R.M.S. pressure amplitude of 1 dyne per
sq. cm. it has dropped to about 20 cycles per sec., extending the range
of audibility downwards by nearly four octaves. Fig. 17.4 gives us the
information at present available as to the limiting frequencies for
audibility at various intensity levels.

Next in importance to the range of sensitiveness is the differential
sensitiveness, i.e. the change in pitch that is just perceptible. Extensive measurements were made by Knudsen.* He used a constant
sensation level of 40 db. for all frequencies and showed that at this
level the sensitiveness of the ear to changes of frequency is much
greater than to changes of intensity, being greatest for frequencies of
from about 600 to 4000. Over this range of frequencies the value of
$\Delta f/f$ is approximately ·003, where Δf is the minimum perceptible change
in the frequency f. These experiments were repeated and extended
by Shower and Biddulph.† They used an improved technique, varying
the frequency sinusoidally from one value to the other about twice
a second, this being found to give the smallest values of $\Delta f/f$. Their
results are shown in fig. 17.9.

This figure shows $\Delta f/f$ plotted against f for various sensation levels.
The maximum sensitiveness is found for a frequency of 2000 and a
sensation level of 70. For these values $\Delta f/f$ is only ·0017, i.e. the ear is
sensitive to a change in frequency of 1 in 600. At frequencies above

---

* Loc. cit.   † *Journ. Amer. Soc. Acoust.*, Vol. 3, p. 275 (1931).

500 the value of $\Delta f/f$ is fairly constant, but it shows a slight upward trend above 8000. At frequencies below 500, Δf is fairly constant, so that $\Delta f/f$ shows a steady increase.

The minimum value of $\Delta f/f$ corresponds to a change in pitch of $100 \log 1\cdot0017/\log 2$ centi-octaves, i.e. 0·24 centi-octave or ·029 of a semitone. Taking Knudsen's values for a sensation level of 40 db., we find that there are 2000 distinguishable tones between the frequencies 50 and 8000.

For a sensation level of 40 decibels and frequency 62 the minimum

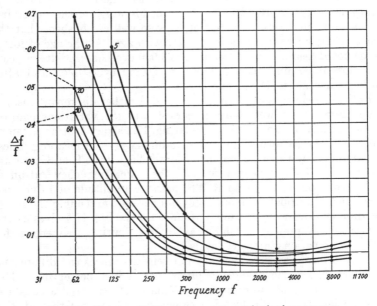

Fig. 17.9.—Variation of $\Delta f/f$ with frequency-sensation level as parameter

value of Δf is about 2 to 3 cycles per sec. It should be remembered, however, that this refers to pure tones. Pure tones of frequencies 60 and 62 will be indistinguishable in pitch, but if the fourth partials are present, they will have a frequency difference of 8 and the notes will easily be distinguished. Thus pitch discrimination is always easier for notes that are not pure.

So far it has been assumed that pitch is completely determined by frequency. Fletcher * has shown that this is not so. Pitch, loudness, and quality are not three simple sensations uniquely related to frequency, intensity, and wave form respectively. Variations in any one of these physical properties of the wave may affect all three

* *Journ. Amer. Soc. Acoust.*, Vol. 6, p. 59 (1934).

sensations. Thus the loudness of notes can be greatly increased by increasing the overtone content, and practically all the loudness of low piano notes is due to the partials. The loudness of complex notes is far from simple and is evidently connected with the masking pheno- menon (p. 484). Most marked, perhaps, is the case of the effect of in- tensity on the sensation of pitch. In addition to the work of Fletcher, this relationship has been studied by Stevens * and Snow †. With some observers no effect of intensity on pitch was recorded, whereas with others changes of sensation level between 40 db. and 120 db. produced changes in pitch as great as 35 per cent. Pure tones were used, and in each case the pitch standard was a pure tone 40 db. above threshold value. According to Stevens a low-pitched sound has its pitch lowered when its intensity is increased, and a high-pitched sound has its pitch raised. The dividing line comes in the region of greatest sensitiveness, and this is taken to suggest that the phenomenon is associated with the resonance characteristics of the ear.

The possibility of developing a purely psychological scale of pitch has been investigated by Stevens, Volkmann and Newman.‡ Observers tried to adjust one tone until its pitch was exactly half that of another tone. Fairly consistent observations for this fractiona- tion of pitch were obtained and frequencies plotted against pitch on this scale. The resulting curve agreed fairly closely with that obtained by integrating just perceptible intervals of pitch. The unit on this scale of pitch is the *mel* and the 1000-cycle tone is arbitrarily assigned the value of 1000 mels.

A point of some interest in this connexion is the duration of a pure tone which is just sufficient to enable a judgment of pitch to be made. Experiments by Mach § suggest that at a frequency of 128 c./sec. some 4 or 5 vibrations are sufficient. The matter has been investigated in more detail by Bürck, Kotowski, and Lichte.‖ Plotting the minimum time required for a judgment of pitch against the fre- quency of the tone, they obtain a curve which strongly resembles the curve representing the variation of pitch sensitiveness with frequency.

A pure tone of short duration is equivalent to a frequency-band with an intensity-spectrum obtained by Fourier analysis. As time elapses this band becomes narrower, and more intense at the ultimate frequency. The experiments have shown that the pitch is recognized when the duration is such that 70 per cent of the energy, corrected for aural sensitiveness, is concentrated in a frequency-band of ± 5 per cent on either side of the tone-frequency. This criterion is justified by a further test in which a click is heard indirectly through a resonant

* *Journ. Amer. Soc. Acoust.*, Vol. 6, p. 150 (1935).
† *Ibid.*, Vol. 8, p. 14 (1936).   ‡ *Ibid.*, Vol. 8, p. 185 (1937).
§ *Deutsch. Natf. Tagebl.*, p. 53 (1871).
‖ *Elek. Nachr. Tech.*, Vol. 12, pp. 278, 326 and 335 (1935).

circuit, the damping in which is adjusted until a definite pitch is detected.

Further light is thrown on the properties of hearing by measurements of the perception of small time-differences at various frequencies, by measuring the interval at which sources of different tones must be switched on in order to make a recognizable difference in the instant of initiation of the respective sounds.* The times involved are somewhat similar to the time required for the recognition of the pitch of a tone. If the pitch of the first tone is established in the ear the second tone will appear to succeed it. Otherwise the two tones will fuse. These experiments are complementary to measurements of the loudness of clicks.† These studies indicate that the ear is linear and aperiodic for sounds at a level which is not excessive. The resonant mechanisms are nearly critically damped. The time constants are between 50 and 150 milli-seconds.

5. Aural Harmonics.

One of the most striking facts about hearing is that tones may be present in the sensation to which there corresponds no constituent simple harmonic vibration in the external stimulus. In these cases Ohm's law (section 5, p. 340) breaks down. These tones are sometimes called subjective tones, but as they are produced in the ear the term aural tones seems more appropriate.

In the discussion of forced and free oscillations in Chapters II and III we confined ourselves to the case where the restoring force is symmetrically and linearly related to the displacement, i.e. the force-displacement graph is a straight line through the origin. Now this double condition represents an ideal case towards which all very small oscillations of elastic bodies tend. As the amplitude is increased, however, a point is soon reached when this ideal is not attained.

We may assume that the relation between acceleration and displacement is given by the equation

$$\ddot{x} + \omega^2 x + a x^2 + b x^3 + \ldots = 0.$$

In general the coefficients are such that for small values of x we can neglect the terms in x^2 and higher powers, and we have the approximate relation

$$\ddot{x} + \omega^2 x = 0.$$

This is the ideal case referred to, and the admissible peak value of x will depend on the values of a, b and c.

---

* Bürck, Kotowski, and Lichte, *Elek. Nachr. Tech.*, Vol. 12, p. 355 (1935).
† *Ibid.*,Vol. 12, p. 326 (1935).

As x is increased the term ax^2 is likely to become effective first and we have the relation

$$\ddot{x} + \omega^2 x + ax^2 = 0,$$

where the third term does not change sign with x. The solution of this equation shows that the effect of this additional term is threefold: (1) a displacement of the mean position, (2) a slight lowering of the frequency, (3) the introduction of the full series of harmonics. Thus harmonic constituents of the tone produced by any musical instrument may be due not merely to the vibration of the string or air column in parts, but to the distortion due to a large amplitude of vibration. Each partial tone may carry its own series of harmonics.

When a vibrating system showing asymmetric and non-linear characteristics is subject to forcing, the resultant motion, as was pointed out by Helmholtz,* is of great interest. Following his treatment, we may take the case of double forcing and write as the equation of motion

$$\ddot{x} + \omega^2 x + ax^2 + F_1 \sin n_1 t + F_2 \sin(n_2 t + \theta) = 0,$$

where $F_1 \sin n_1 t$ and $F_2 \sin(n_2 t + \theta)$ are the applied periodic forces. The equation may be integrated by putting

$$x = \epsilon x_1 + \epsilon^2 x_2 + \epsilon^3 x_3 \ldots,$$
$$F_1 = \epsilon F',$$
$$F_2 = \epsilon F'',$$

and then equating separately to zero the terms multiplied by like powers of ϵ.

This gives

$$\ddot{x}_1 + \omega^2 x_1 + F' \sin n_1 t + F'' \sin(n_2 t + \theta) = 0,$$
$$\ddot{x}_2 + \omega^2 x_2 + ax_1^2 = 0,$$
$$\ddot{x}_3 + \omega^2 x_3 + 2ax_1 x_2 = 0.$$

The first of these equations is equivalent to neglecting the term in x^2. The pulsatances (pulsatance = $2\pi \times$ frequency) involved in the solution are ω, n_1, and n_2. Of these the first is the frequency of free vibration, and if there is any damping this will not appear when the steady state is reached. The two applied frequencies alone will survive and there will be no distortion.

The solution of the second equation involves additional terms with pulsatances $2n_1$, $2n_2$, $n_1 - n_2$, $n_1 + n_2$.

The solution of the third equation brings in terms with pulsatances $3n_1$, $3n_2$, $2n_1 + n_2$, $n_1 + 2n_2$, $2n_1 - n_2$, $n_1 - 2n_2$.

---

* *Sensations of Tone*, Appendix 12.

If we consider first of all the case of single forcing ($F_2 = 0$) then we find that the vibrating system distorts the imposed vibration and, if it is part of a transmission system, adds to the imposed frequency $n_1/2\pi$ the full harmonic series. These tones may, of course, be produced at the source of vibration or in the air, and are then heard by the ear in the normal way.

There is, however, a further possibility. The ear may itself be

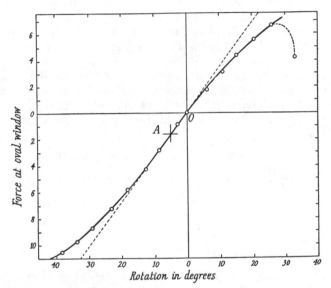

Fig. 17.10.—Graph of the force exerted on the stapes as a function of the degree of rotation of the malleus. Note the non-linearity and asymmetry of the curve as a whole. Point A, at the middle of the central linear portion of the curve, is the point about which the curve is most nearly symmetrical. It does not coincide with the position of rest (O).

Inward rotation of 30° dislocates the malleo-incudal joint. The resulting decrease in pressure on the stapes is indicated by the broken line at the upper end of the curve. The measurements were made on a scale model of the ossicles. (After Stuhlman.)

an asymmetric non-linear transmitter. Helmholtz gave reasons for believing that the tympanic membrane and the ossicles behave in this way and that harmonic tones are generated in the ear. This is now generally agreed to. Dahmann * has obtained positive evidence with respect to the movement of the ossicles, and Stuhlman † has obtained the graph shown in fig. 17.10 by careful observations on a scale model of the ossicles. Here we have the features that show the analysis to be appropriate: (a) a fairly straight middle portion, (b) asymmetry

* *Zur Physiologie des Hörens.* I. Zeitsch. f. Hals-, Nasen-, u. Ohrenheilkundè, Vol. 24, p. 462 (1929).

† *Journ. Amer. Soc. Acoust.*, Vol. 7, p. 119 (1937).

with respect to the origin. (The sigmoid form of the curve is due to the influence of higher powers of x.)

The existence of these aural harmonics can be shown by introducing simultaneously into the ear a strong pure tone of frequency f and another pure tone of variable intensity and frequency. When the frequency of this exploring tone is in the neighbourhood of $2f$, beats are heard between the exploring tone and the aural tone, and this occurs again for frequencies $3f, 4f, \ldots$. Thus for loud pure tones Ohm's law does not hold. Some idea of the intensities of these constituent tones may be obtained by adjusting the intensity of the exploring tone until the beats are most distinct. When this happens

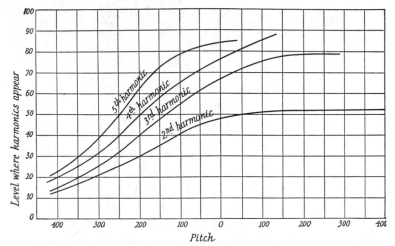

Fig. 17.11.—Sensation levels at which aural harmonics become perceptible

the intensities of the two tones are equal. Experimenting in this way, Fletcher has found for various frequencies of the stimulating pure tone the sensation level at which the various members of the harmonic series become perceptible.* The results are shown in fig. 17.11, where the pitch is measured in centi-octaves from the zero of pitch—1000 cycles per sec.—and the sensation level in decibels above the minimum audible. Obviously these aural tones are generated at a much lower sensation level for low-pitched notes than for high-pitched ones.

The phenomenon is represented from a slightly different angle in fig. 17.12. For any given intensity of fundamental (first harmonic) the intersection of the corresponding line with the ordinates gives the intensity of the other harmonics. Thus for a first harmonic of intensity 100 the other harmonics have the values 87, 74, 61, 48, ... It is in-

---

* Fletcher, *Speech and Hearing*, p. 178 (Macmillan, 1929), from which fig. 17.11 is reproduced by permission.

teresting to translate these intensity levels into sensation levels for a particular tone by reading off from the threshold curve in fig. 17.13 the

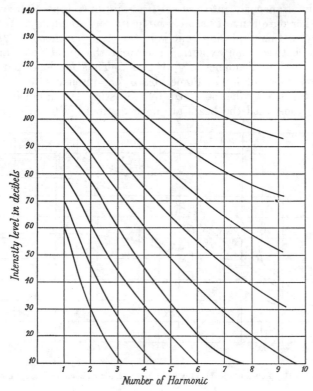

Fig. 17.12.—Relative intensities of aural harmonics

appropriate values. Choosing a 100-cycle tone we have the following results:

Harmonic	Intensity Level	Threshold Level	Sensation Level
1	100	38	62
2	87	20	67
3	74	10	64
4	61	6	55
5	48	3	45

Thus the second and third harmonics actually have a higher sensation level than the fundamental, and the drop in sensation level from the fundamental to the fifth harmonic is only 17 db. as against a drop in intensity level of 48.

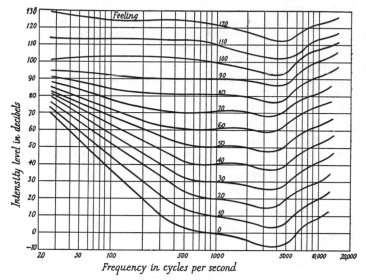

Fig. 17.13.—Intensity levels for the same loudness at different frequencies

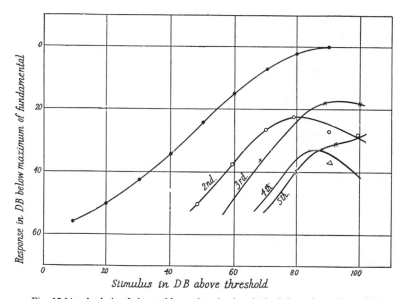

Fig. 17.14.—Analysis of the cochlear microphonics obtained from the cat's ear when stimulated by a pure tone of 1000 cycles. Abscissa values represent the intensity of the stimulus in decibels above the average human threshold. The uppermost curve shows the magnitude of the fundamental frequency in the cochlear microphonics, and the other curves are for the higher harmonics, as indicated.

Another method of research has been opened up by the discovery by Wever and Bray * that when electrodes are placed on the medulla or the auditory nerve of a cat from which the cerebrum has been removed it is possible by listening with telephone receivers to the amplified signals to recognize not only pure tones used as stimuli but even words spoken to the cat. It was later shown that this is in part due to the action of the cochlea as a microphone. This microphonic action is only slightly affected by anæsthetization or even by the death of the animal until the circulation fails. The wave form of the cochlear potential corresponds fairly closely to that of the stimulating sound wave. The complex waves of human speech are reproduced with sufficient accuracy to allow listeners to recognize a speaker by the quality of his voice. This method of the " cochlear microphone " has been applied to the analysis of the response to a strong pure tone by Stevens and Newman.† The microphonic response of the cochlea of a cat to a pure tone of 1000 cycles/sec. is amplified and analysed with a wave analyser. Harmonic constituents up to the fifth are detected and measured and the results are shown in fig. 17.14.

6. Combination Tones.

If two tones are sounded strongly together a third tone can be distinctly heard, whose frequency is the difference of the frequencies of the two generating tones. The discovery of this " difference tone " seems to have been due to the Italian violinist Tartini (1692–1770), who, in 1714, produced it by double stopping on the violin.‡ The phenomenon is also described by the German organist Sorge and seems to have been discovered independently by Romieu § about 1742 or 1743.

These tones are probably the most obvious to the untrained ear in the case of the common police whistle or referee's whistle. When these whistles consist, as they usually do, of two short barrels, each giving a fairly high-pitched note, with a comparatively small musical interval between them, then the blast of the whistle owes its peculiar quality not to either of these notes but to a third—a low-pitched buzz which is quite unmistakable. Its pitch corresponds to the difference in frequency of the notes given by the two barrels. The nature of the phenomenon may be made clear by covering each of the two separate pipes successively with a finger so as to sound the other pipe alone and then while one is sounding removing the finger so that the other pipe comes in. The effect is very striking. Either generator alone gives a feeble, high-pitched note of whistle quality, while the two together generate the penetrating buzz so characteristic of this type of whistle. This tone is known as the first order difference tone and with a little practice it can easily be heard when two notes are loudly

---

* *Proc. Nat. Acad. Sci.*, Vol. 16, p. 344 (1930); *J. Exper. Psychol.*, Vol. 13, p. 373 (1930).
† *Proc. Nat. Acad. Sci.*, Vol. 22, p. 668 (1936).
‡ Tartini, *Dei Principi dell' Armonia Musicale* (1767).
§ *Nouvelle découverte des sons harmoniques graves dont la resonance est très sensible dans les accords des instruments à vent (Assemblée publique de la Société Royale des Sciences*, 1751).

sounded on the organ, or, with rather more difficulty, when a violin is played with loud double stopping.

Young (1800) suggested that these tones were due to beats, and that as the beats got more rapid they finally fused so as to give a tone. This explanation was taken up by König and others, who maintained that the tones were " subjective ".

Helmholtz, on the other hand, held that these tones were produced, as indicated in the previous section, as the result of the double forcing of an asymmetric non-linear system. This led him to the discovery of the summation tone of frequency $f_1 + f_2$, and of some of the other tones mentioned on p. 473. He claimed that at least in some cases the tones were produced outside the ear, and could be reinforced by resonators and detected by their effect on membranes. This was denied by König, Bosanquet and Preyer.

With regard to the contention that the combination tones are really " beat tones " it may be noted that:

(1) This offers no explanation of summation tones.

(2) Combination tones are usually prominent only with strong generators, while beats occur with quite feeble tones.

(3) According to Ohm's law, only simple harmonic motions are perceived as tones. Beats would produce their maximum effect at a point in the basilar membrane sensitive to a frequency $(f_1 + f_2)/2$ and cannot, therefore, produce maximum stimulation at the points corresponding to $f_1 + f_2$ or, in general, $f_1 - f_2$.

(4) The fact that these tones are sometimes· produced outside the ear is now definitely established.

Rücker and Edser * produced combination tones by using a double siren. The sound from this was concentrated by a horn on to a light plate carried by one prong of a heavily mounted tuning-fork. The other prong of the fork carried one of the mirrors of a Michelson interferometer. As the speed of the siren was altered the pitch of the combination tones altered, and when one of these coincided in pitch with the natural frequency of the fork the steadiness of the interference bands observed in the interferometer was at once disturbed. Resonance was established both for the difference tone and for the summation tone. They failed to observe any effect, however, when the combination tone was produced by two tuning-forks.

Similar experiments were carried out by Forsyth and Sowter,† and the disturbance of the bands was recorded photographically. The conclusions of Rücker and Edser were established. It should be noted that in the case of the double siren the two notes act jointly on the mass of air in the wind-chest. W. H. Bragg ‡ points out the essential similarity between this phenomenon, the side bands in wireless tele-

---

* *Phil. Mag.*, (5), Vol. 39, p. 342 (1895).   † *Proc. Roy. Soc.*, Vol. 63, p. 396 (1898).
‡ *Proc. Roy. Inst.* (11th Nov., 1938).

phony, and the Raman effect in the scattering of light. He uses the apparatus shown in fig. 17.15 to illustrate the effect.

A represents a coil seen edgeways, through which either a steady current F_1 or an alternating current $F_1 \sin n_1 t$ can be sent. B is a smaller coil at right angles to A, with its centre coinciding with that of A. Through this second coil a steady current F_2 or an alternating current $F_2 \sin n_2 t$ can be made to pass. The second coil can turn about a vertical axis perpendicular to the plane of the diagram under a torque proportional to the product of the two currents. T is a cylindrical tube in which a slider S is mounted: the slider contains a crystal microphone connected to a loud-speaker. If there are currents in the coils, one or both of which are alternating, the disc D flutters before the mouth of the tube. The tube can be tuned as a resonator by moving the slider. Using frequencies of 50 and 250, the frequencies 200 and 300 are easily found.

Objections have been raised to the form of the equation proposed by Helmholtz, and doubts have been expressed whether the asymmetric term can be large enough to explain the effects. Waetzmann * has argued that the latter objection can be partially met by restoring a damping term which Helmholtz omitted. With regard to the first objection, both Waetzmann and Schaefer † have suggested alternative equations. All the approximate calculations, however, seem to be open to two capital objections:

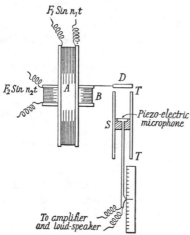

Fig. 17.15.—Apparatus for demonstrating combination tones

(1) Combination tones seem too loud to be due to terms which can be neglected on a first approximation.

(2) The two first-order tones are manifestly very different in intensity, the summation tone being extremely difficult to hear, and the theory seems to offer no explanation of this fact.

Waetzmann has also approached the explanation experimentally. Loading a membrane with a central mass on one side only, he found the curve corresponding to the free vibrations of the membrane, which showed greater amplitude on one side of the undisplaced position. He then recorded the displacement of the membrane under double forcing by two simple tones and performed the Fourier analysis of the resulting curve. The analysis gave the tones f_1 and f_2 (the generators), and in addition the tone $(f_1 - f_2)$ with an amplitude several times that of

---

* *Phys. Zeitschr.*, Vol. 23, p. 382 (1922).   † *Ann. d. Physik*, Vol. 33, p. 1216 (1910).

either generator, a weak tone ($2f_2 - f_1$), and occasionally the summation tone $f_1 + f_2$.

The audibility of the difference tone seems to depend to some extent on its position relative to the two generating tones. If $f_2 < f_1 < 2f_2$, the higher generator is less than an octave from the lower one and the differential lies below this latter tone. On the other hand, if $f_2 > 2f_1$, the interval between the generating tones is greater than an octave and the differential tone lies between the primes. Schaefer finds that in this case it is always very weak.

The difference tone can be well heard with two singing flames. Further, if we have forks of frequency f_1 and f_2 and rest them when sounding on a resonance box tuned to $f_1 - f_2$, the difference tone is produced on the lid of the box and is greatly reinforced. If the two forks are sounded on their own resonance boxes the difference tone is audible only for large amplitudes of vibration.

The beating of a difference tone with one of the generators which produces it has been experimentally demonstrated by Bosanquet and others. If we have two generators whose frequencies form an imperfect octave, we can represent their frequencies by f_1 and $2f_1 \pm \epsilon$. The first-order difference tone is $f_1 \pm \epsilon$, and this makes ϵ beats per sec. with the lower-pitched generator.

Either of these cases can be demonstrated with two tuning-forks of frequencies 256 and 512 respectively. One of the forks is flattened slightly by the addition of a little wax to one of the prongs. The two forks are now sounded together and held over a resonance box or resonator tuned to 256. Beats are distinctly audible.

7. Beating of Combination Tones.

The beating of difference tones with primes indicates how musical intervals may be defined for pure tones. The octave is ordinarily defined by the coincidence of the second partial of the lower note with the fundamental of the higher and the consequent absence of beats. If the notes are pure the interval must be made definite in some other way. In the case of the octave the mistuning will show itself at once, as we have seen above, by the beating of the first-order difference tone with the lower prime. For the fifth we have to call in a second-order difference tone. Thus, if the primes are $2f_1$ and $3f_1 + \epsilon$ we have as the first-order difference tone $3f_1 + \epsilon - 2f_1$ or $f_1 + \epsilon$, and as the second-order difference tone $2f_1 - (f_1 + \epsilon)$ or $f_1 - \epsilon$. This tone, therefore, gives with the first beats of frequency 2ϵ. In the same way with an imperfect fourth we have primes $3f_1$ and $4f_1 + \epsilon$. Here the first-order tone is $f_1 + \epsilon$. The second-order tone with the lower prime is $2f_1 - \epsilon$, while the third-order with the upper prime is $2f_1 + 2\epsilon$. The beat frequency is therefore 3ϵ.

Other intervals involve combination tones of still higher order, so that for strictly pure primes it is doubtful whether the combination tones can play an effective part for these intervals. If, however, the primes are not strictly pure, the combination tones assist. Thus, if each tone carries the second harmonic, we have for the interval of the fourth $3f_1$ and $4f_1 + \epsilon$ with $6f_1$ and $8f_1 + 2\epsilon$ as second partials. These give first-order difference tones $6f_1 - (4f_1 + \epsilon) = 2f_1 - \epsilon$ and $8f_1 + 2\epsilon - 6f_1 = 2f_1 + 2\epsilon$, giving together beats of 3ϵ per sec. In this case the beats occur between first-order tones if the partials are strong enough to act as primes.

8. Aural Combination Tones.

As has already been pointed out, Helmholtz showed that the structure of the drum of the ear has the asymmetric character necessary for the production of these tones, and the fact that the middle ear shares this character has been established by Stuhlmann.* This prepares us for the fact that the quality of musical notes may be considerably modified by this property of the ear. Analysis of the air vibrations corresponding to certain notes shows a surprising feebleness of the fundamental. It may carry only 1 per cent of the total energy, yet it defines the pitch of the note and is the only constituent tone which is ordinarily heard. It may be noted, however, that if the note consists of the harmonic series of partial tones f, $2f$, $3f$, $4f$, . . . , then the first-order difference tone for each successive pair of partial tones has the frequency of the fundamental. Thus the quality of the note as perceived in the inner ear may be something entirely different from the quality as revealed by an analysis of the air vibrations external to the ear, and in particular the fundamental may be greatly strengthened.

Corroboration of this view comes from experiments by Fletcher † using ten separate vacuum-tube generators adjusted to give the frequencies 100 to 1000 at intervals of 100. By suitable switching arrangements any individual components could be eliminated. When they were all impressed upon the receiver, a full tone resulted with a definite pitch corresponding to 100 cycles per sec. The elimination of the 100-cycle component produced no appreciable effect. The note still appeared to have a pitch corresponding to 100. Even with the first seven components eliminated, leaving only 800, 900 and 1000, the pitch corresponded to a frequency of 100. Any three successive components were sufficient to give the tone a pitch corresponding to 100, and with four consecutive components the fundamental was very prominent. When a piece of music is reproduced with all frequencies below 300 suppressed, the quality is affected to an astonishingly small degree.

The simplest explanation of these results is that the mechanism

---

* *Journ. Amer. Soc. Acoust.*, Vol. 9, p. 119 (1937).   † *Ibid.*, Vol. 6, p. 59 (1934).

of the ear displays a non-linear response to external applied forces. This non-linearity produces aural tones: all the summation frequencies, difference frequencies, harmonic frequencies as well as the impressed frequencies produce nerve stimulation. When the fundamental and the first few overtones are eliminated from the external tone, they are again introduced by the ear mechanism as "subjective" tones, although with quite different intensities.

Békésy * maintains that aural overtones are almost certainly produced in the cochlea and difference tones in the middle ear, since their loudness is altered by differences of air pressure and muscle contraction in the ear passages.

The existence of these tones has been established and their intensity estimated by means of the exploring tone method described in a previous section (p. 475). Using two tones at a sensation level of 80 db. and of frequencies 700 and 1200 respectively, and a third exploring tone, Wegel and Lane † established the existence of the following aural tones:

f_1, 1200; f_2, 700; $f_1 + f_2$, 1900; $f_1 - f_2$, 500; $2f_1$, 2400; $2f_2$, 1400; $3f_1$, 3600; $3f_2$, 2100; $2f_1 + f_2$, 3100; $2f_1 - f_2$, 1700; $2f_2 + f_1$, 2600; $2f_2 - f_1$, 200 (?); $4f_2$, 2800; $2f_1 + 2f_2$, 3800; $2f_1 - 2f_2$, 1000; $3f_1 + f_2$, 4300; $3f_1 - f_2$, 2900; $3f_2 + f_1$, 3300; $3f_2 - f_1$, 900.

The only tone absent which theory would have led us to expect was $4f_1$, 4800.

The use of an exploring tone to elucidate the subjective structure of a given tone-complex is criticized by Trimmer and Firestone ‡ on the ground that the exploring tone itself tends to introduce aural tones both by itself and in combination with the tone to be studied, and that it cannot always be assumed that these are negligible. Thus care must be taken to ensure that the exploring tone is not itself contributing to the tone-structure to be explored.

The problem can be approached also by examining the microphonic action of the cochlea. A thorough exploration of the cochlear response of a cat using a wave analyser gave a total of 66 different tones in the frequency range 100 to 8000 when two pure tones were used as the stimulus. Their frequencies were 700 and 1200 and their sensation level 90 db. above threshold. The list included 4 harmonics of 700, 3 harmonics of 1200 and 27 combination tones, all with intensities exceeding 1 per cent of the stimulating tones.

Of course any mechanical system to which the vibrations are communicated may give rise to these tones. Since the adiabatics for air are curved, there is an asymmetry in the relation between pressure difference and condensation. Thus with sufficiently loud sounds combination tones may be produced in the medium. They may also

---

* *Ann. d. Physik*, Vol. 20, p. 809 (1934).   † Fletcher, *Speech and Hearing*, p. 176.
‡ *Journ. Amer. Soc. Acoust.*, Vol. 9, p. 24 (1937).

be produced in the receiving mechanism—not only in the ear but in a microphone.

9. Masking of Sounds.

If, while we are listening to a continuous sound, another sound is started with a low but gradually rising intensity, there may come an instant when the first sound ceases to be audible; it is said to be masked by the second sound. Early experiments by Mayer * indicated that a tone of high pitch can easily be masked by a tone of low pitch, but that it is much more difficult to mask a tone of low pitch by using a tone of high pitch. The matter has been further studied by Wegel and Lane.†

The curves in fig. 17.16 indicate results obtained at the Bell Telephone Laboratories. The masking tone is held steady at a frequency of 200 and an intensity level of 20 db. above threshold. Another tone of frequency 100 cycles per sec. is then produced, and its intensity is gradually raised until it just becomes audible. The intensity at which it now becomes audible is a new threshold value, and the difference in decibels between this intensity and the ordinary threshold intensity is called the *threshold shift*, and is plotted against the frequency 100. The same process is repeated with notes varying in frequency up to 4000, the masking tone being maintained steady at frequency 200 and sensation level 20 db. The results when plotted give the lowest curve in the first figure of the diagram.

This curve shows that for frequencies from 100 to about 700 the masking effect of the tone of frequency 200 is considerable, rising to about 10 db. threshold shift for tones of frequency about 180 and to about 13 db. or 14 db. for tones of frequency about 270. Above frequencies of 700 there is no threshold shift at all; that is, the tone is audible at the same level of intensity whether the masking tone is sounding or not.

The intensity of the masking tone is now raised to 40 db., 60 db., and 80 db. respectively above threshold and the whole series of observations from frequency 100 to frequency 4000 is repeated in each case. These observations when plotted give the other curves of the first diagram. It is seen at once that a 200-cycle tone of intensity 80 db. above threshold gives considerable masking all over the frequency range, but a greater threshold shift for notes of higher frequency than for notes of lower frequency than the masking tone. The other diagrams show the effects of masking tones of frequencies 400, 800, 1200, 2400 and 3500 cycles per sec.

Thus Mayer's deduction requires qualification. A low tone must be raised to a very high intensity before it will mask a high tone far

---

* *Phil. Mag.*, Vol. 11, p. 500 (1876).   † *Phys. Rev.*, Vol. 23, p. 266 (1924).

removed in frequency, and a high tone will mask one of lower pitch if the frequencies are near together.

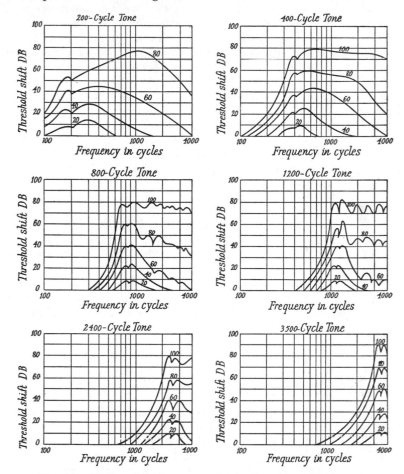

Fig. 17.16.—Masking effect of pure tones of various intensities and frequencies.
(From Fletcher, *Speech and Hearing* (Macmillan, 1929), by permission)

10. Noise.

The increase of noise due to the increased use of machinery, the development of mechanical transport and other causes has focused public attention on the subject, and a scientific study of its physiological and psychological results has been demanded. This has involved the necessity of measuring and analysing noise, so that we may be in a position to eliminate as far as possible all unnecessary noise and reduce necessary noise to a minimum.

Noise is defined as " sound not desired by the recipient ". This definition may seem somewhat subjective, as indeed it is, but it has its uses. It allows for the obvious fact that what is one man's noise may be another man's music; indeed, what is one man's noise at one moment may be the same man's music at another moment.

The most important characteristic of noise is loudness, and several methods of measuring this are available. From the definition already given (section 3, p. 464) it is obvious that for subjective measurement a standard tone must be adjusted in intensity until it is equal in loudness to the noise to be measured. The interval between the intensity of the standard tone and its threshold intensity measured in decibels gives the loudness of the noise in phons.

Measurements have been made by Davis * and others with a tuning-fork. The intensity of the sound emitted by a tuning-fork may be represented by the equation

$$I_t = I_0 e^{-at},$$

where I_t is the intensity at time t, I_0 the initial intensity, t the time in seconds, and a a constant depending on the fork.

Since $10 \log_{10} I_0 / I_t$ is the difference in intensity in time t measured in decibels, the decay in intensity in time t is $\Delta \times t$, where Δ is a constant depending on the fork. Hence if the fork takes t sec. to decay to an intensity equal in loudness to the noise, and N is this sensation level and S the initial sensation level of the fork in decibels above the threshold,

then $$N = S - (\Delta \times t).$$

If the vibrations of the fork are allowed to decay until its note is just masked by the noise,

$$N = S - (\Delta \times t) + M,$$

where M is the difference between the matching value and the masking value, a quantity which varies a little with the nature and pitch of the noise but is fairly constant at 15 to 20 db. If the frequency of the fork is 1000 cycles/sec., then N is the loudness in phons.

The method has the advantage of great simplicity, and the results compare favourably with those obtained by much more elaborate and expensive apparatus. It has, however, some disadvantages. The first it shares with some other instruments: it is dependent on a subjective judgment. Secondly, it is not applicable to sounds of short duration or to rapidly varying sounds. Thirdly, it cannot be used for very intense sounds, as the initial loudness of the fork is not sufficiently great.

Among audiometers of rather more complicated nature may be mentioned the Siemens-Barkhausen instrument. It consists essentially of an electric diaphragm buzzer of standard frequency, the current from which is led to a telephone

* *Nature*, Vol. 125, p. 48 (1930).

against one ear. The telephone may be placed in close contact with one ear and the other ear left open to receive the noise. The adjustment of the telephone by an attenuator is then made for equality. Alternatively, the ear-piece may hold the diaphragm away from the ear and allow mixing of the noise in the same ear. In this case adjustment is made for masking. The telephone receiver may be calibrated by placing it tightly over an artificial ear canal communicating with the diaphragm of a calibrated microphone. It is graduated to read decibels above threshold intensity.

An instrument designed by the Western Electric Company uses valve oscillators of eight different frequencies and measures the rise of the threshold of audibility due to the noise by admitting noise and sound from the oscillators to the same ear. This rise of the threshold of audibility, of course, is what the telephone engineer is particularly interested in.

In all these cases we use aural matching and the instruments are said to be *subjective*. Some time ago the Radio Corporation of America introduced an instrument designed to eliminate this subjective judgment. Obviously a mere integration of the total energy is useless owing to the relative insensitiveness of the ear to very low and very high frequencies, and in this instrument a microphone and amplifier are connected to an attenuator which reduces the response at each frequency in such a way as to simulate the action of the ear. Strictly speaking, this means different relative attenuation at different noise levels, but it is found sufficient to have the instrument adjustable for the levels 40 db. to 90 db. A similar instrument has been designed in the National Physical Laboratory and is being produced on a commercial scale. It is a direct-reading instrument giving a range of from 50 to 130 phons.

It is only rarely that noise produces any physical injury. Boiler-maker's deafness is a well-known occupational disease, but it arises only after prolonged exposure of the subject to a very intense noise level far exceeding anything met with in ordinary life. Only very rarely is the normal person subjected to sufficiently persistent intense noise to produce any permanent effect on auditory efficiency.

On the other hand, temporary effects are noticeable at levels of 100 db. for tones of frequency about 1000. The threshold of audibility may be temporarily raised by about 20 db., but the effect passes off after a comparatively short time. Airman's deafness is an illustration of this, but with ordinary people the conditions are very rarely realized.

Evidence as to the effect of noise on output is somewhat conflicting. Laird * has measured the oxygen consumption of typists working at different noise levels and found a considerable increase at high levels. On the other hand, Weston and Adams † found the output of weavers only slightly increased when they were protected by ear defenders. It was clear from their results, however, that adaptation to the noise

---

* *Journ. Nat. Inst. Industr. Psychology*, Vol. 4, p. 259 (1929); *Journ. Appl. Psychology*, Vol. 17, p. 320 (1933).

† *Industrial Health Research Board, Report* 65.

is a process which the worker undergoes daily, and that the adaptation wears off and efficiency drops when fatigue sets in. Pollock and Bartlett * found that the performance of mental tasks is not prejudicially affected after a preliminary period of adaptation even when the noise level is considerable and the tasks complex. Of course in all these cases there is one important factor which still remains in doubt. No one works normally at maximum output, and the maintenance of the normal output at a high noise level may make greater demands on reserves and be more costly than we think.

So far as distraction is concerned loudness is again a primary factor, but above frequencies of 500 or so annoyance seems to increase more rapidly than loudness, which suggests that high-pitched sounds are inherently distracting, as are also sounds containing high-pitched or inharmonic partials. Unfamiliarity, uncertainty as to cause, and uncertainty as to direction of source are also factors tending to increase the distraction.

Doctors have called attention to the effect of noise on sleep. Even when the subject is unconscious of the noise and is neither kept awake nor roused by it, physiological effects are produced which may indicate that the restorative quality of the sleep is being impaired.

There remains the effect of noise on the nervous system. This is very difficult to assess. The point of view of the medical profession is stated by Lord Horder † as follows: " Doctors are definitely convinced that noise wears down the human nervous system, so that both the natural resistance to disease and the natural recovery from disease are lowered. In this way noise puts health in jeopardy, and most intelligent folk can understand this from its effect upon themselves."

Bartlett ‡ sums up the situation as follows:

" We can also say two other things: the first is that, on the whole, noise, however intense it is, is not very likely to disturb the people who make it, or even the people whose exposure to it is regular and long continued; and the second is that probably the disturbing effects of noise are at their maximum for people who have to do mental work, but are for some reason bored, tired, forced into a job which is a bit too difficult for them or not quite difficult enough or in which they are only moderately interested. If any community contains a considerable number of people of whom these things are true, complaints of noise will be common. As a distraction, however, while its effects do not justify the sensational statements that are often made, it is certainly harmful enough to provide a justification for all the efforts that can be made towards its reduction."

The most satisfactory attack upon unnecessary noise is that directed against the source. Here a good deal of progress has been made. The motor-horn has been silenced at night in built-up areas. Wireless loud-speakers and gramophones are controlled by by-laws. A special study is being made of the noises due to aeroplanes, and the under-

---

* *Industrial Health Research Board, Report* 65.   † *Quiet*, Vol. 1, p. 5 (July, 1937).
‡ *The Problem of Noise* (Cambr. Univ. Press, 1934).

ground railways are being silenced by the use of longer lengths of rail and by the use of absorbents on the walls of the tunnel. Now that quantitative measurement of noise is possible, new methods of attack on the problem are being opened up almost daily.

Three tables are appended * giving loudness levels due to (a) Traffic Noises, (b) Road Transport Noises, (c) Noises from various sources.

TABLE IX.—NOISE LEVELS

Very Loud Noises

Source	Observer's position	Loudness
		phons
Aeroplane	10 ft. from airscrew	120 to 130
,,	in cabin	90 to 110
Riveting machine	35 ft. away	102
Pneumatic drill	10 ,,	90 to 100
Ship's siren	115 ,,	98
Niagara Falls	noisiest location	90

British Road Transport Noises

Source	Observer's position	Loudness
		phons
Tram	in street	91
Motor-bus	inside	64 to 74
Quiet motor-car,		
40 m.p.h.	inside	75
Motor-horn	20 ft. away.	94 to 102

Traffic Noise Measurements in London

Microphone suspended above Pavement

Location	Average Loudness	Peak Loudness
	phons	*phons*
In front of St. Paul's Cathedral	74	77
Lombard Street	74	80
Mansion House	73	78
Victoria Street	73	77
Trafalgar Square	72	—
Adelphi	62	66
Fleet Street (Law Courts)	62	70
Temple Gardens	53	67
Regent's Park (quiet period) ..	52	—

* From N. W. McLachlan, *Noise* (Oxford Univ. Press, 1935).

11. The Hearing of Beats.

The phenomenon of superposition explains the fact that when two continuous notes are admitted both to both ears or both to one ear, beats are heard whose frequency is the difference in frequency of the two notes. If the waves corresponding to the two notes act on the same part of the hearing mechanism, we should expect these alternations in amplitude of vibration and therefore in loudness. These beats are difficult to hear if they are very slow, and are best ·heard when they have a frequency of about 3 per sec. The effect is that of a single throbbing tone of intermediate pitch called the *intertone*. As the interval between the two sources is increased a point is reached when it is recognized that there are two notes involved.* This " resolution " of the two components is only achieved by the ear at greater frequency differences (about 8 per sec.) than are required to distinguish two notes sounded successively. As the interval between the two notes is increased the intertone disappears, the frequency of the beats increases and the sensation becomes unpleasant. Helmholtz attributed all discord in music to rapid beating between the fundamental tones of chords or between their partials. The unpleasantness, however, does not increase without limit. It reaches a maximum for a beat frequency which depends on the frequencies of the two notes involved and which is lower the lower these frequencies are. Further widening of the interval between the two notes is accompanied by decreasing unpleasantness, enfeeblement of the beats, and finally complete disappearance of the beats. An attempt to measure roughness has been made by Békésy,† but the project is beset with many difficulties and only a beginning has been made.

Beats may be heard not only when the sound waves from both beating sources reach both ears but also when the waves from each beating source are led to one ear only. The phenomenon is one of considerable interest and has been studied by Lane.‡ Two tones capable of giving moderately slow beating in the ordinary way are led separately to two telephone ear-pieces attached to the two ears so that only one tone reaches each ear. One of the tones is maintained steadily at an intensity of about 80 decibels above the threshold of audibility. The other is started at zero intensity and gradually increased. At first nothing but a steady tone with the frequency of the louder tone is heard. When the intensity of the weaker tone reaches a level of 5 or 10 db. above threshold audibility very faint beats become perceptible. At about 25 or 30 db. the beats reach their maximum distinctness; as the intensity of the variable tone is further

* Wever, *Psychol. Rev.*, Vol. 36, p. 402 (1929).
† *Zeits. f. tech. Phys.*, Vol. 16, p. 56 (1935).   ‡ *Phys. Rev.*, Vol. 26, p. 401 (1925).

increased the distinctness diminishes and at 45 or 50 db. the beats disappear. If the intensity of the variable tone is still further increased, beats are again heard when this reaches about 60 db., to become very distinct at 80 db. and disappear at 100 db. These two sets of beats are quite different in character, and for reasons which will appear later are distinguished as *subjective* or *objective* according as they occur for sources of nearly equal intensity or for sources of very unequal intensity.

When beats are heard in the ordinary way they are most distinct when the two tones have the same intensity and are inaudible if they differ by more than about 30 db. In the case of binaural hearing the beats are most distinct when there is a difference in intensity of about 55 db. This suggests at once that the beats are heard in the ear to which the weaker tone is led and that the stronger tone is conducted across the head and loses about 55 db. in its passage. This view is confirmed by the fact that for a person entirely deaf in one ear the average difference in intensity required for minimum audibility between a tone in the good ear and in the bad ear is about 55 db. It is also confirmed by a masking experiment. A tone of one frequency has superposed on it in the same ear a tone of another frequency and the intensity of the second tone is increased until the first tone becomes inaudible. The tone of variable intensity is then transferred to the other ear and again increased in strength till the first tone becomes inaudible. The intensity of the variable tone will then be found to be about 55 db. greater than was necessary when the masking tone was applied to the same ear as the tone to be masked.

The subjective beats which occur when the two tones are of nearly equal intensity must have an entirely different origin. They are probably due to the fact that localization of a source of sound seems to depend on the capacity of the ear to appreciate differences in time of arrival of sound waves at the two ears. This question will be raised again in the next section; meanwhile it is only necessary to say that if the tones from two tuning-forks of slightly different frequency are led separately to the two ears respectively the observer experiences a sensation of continuous change of sound direction. It is as if two compressions arriving simultaneously at the two ears gave the impression of a source of sound situated in the median plane of the head. The tone of greater frequency then gets in advance, and if it is being led to the right ear the source of sound appears on the right-hand side. As this tone continues to gain the phase difference passes through π, and the source of sound appears to change to the left-hand side. This experiment is due to Rayleigh, and Lane maintains that when the difference of frequency exceeds one or two vibrations per second the sensation becomes the so-called subjective binaural beating.

12. Perception of Sound Direction.

The perception of sound direction without movement of the head requires the use of two ears, and with low-pitched sounds even rotation of the head may fail to give information as to the direction of a source of sound if one ear is stopped. When both ears are used the discrimination between right and left is made with ease and certainty even for pure tones; discrimination between front and back is much more difficult, and in the case of pure tones almost impossible. The phenomenon was studied very thoroughly by Rayleigh.* The obvious explanation of the ability to discriminate is that a source of sound produces a difference of intensity at the two ears and that the subject locates the source of sound in the direction of the ear receiving the greater intensity. Where there is any uncertainty the subject tends to swing the head round until the source lies on the line joining the two ears and the difference in intensity is a maximum. Rayleigh showed that however plausible this explanation may seem, it can only have a very limited application. The head is an effective obstacle only for sounds for which the circumference of the head is comparable with the wave-length of the sound. Thus if we treat the head as a sphere of radius a and compare the sound intensity I_R at the right ear presented directly to the source, with the intensity I_L at the left ear shielded by the sphere, we have the following results:†

$\dfrac{2\pi a}{\lambda}$	I_R	I_L	$\dfrac{I_R - I_L}{I_R}$	
$\frac{1}{2}$	·294	·260	$\frac{·034}{·294} = 12$	per cent
1	·503	·285	$\frac{·218}{·503} = 43$	,,
2	·690	·318	$\frac{·372}{·690} = 54$	,,

For the head $2\pi a = 2$ ft., so that if $2\pi a/\lambda = \frac{1}{2}$, $\lambda = 4$ ft., or $f = 256$. It can be shown that for $f = 128$ the intensity difference is less than 1 per cent. It seems, therefore, as if in the case of low-pitched pure tones, at least, the explanation of the correct location of a source of sound must be sought elsewhere.

The possibility that phase difference is the effective factor was also suggested by Rayleigh and investigated experimentally. He devised the experiment on binaural beats referred to on p. 491. Two forks, associated with resonators and giving a slow beat cycle, are acoustically insulated in separate rooms and sound is led by pipes to points near the two ears of the observer. Distinct alternations of sensations of right and left are observed. When the vibration of greater frequency is on the right, sensation of right follows agreement of

* *Nature*, Vol. 14, p. 32 (1876); *Phil. Mag.*, Vol. 3, p. 546 (1877); *ibid.*, Vol. 13, p. 340 (1882).   † Rayleigh, loc. cit.

phase and sensation of left follows opposition of phase. Rayleigh concluded that both intensity and phase difference are effective, the former being the main factor for high frequencies and the latter for low frequencies.

Subsequent investigations by Stewart * confirmed the importance of the two factors. By varying the intensity ratio at the two ears he found that the apparent displacement from the median plane of the single source of sound into which the two separate sources at the two ears seems to fuse is given by

$$\theta = K \log_e \frac{I_R}{I_L}.$$

This formula is established for frequencies 256, 512, 1024. The actual values of I_R and I_L for definite values of θ for a real source are calculated, and so great a discrepancy is found between the experimental value I_R/I_L required to produce the sensation of a phantom source in a position defined by θ and the calculated value of I_R/I_L for an actual source in the same position that it is inferred that intensity cannot be an important factor in the frequency range 256–1024. Experimenting with phase difference, Stewart found a linear relation between the apparent angular displacement of a source from the median plane and the difference of phase being artificially produced at the two ears. When the two are plotted they give different straight-line relations for different frequencies and the slope of the line is found to be proportional to the frequency. The experimental value of the phase difference at the two ears leading to a judgment of a single source in a plane making an angle θ with the median plane agrees well with the calculated value for a real source in that position for frequencies up to about 1200.

A valuable report on the subject has been issued by the Medical Research Council.† This report points out that the effect attributed to phase difference may be due simply to time difference in arrival at the two ears, and that this is more likely to be directly sensed than the fraction (time difference)/period. Stewart's work is consistent with this interpretation. Further experiments are cited to show that any given deviation always requires the same time interval no matter what the frequency of the note. The intensity factor is rather discounted as involving much greater intensity differences than those actually experienced. It is also pointed out that moderate deafness in one ear or the partial closing of a tube through which the sound reaches one ear does not affect localization.

Further, it is to be noted that in work with sound locators the mean angle of error in setting, for a given observer, is practically independent of the distance of the source so long as this is not so

---

great as to make hearing difficult. This is what we should expect if the time difference at the horns is the deciding factor. It is not what we should expect if the deciding factor were either the absolute difference of intensity or the relative difference of intensity. It is also found that in working under the best possible conditions with the most modern forms of locators the accuracy of working approaches the limit set by the shortest perceptible interval of time as determined by other methods. The suggestion that time difference rather than phase difference is the deciding factor is strengthened by the observation that complex sounds are located with greater precision and certainty than pure tones. Now each constituent of the complex sound will give different phase difference, but all constituents will give the same time difference.

Against this Stevens and Newman * have shown that errors of judgment in locating pure tones are a maximum for frequencies in the neighbourhood of 3000, which is about the region of frequency too high for phase discrimination and too low for good intensity discrimination.

It may be fairly claimed, then, that the available evidence points strongly to the conclusion that the power of assigning a direction to the source of sound depends on the ability to appreciate a time difference of the arrival of the sound or some prominent feature of its wave form at the two ears. Above a frequency of about 1200 intensity may play some part, but the evidence for this is not conclusive.

13. Theories of Hearing.

From a consideration of the mechanism of the ear and the phenomena of hearing we pass to a consideration of the way in which the mechanism operates, and here we pass from established fact to theory. One of the earliest theories was the resonance theory. It seems to have been suggested, first by Cotugno (1736–1822) and later by Charles Bell,† that the fibres of the basilar membrane play the part of resonators, taking up from the vibrations communicated to the fluid in the cochlea the vibrations of the frequency to which they are tuned and, because of their damping, vibrations of neighbouring frequencies. This theory was adopted by Helmholtz in his *Sensations of Tone* (1863), probably independently, and put on a firm physical basis. The facts which the theory was then called upon to explain were as follows:

(1) The ear is sensitive over a range of ten or eleven octaves.

(2) Pitch discrimination over the middle of the range of audibility is very acute, but it becomes much less so at both ends of the range.

(3) Beats are heard when two pure tones of nearly equal frequency

---

* *Proc. Nat. Acad. Sci.*, Vol. 22, p. 668 (1936); *Amer. Journ. Psychol.*, Vol. 48, p. 297 (1936).

†*Anatomy and Physiology of the Human Body* (1826).

are sounded simultaneously, but only when the frequency ratio of the two tones, i.e. the musical interval between them, is not too large.

(4) Trills performed on two notes are clear-cut and distinct provided they are not too rapid, but rapid trills which may be quite distinct in the treble are not distinct in the bass.

(5) When two or more notes differing widely in pitch are sounded simultaneously, the ear hears each separately, and it can even hear separately the constituent partial tones of an ordinary musical note.

If now we assume the existence in the ear of a series of resonators covering something like the range of frequency to which the ear is sensitive and subject to damping, these facts may be explained.

(1) A pure tone will excite a small group of these resonators and each will stimulate its corresponding nerve cells, the pitch of the tone being determined by the resonator giving maximum response.

(2) Over the middle of the range it will be possible to distinguish two maxima fairly close together, while at the ends of the range the end resonators will be stimulated by two tones whose frequencies lie beyond the proper frequencies of the end resonators and no true maxima will exist.

(3) Beats imply the simultaneous action of the two beating tones on certain resonators and can therefore be heard only when the two groups of resonators which respond to the two tones separately have certain members in common. When the beating tones are too widely separated in pitch, the two groups of resonators will be entirely distinct and no beats will be heard.

(4) The fact that trills can be clearly heard implies that the damping must be fairly considerable. The fact that trills are more clear in the treble than in the bass when performed at the same rate is what would be expected if the resonators fall to any given fraction of their initial amplitude in the same number of vibrations. This would mean that it would take much longer for the amplitude to fall to one-tenth of its initial value in the case of the notes in the bass than with notes in the treble.

(5) Any number of groups of resonators may be simultaneously stimulated and each group can produce its separate nervous stimulus.

Now it must be said at once that there is no conclusive evidence of the existence of such a series of resonators. The possibility that the transverse fibres of the basilar membrane may so act was, as we have seen, one of the earliest suggestions, and it has not yet been abandoned. We know that the fibres vary in length and thickness. There is reason to believe that they vary in tension, the shortest and lightest being nearest to the oval window and most tightly stretched. They are differentially loaded in the same sense by the liquid in which the membrane is immersed, and if we take all these facts into consideration the possible range of frequency is of the order of the range of audible frequencies. Also, since they must be fairly heavily damped a group will be stimulated by any pure tone, and the louder the tone the larger will be the group.

Several attempts have been made by Hartridge to establish the existence of these resonators by examining the sensation produced by a sudden phase change of π in the stimulating tone. On the resonator theory we should expect a momentary silence while the excited resonators came to rest and started again. This Hartridge claimed to have observed.* As his interpretation of the observed sensation was not accepted, he returned to the subject again † and, using another technique (a siren in which all the holes were equally spaced except one pair for which the distance was halved), found an instant of silence in each revolution of the disc. In collaboration with Hallpike and Rawdon Smith ‡ he observed the electrical response of the cochlea and of the auditory nerve of the cat to phase reversal in a stimulating tone. The variations in the potential were recorded by a cathode ray oscillograph. The record from the auditory nerve showed the silence. The record from the cochlea, on the other hand, showed an accurate and immediate reproduction of the change in the stimulating tone without any interruption, suggesting that the part of the cochlea responsible for the microphonic action is not resonating in character. Ot course the part responsible for the microphonic action may not be the same as the part responsible for pitch perception, but this view seems difficult to maintain in view of the close correlation between pitch perception and the electrical response of the cochlea.

However slender the evidence may be for the existence of a series of tuned resonators or for their identification with the fibres of the basilar membrane, there is very strong evidence that the perception of frequency is spatially distributed along the membrane. Experiments have been made on animals by subjecting them to prolonged sounds of high intensity. They have afterwards shown localized damage of the cochlea near the base for high-pitched sounds and near the apex for low-pitched sounds, and have also shown deafness for tones of pitch near to that of the stimulating tone. An examination of the microphonic response of the cochlea for various frequencies has given similar results. It has also been found by Hallpike and Rawdon Smith § that if in the measurement of the microphonic response of the cat an electrode is inserted at the base of the cochlea the response is greatest for high frequencies, while if it is inserted at the apex the response is greatest for low frequencies. Their results are shown graphically in fig. 17.17. Held and Kleinknecht ‖ have produced localized damage of a small area of the basilar membrane of a guinea-pig by means of a very fine drill and found that the animal showed a selective deafness to tones of a particular pitch.

Additional evidence is obtained from the microphonic action of the cochlea of a guinea-pig by Stevens, Davis and Lurie.¶ By measuring the electrical response in the cochleas of guinea-pigs to pure tones before and after the production of localized lesions of the basilar membrane and afterwards subjecting the basilar membrane to careful histological examination, a correlation between position on the membrane and frequency response is obtained. In fig. 17.18 the circles represent results obtained by this method, position on the membrane being plotted against frequency.

The results can be compared with results deduced for the human ear on certain assumptions. If it is assumed that the ear can always discriminate in pitch between two tones whose maxima are separated

* *Brit. J. Psychol.*, Vol. 12, p. 142 (1921). † *Proc. Phys. Soc.*, Vol. 48, p. 145 (1936).
‡ *Proc. Roy. Soc.*, Vol. 122, p. 175 (1937) § *J. Physiol.*, Vol. 81, pp. 25, 395 (1934).
‖ *Pflügers Archiv.*, Vol. 216, p. 1 (1927). ¶ *J. Gen. Psychol.*, Vol. 13, p. 297 (1935).

by a certain minimum distance on the basilar membrane, then just
perceptible pitch difference (difference limens) will correspond to equal

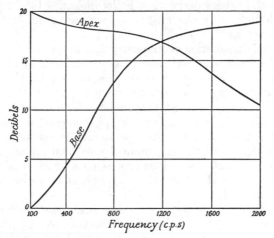

Fig. 17.17.—Graphs showing the relative responses obtained from basal and
apical electrodes on the cochlea of the cat, for various stimulating frequencies.
Note that the curves intersect at approx. 1200 c.p.s.

steps along the basilar membrane. Taking the maximum and minimum
audible frequencies for the two end-points and dividing the membrane

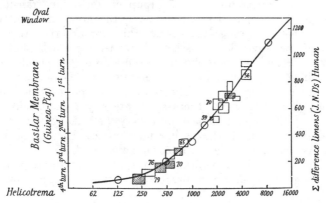

Fig. 17.18.—The correlation between the position of damage on the basilar membrane
and the associated change in the audiograms. The solid line represents the integration of the
data for human pitch discrimination, as explained in the text. The width of each rectangle
represents the frequency range within which deviation from normal sensitiveness occurs,
and its height represents the zone on the basilar membrane separating definitely normal
from definitely abnormal hair cells. The centres of the circles indicate the centres of the
peaks or depressions in the audiograms and the centres of normal or abnormal regions of
the organ of Corti.

up into the 1200 or so equal steps, we can plot position on the basilar
membrane against frequency, and we get the solid line of fig. 17.18.

The end portions of the curve are a little uncertain, as they depend very largely on the loudness level selected for the observations, but this assumption and others make very little difference to the part of the curve which represents the range of frequency from 500 cycles/sec. to 10,000 cycles/sec.

This spatial distribution of frequency does not, of course, require the existence of a series of resonators; it only requires a point of maximal stimulation of the membrane whose position varies with frequency. Even so, however, the view is not without its difficulties. The region of the basilar membrane which is stimulated by a loud pure tone must be considerable if it is to explain the phenomenon of masking. To account for sensitiveness to small pitch differences we must assume that a displacement of the maximum by 0·02 mm. along the basilar membrane can be detected. This represents a space sensibility much greater than that of the finger-tip, although not greater than that of the retina of the eye.

As an alternative theory it has been held that the whole basilar membrane responds to all loud tones and that the frequency of the stimulating tone is the same as the frequency of the impulses conveyed by the nerve. Now it is impossible for any single nerve fibre to carry high-frequency signals. After each signal has passed there is a recovery period during which the nerve fibre cannot pass another signal. The limit to the frequency which one fibre can transmit is about 1000 cycles/sec., but by co-operation a group of fibres can transmit frequencies up to 2000 cycles/sec. or more, the fibres transmitting in rotation. There is strong evidence for this, but unfortunately no indication of the direct transmission of frequencies much above 2000 cycles/sec. Thus the microphonic response from the cochlea occurs at all audible frequencies, but the potentials in the auditory nerve exhibit no high frequencies. The variation of pitch with intensity also tells against this view. Increase of intensity does not change the frequency of the signals, but it may very well change the point of maximal stimulation on the basilar membrane. There is still much work to be done, but the correlation between pitch sensation and position on the basilar membrane satisfies most of the experimental results and gives an easy and direct explanation of the phenomena of analysis.

14. Deafness.

Deafness may be conveniently rated by specifying the hearing loss (H.L.) given by

$$\text{H.L.} = 10 \log_{10} \frac{I}{I_0},$$

where I is the threshold intensity for the patient's ear and I_0 is the threshold intensity for the normal ear. Strictly speaking, for a complete specification each ear must be tested over the whole frequency range with pure tones. This involves the use of expensive apparatus, but the results so obtained are invaluable from the point of view of diagnosis

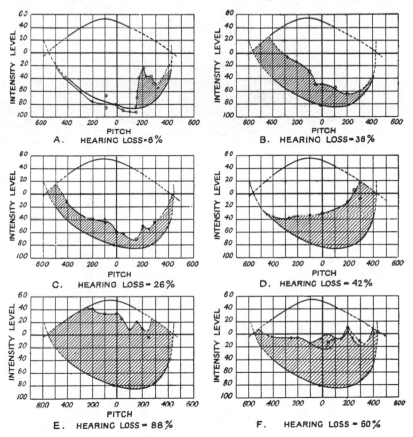

Fig. 17.19.—Audiograms for typical cases of deafness

The whole area enclosed represents the sensation area for a normal ear, the shaded portion the insensitive region for the ear examined. A shows hearing loss for high notes with slightly increased intensity for notes of low and middle pitch. B shows hearing loss mainly for low notes. E shows nearly total loss of hearing. The units on the vertical scale are decibels of intensity level above or below the intensity level corresponding to maximum range of pitch. The units on the horizontal scale are centi-octaves of pitch above and below a frequency of 1000. 1 centi-octave = 12 cents = 3 savarts (approx.).

and will no doubt soon completely supersede the older and more approximate methods. The results can be plotted as shown in fig. 17.19.

Fletcher * relates hearing loss as defined above with the results obtained by more rough-and-ready methods. Hearing can, for instance,

* *Speech and Hearing*, p. 198.

be tested by the distance at which the subject can interpret numbers called by a speaker. It is difficult to control the intensity of the sound waves from the speaker or to specify it; it is very difficult to avoid reflections indoors and noise disturbances out of doors. Eliminating sources of error where possible and allowing for them where they cannot be eliminated, it is found that for a normal ear the distances at which the subject can interpret correctly 50 per cent of a series of numbers are for the average whisper 40 feet, for a loud whisper or quiet voice 222 feet, for a medium loud voice 1250 feet, and for a very loud voice $1\frac{1}{3}$ miles. The way in which these distances are affected by hearing loss is shown in the following table.

Maximum Distances in a Quiet Place free from Reflections for Interpreting Called Numbers by Persons having various Amounts of Hearing Loss

Hearing Loss	Average Whisper	Loud Whisper or *pp* Voice	*mf* Voice	*ff* Voice
0	39·5 ft.	222 ft.	1250 ft.	$1\frac{1}{3}$ miles
5	22·2 ft.	125 ft.	704 ft.	3950 ft.
10	12·5 ft.	70 ft.	395 ft.	2220 ft.
15	7·0 ft.	39·5 ft.	222 ft.	1250 ft.
20	4·0 ft.	22·2 ft.	125 ft.	704 ft.
25	2·2 ft.	12·5 ft.	70 ft.	395 ft.
30	15 in.	7·0 ft.	39·5 ft.	222 ft.
35	8·5 in.	4·0 ft.	22·2 ft.	125 ft.
40	4·7 in.	2·2 ft.	12·5 ft.	70 ft.
45	2·7 in.	15 in.	7·0 ft.	39·5 ft.
50	1·5 in.	8·5 in.	4·0 ft.	22·2 ft.
55	0·8 in.	4·7 in.	2·2 ft.	12·5 ft.
60	—	2·7 in.	15 in.	7·0 ft.
65	—	1·5 in.	8·5 in.	4·0 ft.
70	—	0·8 in.	4·7 in.	2·2 ft.
75	—	—	2·7 in.	15 in.
80	—	—	1·5 in.	8·5 in.
85	—	—	0·8 in.	4·7 in.
90	—	—	—	2·7 in.
95	—	—	—	1·5 in.
100	—	—	—	0·8 in.
110 115 }	May be reached by speaking-tube			
120	Totally deaf			

Similar tests may be made using the tick of a watch or the click of two coins.

It is remarkable that a 50-db. hearing loss produces hardly noticeable deafness; at 80 db. ordinary conversation can still be followed; at 100 db. apparatus is required, and above this the threshold of feeling is approached and deafness is complete.

CHAPTER XVIII

Recording and Reproduction of Sound

1. Sound Recording.

The remarkable development which has taken place in the gramophone during the last thirty years is based to some extent on the perfection of the method of recording sound on discs in such a way that the sounds can be reproduced at will. Just because it can give us the music we want at the moment when we want it, there seems to be an obvious field for the gramophone which the wireless can never successfully invade. Even with the resources of a number of foreign broadcasting stations at his disposal, the fastidious music lover is likely to have many opportunities for listening to music at times when the programmes offered make no appeal. For cinema films, too, the sound recording is frequently on discs, although it seems obvious that here recording on film must ultimately supersede the disc method.

The first sound records were made by Leon Scott in 1857 using the " phonautograph ". The records were scientific curiosities used neither for purposes of analysis nor for reproduction. In 1877 Edison used the principle of the phonautograph to record sounds by indenting a trace of tinfoil covering the face of a metal cylinder. The tracing point made a track of varying depth (hill and dale recording). If after the track had been made the tracing point was started at the beginning of the track and the cylinder rotated, the point reproduced its own motions, communicated them to the attached membrane, and so reproduced the sounds which had been the original cause of its vibration. In 1878 Bell recorded by a similar method on wax cylinders, the material being not merely indented but cut out. He recorded with a sharp stylus and stiff membrane and reproduced with a blunt stylus and limp membrane. The records were duplicated by an electrotype process and cast in wax, so that a softer wax could be used for recording and a harder wax for reproduction. In this same year Edison embodied these discoveries in the phonograph, the first practical talking machine. The next step was the gramophone patented by Berliner in 1887. The record was a disc instead of a cylinder and the track was a wavy furrow of uniform depth, the vibration of the recording stylus being across the track instead of up and down in it. The record was hand-driven and the sound-box had a small conical horn attached. Later developments have consisted for the most part in the perfecting of the various elements in this early machine. A clockwork motor was introduced as driver, the record material was improved and the processing of the records made more efficient. The theory of the horn was developed and the design modified accordingly. Two new principles were introduced, that of electrical recording in 1924, and that of electrical reproduction in 1925, with advantages which will be at once apparent.

In the case of recording, the energy available for the work of cutting a record was at first entirely derived from the sound waves emitted by the source. The output was at best very small, and to get reasonable

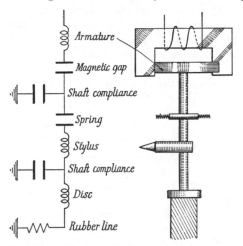

Fig. 18.1.—Diagram illustrating Maxfield and Harrison's recorder, with equivalent electrical circuit

results at all the source had to be very close to the instrument, and a large horn had to be used to concentrate the sound on the diaphragm. This was a cramping condition for an individual performer, and any attempt to record an orchestral performance involved severe crowding of the performers. To record from a large orchestra or to record under ordinary concert conditions was impossible.

A further difficulty arose from the fact that, in the mechanical system by means of which the energy of the sound waves was finally applied to the cutting tool, resonances were almost inevitable, and these could not be eliminated by large damping owing to the small amount of energy available. With the development of the wireless valve, however, distortionless amplification in almost any ratio can be applied to an electrical microphone, and there is the further advantage that by the use of lines the recording can be done at a point remote from the performance.

The record cutter was designed by Maxfield and Harrison * by applying to the mechanical system the principles of the electrical filter. Fig. 18.1 shows the essential parts of the mechanism, and on the left the corresponding elements of the analogous electrical filter. The current from the microphone is led to an electromagnet between the poles of which an armature is free to rotate. The armature is fixed to a shaft controlled by springs and carrying the recording stylus. In order to avoid selective frequency response it is essential that

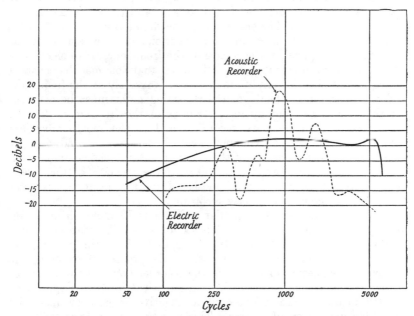

Fig. 18.2.—Response curve of Maxfield and Harrison's recorder compared with the response curve of an earlier acoustic recorder. The acoustic recorder curve is an example only, as the form varied greatly with the adjustment and from one instrument to another. The relative levels are quite arbitrary.

the far end of the mechanical filter shall be terminated by a non-reactive mechanical resistance of appropriate value. This is secured by using a rod of gum rubber about 25 cm. long such that the torsional waves transmitted along it and reflected at the farther end are dissipated in the double journey. These principles of design were first laid down by Maxfield and Harrison † and marked an epoch in the perfection of recording and reproduction. The response curve of the electrical recorder as compared with that of an earlier acoustic recorder is shown in fig. 18.2.

* *Bell System Tech. Journ.*, Vol. 5, p. 493 (1926).
† *Journ. Amer. Inst. of Elec. Eng.*, Vol. 45, p. 243 (1926).

2. Recording on Discs.

The recording machine consists essentially of a heavy turntable, driven at a constant speed of rotation by means of clockwork operated by a weight. The recording point has a slow traverse across this along a radius of the disc, either from circumference to centre in the case of the ordinary record or from centre to circumference according to present practice for a record for use with a film projector. Sound pressure is converted by the microphone into voltage variations and these are amplified, corrected for distortion, and passed to an electro-mechanical recorder. The energy of the needle in vibration as it passes round the groove of a record is proportional to the square of the amplitude multiplied by the square of the frequency, or to the square of the velocity amplitude simply. In order that this may be constant for all frequencies the amplitude must vary inversely as the frequency, and the maximum velocity of the recording point must be constant for the same input energy for all values of the frequency. This is known as constant-velocity recording and is the most convenient for reproduction, as the common sound-box gives a sound pressure proportional to the velocity of the needle point and the common pick-up gives an E.M.F. proportional also to the velocity of the needle point. Recorders are specially designed on the principles set out above to give constant-velocity recording.

The recording wax is a circular slab about 13 inches in diameter and $1\frac{1}{2}$ inches thick, which is composed of a metallic soap and has a highly polished plane surface. It is brought to the optimum temperature, and the wax shavings produced in the process of recording are removed by a suction pipe close to the recorder box. The wax surface is then rendered conducting by brushing it with graphite or sputtering it with metal. From the record a negative is now produced by the electrodeposition of copper. This negative is a copper shell, the master shell, and could be used for the stamping of records directly. This would of course cause wear and a new recording would be necessary. To avoid this a second electrodeposition of copper is made, this time on the master shell, the surface of which is treated so that it can be separated from the deposited copper. This process gives a metallic replica of the wax, a positive known as the "mother shell". The electrodeposition is repeated on this and yields a new negative called the "matrix shell", which is backed and mounted in a press for the stamping of the actual records.

The material of which the records are made is an intimate mixture of shellac, copal, resin, slate powder and carbon black. The mixture is passed along heated rollers, then cooled, and delivered in thin brittle sheets. The hydraulic press has a pair of heavy steel jaws in which are fixed the dies holding the matrices. These dies are hollow and

are fitted with a series of pipes through which steam or cold water
can be passed. The labels are put in position above and below the
lump into which the record material has been converted from its
" biscuit " form, and the pressing is carried out for about a minute
with the press steam-heated. Cold water is then run through and
the edges of the records trimmed and polished. When speed is essential
the whole series of processes can be carried through in a few hours,
although normally it takes several days. Until comparatively recently
the material contained abrasive purposely introduced to grind the
steel needle-point used in playing to the shape of the groove. The
abrasive, however, adds to background noise, and with the use of
reproducers of lower mechanical impedance homogeneous, non-
abrasive material is replacing the older type.

In order that there may be a long playing time the groove must
be as narrow as possible and successive grooves as close as possible.
The needle-point cannot in practice be reduced below a diameter of
about ·003 in., and even this figure gives a load on the point of several
tons weight per square inch. The groove has a width of ·006 in. and
the wall dividing two grooves a width of ·004 in. As the product of
frequency and amplitude must be kept constant for constant intensity
over all frequencies, low-frequency notes must have a large amplitude
and two successive grooves tend to cut into one another if this minimum
separation is not maintained. The distance between two successive
grooves measured from centre to centre is thus ·01 in. Since the needle
point has a diameter of ·003 in. it cannot take a bend of less diameter.
Therefore to reproduce a frequency of 5000 the disc must be run at
a speed relative to the needle point of $5000 \times \cdot003$ in. per sec. or 900 in.
per min. To obtain this speed on a groove of 2 in. radius, which is the
minimum used in practice, requires $900/4\pi$ revolutions per min. or
about 72 r.p.m. The speed chosen in practice is usually 78 r.p.m. This
determines the playing time for a given size of record. Thus if the
outermost groove has a diameter of 12 in. and the innermost a diameter
of 4 in., then the difference in radius is 4 in., and since the pitch of the
groove is ·01 in. this allows for 400 revolutions. The time is $400/78 =$
5·13 min. The total length of the trace is the mean circumference
multiplied by the number of revolutions $= \pi \times 8 \times 400 = 10,050$ in.
$= 837$ ft. or nearly a sixth of a mile.

Attempts are now being made to develop commercially the " hill
and dale " method of recording, and records have been produced *
which give a wider range of frequency than the lateral cut. The closer
groove spacing possible with an amplitude which is vertical instead
of horizontal and the use of a slower speed of rotation (33⅓ r.p.m.) has
made it practical to provide a 12-in. record which for music has a
playing time of from 10 to 20 minutes.

* *Rev. Sci. Inst.*, Vol. 5, p. 179 (1934).

The limitations of the method of disc recording are obvious. Better-quality reproduction is now demanded, and for the bass register this involves a wider pitch for the record groove and for the high-frequency components a faster speed. Both these changes would diminish the playing time, which is already too short. It seems that so far as these requirements are concerned it is impossible to avoid compromise. On the other hand, record material may be modified so as to give less surface noise, longer life and a cheaper record more easily carried and stored.

3. Recording on Film.

The possibility of recording and reproducing sound by a variation of a light beam seems first to have suggested itself about 1900. About this time Ruhmer is said to have produced photographic records using an arc, the light from which was varied by superposing the alternating current from a microphone on the current through the arc. The sound was afterwards reproduced by running the record in front of a constant arc so as to vary the light falling on a selenium cell. The variable current from the cell worked a loud-speaker. In 1906 Lauste applied to the British Patent Office for a patent for a " new and improved method of and means for simultaneously recording and reproducing movements and sounds ". The patent was accepted on 10th August, 1907, but it expired before it was worked. It appeared at a time when the development of the silent film was too rapid and when the unamplified voices were too thin to please an audience in a large hall; Lauste was twenty years ahead of his time. Meantime in 1923 de Forest took out patents for recording and reproducing on film with amplifiers, a demonstration was given at Finsbury Park Cinema, and in 1927 commercial backing was obtained on a large scale. The première of " The Jazz Singer " in September, 1928, and its run subsequently at the Regal Theatre, Marble Arch, marked the beginning of a spectacular development. The silent film was completely superseded in a few weeks almost. The demand for the new sound-film apparatus far outstripped the supply and skilled operators were unobtainable. Saturation in the matter of the number of theatres does not yet seem to have been reached, and the demand of the public is so uncritical that at most provincial theatres, at any rate, the standard of reproduction is far below what modern technique is capable of giving.

4. Variable-density Recording.

There are two methods of recording in use. In one of these the illumination fills the whole width of the sound track, but its intensity is varied so that the record varies in density. A reproduction of a piece of variable-density recording is shown on the right in fig. 18.3. The slit whose image is projected on the moving film is illuminated with light of variable intensity. The intensity can be varied in one of two ways. We may either modify the source of light or modify the beam after it has left the source. The variable arc already referred to is an example of the former device. If a mercury arc is used the changes of intensity may be made very rapid. De Forest applied amplified microphone currents to an electric glow lamp. The difficulties inherent in the method are (1) weakness of the source of light,

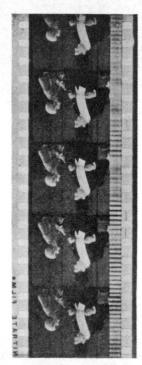

Fig. 18.3.—Sound track

Films showing the two classes of sound track, in the correct position for passing through the projector, viewed from the condenser side

(2) difficulty of securing a proportionality between current strength and light intensity throughout the whole range of frequencies. The method has now been superseded.

The alternative course is to modify the light beam by passing it through some sort of " light valve " operated by the microphone currents. This allows of the use of a very intense source of light and a very large range of values for the transmitted light.

One form of valve is shown in fig. 18.4. It consists of a narrow slit between two strips of duralumin ribbon. The strips carry the amplified microphone currents and are situated in a strong transverse magnetic field, the pole-pieces of the magnet being perforated to transmit the beam. The strips are subject to electrodynamic forces tending to open or close the slit and depending on the microphone current. The disadvantage of this method as compared with the

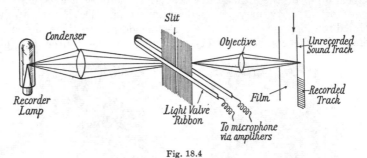

Fig. 18.4

variable glow lamp is the inertia of the ribbon, which is small but causes trouble at high frequencies.

5. Variable-width Recording.

Another method of light recording is to have a constant source illuminating a variable width of the slit whose image is being projected on the moving film. This results in a record which has one edge clear and one uniformly dark, the appearance being as shown on the left in fig. 18.3. This result is secured by reflecting the light from the source on to the slit by means of an oscillograph mirror. The oscillograph may be a wire loop carrying the amplified speech currents and having the mirror attached, and it is suspended with the plane of the loop parallel to the lines of force of a strong magnetic field.

The oscillograph may also consist of a moving magnet or it may embody the principle of the string galvanometer, a single duralumin ribbon being suspended in a strong magnetic field and carrying the microphone current. If the ribbon is designed with a natural frequency of about 10,000 it will compensate by resonance for high-frequency loss.

This method obviously allows of 100 per cent modulation if the peaks run right across the track and if the transparent section transmits completely and the dark section is completely opaque.

Variable-width recording gives negatives which are easier to handle than those given by the variable-density method. The former method produces a black-and-white record, the latter a record which must be developed to just the right point to give the best variation in density.

In the actual talking-picture film the width available is about one inch and of this nine-tenths is devoted to the picture and one-tenth to the sound. The film moves through the apparatus with a speed of

90 ft. per min. or 18 in. per sec.—by jerks through the picture projector and steadily through the sound projector. The finest slit image which can usefully be projected on the moving film is about ·002 in. This gives us for the upper limit of possible frequency 18/·002 = 9000, which compares favourably with that achieved by the disc. This limit was also set by the size of the film grain, but improvements in the film have already removed this cause of limitation and a greater fineness of slit may soon be achieved also.

The processing of the film is automatic, the exposed film being driven through a series of tanks in which the film hangs in loops of length varying with the time required for that particular stage of the process.

In a new method of recording * known as the Phillips - Miller, an opaque layer is removed from a travelling film by a chisel C operated by the microphone current. The film itself has three layers. The lowest and thickest (B) is translucent. On top of this is another translucent layer C_{ht} into which the chisel digs, removing a strip of varying width

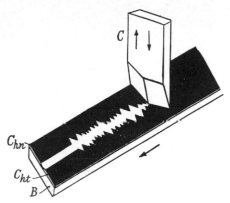

Fig. 18.5.—The Phillips-Miller method of recording

from the top opaque layer C_{hn}. The process, which seems to have considerable possibilities, will be understood by studying fig. 18.5. The angle of the chisel edge is such that an alteration of width of 2 mm. in the cut is produced by a vertical displacement of ·05 mm.

It is obvious that recording on film has many advantages for use in sound films. Synchronism between pictures and sound may be made automatic and transport is greatly simplified. The technique of processing sound films is still very young and may be expected to show considerable improvement. If this type of recording could be adapted to the gramophone a much longer playing time would be possible and records would be lighter. Expense at present makes this use of the film impossible.

6. Magnetic Recording.

A method of recording on a magnetic wire was first introduced by Poulsen about 1900 under the name of the " telegraphone " and was used for recording telegraph signals for subsequent transcription.

---

* *Soc. Franc. Phot. et Ciné Bull.*, Vol. 23, p. 210 (1936). Further improvements are described in *Revue Générale de l'Electricité*, Vol. 42, p. 148 (1937).

In 1924 Stille, a German engineer, substituted a tape for the wire and made other improvements. The system was taken up by the B.B.C. in 1930 under the name of the "Blattnerphone", and after some further developments of method was introduced into the Empire Broadcast on Christmas Day, 1932, and has since been in fairly constant use for certain types of programme item.

The method depends essentially on two properties of the magnetic tape, remanence and coercivity. It must retain the magnetization which is imposed on it and it must resist the demagnetizing effect due to the field between neighbouring portions.

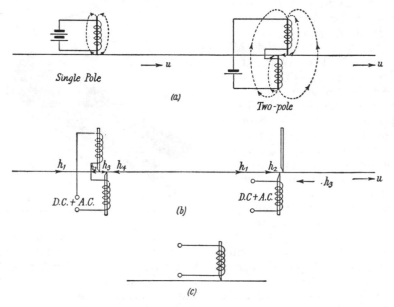

Fig. 18.6.—(a) Wiping head; (b) Recording head; (c) Reproducing head

The apparatus has been described by Barrett and Tweed * and consists of four essential parts:

(1) A magnetic tape driven at constant speed.

(2) A wiping head to magnetize the tape.

(3) A recording head to vary the magnetization by amplified microphone currents.

(4) A reproducing head where the passage of the magnetic variations of the tape may generate an induced alternating current which will actuate a loud-speaker.

(1) The tape is usually of tungsten magnet steel of high coercivity and remanence. It is about 3 mm. wide and about 0·08 mm. thick. One spool has to run for about half an hour at a speed of some 90 metres per minute, so that about 2700

* *J. I. E. E.*, Vol. 82, p. 265 (1938).

metres are required. As the tape is rolled in 1000-metre lengths, soldered joints are necessary and introduce some difficulties.

(2) The wiping head carries a direct current sufficient to saturate the tape, which leaves the head with its maximum remanent induction. The head may consist of a single pole-piece or a double pole-piece as shown in fig. 18.6. The direction of magnetization is shown by the arrows.

(3) The recording head is designed to produce the largest possible variations in flux consistent with linearity. As the length of tape in the magnetizing field must be very small for the recording of high frequencies, it is applied through sharpened pole-pieces, which are strips of magnetic alloy. The magnetization may be longitudinal, or parallel to breadth or depth. It is found that longitudinal with a depth component is best—i.e. with the pole-pieces on opposite sides of the tape. Arrangements in actual use are shown in fig. 18.6. The microphone current is superimposed on a steady demagnetizing current sufficient to bring the tape to a suitable magnetic state.

(4) The reproducing head (fig. 18.6) consists as a rule of a single pole-piece with one end in contact with the tape and wound with a coil in which the variations of magnetic flux give a variable current.

The method is particularly suitable for quick reproduction and for long programmes to be repeated as a whole. The records do not deteriorate appreciably with repeated reproductions. The other outstanding advantage of the method is that a used tape inserted into the apparatus is "wiped" clean by the wiping head and thus prepared for a new recording. Thus a record can be replayed at once, and if it is unsatisfactory the item can be re-recorded on the same tape. Some tapes have remained in good condition after as many as sixty recordings and hundreds of reproductions.

7. Microphones.

The microphone is essentially an arrangement for transforming sound into variations of electrical quantities. It is the first element of the telephone (the transmitter), in which case the variations of electric current are reconverted into sound by the receiver at a distant point. It is the first element of a broadcasting arrangement, in which case the electrical oscillations are reconverted into sound at a distant point by the loud-speaker. Finally, it is the first element of all processes for the electrical recording of sound either mechanically on disc, optically on film, or magnetically on steel tape. The sound waves impinge on a mechanical system, usually a diaphragm but sometimes a ribbon, and set it in vibration. In some types of microphone the processes are reversible. Just as a dynamo-electric generator may be run as a motor by passing current through the windings, so a microphone transmitter may often be used as a receiver or loud-speaker, changes in electrical current setting the diaphragm in vibration and reproducing sound.

When good quality reproduction is required it is important that any resonance of the mechanical system on which the sound waves impinge should be avoided. Diaphragms are sometimes very tightly stretched so as to have a natural frequency well above the range which is important in speech or music. The ribbon microphone, on the other hand, is light and limp and heavily damped.

8. Carbon Microphones.

One of the earliest forms of transmitter, still one of the most widely used, depends on the variations of electric current produced by variations of pressure at loose contacts. In one of the first forms the current was transmitted through a nail which rested on two others, the arrangement being attached to a board which was set in vibration by speech sounds. It was soon found that carbon was the most efficient material, and in the modern telephone transmitter an electric current is modulated by the variation in resistance of carbon granules as a result of the motion of a diaphragm which confines them and which responds to rapid changes in air pressure.

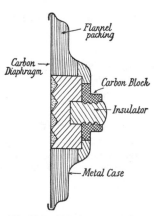

The granules are prepared from carefully selected anthracite. They are ground to the required size, washed to free them from dirt and from magnetic material, and put through a mesh of the required size. They are then heated to a fairly high temperature in an atmosphere of hydrogen.

Fig. 18.7.—Telephone transmitter

The current passes from granule to granule through minute irregularities in the surfaces in contact, and these points of contact increase in number with pressure and so lower the resistance of the mass. The hiss associated with the carbon microphone is attributed to local heating at the points of contact. One advantage of the carbon microphone is that fairly large currents may be obtained without amplification. The sound energy is not transformed into electrical energy but is used to modify a current independently produced by a battery. The magnitude of this current is limited mainly by the hiss to which reference has just been made. The usefulness of the carbon microphone is somewhat prejudiced by a tendency of the carbon granules to " pack ". When this happens the resistance of the microphone falls and it becomes very insensitive.

Three types of carbon microphone may be mentioned:

(a) *The ordinary telephone transmitter.*—There are numerous forms all belonging to this general type, one of which is illustrated in fig. 18.7. The sound waves impinge on a carbon diaphragm, the vibrations being damped by soft packing round the edges so as to avoid sharp resonance. The diaphragm is held in a metal case and the current from a battery passes through the case to the diaphragm and from the central portion of the diaphragm through the carbon granules to the carbon block which forms the other terminal of the arrangement.

(b) *The button microphone.*—This has been largely used for hydrophone work. It can be screwed on to the centre of a large diaphragm which is used to pick up vibrations under water. The arrangement is shown in fig. 18.8.

(c) The Reisz microphone is shown in fig. 18.9. It is used a good deal for broadcasting purposes. It consists essentially of a marble block with its front surface recessed to hold a layer of fine carbon granules between two carbon electrodes. It will be noticed that in this type of microphone the current passes parallel to the diaphragm, instead of nor-

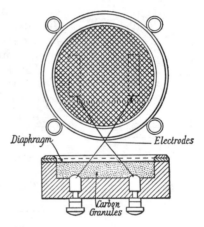

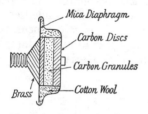

Fig. 18.8.—Button microphone

Fig. 18.9.—Carbon microphone, transverse current type

mally to it as in the other types noted. The granules are retained in position by a non-resonant membrane of thin oiled silk or mica. The thickness of the layer is 1 to 2 mm. and is chosen to be just sufficient for practically complete absorption of the sound waves. This type of carbon microphone is less sensitive than the others; it shares with them the disadvantage of a slight hiss and when subjected to excessive peaks of sound pressure it gives the phenomenon known as " blasting ", but if the sound pressure on the diaphragm is kept below about 20 dynes per sq. cm. it can be used as a high-quality instrument. It gives very little distortion and can be used either for broadcasting or for recording on wax or film.

9. Condenser Microphones.

In a letter to Tait in 1863 Kelvin refers to the sounds produced by a condenser when charged and discharged. Shortly after this the possibility of using a condenser as a telephone was recognized and pursued by numerous investigators. The instrument in very much the form in which it is now used was first

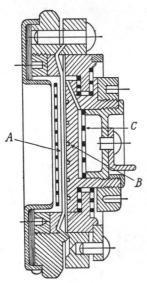

Fig. 18.10.—Condenser Microphone

described by Wente.* In this paper he gives the result of a calibration over a frequency range from 0 to 10,000 cycles per second. The sensitiveness is nearly uniform and the apparatus is easily portable and has no delicate parts. It can be used either as receiver or as transmitter, its great merit being its freedom from distortion and its only serious defect its lack of sensitiveness. The almost unlimited distortionless amplification which can now be achieved renders this defect comparatively unimportant.

The apparatus (fig. 18.10) consists of a thin metal diaphragm A under tension separated by a small distance from a plane metal plate B, the diaphragm and plate forming together an air condenser of variable capacity. C is a compensating diaphragm forming part of an air damping system. The microphone is placed in an electrical circuit as shown in fig. 18.11.

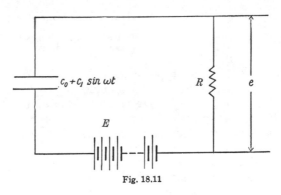

Fig. 18.11

If the area of the plates of the condenser is A and if x_0 is the equilibrium distance between the plates, we have for the capacity at any instant t

$$C = \frac{KA}{4\pi(x_0 + a \sin\omega t)},$$

* Phys. Rev., Vol. 10, p. 39 (1917).

where we assume that the motion of one plate is simple harmonic and its amplitude is a. K is the dielectric constant.

If $\qquad\qquad C_0 = \dfrac{KA}{4\pi x_0}$ is the equilibrium capacity,

$$C = \frac{C_0}{1 + \dfrac{a}{x_0}\sin\omega t}.$$

If a is small compared with x_0

$$C = C_0\left(1 - \frac{a}{x_0}\sin\omega t\right)$$
$$= C_0 + C_1 \sin\omega t,$$

where $2\pi/\omega$ is the frequency and C_1 depends on the amplitude.

Since $\qquad\qquad E - Ri = \dfrac{1}{C}\int i\,dt,$

$$(C_0 + C_1\sin\omega t)R\frac{di}{dt} + (1 + RC_1\omega\cos\omega t)i - EC_1\omega\cos\omega t = 0.$$

Let $\qquad\qquad i = \Sigma i_n \sin(n\omega t + \phi_n).$

By substitution and determination of coefficients

$$i = \frac{E}{R}\left(\frac{C_1}{C_0}\right)\cos\phi_1 \sin(\omega t + \phi_1)$$

$$- \frac{1}{2}\frac{E}{R}\left(\frac{C_1}{C_0}\right)^2\cos\phi_1 \sin(\phi_1 - \phi_2)\sin(2\omega t + \phi_2)$$

together with terms of higher order in C_1/C_0.
  In this expression

$$\cot\phi_1 = C_0R\omega, \quad \tan(\phi_1 - \phi_2) = 2C_0R\omega.$$

For the highest efficiency R should be made large in comparison with $1/C_0\omega$, and in this case

$$E = Ri = \frac{EC_1}{C_0}\sin(\omega t + \phi_1) - \frac{EC_1{}^2}{2C_0{}^2}\sin(2\omega t + \phi_2).$$

It follows that in order to get a pure sine voltage we must make C_1 small compared with C_0. This involves limiting the amplitude.

In the instrument described by Wente in his later paper * the microphone has a natural frequency slightly over 10,000 cycles/sec. and a damping constant of 14,000. The diaphragm is of steel 0·0051 cm. in thickness, stretched so that its natural frequency in air is 7000. Annular grooves are cut into the back-plate to give the required damping. The air gap is 0·0025 cm. and the space surrounding the back-plate is sealed off completely so as to exclude moisture.

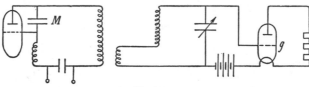

Fig. 18.12

A condenser microphone embodying some unique features has been devised by Riegger †. The condenser whose capacity variations are determined by the sound waves is included in a high-frequency oscillating circuit as shown in fig. 18.12. The result is, of course, a modified frequency of oscillation in the circuit. This oscillating circuit is inductively coupled with a second circuit whose frequency is adjustable. The current in this second circuit will depend on its frequency and will be a maximum at resonance. If the frequency of this resonating circuit is so arranged that the oscillations in the microphone circuit produce in it a current about half that obtained for resonance, then, as is shown in fig. 18.13, small changes in frequency in the microphone circuit will cause large changes of current in the resonating circuit.

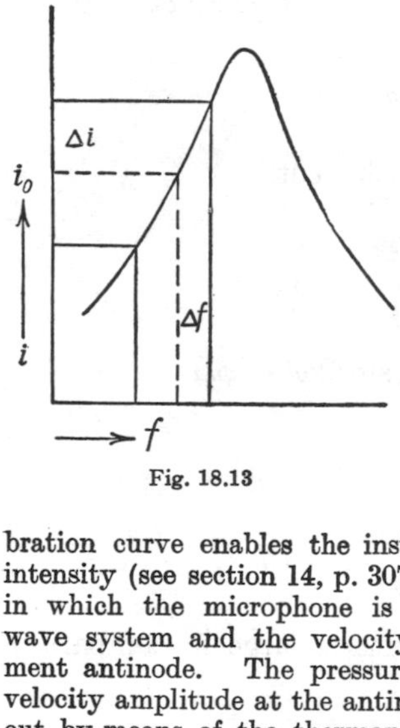

A similar microphone is described by Trendelenburg ‡, and is shown in fig. 18.14. Its great merit is that it shows no resonance in the audible range. The oscillatory system consists of the thinnest metal foil, which is placed between two silk sheets and forms the back plate of the condenser. The front plate is perforated.

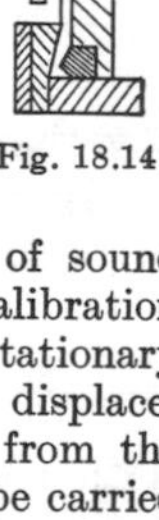

The performance of an improved design described by Bull § is indicated in fig. 18.15. This calibration curve enables the instrument to be used for measurements of sound intensity (see section 14, p. 307). The calibration may be a pressure calibration in which the microphone is placed at a displacement node in a stationary wave system and the velocity measured by a Rayleigh disc at the displacement antinode. The pressure amplitude at the node is calculated from the velocity amplitude at the antinode. The pressure calibration can also be carried out by means of the thermophone or pistonphone (section 14, p. 309). Alternatively, the calibration may be carried out in the field of free progressive waves.

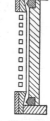

Fig. 18.13

Fig. 18.14

* *Phys. Rev.*, Vol. 19, p. 498 (1922).

† *Wiss. Veröff. a. d. Siemens Konzern*, Vol. 3/2, p. 67 (1924); Vol. 5/2, p. 120 (1926).

‡ *Zeitschr. f. tech. Phys.*, Vol. 5, p. 236 (1924); Vol. 7, p. 630 (1926).

§ *J. Sci. Inst.*, Vol. 13, p. 39 (1936).

The result in this case will differ from the result for the pressure calibration, owing to diffraction. For wave-lengths large compared with the external dimensions of the microphone the pressure at the face of the diaphragm is the same as would have existed in the undisturbed wave. At higher frequencies, where the

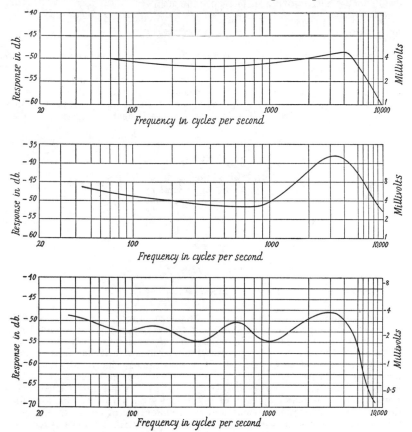

Fig. 18.15.—Calibration of condenser microphone

(a) Pressure calibration ;   (b) Field calibration for direction normal to diaphragm ;
(c) Field calibration for direction parallel to diaphragm

dimensions of the microphone are comparable with the wave-length, the wave-front is reflected and the pressure approaches a value twice that which would have existed in the undisturbed wave. Obviously this effect begins at a frequency of about 1200, and can only be obviated by an indirect method such as those mentioned in section 14, p. 307.

10. **Electrodynamic Microphones.**

Here we make use of a principle applicable either to transmitters or to receivers. If a variable current is passed through a conductor in a magnetic field, the conductor is acted on by a variable force, and if the current is oscillatory the conductor is set in vibration. Conversely, if a conductor is made to oscillate in a magnetic field an oscillatory electromotive force is produced in it.

(a) *Moving-coil type.*—One form of instrument * is shown in fig. 18.16.

The diaphragm m_0 is given increased stiffness by being made dome-shaped in its central portion. The coil, consisting of a large number of turns of fine wire, is rigidly attached to the diaphragm and surrounds the central portion. It works in the circular gap between the central pole-piece and the peripheral pole-piece of a " pot " magnet. The peripheral portion s_0 of the diaphragm is plane. Since the voltage generated by a coil moving in a magnetic field is proportional to the

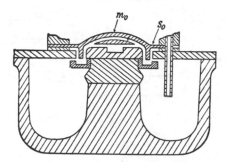

Fig. 18.16.—Moving-coil microphone

velocity, it follows that if the induced voltage is to represent the pressure the coil must have the same velocity per unit of pressure in the sound wave at all frequencies. This is equivalent to saying that if the diaphragm has a constant effective area the mechanical impedance (force per unit velocity) of the diaphragm must be the same at all frequencies. In the instrument shown this condition is practically achieved over a frequency range from 45 to 1000, the sensitiveness being about $9 \cdot 5 \times 10^{-2}$ milli-volts per dyne per sq. cm. pressure. Used with a transformer giving a step-up ratio of 100 to 1, it gives a sensitiveness exceeding that of the condenser microphone and great uniformity of response. Owing to this greater sensitiveness and to the fact that no polarizing voltage is required, this type of microphone has superseded the condenser microphone for many purposes.

(b) *Ribbon type.*—In this type the moving conductor is not a coil but a very thin corrugated strip of aluminium foil. The principle was first applied by Gerlach and Schottky.† A detailed investigation of the instrument was made by Olson.‡

The ribbon is surrounded by a baffle which increases the sound path from back to front of the ribbon, and the force causing motion of the ribbon is the

* Wente and Thuras, *Journ. Amer. Soc. Acoust.*, Vol. 3, p. 44 (1931).
† *Phys. Zeitschr.*, Vol. 25, p. 276 (1923).
‡ *Journ. Amer. Soc. Acoust.*, Vol. 3, p. 56 (1931).

difference in pressure between the front and the back arising from the phase difference due to this path. If the ribbon is very light it will take up the whole motion of the air, and for this reason it is said to be a " velocity " microphone.

As in the case of the moving coil, the ideal to be aimed at is a mechanical impedance of the ribbon independent of the frequency over the range within which the instrument is to be used. By careful designing this has been secured and a uniform sensitiveness of about 1·2 milli-volts per dyne per sq. cm. pressure has been obtained over a frequency range from 100 to about 6000. The system is free from resonances, the natural period of the ribbon being below the range of audibility. This microphone has marked directional properties. For a source of sound in the plane of the ribbon, equal pressures are applied to the ribbon in front and behind and there is no movement. The maximum response is for a source on the normal to the plane of the ribbon, and the response falls off rapidly with the increase of the angle between this normal and the direction from the ribbon to the source. For this reason any particular source can be selected by a suitable orientation of the microphone and the difference of sound level between the source and the general background of noise can be enhanced. The microphone can be used to diminish the effects of excessive reverberation.

When used for the measurement of the power of a source of sound of definite frequency this microphone can be made the basis of a null method due to Gerlach. An oscillating current of the same frequency as the source of sound is sent through the ribbon and the phase and amplitude of the current are adjusted until the ribbon is held still, the electrodynamic forces due to the oscillating current exactly balancing the mechanical forces due to the air waves. From the amplitude of the current and the strength of the applied magnetic field the intensity of sound at the ribbon may be calculated.

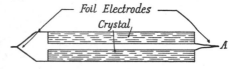

11. Crystal Microphones.

Reference has already been made to the phenomenon of piezo-electricity in connexion with the quartz oscillator (sections 5, p. 220, and 9, p. 323). The phenomenon is utilized in the crystal microphone, and Rochelle salt, which has a high piezo-electric coefficient, is used.

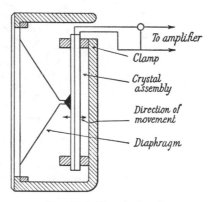

Fig. 18.17.—Crystal microphone

Thin slices of the crystal are mounted as shown in the upper diagram of fig. 18.17. When the double sheet is bent under the action of the sound waves, one layer is thrown into compression while the other is thrown into tension. The electrodes are connected so that the effects are added. The mounting is shown in the lower diagram. It is, of course, also possible to mount the crystal so that it forms the diaphragm of the microphone. Two crystal slices about a quarter of an inch square are mounted in an insulating holder with an air chamber between. When a compression arrives from a source in the plane of the slices both are bent inwards, and conversely for a rarefaction. With suitable electrode connections the effects are again added, and a battery of these crystal elements can be combined to form one microphone.

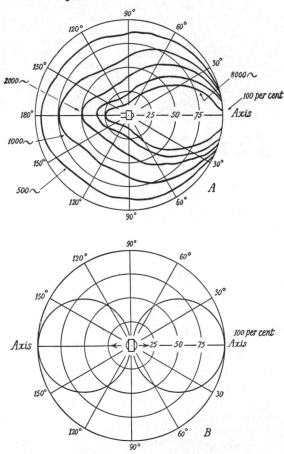

Fig. 18.18.—Microphone polar curves

A Directional microphone.   *B* Bi-directional microphone.

12. Comparison of Microphones.

Most microphones show a directional effect, that is, the response depends not merely on the intensity of the sound but also on the direction along which it reaches the microphone. This shows itself

in broadcasting by a variation in the ratio of the loudness of the direct
sound and the loudness of the general reverberation associated with
it, and in order to get natural effects this property of the microphone
must be taken into consideration.   The directional effect is a result
of diffraction, as will be seen from fig. 18.18.   For a frequency of 500
the response of the microphone varies very little with direction, but
for a frequency of 8000 the response for sounds coming from behind

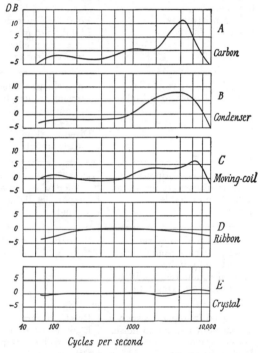

Fig. 18.19.—Microphone response curves

is only 25 per cent of that for sounds coming from in front.   All diaphragm microphones yield results similar to those represented in the
upper polar diagram, for they are pressure-operated.   Pressure is, of
course, a scalar quantity and a velocity-operated microphone behaves
differently, as is shown in the case of the ribbon microphone in the
lower diagram.   This microphone is bi-directional, responding equally
to sounds from behind and in front, but not at all to sounds coming
from directions in the plane of the ribbon.

Comparative response curves are shown in fig. 18.19, but these refer,
of course, to individual microphones and can only be taken to represent
the general type of curve applying to any given class of microphones.

The advantages and disadvantages of the various types have been summarized by Greenlees * as follows:

Advantages and Disadvantages of Microphones

Type of Microphone	Advantages	Disadvantages
Carbon	Robust. Reliable. High sensitiveness. Relatively low cost.	Irregular frequency response. Background hiss. Polarizing current required. Liability to pack. Directional effects, frequency discrimination.
Condenser	Good frequency response. Absence of background noise.	Requires associated amplifier, owing to high impedance, Fragile and affected by moisture. Directional effects, frequency discrimination.
Moving-coil	Good frequency response. Absence of background noise. Robust and reliable. Sensitive.	Directional types have frequency discrimination. Diaphragm liable to flutter in wind.
Ribbon	Very good frequency response. Absence of background noise. Robust and reliable. Good directional effect, little frequency discrimination.	Relatively low output. Very liable to wind flutter.
Crystal	Very good frequency response. Absence of background noise. Non-directional types have little frequency discrimination with direction.	Relatively low output. High capacity impedance requires local amplification. Diaphragm types have directional effects with frequency discrimination.

13. Reproduction from Disc (Mechanical).

The recorded sound may be reproduced from the disc in either of two ways. It may be reproduced by means of a sound-box which transforms the vibration of the needle point as it traverses the record groove into sound waves by a purely mechanical transformation; or it may be reproduced by transforming the vibrations of the needle point into a variable electric current by means of a " pick-up ",

* *Amplification and Distribution of Sound* (Chapman & Hall, 1938).

amplifying this and then transforming it into sound waves by the use of some form of loud-speaker. The sound-box used in the modern gramophone has reached a high state of perfection, and there are competent critics who, for reproduction in a moderate-sized room where great intensity is not required, prefer its reproduction to that of the pick-up. In a large room or hall, however, it gives insufficient loudness and the electrical method is essential.

The essential features of the sound-box are shown on the left in fig. 18.20. The needle point is one end of a lever which is pivoted just above the point and carries the vibrations to the central point of the diaphragm or by means of a " spider " to a ring surrounding the centre. For the diaphragm numerous materials have been tried, including iron, copper, aluminium, paper, parchment, wood, glass and mica. It is important that the diaphragm should be light and that it should have as high a natural frequency as possible. Up to that frequency it vibrates as a whole. Above that frequency it tends to vibrate in parts, with marked loss of efficiency. Now the fundamental frequency for a diaphragm varies as $\sqrt{(\text{Stiffness}/\text{Mass})}$, and this ratio is high for mica, thin glass and thin aluminium under tension. Further, for any given material the fundamental frequency varies as t/d^2, where $t =$ thickness and $d =$ diameter. Hence, for the same fundamental frequency, if d is doubled t is quadrupled, and the mass is increased 16 times. This large increase in mass sets a limit to the size of the diaphragm which can be used.

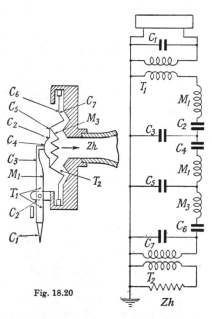

Fig. 18.20

As in the case of the recording mechanism, so also in that of the sound-box, the relation of the various parts is determined by the application of the principles of electrical transmission as developed by Maxfield and Harrison so as to give a matched impedance system providing a one-directional flow of energy. The electrical analogues to the various parts of the H.M.V. sound-box are shown in the right in fig. 18.20, which is taken from a paper by Whitaker.[*]

*Physics in Sound Recording, Institute of Physics, November, 1931; see also West, Roy. Soc. Arts Journ., Vol. 79 (1931).

14. Reproduction from Disc (Electrical).

Electrical reproduction involves the use of a pick-up, an amplifier system and a loud-speaker. In the design of these units very great advances have been made. Even where small intensities are required there are those who prefer electrical reproduction, and where large intensities are required there is no option. If price is no consideration the amplifier and loud-speaker may be designed to correct errors inherent in the pick-up. In all its various forms the method of the pick-up involves three processes: (1) the vibration of the needle generates an E.M.F. with a wave form corresponding to the wave in the groove, (2) this varying E.M.F. is amplified, and (3) a loud-speaker converts the electrical power back into sound.

Since the pick-up is only a specialized type of microphone contrived so as to transform mechanical vibrations into variations of E.M.F., any of the principles upon which the microphone is based is available for the design of the pick-up. Thus we can have (1) the electro-magnetic type, operating either as a moving coil in a magnetic field or as a moving magnet in the neighbourhood of a fixed coil. In either case the E.M.F. developed is proportional to the rate of change of magnetic flux and therefore to the velocity of movement of the armature. In (2) the resistance type, the electrical resistance of carbon is varied by the varying pressure exerted by the pick-up needle. In (3) the electrostatic type, the movement of the needle varies the capacity of a condenser. These pick-ups have a very low output and require large amplification. In (4) the piezo-electric type, the variations of pressure on a suitably chosen crystal produce the necessary variations of E.M.F. Of these four possible types we shall give further consideration to two, the electromagnetic and the piezo-electric.

The success of the moving-coil loud-speaker raised great hopes of the successful design of a moving-coil pick-up, but these hopes have not so far been realized. The scale of the apparatus is so different in the two cases that the comparison is illusory. The coil attached to the needle must be small, light and rigid, and this means a very low output requiring considerable amplification. The design of the magnets also presents difficulties. The main line of development has therefore been in the direction of the " moving-iron " form, in which an iron armature varies its position in the magnetic field by rotation about a pivot in the centre. A diagram is given in fig. 18.21. The pick-up is a miniature electric generator, consisting of a small steel armature moving with the needle and swinging in the field of a permanent magnet. Around this armature is a coil c of fine wire forming the winding, the ends being connected through the volume-control to the amplifier and loud-speaker. The volume-control is a feature possible in electrical reproduction only. No real control of loudness is possible with the mechanical gramophone.

In the crystal pick-up Rochelle salt crystals are used, as in the crystal microphone. They are strained by the movement of a pivoted stylus bar which carries the needle at its lower end. Both this pick-up and the magnetic one can be arranged to give a suitable response curve which emphasizes the bass and so makes large-amplitude recording unnecessary.

The scratch reducer is an electrical filter designed to reduce the audio-frequencies that constitute the scratch. The frequencies of this noise may be above the range of the recorder, in which case they

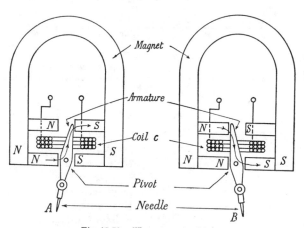

Fig. 18.21.—The magnetic pick-up

may be cut out with advantage. Such audio-frequencies as lie within the range of the recorder, however, cannot be cut out without impairing the fidelity of the reproduction.

With the earlier forms of pick-up the great disadvantage was the extremely heavy record wear. As the pick-up took far less useful work off a record than a sound-box this was somewhat surprising. It was found to be due to the fact that the needle was mainly controlled by a series of masses and springs which introduced reactive forces on the record. Attention to this point in the design has resulted already in considerable improvement, and pick-ups are now available which produce less wear on the record than an ordinary sound-box.

15. Reproduction from Film.

In reproduction from ordinary sound film the sound track passes with uniform speed through the sound-gate. As the film passes through the picture-projector in jerks, there must be some slack between the projector and the sound-gate and adjustment must be made for the fact that the sound which is being reproduced at any

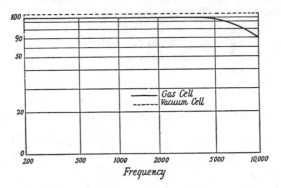

Fig. 18.22.—Frequency response for gas and vacuum cells

Reproduced by permission from Pender-MacIlwain, *Electrical Engineers' Handbook, Communication-Electronics* (John Wiley & Sons, Inc., New York)

instant is not that recorded at the side of the picture which is being projected at that instant. The exciting light must be as bright as

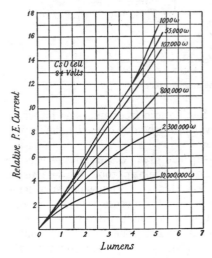

Fig. 18.23.—Current-illumination curves for gas cell with various series resistances

Reproduced by permission from Pender-MacIlwain, *Electrical Engineers' Handbook, Communication-Electronics* (John Wiley & Sons, Inc., New York).

possible and must be concentrated on a depth of film not exceeding ·002 in. This may be achieved by using a real slit of this depth or, better still, the reduced image of a larger slit, so that choking with dust may be avoided. Having passed through the film, the light now falls on the light-sensitive element. In Lauste's original patent this was a selenium cell, the variable resistance of which yielded a varying current in a suitable circuit. The disadvantages of this device were found to be (1) lag, and (2) loss of high frequencies. By the use of very thin layers these disadvantages may be very largely overcome and the method has been successfully used on a commercial scale. More commonly, however, the light-sensitive unit is a photo-electric cell.

One type of photo-electric cell which is in common use consists of a central anode surrounded by a semi-cylindrical cathode coated with the light-sensitive material. This consists as a rule of the alkali metals in some form. The sensitiveness of the pure metals, however, is far below that of the same metals when given special treatment. The most sensitive cell at present in use consists of a silver plate which is oxidized and subsequently exposed to caesium vapour. The anode is connected to a positive high tension of about 90 volts. The cell may be evacuated or may contain gas. In the former case the current consists entirely of electrons emitted from the cathode. In the gas-filled cell the introduction of a trace of argon up to a pressure of 0·5 mm. of mercury gives an amplification of the current by ionization, but this must not be allowed to produce a visible glow

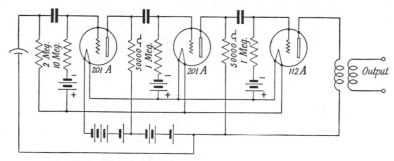

Fig. 18.24.—Three-stage amplifier for interrupted photo-electric currents

discharge or the sensitive surface will be injured. These gas-filled cells are slightly less effective at high frequencies, as can be seen from fig. 18.22. With a suitable series resistance the relation between the photo-electric current and the intensity of the light is very nearly linear, as may be seen from fig. 18.23. The connexions for a three-stage amplification are shown in fig. 18.24.

16. Loud-speakers.

Just as the microphone is the first step in the process of electrical recording, so the loud-speaker is the last step in the process of electrical reproduction, whether from disc or film. It is therefore essentially a microphone worked backwards, and almost any principle which can be used as the basis of the action of a microphone can also be made the basis of the action of a loud-speaker. The requirements for a loud-speaker are (1) same pressure amplitude of air wave for the same value of the applied force at all frequencies, (2) freedom from asymmetrical distortion, i.e. freedom from the radiation of constituent tones not present in the original sound, (3) efficient damping of impulsive sounds. A weak or missing frequency range is very noticeable even to an untrained ear, except when it lies below about 400 or above about 3000. Similarly, an abnormally loud range distorts quality very noticeably. Asymmetrical distortion gives an unnatural ring to the reproduction and plays havoc with vowel sounds.

On the whole we may divide loud-speakers into two main classes, those with horns and those without. When a vibrating diaphragm is working into free air the mechanical impedance of the diaphragm is fairly large, while that of the air in free space is very small. The transmission is very inefficient in these circumstances, and in order to obtain sufficient sound output it is necessary to use a large diaphragm and considerable amplitude. The use of these in no way improves the efficiency but, partly by resonance, secures good low-frequency radiation of sound; indeed, low frequencies are apt to be overdone in practice and the arrangement has the further disadvantage that there is little damping and crisp staccato effects are spoiled in reproduction.

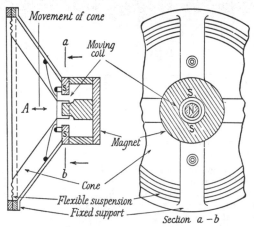

Fig. 18.25.—Moving-coil loud speaker unit

Loud-speakers based on the large diaphragm and without horns have been developed principally for home use, owing to the size and cost of large horns. For efficiency the diaphragm ought to be set in a baffle board in order to prevent circulation of air between front and back. In the case of low frequencies the baffle board must be large, the diameter of the circle or the side of the square being not less than $\lambda/2$. For reproduction down to a frequency of 100 this means a baffle board about 6 feet square.

The commonest loud-speaker using the large diaphragm and no horn is probably the cone diaphragm driven by a moving-coil mechanism, somewhat similar to that already described in connexion with the microphone (fig. 18.25). The field electromagnet is designed to produce a strong magnetic flux across an annular gap. The voice-coil, to which the variable current is led, is attached to the conical diaphragm and is free to move in the gap. The relation between the current and the driving force is linear and the force is independent of the position of the coil in the gap for considerable movement. The diaphragm may be made of stiff paper of radius 10 to 15 cm., supported round the periphery by a flexible annular strip of leather or rubber. McLachlan and Sowter * have shown that this flexible support acts as an auxiliary resonant diaphragm at low frequencies. If the cone has circular corrugations it will move as a whole at low frequencies, being effectively a single mass, but at high frequencies it will be equivalent to a series of masses connected by springs. By translating this into terms of inductances and compliances a diaphragm can be designed giving a fairly uniform response from about 90 to 3500. To obtain a uniform response over a wider range the moving coil and the cylindrical strip on which it is mounted may also be divided by corrugations giving a series of masses and compliances, and with suitable design a fairly uniform response from 80 to 10,000 can be secured.†

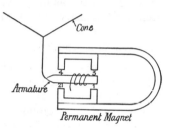

Fig. 18.26.—Magnetic loud-speaker mechanism

In the coil-driven cone speaker the efficiency is small, something like 1 per cent, but it is possible to get a fairly uniform frequency response and to radiate large power without appreciable asymmetric distortion.

The coil drive may of course be applied to a plane diaphragm, and this is done in the H.M.V. loud-speaker. The diaphragm has a diameter of about 30 in. and consists of a flat sheet of duralumin about ·002 in. thick, stretched almost to its elastic limit and bolted to stout aluminium rings round its edge. The moving coil is mounted on the diaphragm eccentrically so as to allow of modes of vibration having nodal diameters. The large diameter of the diaphragm eliminates circulation to a large extent and the arrangement gives a fairly uniform response from 50 to 5000.

The large diaphragm required in lieu of a horn may also be driven by an arrangement of the "moving-iron" type, but this is less common. If the diaphragm is itself the armature it is hardly possible to get sufficient clearance between it and the magnet to allow sufficient amplitude at low frequencies. Numerous possible alternatives have been attempted.‡ A typical arrangement is shown in fig. 18.26. The armature has to be controlled by a spring of fair stiffness to return it to its zero position after displacement, and this involves a resonance point in the audible range below which the low-frequency response is greatly curtailed.

Loud-speakers in which the diaphragm radiates direct into the

* *Phil. Mag.*, Vol. 2, p. 771 (1931).　　† Olson, *Proc. Inst. Rad. Eng.* (Jan., 1934).
‡ Hanna, *Proc. Inst. Rad. Eng.* (Aug., 1925).

air have also been designed by using the attraction between two oppositely charged plates. One of these plates is fixed, the other is the diaphragm. A fairly high polarizing E.M.F. is applied between them and this is varied by the audio-amplifier. The theory is discussed by Hanna * and by Olson and Massa.† The driving mechanism is simple and the force is applied over the whole diaphragm, but the efficiency is low and the high polarizing voltage required places this speaker at a disadvantage as compared with the other types just discussed.

Mention should also be made of the eddy-current loud-speaker devised by Hewlett,‡ of which a careful quantitative study has been made. It is capable of giving a pure tone of constant and measurable pitch and intensity over a wide range.

17. Horn Loud-speaker.

When a diaphragm is set in motion in free space the air in front of it is given a certain velocity and a pressure is set up which reacts on the diaphragm. This pressure is proportional to the air particle-velocity, and must obviously be small compared with the forces due to the inertia and stiffness of the diaphragm itself. The diaphragm, therefore, works with a very small load and so its motion is almost entirely determined by its own stiffness and mass. Its own natural frequencies will be pronounced and the useful work done by the diaphragm on the air will in general be small.

Thus the first function of the horn is to load the diaphragm. If the horn is removed the sound energy is at once reduced and the diaphragm if magnetic may increase its amplitude so that it chatters against the pole-pieces. A receiver element without a horn is like a motor without a load or like a closed oscillation circuit without an antenna. The horn is the antenna of the loud-speaker. The other functions of the horn were first discussed by Hanna and Slepian.§

The horn must be designed to meet three requirements:

(1) A given applied force acting on the diaphragm must cause the air at the throat of the horn to have a nearly uniform velocity over the whole audio-frequency range. This is secured by proper design of the air chamber above the diaphragm and the choice of a suitable area for the throat of the horn.

(2) The area of the mouth of the horn must be such that little sound energy is reflected, otherwise air-column resonances will occur.

---

* *Journ. Amer. Soc. Acoust.*, Vol. 2, p. 143 (1931).

† *Applied Acoustics*, p. 177 (Blakiston, 1934).   ‡ *Phys. Rev.*, Vol. 19, p. 52 (1922).

§ *Journ. Amer. Inst. Elect. Eng.*, Vol. 43, p. 250 (1924). See also Webster, *Proc. Nat. Acad. Sci.* (1919); Hanna, *Journ. Inst. Rad. Eng.* (Aug., 1925); Maxfield and Harrison, *Trans. Amer. Inst. Elec. Eng.* (1926); Ballantine, *Journ. Frankl. Inst.* (Jan., 1927); Hanna, *ibid.* (June, 1927); Hanna, *Trans. Amer. Inst. Elect. Eng.*, Vol. 47 (1928); Olson and Massa, *Applied Acoustics*, pp. 181 *et seq.*

(3) The law of increase of area of cross-section with length and the rate of increase must secure the maximum transmission of sound energy and a constant ratio of pressure and air velocity at the throat over the whole audio-frequency range.

We consider first of all the throat of the horn and the air chamber into which the diaphragm works; this is a coupling between the diaphragm and the air within the horn. If the air chamber has a small volume, almost all the air displaced by the movement of the diaphragm will pass into the horn. If the throat area is small compared with the diaphragm area, the air in the throat will be given a proportionately high particle-velocity, and as the pressure generated is proportional to this velocity the reaction on the diaphragm will be correspondingly high and the work done on the air correspondingly great. It is in this way that the diaphragm is loaded. The load increases the useful work done by the diaphragm and smooths out its possible resonances. It would seem that the smaller the area of the throat the more efficient the arrangement. A limit is set to this, however, by the energy used up in overcoming viscous resistance if the diameter of the throat is less than a certain value. As we shall see later, the smaller the throat the longer the horn must be, and this is an additional disadvantage.

The next point to be considered is the area of the mouth of the horn. This must be large enough to give negligible reflection in the audio-range. When waves escape from the confining walls of the horn there is an " open-end " reflection resulting in resonance if the frequency happens to be that of one of the proper tones of the horn. It was at one time thought that the chief function of the horn was to act as a resonator, but horns are now designed so as to suppress resonances. The wider the mouth of the horn the less reflection there is, and as a practical limit we may take the diameter of the open end to be at least one-quarter of the longest wave-length to be radiated.

It now remains only to decide on the shape of the horn and its rate of expansion. For reasons indicated in Chapter IV the shape chosen is the exponential and the rate of expansion is fixed by the lowest frequency which it is desired to radiate. The exponential horn is a high-pass filter and its cut-off is determined by its rate of expansion. A low cut-off means a slow rate of expansion, and as we are already committed to a small throat and a large mouth there is no escape from the long horn, the ideal length being 15 to 25 feet, as indicated in section 6, p. 119.

A practical design by McLachlan * is shown in fig. 18.27. It is a moving-coil type and the diaphragm, which is shaped to give rigidity, is within the coil. The coil and diaphragm are attached to a flexible annulus, the outer edge of which is securely clamped to the electromagnet. The obstruction H, apart from reducing the throat area and thereby increasing the air particle-velocity, acts as a

* *Nature*, Vol. 128, p. 517 (1931).

" phase equalizer ". The clearance between the diaphragm and H gradually increases with the radius. Thus during vibration the velocity of the air particles most remote from the horn is increased, so that up to quite high frequencies the pressure from all parts of the diaphragm arrives in the main column in substantially the same phase. With a long exponential horn this arrangement will give efficiencies in the neighbourhood of 30 per cent over a considerable range of frequencies as against 1 to 10 per cent for the cone loud-speaker without horn.

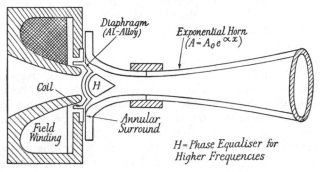

Fig. 18.27

The horn loud-speaker is thus a more efficient instrument, and when well designed it gives better reproduction, particularly in the high-frequency range. But it has one notable disadvantage. The horn required for the best reproduction is impossibly large for a private house and cannot always be accommodated in a picture-house. In these circumstances it was only to be expected that an attempt should

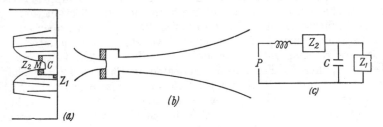

Fig. 18.28.—(a) Cross-sectional view of compound horn loud-speaker ; (b) Equivalent of the compound horn loud-speaker showing the low-frequency horn developed ; (c) Equivalent electrical circuit of the dynamical system.

be made to combine the good reproduction of the long horn with the compactness of the hornless type. Various attempts have been made to achieve this by bending the horn and even by folding it in a cabinet. In some cases very good results are obtained. A more ambitious scheme has been attempted by Olson and Massa * in their compound

* *Journ. Amer. Soc. Acoust.*, Vol. 8, p. 48 (1936).

horn loud-speaker. In view of the fact that a folded horn tends to give defective high-frequency reproduction owing to interference of the shorter waves, they add a short straight horn for high frequencies and work both horns from the same unit. The apparatus is shown in fig. 18.28. The long horn terminates in an annular opening surrounding the mouth of the short horn. The response characteristic is fairly smooth from 50 to 10,000.

18. Task of Reproduction.

Ideal reproduction involves the radiation of air waves identical in composition with those originally received within the audible range. This requires an apparatus capable of handling air waves of frequencies

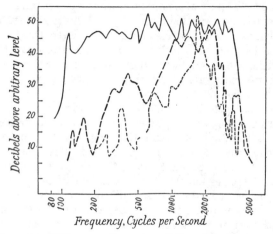

Fig. 18.29.—Gramophone 1897 - - - -   Gramophone 1912 —·—   Gramophone 1928 ——

between about 25 cycles/sec. and 25,000 cycles/sec. and of power between limits in the ratio of $10^{14} : 1$. Within this range there must be no frequency distortion; the ratio of the intensities of the component frequencies must remain unchanged. There must also be a complete absence of asymmetric or non-linear distortion; no new frequencies may appear. It is very important to know how far these requirements are achieved in actual practice, and every manufacturing firm producing gramophones or wireless sets has its methods of test. Fairly rigorous methods are discussed by Ballantine,* Fay and Hall † and Davis.‡ The kind of progress which has been made towards the ideal in the case of the gramophone is shown in fig. 18.29, taken from the paper by Whitaker already quoted. It represents the

---

* *Journ. Amer. Soc. Acoust.*, Vol. 5, p. 10 (1933).   † *Ibid.*, Vol. 5, p. 46 (1933).
‡ *Phil. Mag.*, Vol. 15, p. 309 (1933).

progress achieved by the H.M.V. gramophone between 1897 and 1928. There is a notable extension in the bass and an increasing gain in the flatness of the response curve. The corrugations in the 1928 curve, however, are still considerable, and show how far short of achieving the physical ideal the instrument then was.

Fortunately, however, we are primarily concerned with the judgment of the ear and the ear is on the whole a tolerant judge. We can narrow the range of frequencies. If we omit all frequencies below 50 cycles/sec. and all frequencies above 5000 cycles/sec. the average ear remains fairly well satisfied. This is about the range of a good domestic loud-speaker. A very good and carefully designed loud-speaker may give from about 40 cycles/sec. to 7000 cycles/sec., while an additional loud-speaker unit (compound or otherwise) will extend this range upwards to 12,000. We may also narrow down the power range. It is never desired to reproduce very loud sounds, and the power ratio covered in orchestral music does not exceed $10^8 : 1$. Even this, of course, is very considerable and it is difficult to get good reproduction at low intensities without overloading at high intensities. So far as distortion is concerned we may safely say that the distortion represented by the departure of the 1928 response curve in fig. 18.29 from a straight line would pass completely unnoticed by the great majority of listeners.

So far as the telephone engineer is concerned, of course, the only requirement is intelligibility, and this is tested by the articulation tests already referred to in section 12, p. 362. Articulation is mainly dependent on the high-frequency range; f, v and th require very high frequencies and are responsible for 50 per cent of telephone mistakes.

While good articulation is a sufficient criterion for telephone conversation, it is not sufficient for broadcasting, where a sustained talk even with perfect articulation might very soon become intolerable. Here naturalness is a further requirement both for speech and for music, and this is a demand much harder to meet. Together with those already considered, it limits us to reproduction at about the original loudness level. The ear is more sensitive to frequencies at the middle of the range than to those near the low-frequency end of the range. It follows that if while keeping the ratio of intensities for the various frequencies constant we raise the whole loudness level, the bass is emphasized, while lowering the loudness level weakens the bass. This physiological distortion can easily be tried out on any broadcasting set and explains the unnatural impression created by the speaking voice when the reproduction loudness level is too high. Apart from this particular type of physiological distortion, the production of the subjective tones referred to in section 5, p. 472, gives physiological distortion of another type.

Another requirement for naturalness is what is called " auditory perspective ". To give perfect reproduction of an orchestra in this respect would involve a separate pick-up microphone for each instrument connected to a separate loud-speaker unit suitably placed in a similar room for reproduction. Fortunately again, the ear is not so exacting as the physics of the problem might lead us to fear. The necessary conditions are discussed by Fletcher and others * and by Aigner and Strutt,† and it has been shown that it is generally sufficient to have two microphones, one on each side of the platform at the sending end, and two loud-speakers similarly placed in the reception hall.

* *Bell Syst. Tech. Journ.*, Vol. 13, p. 239 (1934).
† *Zeits. f. tech. Phys.*, Vol. 15, p. 355 (1934).

CHAPTER XIX

Acoustics of Buildings

1. Source of Sound in an Enclosure.

Clearly if we have a source of sound in an enclosure with perfectly reflecting walls there will be practically no dissipation of energy and the energy-density in the room will build itself up indefinitely so long as the source continues. If, on the other hand, the walls are completely absorbent no sound will be reflected and the situation in the enclosure will be the same as if the boundary walls were removed —the energy-density will diminish from the source outwards and the intensity will vary inversely as the square of the distance from the source. In most actual cases of buildings we have to deal with an enclosure whose walls reflect fairly copiously but show a definite amount of absorption which limits the maximum to which the loudness of a sound in the room can rise when the source is continuously sounded.

In order to develop a formula which will enable us to represent the phenomenon analytically, let us assume that the interior of the enclosure has a homogeneous distribution of energy and intensity immediately the source starts to sound.

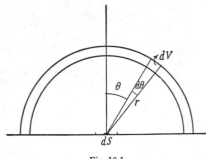

Fig. 19.1

If E is the value of the energy-density and the energy stream is the same in all directions, then in any element of volume dV the amount of energy is $E\,dV$. Of this energy the fraction moving in a direction which will ultimately pass through the element of area dS (fig. 19.1) is $(d\omega/4\pi)E\,dV$, where $d\omega$ is the angle subtended by dS at the element of volume dV.

But
$$d\omega = \frac{dS\cos\theta}{r^2},$$

536

where θ is the angle between the normal to dS and the direction from dS to dV, and r is the distance from the element of volume to the element of area.

Now with centre at dS and radii r and $r + dr$ describe two circles. From the element of area dS draw two lines intersecting these circles and making with the normal to dS angles θ and $\theta + d\theta$ respectively. If the figure is now rotated about the normal the small area lying between the two circular arcs and the two lines will sweep out an element of volume which we may take as dV.

We then have

$$dV = \text{Area} \times \text{Length of path}$$
$$= r\,d\theta\,dr \times 2\pi r \sin\theta$$
$$\therefore \ dV = 2\pi r^2 \sin\theta\,d\theta\,dr.$$

The energy in this element of volume which will ultimately fall on dS is given by

$$\frac{d\omega}{4\pi}E\,dV = \frac{E\,dS\cos\theta\,dV}{4\pi r^2}$$
$$= \frac{E\,dS\cos\theta\sin\theta\,d\theta\,dr}{2}$$
$$= \frac{E\,dS\sin 2\theta\,d\theta\,dr}{4}.$$

If we extend this to the whole shell between the two hemispheres, the energy falling on dS becomes

$$\tfrac{1}{4}E\,dS\,dr\int_{\theta=0}^{\theta=\pi/2}\sin 2\theta\,d\theta = \tfrac{1}{4}E\,dS\,dr.$$

To get the energy striking dS per second we must integrate for r from 0 to c, and we obtain

$$\tfrac{1}{4}E\,dS\int_{r=0}^{r=c}dr = \tfrac{1}{4}Ec\,dS.$$

Let a be the coefficient of absorption, i.e. the fraction of incident energy absorbed. Then the energy absorbed by the element of surface per second is $\tfrac{1}{4}Eca\,dS$.

$\therefore$ Energy absorbed in whole enclosure per second

$$= \tfrac{1}{4}Ec\int a\,dS = \tfrac{1}{4}EcA,$$

where $A = \int a\,dS$ is the total absorption of all the surfaces.

Let $\bar{E}$ be the rate of emission of the source, V the volume of the enclosure, EV the energy in the enclosure at a given instant.

Then the rate of increase of energy is $\bar{E} - \frac{1}{4} EcA$,

which is equal to $\quad\quad\quad \frac{\partial}{\partial t}(EV)$ or $V\frac{\partial E}{\partial t}$.

Put $\quad\quad\quad\quad\quad\quad\quad \frac{Ac}{4V} = b$,

then $\quad\quad\quad\quad\quad\quad V\frac{\partial E}{\partial t} = \bar{E} - bVE$,

$$\frac{bV\,dE}{\bar{E} - bVE} = b\,dt,$$

or $\quad\quad\quad \log(\bar{E} - bVE) = -bt + C.$

If we measure t from the instant when the source starts, then for $t = 0, E = 0$;

$$\therefore\ C = \log\bar{E},$$

$$\therefore\ \log\left(1 - bV\frac{E}{\bar{E}}\right) = -bt,$$

or $\quad\quad\quad\quad 1 - bV\frac{E}{\bar{E}} = e^{-bt}$

or $\quad\quad\quad E = \frac{\bar{E}}{bV}(1 - e^{-bt}) = \frac{4\bar{E}}{Ac}(1 - e^{-Act/4V}).$

For the steady state we put $t = \infty$ and the maximum energy-density $\hat{E}$ is given by

$$\hat{E} = \frac{\bar{E}}{bV} = \frac{4\bar{E}}{Ac}.$$

For decay of intensity we have as before the relation

$$\log(\bar{E} - bVE) = -bt + C.$$

In this case when $t = 0$, $E = \hat{E}$ and $\bar{E} = 0$,

$$\therefore\ \log(-bV\hat{E}) = C,$$

$$\therefore\ E = \hat{E}e^{-bt}$$

$$= \frac{4\bar{E}}{Ac}\,e^{-Act/4V}.$$

The term usually applied to the persistence of audible sound after the source has ceased to operate is *reverberation,* and the time of reverberation T is defined as the time taken for the energy-density to fall to the minimum audible value from an initial value 10^6 times as great, i.e. a range of 60 decibels.   In this case

$$\log_e \frac{\hat{E}}{E} = \log_e 10^6.$$

$$\therefore \ bT = 6 \log_e 10,$$

or
$$T = \frac{24 \log_e 10 \cdot V}{Ac} = \frac{kV}{A}.$$

For measurements in feet $k = \cdot 05$; for measurements in metres $k = \cdot 16$.

The time of reverberation is the most important criterion of the suitability of a room for public speech or for music, and this particular definition was adopted by W. C. Sabine * partly owing to the fact that the standard source of sound which he used for experimental purposes gave an initial energy level in the rooms in which he tried it of about 10^6 times the minimum audible.

In the above discussion, in which we have followed fairly closely the analysis of Franklin,† several assumptions have been tacitly or explicitly made.   These may be summarized as follows:

(1) The rate of emission of energy by the source is constant and is independent of the energy level in the enclosure.

(2) The energy distribution is uniform in all parts and the transmission of energy equal in all directions.

(3) Superposition effects may be neglected.

(4) The dissipation of energy is confined to the bounding surfaces of the enclosure and the dissipation taking place in the air in the enclosure is negligible.

(5) The coefficient of absorption of the surfaces is independent of intensity.

The relation $T = kV/A$ was first deduced experimentally in the course of his study of the acoustics of halls by W. C. Sabine, and the close agreement between his experimental results and the theoretical relation just established would seem to justify the assumptions made.

More recently M. J. O. Strutt ‡ has shown from much more general considerations that the time of reverberation as here defined is, for large enclosures, proportional to the quotient of the volume and the total absorbing power and is independent of the position of the source and the shape of the enclosure.   His assumptions do not involve a uniform distribution of the energy in the steady state, but they do involve a *large* enclosure, i.e. one for which the frequency of

---

* *Collected Papers on Acoustics* (Harvard Univ. Press, 1922).
† *Phys. Rev.*, Vol. 16, p. 372 (1903).   ‡ *Phil. Mag.*, Vol. 8, p. 236 (1929).

the source is much higher than the lowest of the resonance frequencies of the enclosure, and consequently one in which the linear dimensions are large compared with the wave-length of the sound.

2. Decay of Sound Energy of Free Vibrations in an Enclosure.

The air in any enclosure has a large number of possible modes of vibration, corresponding to the partial tones which it would emit if vibrating freely.

Thomas Young * calls attention to these partial tones in the following passage:

" When the walls of a passage, or of an unfurnished room, are smooth and perfectly parallel any explosion, or a stamping with the foot, communicates an impression to the air, which is reflected from one wall to the other, and from the second again towards the ear, nearly in the same direction with the primitive impulse. This takes place as frequently in a second, as double the breadth of the passage is contained in 1130 ft.; and the ear receives a perception of a musical sound, thus determined in its pitch by the breadth of the passage. On making the experiment, the result will be found accurately to agree with this explanation. If the sound is predetermined, and the frequency of vibrations such as that each pulse, when doubly reflected, may coincide with the subsequent pulse proceeding directly from the sounding body, the intensity of the sound will be much increased by the reflection; and also, in a less degree, if the reflected pulse coincides with the next but one, the next but two or more, of the direct pulses. The appropriate notes of a room may readily be discovered by singing the scale in it; and they will be found to depend on the proportion of its length or breadth to 1130 feet."

In general when a source is sounding in the enclosure the vibrations are forced and the air is not thrown into resonant vibration. Nevertheless, it seems at least possible that in this case the air reverts to free vibration when the source ceases to sound, and that the reverberation which follows the stopping of the source is the decay of these free vibrations. This seems most probable if the value of a, the absorption coefficient, is small.

For a rectangular room bounded by reflecting surfaces whose linear dimensions are l_1, l_2, l_3 the possible frequencies for free vibrations are given by

$$f = \frac{c}{2}\left(\frac{p^2}{l_1{}^2} + \frac{q^2}{l_2{}^2} + \frac{r^2}{l_3{}^2}\right)^{\frac{1}{2}},$$

in which c is the velocity of sound and p, q, r are integers.

If we cover two pairs of opposite faces with complete absorbent we have essentially a one-dimensional system and

$$f = \frac{cp}{2l_1},$$

* *Works*, edited by Peacock, Vol. I, p. 73 (1855).

which gives the possible frequencies for an organ pipe closed (or open) at both ends.

Knudsen * calculated the first thirty-four possible values of f for a room 8 ft. × 8 ft. × 9·5 ft., assuming the velocity of sound to be 1125 ft. per sec., and found the values to lie between 59·1 cycles/sec. and 231·4 cycles/sec. A constant-output source whose frequency could be varied between these limits was operated in the room and the resulting intensity estimated (1) by oscillograph, (2) by aural observation made just outside the door. Every frequency predicted by theory was verified by experiment. When a note of frequency corresponding to the lowest frequency mode ($p = 1$, $q = r = 0$) was sounded, exploration of the air in the room by moving the oscillograph from point to point gave clear evidence of the existence of the corresponding mode of vibration. Observations made with the oscillograph during decay were most instructive. The predominant frequency in the record of the decaying sound was not the frequency of the source which had just ceased but the nearest frequency in the calculated series corresponding to possible modes of vibration. Further, the oscillograph record often showed beats, and these could always be identified as due to two neighbouring members of the series of free vibrations. It is clear, therefore, that the decay of free vibrations is an important element in the phenomenon of reverberation.

3. Discontinuous Decay of Sound Energy in an Enclosure.

The decay of sound energy in an enclosure with partially absorbing boundaries has been subjected to a fundamentally different treatment by Schuster and Waetzmann,† and by Eyring.‡ The method can be

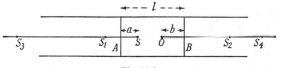

Fig. 19.2

best understood by considering each reflected beam of sound as a direct beam coming from the image of the source as formed by reflection at the surface.

To simplify matters assume the enclosure to be a tube AB with partially absorbing ends and perfectly reflecting sides. Let the source be situated at S (fig. 19.2) and the point of observation at O. When the source is first started O receives no sound until the instant $(l - a - b)/c$,

* *Journ. Amer. Soc. Acoust.*, Vol. 4, p. 20 (1932).

† *Ann. d. Physik*, Vol. 5, p. 671 (1929).

‡ *Journ. Amer. Soc. Acoust.*, Vol. 1, p. 217 (1930).

when it receives the direct beam from S. The intensity at O remains constant at this value until it receives the reflected beam from A at the instant $(l + a - b)/c$, when the intensity suddenly increases. The new beam has an intensity $I(1 - a)$. Presently it receives the beam reflected from B at the instant $(l + b - a)/c$, and this beam also has an intensity $I(1 - a)$, A and B being assumed to have the same coefficient of absorption a. The result is the same as if the source, its image in A and its image in B had all started simultaneously, the sound reaching O from the two images in the order of their remoteness. Second reflections must, however, be taken into account. S_1, the image of S in A, will produce an image S_4 in B and S_2, the image of S in B, will produce an image S_3 in A. Whereas S_1 and S_2 have intensities $I(1 - a)$, the images S_3 and S_4 have intensities $I(1 - a)^2$. Subsequent reflections give more remote images of further diminished intensity.

During decay the converse process takes place. When the source of sound is stopped all the images are simultaneously extinguished, but while the direct beam from the source stops almost at once, sound from the images continues to reach O, the contributors of the various sources being cut off again in order of the remoteness of the image.

By applying this method to an enclosure of any shape Eyring has obtained the formula

$$T = \frac{kV}{-S \log_e (1 - \bar{a})}$$

for the time of reverberation as defined by Sabine. In this formula k has the same value as in the formula developed by Franklin, V is as before the volume of the enclosure, S is the total area of the boundary walls, and $\bar{a}$ is the average coefficient of absorption defined by the relation

$$\bar{a} = \frac{a_1 s_1 + a_2 s_2 + a_3 s_3 + \cdots}{s_1 + s_2 + s_3 + \cdots},$$

where a_1 is the coefficient of absorption of the area s_1, a_2 that of the area s_2, and so on.

Thus
$$\bar{a} = \frac{\Sigma as}{\Sigma s} = \frac{\Sigma as}{S}.$$

These two formulæ

$$T = \frac{kV}{A} = \frac{kV}{\Sigma as} \text{ (Franklin)},$$

and
$$T = \frac{kV}{-S \log_e (1 - \bar{a})} \text{ (Eyring)},$$

look as fundamentally different as the methods by which they are derived. It is worth while, however, to observe that if $\bar{a}$ is small

$$\log_e (1 - \bar{a}) = -\bar{a}$$

and the second formula reduces to

$$T = \frac{kV}{S\bar{a}} = \frac{kV}{\Sigma aS} = \frac{kV}{A},$$

which is identical with the first.

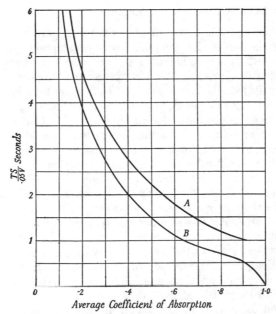

Fig. 19.3.—Comparison of reverberation formulæ: *A* Sabine; *B* Eyring

Where $\bar{a}$ is large, however, the two formulæ lead to different values of T, and in this case there is no doubt that the second formula is to be preferred. If, for instance, the walls of the enclosure are completely absorbent, $\bar{a} = 1$ and the formulæ reduce to

$$T = \frac{kV}{S} \quad \text{(Franklin)},$$

$$T = 0 \quad \text{(Eyring)}.$$

In this case since there is no reflection there is no reverberation, and the second formula gives the correct result. Fig. 19.3 gives a comparison of the values of T for various values of $\bar{a}$ calculated by the two formulæ, from which it appears that the difference is about 10 per cent for $\bar{a} = 0.2$ and about 30 per cent for $\bar{a} = 0.4$.

A further modification of Eyring's formula is suggested by Millington.* This relationship is

$$T = - \frac{0.05V}{\Sigma S_1 \log_e(1 - a_1)}$$

where S_1 and a_1 are corresponding values of area and coefficient of absorption. For small values of a this modified formula, like the Eyring formula, approximates to the simpler formula used by Sabine, and when a is large it fits the experimental values well.

4. Time of Reverberation for an Enclosure.

Before the analysis given in the preceding paragraphs had been worked out the subject had acquired very great practical importance. The design of rooms and halls for public speech or music had, until 1900, no scientific basis; in fact, the problems involved had not even been clearly stated. It was recognized that some buildings were good and some bad, but few people had ever asked themselves the question " In what does this goodness essentially consist?" That it consists, for public speech at least, in avoiding a reverberation which is too protracted seems first to have been clearly stated by Dr. D. B. Reid.† He says: "Any difficulty in the communication of sound in large rooms arises generally from the interruption of sound produced by a prolonged reverberation." Clearly if the reverberation of a syllable persists so as to prolong the sound while several successive syllables are pronounced, intelligibility will suffer and acoustic conditions will be bad.

The first systematic investigation of the problem of good hearing was undertaken by W. C. Sabine ‡ at Harvard when he was consulted about the Fogg Art Museum of that university. Here the acoustic conditions were so bad that a speaker could hardly make himself intelligible. A rough test showed that when it was empty, the time of reverberation for a syllable spoken in an ordinary tone of voice was about $5\frac{1}{2}$ sec., a period of time during which the original syllable would have been followed by some twelve or fifteen others. When the hall was filled with an audience the conditions were much improved, but still far from satisfactory. The first requirement was obviously to reduce the time of reverberation. In order to get accurate results it was necessary to work with a definite source of sound and to measure accurately the time of reverberation of the hall under different conditions. The source of sound chosen was an organ pipe of the Gemshorn Stop with a frequency of 512. The wind, supplied from a double tank, was turned on and off by an electropneumatic valve. The time of reverberation was at first measured by a stop-watch which was started at the instant when the source of sound ceased to act and stopped at the instant when the sound ceased to be audible. It might

* *Journ. Amer. Soc. Acoust.*, Vol. 4, p. 69 (1932).   † *British Association Report* (1835).
‡ Loc. cit.

reasonably be objected that the latter instant is not a very definite one, but the consistency of the observations by the same observers at different times and by different observers at the same time is a sufficient answer to this objection. A more accurate method was adopted later, when the instant at which the air supply to the pipe was cut off was electrically recorded on a chronometer and the only duty of the observer was to press the key when the sound ceased to be audible.

Experiments were first made on the effect of introducing cushions from a neighbouring lecture room. When the length x of cushions introduced was plotted against the reciprocal of the time of reverberation the resulting graph was a straight line intercepting the x-axis at -146. This point corresponds to an infinite time of reverberation and therefore no absorption, and suggests that the absorption of all the surfaces originally present in the room was equivalent to 146 metres of cushion. This gives us the empirical relation

$$AT = K,$$

where A is the total absorption, T the time of reverberation, and K a constant for the room.

Experiments in other rooms of different volumes showed that for each room a similar relationship held, A being measured in terms of the same cushions. On comparison of the constant K with the volume V for each room it was found that the ratio K/V was approximately constant. We thus have, dividing both sides by V,

$$\frac{AT}{V} = \frac{K}{V} = k,$$

where k is now a constant applicable to all the rooms. That is,

$$T = \frac{kV}{A},$$

which is of the same form as the equation already deduced by theoretical treatment.

The great weakness in this empirical relation is that A is measured in terms of length of a particular type of cushion, a purely arbitrary unit. Sabine got over this difficulty by treating open window as a complete absorber and rating the cushions in terms of this unit by finding what area of open window produced the same diminution in the time of reverberation as so many metres of cushions. Taking A in terms of this unit he obtained the relationship

$$T = \frac{\cdot 171V}{A} \text{ (in metres)},$$

$$T = \frac{\cdot 053V}{A} \text{ (in feet)},$$

equations which compare very closely indeed with those obtained in
the earlier sections.

Typical graphs showing these results are given in fig. 19.4. On the
left we have I/I_0 plotted against t, where I is the intensity at any
instant and I_0 is the minimum audible intensity. The figure is drawn
for the case where

$$\hat{I} = \tfrac{1}{4}c\hat{E} = \frac{\bar{E}}{A} = 10I_0.$$

The initial part of the curve represents the growth equation

$$\frac{I}{I_0} = 10(1 - e^{-Act/4V}).$$

The second part of the curve represents the decay equation

$$\frac{I}{I_0} = 10\,e^{-Act/4V}.$$

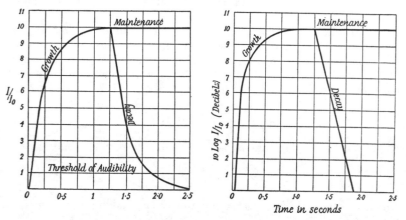

Fig. 19.4.—Growth and decay of sound intensity in an enclosure

The maximum intensity attained is for convenience the maximum
used by Sabine multiplied by 10^{-5}.

In the right-hand diagram we have $10 \log I/I_0$, i.e. the intensity level,
plotted against t.

The intensity level corresponding to the minimum audible now
becomes the new zero, and it is reached at the same instant by
the growth curve and again by the decay curve as the threshold of
audibility is by the two curves in the left-hand diagram.

5. Coefficients of Absorption.

The absorption of sound is essentially the dissipation of the sound energy into heat, and in so far as it is affected by a bounding surface it is mainly due to one of two causes, porosity and flexural vibrations. The theory of the action of pores has been discussed by Rayleigh * and Paris.† It accounts for the high coefficient of felt, carpets, rugs, &c., and a number of proprietary products now manufactured in large quantities. The absorption coefficient of any given material increases with the thickness used, up to a certain limiting value. The marked difference which is found in the coefficient for painted and for unpainted brick at once shows the importance of porosity.

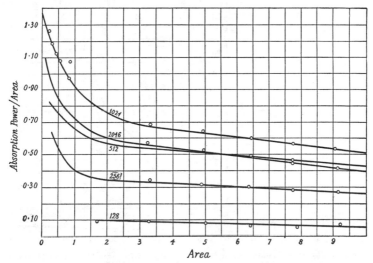

Fig. 19.5.—The numbers give the frequencies of the test tones

In the case of flexible materials not rigidly mounted the material is of course set in vibration and the damping forces called into play dissipate the sound energy.

A comparison of the results of measurements brings out two important points. In the first place, there is a marked and consistent difference between the coefficients obtained by the stationary-wave methods and those obtained by the reverberation-chamber methods. Generally speaking the reverberation coefficient is greater than the stationary-wave coefficient, and the discrepancy is greater at low frequencies than at high. In the second place, the coefficient is greater when measured for small samples than when measured for large ones. This effect again is more marked for sources of high pitch than for those of low pitch. The results for a highly absorbent felt are shown in fig. 19.5.

* *Phil. Mag.*, Vol. 39, p. 225 (1920).   † *Proc. Roy. Soc.*, A, Vol. 115, p. 407 (1927).

It will be noticed that for high frequencies the coefficient is sometimes considerably greater than unity. The explanation of these facts is fairly obvious. The edges screen the centre of the area, and sound waves approaching the centre nearly tangentially are largely absorbed in the marginal regions of the specimen. Further, the dimensions of the sample are small compared with the wave-length and diffraction effects come in.

If, for instance, we had a small absorbent patch on the walls of the test chamber and perfectly reflecting walls elsewhere, dissipation

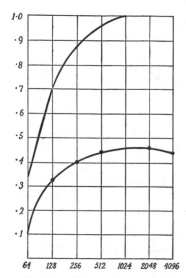

Fig. 19.6.—Absorption coefficient for an audience; lower curve per person, upper curve per sq. metre.

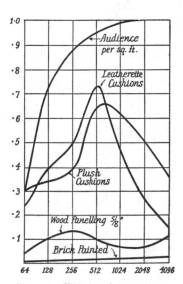

Fig. 19.7.—Variation of absorption coefficients with pitch

would take place only at the patch and energy would flow toward the absorbent area from all parts of the room. The net energy flux incident upon the absorbing surface would be greater than that toward an equal non-absorbing area, and this difference would be greater the greater the absorptivity and the smaller the area.

The coefficient of absorption varies markedly with frequency. As a rule it increases with increasing frequency, but if the coefficient is plotted against frequency every kind of curve can be obtained by selection from the large number of materials for which measurements have been made. Some absorb most strongly in the region of low frequency; some absorb most strongly in the region of high frequency: some show a maximum with diminution for lower and higher pitch; some are claimed to be " straight-line absorbents ", which means that they absorb equally strongly throughout the range of audible frequencies.

These variations of absorbing power have important consequences for music. We may choose an absorbent effective in regions of high pitch which will increase the relative importance of fundamentals and conduce to purity of tone. Or we may choose one absorbing mainly at low frequencies, which will tend to emphasize high partials and increase brilliance of tone. An audience tends to disturb the balance of an orchestra or choir by absorbing mainly above middle pitch, and the very different acoustic conditions obtaining at rehearsals in any empty hall and in a "full house" account for some unexpected failures and a few unexpected successes.

In some cases it is obviously necessary that we should measure the absorption of individual objects instead of area. For instance, the audience is known to be one of the most important elements in the acoustic problem. Rooms which are impossible owing to reverberation when empty are at least tolerable when full. The measurement in this case presents no new difficulty. The time of reverberation of a room may be measured with an audience and closed windows. The audience is then cleared and windows opened until the same time of reverberation is attained. This gives a not very flattering equivalence between

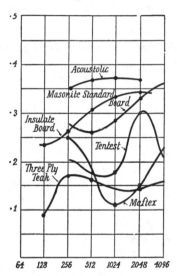

Fig. 19.8.—Variation of absorption coefficients with pitch

persons and open window space. Sabine's early figures suggested 4·7 sq. ft. of open window per person, and in practical work this figure is still largely used, although more recent determinations suggest that this value is rather high. Chrisler * gives 4·1 as the value for a frequency of 512. An audience may of course also be rated per unit of area, and both methods are shown in fig. 19.6 (in square metre units instead of square feet, from W. C. Sabine's early results). A selection of typical absorption curves is shown in fig. 19.7. There has been tremendous activity in the production of patent absorbing materials, and the results for some of these are shown in fig. 19.8. Great progress has been made since the early days when felt was almost the only suitable material available. More modern materials are cheaper, cleaner, less inflammable and equally effective.

* *Journ. Amer. Soc. Acoust.*, Vol. 2, p. 127 (1930).

From what has already been said it will be obvious that a coefficient of absorption is not an exactly determined quantity. The method of measurement, the size of the sample, the method of mounting, &c., all affect the result and exact agreement will not be attainable until it is possible to prescribe these conditions with precision. Fortunately, however, for practical purposes the approximate value is all that is required, and this can be interpreted in the light of the information available as to the conditions of measurement.

It is commonly assumed that absorption takes place only at the surfaces, but it has been shown that for moist air and high frequencies considerable absorption takes place in the air itself (see Chapter V, p. 130).

6. Measurement of Coefficients of Absorption.

Reference has already been made in Chapter VIII (p. 205) to the stationary-wave method of measuring absorption coefficients. As a method it is open to one serious criticism—it measures the coefficient of absorption for normal incidence only, though in actual position in a room the absorbent surface is exposed to beams of sound incident at all possible angles. It is also open to the objection that the material can be used only in small samples, and that it is almost impossible to mount the sample in conditions similar to those occurring when the material is mounted in bulk. In any case, what is measured is the ratio of pressure amplitudes or velocity amplitudes in the direct and reflected wave trains respectively.

The measurement can be approached in a way which links it up much more directly to reverberation theory. We have already (p. 538) derived the relation

$$V \frac{\partial E}{\partial t} = \bar{E} - \tfrac{1}{4} EcA \ ;$$

$$\therefore \text{ if } \bar{E} = 0, \ \frac{\partial E}{\partial t} = - \frac{EcA}{4V}.$$

It has also been shown that for the decay of sound in a room after the source has been cut off we may write

$$E = \hat{E} \, e^{-(Ac/4V)t},$$

where E is the energy-density (supposed uniform) in the room t sec. after the source has been cut off. Further, $\hat{E} = 4\bar{E}/Ac$.

Suppose we have two sources whose outputs are $\bar{E}$ and $\bar{E}'$ respectively, giving maximum energy-densities of $\hat{E}$ and $\hat{E}'$ respectively. Let E_0 be the minimum audible energy-density and T and T' the respective times of decay to the threshold of audibility. Then

$$E_0 = \hat{E}e^{-bT}, \ E_0 = \hat{E}'e^{-bT'},$$

where
$$b = \frac{Ac}{4V};$$

$$\therefore \frac{\hat{E}'}{\hat{E}} = e^{b(T' - T)},$$

or
$$\log \hat{E}' - \log \hat{E} = \frac{Ac}{4V}(T' - T),$$

$$\therefore A = \frac{4V}{c} \frac{\log \hat{E}' - \log \hat{E}}{T' - T}.$$

Test chambers for measurements of absorbing power have to be very carefully constructed. They must exclude all extraneous sound; they must have a small absorbing power so as to give a long time of reverberation; they must be large enough to contain considerable samples of absorbing material. Sabine's method of calibrating his chamber was to take four organ pipes as nearly identical as possible, and find the value of T for one, two, three and four pipes respectively, combining the pipes in every possible way so as to eliminate possible differences. If $\hat{E}'$ is the initial intensity produced by n pipes, $\hat{E}$ the intensity produced by one pipe, T_n the time of reverberation for n pipes, and T_1 the time of reverberation for one pipe, then

$$A = \frac{4V}{c} \frac{\log n}{T_n - T_1}.$$

Plotting $\log n$ against $T_n - T_1$ gives a straight line, and the slope of this line multiplied by $4V/c$ gives the absorption of the chamber. As the absorption varies with the frequency, this must be done for several frequencies, and the method adopted by P. E. Sabine [*] at the Riverbank Laboratories used the frequencies 128, 256, 512, 1024, 2048, 4096.

Taking the equation for a single source, we have

$$\frac{\hat{E}}{E_0} = e^{bT_1}.$$

But
$$\hat{E} = \frac{4\bar{E}}{Ac},$$

$$\therefore \frac{4\bar{E}}{AcE_0} = e^{bT_1},$$

or
$$\log \frac{4\bar{E}}{AcE_0} = \frac{AcT_1}{4V},$$

$$\therefore T_1 = \frac{4V}{Ac} \log \frac{4\bar{E}}{AcE_0}.$$

[*] *Journ. Frankl. Inst.*, Vol. 207, p. 341 (1929).

This equation enables us to determine $\bar{E}/E_0$ for this particular source and observer. The equation then enables us to plot time of reverberation against absorbing power, and hence from the time of reverberation to calculate the coefficient of absorption of any material placed in the chamber.

The defects of the method are fairly obvious, but it yields unexpectedly good and consistent results. The measurement of the time of reverberation is a difficult one to make and requires absolute silence if the end-point is to be exactly marked. Further, as T is at the best small, great accuracy is impossible. Finally, it is open to the disadvantage of subjectivity with its inevitable uncertainty of judgment and possible variation of sensitiveness.

A variation of the experimental method which has certain advantages is the substitution of a loud-speaker of variable output for the series of organ pipes. For a good-quality moving-coil loud-speaker

$$\bar{E} = kC^2,$$

where $\bar{E}$ is the sound output, C is the input alternating current, and k is a constant. We therefore have

$$A = \frac{4V}{c} \left(\frac{\log C_1{}^2 - \log C_2{}^2}{T_1 - T_2} \right).$$

This gives a much wider range of initial intensity.

With a view to eliminating uncertainties involved in judgments by ear several modifications of the method have been adopted. Wente and Bedell * have used a relay and chronograph. In effect this involves the use of a microphone, the amplified current from which attracts an armature. When the current falls below a certain value the armature is released and a record made on a revolving drum. The paper on the drum can thus be made to give a record of the time taken to fall from the initial value to another set by the sensitiveness of the armature. In this experiment it is this second value that is varied. Instead of a variable initial intensity produced by from one to four pipes and a constant final intensity fixed by the threshold of audibility, we have a fixed initial intensity and a variable final intensity produced by varying the sensitiveness of the instrument. Other automatic methods dispensing with the ear have been used by Norris,† Hunt ‡ and others.

Measurements have also been made by using an oscillograph to record the actual decay of sound in a room. The fluctuations of intensity make it difficult to obtain exact data, but by taking special precautions Chrisler and Snyder § obtained curves of decay which

---

* *Journ. Amer. Soc. Acoust.*, Vol. 1, p. 422 (1930).
† *Journ. Amer. Soc. Acoust.*, Vol. 3, p. 361 (1932).   ‡ *Ibid.*, Vol. 5, p. 127 (1933).
§ *Bur. Stands. Journ. Res.*, Vol. 5, p. 957 (1930).

proved to be logarithmic and used these to·check the results obtained by ear. Fig. 19.9 shows how close the values of A lie for the various frequencies from 128 to 4096.

It is possible, of course, to determine A by quite a different relationship. We may use a source of known output and measure the maximum energy-density in the enclosure when the source is sounding. Since

$$\hat{E} = \frac{4\bar{E}}{Ac},$$

$$A = \frac{c\hat{E}}{4\bar{E}}.$$

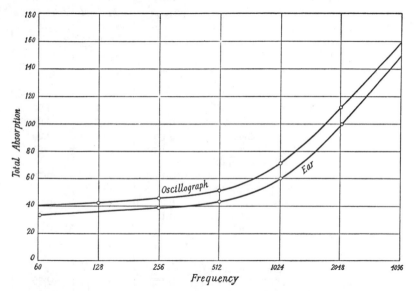

Fig. 19.9.—Comparison of absorption measurements by ear and by oscillograph

Now add the new absorbent A' and we shall get a new value $\hat{E}'$ for the maximum energy-density. Then

$$A + A' = \frac{c\hat{E}'}{4\bar{E}},$$

$$\therefore \ A' = A\left(\frac{\hat{E}'}{\hat{E}} - 1\right).$$

$\hat{E}'/\hat{E}$ is calculated from $\hat{I}'/\hat{I}$, the ratio of the intensities, which can be measured by any of the methods outlined in Chapter XI. This method of determining A' has the advantage of eliminating the ear,

TABLE X

Absorption coefficients of various Materials

Material	Frequencies in cycles/sec.		
	250	500	1000–2000
Ordinary wall and ceiling surfaces:			
Lime plaster	0·02–0·03	0·03–0·04	0·03
Hard plaster	0·01–0·02	0·01–0·02	0·02–0·03
Unpainted brick	0·03	0·03	0·05
Wood-panelling, 3-ply	0·01–0·02	0·01–0·02	0·01–0·02
Curtains:			
Cretonne	—	0·15	—
Medium weight	—	0·2–0·4	—
Heavy, in folds	—	0·5–1·0	—
Floor coverings:			
Wood block in mastic	0·03	0·06	0·10
Cork carpet, ¼ in. thick	0·03	0·07	0·20
Porous rubber sheet, ¼ in. thick ..	0·05	0·05	0·20
Axminster carpet, ¼ in. thick ..	0·05	0·10	0·35
„ „ on ¼ in. felt under-lay	0·15	0·40	0·65
„ „ on ¼ in. rubber underlay ..	0·05	0·20	0·45
Turkey carpet, ½ in. thick	0·10	0·25	0·30
„ „ on ½ in. felt underlay	0·30	0·50	0·65
Special absorbents:			
Acoustic plasters (½ in. to 1 in. thick) on stone	0·15	0·25	0·30
Fibre boards, plain, ½ in. thick, on battens	0·30–0·40	0·30–0·35	0·25–0·35
Medium efficiency tiles, on battens ..	0·40	0·40	0·50
High efficiency tiles, with perforated surfaces, on battens	0·50	0·80	0·85
Acoustic felts, 1 in. thick, perforated covers on hard surface	0·30	0·70	0·80
Acoustic felts, ½ in. thick, on battens	0·25	0·45	0·70
Wood wool-cement board, 1 in. thick, on battens	0·30	0·60	0·70
Sprayed asbestos, 1 in. thick ..	0·50–0·60	0·65–0·75	0·60–0·75
Slag wool or glass silk about 2 in. thick, on battens	0·70	0·85	0·90
Cabot quilt, 3-ply, 2 layers	0·40	0·70	0·70

Material	Frequencies in cycles/sec.		
	250	500	1000–2000
Individual objects in open window units (ft.):			
Audience per person	4·3	4·7	5·0
Chairs, bent ash	0·16	0·17	0·21
Cushions, hair, 2¾ sq. ft. under canvas and plush	1·1	1·8	1·5

but it has the same disadvantages as all instrumental methods of determining the *average* sound intensity throughout a volume.

Table X exhibits the results of measurements, mostly based on work done at the National Physical Laboratory. These results are in fair agreement with similar figures from other laboratories, but methods of measurement must be more carefully standardized before close agreement can be expected.*

If comparative measurements are sufficient they can be very quickly and accurately made by a method † used by the Electro-acoustical Engineering Co. of America. The reverberation chamber with the usual highly reflecting walls is built with a recessed cavity about 4 ft. wide, 6 ft. deep, and extending the whole height of the chamber. Over the front of this cavity there slides vertically a solid steel shutter made of 2-in. planks covered with ½-in. polished steel plates. The cavity is filled with absorbing material, loosely packed near the shutter and more densely packed near the wall remote from the opening, so as to form an almost complete absorber for all wavelengths. A sample of the material is introduced into the room with the shutter closed and the intensity of sound at the microphone is read on the amplifier output meter. After the reading is noted the sample is removed and the shutter is opened until the meter reading is the same as with the sample present. If the sample is always of a standard size it is obvious that the shutter can be graduated so as to read percentage absorption direct. In this method it is not necessary to know the total absorption of the chamber. Here again we are faced with the difficulty of determining the average intensity in the chamber and therefore of making that as uniform as possible.

The highly reflecting walls produce a very marked and very complicated superposition pattern depending on the position of the source. The intensity therefore varies from point to point in a very marked way. Not only so, but the superposition pattern varies with wavelength and is different for each partial tone present. As the absorption

* See Willig, *Journ. Amer. Soc. Acoust.*, Vol. 10, p. 293 (1939).
† Olson and Massa, *Applied Acoustics*, p. 332.

varies with pitch the relative importance of these partials varies progressively. Finally, the sporadic changes in intensity which occur at any one point during the decay of sound in a room are very marked and make the regular decay curve difficult to disentangle. To eliminate these difficulties the following precautions are adopted: (a) observations are made at a number of points, (b) a large slowly revolving steel mirror is used to produce a cyclic change of the interference pattern, (c) the source is a " warble " tone, the frequency varying cyclically between two limiting frequencies, (d) the source is made to revolve slowly.*

In reverberation measurements it is usual to assume that there is no reaction on the source, i.e. that its output is independent of its position and of the absorption in the room. Under the conditions outlined above this is probably true. It is further assumed that absorption is a surface effect and not a volume effect. That this is not strictly true has been shown by Knudsen.† It appears that for comparatively low frequencies the volume absorption is negligible, but that for frequencies over 2000 it depends on relative humidity.

7. Time of Reverberation and Acoustic Design.

We are now equipped with the data required to calculate the time of reverberation as defined by either of the two formulæ already given. As most buildings are relatively " live ", i.e. have a small average coefficient of absorption, the simpler formula of W. C. Sabine gives us a sufficiently close approximation. A typical calculation by Bagenal ‡ for Queen's Hall, London, is shown below.

The volume referred to is of course the air volume contained by all the bounding surfaces of the room and is calculated from the internal dimensions. The volume per seat is shown because of its value as an index of acoustic conditions. The larger this figure the greater the time of reverberation tends to be and the less satisfactory the acoustic conditions. The first two columns in the above table give the nature of the surface; the third column gives the area in square feet in the case of surfaces or the number in the case of chairs or persons; column 4 gives the coefficient of absorption; column 5 is the product of 3 and 4 and gives the number of " open window units " of absorption (O.W.U.). Column 6 gives any reason known for adjusting the figures in column 5; and column 7 gives the net value of the absorption. It will be noted that, allowing 10 per cent for the shading of the floor by chairs and 25 per cent for the sound transmitted by the glass, the total permanent absorption is 5684. Adding the orchestra and choir, we get rehearsal conditions, 7282. For the audience we subtract the absorption per seat from the absorption per person and get total absorption with one-third of the seats full, 9577, and with all seats full, 14,170. From these values of the total absorption the corresponding times of reverberation are calculated.

* Knudsen, *Phil. Mag.*, Vol. 5, p. 1240 (1928).
† *Journ. Amer. Soc. Acoust.*, Vol. 3, p. 126 (1931).
‡ Bagenal and A. Wood, *Planning for Good Acoustics*, p. 112 (Methuen, 1931).

QUEEN'S HALL

Volume 422,000 c. ft. Seating 2026. Volume per seat audience 208 c. ft.

Absorbent	Remarks	Area (sq. ft.) or Number	Coefficient	Absorption O.W.U.	Adjustment	Net Absorption O.W.U.
Hard plaster	Early fibrous on wood	19,400	0·025	485	—	485
Glass	Responds to low tones	1,000	0·027	27	Add 25 per cent for transmission	34
Vents	—	180	0·5	90	—	90
Wood panelling	Responds to middle and upper middle tones	5,080	0·1	508	—	508
Dado linings	Corrugated fibre	1,500	0·1	150	—	150
Oil-painted canvas over wood	Muffled middle tone	1,200	0·12	144	—	144
Wood floor and staging	—	11,250	0·06	675	Less 10 per cent for shading	608
Carpeting	Large part on felt mat	4,790	0·2	958	,,	863
Linoleum on wood	Balcony only	3,280	0·03	98	,,	89
Organ case	Pipes, wood, small curtains	1,000	0·08	80	—	80
Upholstered seats	Horsehair and cloth half backs, 1200 with arm pads	2,026	Average 1·3 per seat	2633	—	2633
				Total permanent absorption, 5684		
Average orchestra	On wooden chairs	90	Per person 4·7	423	—	423
Average choir	On staging	250	4·7	1175	—	1175
Audience full	Coefficient 4·7 — 1·3	2026	3·4	6888	—	6888
Audience one-third	,,	675	3·4	2295	—	2295

Time of reverberation:

Hall empty	(·05 × 422,000)/5684	= 3·7 sec.
Rehearsal conditions	(·05 × 422,000)/7282	= 2·9 sec.
One-third audience	(·05 × 422,000)/9577	= 2·2 sec.
Full audience, choir and orchestra	(·05 × 422,000)/14,170	= 1·5 sec.

Clearly the formula puts us in a position to correct a room in which the reverberation is considered excessive by the introduction of an appropriate amount of absorbent applied to walls or ceiling. The procedure will be clear from an actual case, that of the University Examination Hall at Cambridge. Built originally to accommodate candidates in University Examinations, it came to be used also for lectures, especially in connexion with the Summer Schools held under the auspices of the Extra-mural Board. With large audiences conditions were quite tolerable, but with small or medium audiences the conditions were very difficult, especially for foreign students. The following table indicates how the absorption of the various surfaces was calculated.

REVERBERATION BEFORE CORRECTION

Vol. 162,000 c. ft. Seating 1000. Vol. per seat 162 c. ft.

Absorbent	Remarks	Area (sq. ft.) or Number	Co-efficient	Units of Absorption O.W.U.	Adjustment	Net No. of Units of Absorption O.W.U.
Hard plaster ceiling and part walls	Lime plaster distempered	10,400	0·025	260	—	260
Glass	—	1,260	0·027	34	—	34
Wood panelling	Oil painted	3,370	0·06	202	—	202
Floor	Cork	5,400	0·04	216	Less 10 per cent for shading	195
Wood chairs	—	1,000	0·1 per chair	100	—	100
				Total permanent absorption		791
Full audience	On wood chairs	1,000	4·7 less 0·1=4·6	4600	—	4600
Half audience	,,	500	,,	2300	—	2300

In this case the volume of the hall is 162,000 c. ft., and if we calculate t, the time of reverberation for full audience and half audience from the simple formula already given,

$$t = 0·05 \ V/A,$$

we get

$$t \text{ for full audience} \quad 1·5 \text{ sec.};$$
$$t \text{ for half audience} \quad 2·6 \text{ sec.}$$

Thus the time of reverberation was satisfactory for a full audience but excessive for a half audience, and this accounted for the numerous complaints received when the hall was used as a lecture-room, especially with small audiences.

A wall treatment was recommended rather than a ceiling treatment, for reasons of cost. The available wall area above the wood panelling of the room amounted to 2040 sq. ft., and on this was placed, in the form of large panels, two layers of triple-ply Cabot quilt, screened with canvas and distempered. The treatment is practically invisible, and the above table has now to be modified as follows:

Hard plaster	10,400 less 2040 = 8360 sq. ft.	0·025	209 units
Triple-ply quilt, two layers and canvas	2040 sq. ft.	0·7	1428 units
Remainder as in above table			531 units
Total permanent absorption			2168 units

t for full audience	1·2 sec.;
t for half audience	1·8 sec.

This gives good audibility with a full audience and a very marked improvement for smaller audiences. The hall is also used on occasions for music and is considered good.

It will at once be apparent that all the data required for a calculation are available in advance of actual construction, and that therefore it is possible to design in advance instead of building first and correcting afterwards. It is essential, however, that we should know what time of reverberation to aim at. We might expect that for public speech a very short time of reverberation would be preferred. This would avoid overlap of syllables and give clear articulation. This is the condition found in the open air, where reverberation is absent and the only difficulty which faces a speaker is that of generating sufficiently intense sounds to reach the whole of his audience. Incidentally, it may be noted that the Greek and Roman theatres avoided the difficulties of reverberation by being open to the heavens, and this partly accounts for the high praise which their acoustic qualities have quite rightly won. But a speaker does not prefer these conditions, either in the open air or in a highly absorbing room. The room appears to him to be "dead", and he misses the sense of power which a little reverberation gives him. He has to work harder to produce the same loudness.

The most acceptable conditions for speaker and audience seem to correspond to a time of reverberation of about 1 sec. for small rooms, increasing to 1·5 sec. or even 2 sec. for large rooms, where in any case speaking tends to be more deliberate. The rapidity of speech is of course very important, and by speaking slowly and not too loudly a speaker can make himself intelligible in a room with a time of reverberation far above the preferred value. An attempt has been made to estimate "articulation" numerically, the percentage articulation being the percentage of meaningless syllables correctly heard in an auditorium by the average observer. The syllables are called in groups

of three by a speaker and recorded by a group of observers. Knudsen *
has done this for a number of rooms similar in shape and varying
in volume from 200,000 to 300,000 c. ft., with the results shown in
fig. 19.10.

This is not of course directly applicable to connected speech, where
a large proportion of the syllables wrongly recorded would have been
rightly inferred from their context. Tests made by Fletcher † indicate
that 70 per cent articulation corresponds to 98 per cent intelligibility,

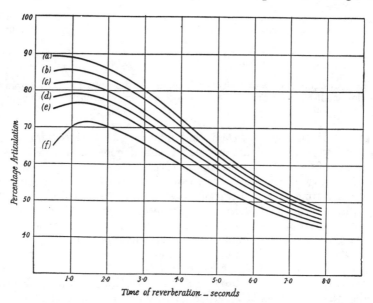

Fig. 19.10.—Group of curves showing how the loudness of a speaker's voice affects
the hearing of speech in auditoriums. These curves are for an auditorium having a
volume of 400,000 cu. ft.

(a) Speech amplified;   (b) Loudest speaker in this series;   (c) Moderately loud speaker;
(d) Average speaker;   (e) Moderately weak speaker;   (f) Weakest speaker in this series

while 80 per cent articulation gives 99 per cent intelligibility. It seems
fair to conclude, then, that, given a speaker sensitive to the conditions,
a time of reverberation of 2·5 sec. is manageable. These results are of
course dependent to some extent upon loudness, as is seen in fig. 19.10.
The stronger the source, the shorter is the value of the time of reverberation which gives the highest percentage articulation. The effect
of reverberation is also seen in fig. 19.11, which gives some results of
Knudsen (loc. cit.).

The matter of musical taste is not less important. We can approach
the quest for the preferred time of reverberation either by attempting

* *Journ. Amer. Soc. Acoust.*, Vol. i, p. 57 (1929).   † *Speech and Hearing*, p. 266.

to adjust various rooms to suit musical taste or by calculating the
time of reverberation for a series of rooms pronounced good for their
purpose by qualified musical critics. W. C. Sabine used both methods.
He arranged for the performance of a selection of pianoforte pieces
in a series of five different rooms before a group of experts. Each
room was then adjusted by adding or removing absorbing material
until the experts pronounced it just right. He found that musical taste
was unexpectedly accurate, the calculated time of reverberation in
each case lying between 0·95 and 1·05 sec. The other experiment he
carried out in connexion with the design of a new concert room at
Boston. Expert opinion settled on the Leipzig Gewandhaus as the

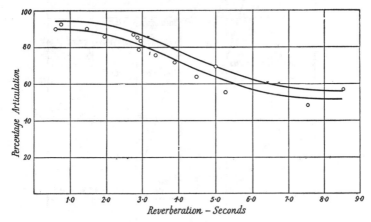

Fig. 19.11.—Curves showing the interfering effect of reverberation upon the hearing of speech
The lower curve represents the most probable fit with the observed data. The upper curve
has been corrected for loudness, and corresponds to a loudness of 70 db.

best concert room in Europe, and having calculated its time of reverberation he set himself to design the new concert room with the same
time of reverberation. The experiment was a complete success and
the new concert room which he designed has earned high praise.

It seems obvious that different types of music will demand different
times of reverberation. When the music depends for its effect on
precision of detail, as commonly in chamber music, a short time of
reverberation seems indicated, but with music depending on massiveness and power, as in the case of choral and organ music, a longer
time of reverberation is called for. Musicians and singers, like speakers,
demand some reverberation and strongly resent having to perform
in a room which is acoustically dead. There are grounds for thinking that in this matter the taste of the artist and of the audience is
not identical, and that for this reason it is desirable to surround the

artists with highly reflecting surfaces and to introduce the required absorbent at the farther end of the room. In fig. 19.12 the times of reverberation for a number of well-known buildings are plotted against the cube root of the volume. The time of reverberation is

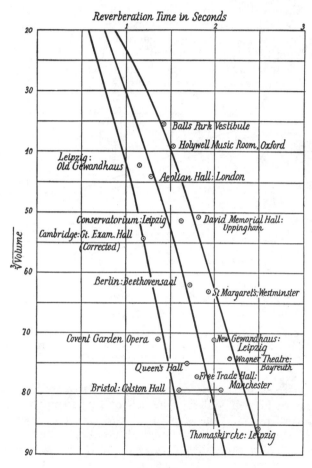

Fig. 19.12

calculated for full audience and frequency 512. The points all lie in a comparatively narrow band and represent a strong case for the contention that there is at least an " acceptable range of reverberation times ", a phrase which P. E. Sabine urges in preference to the commonly used term " optimum time of reverberation ".

The Hastings White Rock Pavilion is an example of a building in the design of which acoustic requirements were regarded as of considerable importance. The analysis is as follows:

Absorbent	Remarks	Area (sq. ft.) or Number	Coefficient	Absorption O.W.U.	Adjustment	Net Absorption O.W.U.
Plaster, hard	Keene's or fibrous	22,500	0·02	450	—	450
Wood, platform floor and staging	Oak	1,175	0·06	70·5	Less 10 per cent for shading by players	63
Wood, panelling round orchestra	Oak, ½ in. 5-ply panels, 2-in. air space	526	0·1	52·6	—	52·6
Wood, doors	Oak, 2-in.	774	0·06	46·4	—	46·4
Glass, laylight and windows	—	224	0·027	6	—	6
Carpet area on ground floor promenades	Five-frame Wilton on thick under-mat	9,600	0·25	2400	Less 10 per cent for shading by seats, &c.	2160
Curtains	Thin	224	0·15	33	—	33
Vents	—	100	0·5	50	—	50
Upholstered seat, arms not upholstered	Goat hair	1,400	1·7 per seat	2380	—	2380
Settees, large upholstered	Seating each 5 people	15	20 units each	300	—	300
		Total permanent absorption			.. ..	5541
Audience full	Take coefficient at 4·7 − 1·7 = 3·0	1400	3·0	4200	—	4200
Audience one-third		466	3·0	1398	—	1398
Rehearsal average orchestra	Neglect platform chairs	40	4·7	188	—	188

Volume 280,000 c. ft.   Volume per seat of audience 200 c. ft.

Time of reverberation T $\begin{cases} \text{Full audience} & 1\cdot44 \text{ sec.} \\ \text{Audience and orchestra} & 1\cdot4 \quad ,, \\ \text{Rehearsal} & 2\cdot44 \quad ,, \\ \text{Hall empty} & 2\cdot5 \quad ,, \end{cases}$

The time of reverberation with the hall full is only 1·4 sec., falling on the lower limit of the reverberation values given in fig. 19.12. This provides clear speech conditions, and to maintain these conditions with a small audience upholstered seats and thick carpeting are provided. As a result of this the total variation between hall full and hall empty is only about 1 sec.

Recording and broadcasting studios present a very special problem. They involve at the moment of reproduction a single channel from the source and so are in a sense equivalent to monaural listening, as contrasted with binaural listening where the sound is separately conducted from the source to each of the two ears. Now binaural listening seems to enable the observer to deal successfully with a greater amount of reverberation, perhaps because location of the direction of the source is facilitated and therefore discrimination between direct and reflected sound is made easier. This suggests the desirability of a shorter time of reverberation.

In addition to this the reverberation in the studio is reproduced and superimposed on the reverberation in the listening room or picture-house, which almost suggests the desirability of eliminating the reverberation completely.

As a matter of fact, in the early days of broadcasting this was attempted, and the performers were placed in rooms so " dead " that artistic satisfaction was impossible. Not only did the " dead " room seem oppressive, but it was realized that reverberation considerably eased for singers and orchestra the strain of keeping in tune. For this reason there was developed the " live "- and " dead "-end studio in which the artistes are placed in one end and all the absorbent in the other.

So far as musical recording is concerned, there seems to be no necessity for a very low time of reverberation. Successful records have been made by the Philadelphia Symphony Orchestra in an empty hall for which the time of reverberation was 2·3 sec., and P. E. Sabine * tells how he was able to vary the time of reverberation of a broadcasting studio from 0·25 sec. to 0·64 sec. in three steps. Of the listeners 16 preferred the shortest time of reverberation, 32 the medium time, and 73 the longest time (which, of course, is still short).

In general, however, there seems to be no doubt that on the one hand a fairly short time of reverberation is desirable, and that on the other hand there are objections to excessive absorption. It has been suggested † that the effect of diminished reverberation may be obtained by changing the proportion of direct sound to reflected sound. There are two ways in which this may be achieved. One is to place the artistes near to the microphone—a practice which bristles with difficulties. The other is to use a directional microphone which will discriminate between the sound direct from the source and the sound

---

* *Acoustics and Architecture*, p. 168 (McGraw-Hill, 1932).
† Olson and Massa, *Applied Acoustics*, p. 343.

reflected from surfaces and constituting the reverberation. The latter plan has given good results.

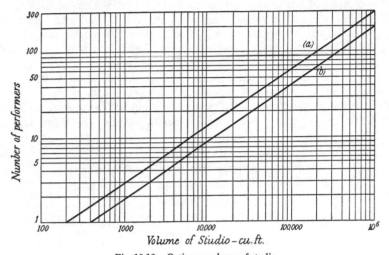

Fig. 19.13.—Optimum volume of studio
(a) Maximum number of performers;   (b) Optimum number of performers

In these matters the experience of the B.B.C. is of great value, and the results of this experience together with an account of experi-

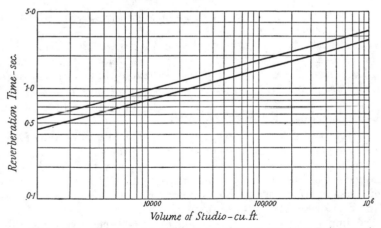

Fig. 19.14.—Optimum reverberation time for studios (based on data due to F. R. Watson)

ments on coefficients of absorption have been given by Kirke and Howe.* In the matter of time of reverberation at the standard fre-

* *Journ. Inst. Elect. Eng.*, Vol. 78, p. 404 (1936).

quency of 512, B.B.C. design is based on curves given by F. R. Watson.* The need for varying sizes of studio is imposed by the need for different types of musical performance, and fig. 19.13, based on a graph first given by Watson, shows the relationship between size of studio and number of performers in the form in which it is given by Kirke and Howe. Fig. 19.14 shows the corresponding relation between size of studio and time of reverberation. Another matter of great importance is the best form for the reverberation/frequency curve. For a time the " straight-line absorption " was aimed at, i.e. efforts were made to secure equal absorption at all frequencies. The studios which without exception have proved the most satisfactory, however, have had a

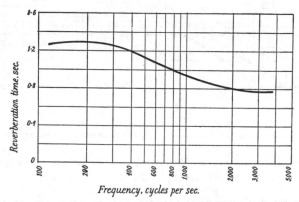

Fig. 19.15.—Reverberation characteristic of Cardiff studio

reverberation/frequency curve of the form shown in fig. 19.15, which refers to the Cardiff studio. The absorption is relatively constant up to a frequency of 600 or 700 and then increases slightly in the range of higher frequencies.

8. Other Conditions for Good Acoustics.

We have so far treated reverberation as the only important factor in acoustic design and have neglected entirely the shape of the room. For small rooms reverberation is the main factor to be considered. In large rooms, however, the general design is important, and we ought to aim at securing three conditions: (1) adequate loudness, (2) uniform distribution, (3) absence of echoes.

The importance of adequate loudness has been investigated by Fletcher, and his results are shown in fig. 19.16. It will be seen that speech is most easily intelligible when the sensation level is about 75 decibels, which is greater than that for ordinary conversation. If

* *Acoustics of Buildings* (Wiley, 1923).

the sensation level lies between 50 db. and 110 db. the articulation is 90 per cent, which is entirely satisfactory. Below 50 db. the articulation drops off rapidly as the loudness is diminished.

Measurements of the loudness actually attained by speakers have been made by Knudsen,* and he has deduced from these measurements the power output of the speakers. Thus if $\hat{E}$ is the average energy-

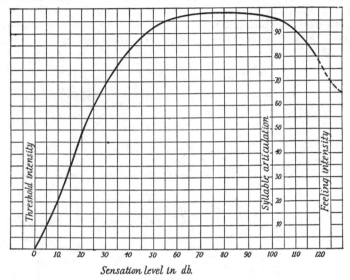

Fig. 19.16.—Articulation and loudness. The figures were originally given in terms of sensation level and this measurement has been retained

density of the sound in the hall during a speech and S is the corresponding sensation level which is measured, then

$$S = 10 \log_{10} \frac{\hat{E}}{E_0},$$

where E_0 is the minimum audible energy-density for speech.

Knowing S and E_0, we can calculate $\hat{E}$, and then since $\hat{E} = 4\bar{E}/Ac$, we can calculate $\bar{E}$, the power output of the source.

For five speakers in a room of volume 770 c. m. the average power ranged from 4·5 microwatts to 66·2 microwatts, and the average for the five being 27·4 microwatts, and the average sensation level attained was 50·7 db. With eight speakers in a room of larger dimensions the average power output was 48·9 microwatts and the average sensation level 45·7 db. Thus although the speakers increased their output, they did not succeed in attaining the same sensation level.

Adequate loudness is secured by the reflecting properties of the walls, floor and ceiling. Without reflectors the carrying power of the unaided human voice is comparatively poor. Andrade * refers to an experiment by M. Gustave Lyon, the designer of the Salle Pleyel in Paris, in the course of which two observers were suspended below two small balloons in mid-air and, being deprived of all reflecting surfaces, found it impossible to communicate with one another at distances exceeding about 11 metres. This figure seems unreasonably low, but everyone who has spoken in the open air is alive to the value of reflecting surfaces. A wall behind the speaker economizes effort tremendously,

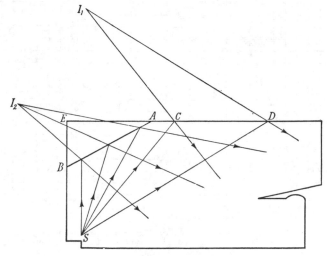

Fig. 19.17

and the excellence of the Greek theatres, to which reference has already been made, though due in part to the absence of reverberation, is also due in part to their effective use of reflecting surfaces. The reconstruction of the Stage House at Oropos showed that the actors had a reflecting wall behind them and another excellent reflector in the large paved area in front, from which the sound was sent up over the tiers of the auditorium.

In a rectangular hall it is obvious that each of the six bounding surfaces gives rise to a sound image of the source, and these images in turn act as sources, each producing a new set of secondary images, and so on. The application of the principles of geometrical optics to the design of an auditorium suggests modifications in the rectangular shape. If we consider, for instance, the section in fig. 19.17, it will be apparent that I_1 is the image of S in the ceiling, and that the useful

* *Nature*, Vol. 130, p. 332 (1932).

part of the ceiling for reinforcing sound at the back of the hall is CD. If we introduce a splay AB, we substitute a useful reflecting surface for the comparatively useless part AE of the original ceiling and get a useful beam under the gallery. The phenomenon is of course very greatly modified by diffraction, but the advantage of applying these principles to design is established. A glance at fig. 19.17 will convince us that there is a similar case for side splays on plan. Two developments of the design suggest themselves—the fan-shaped plan where the side walls are all splay, which has been found very satisfactory, and the paraboloid reflector, as used at the Hill Memorial Hall, Ann Arbor, Michigan. In this case the whole back ceiling and side walls in the neighbourhood of the speaker form an immense paraboloidal reflector with the speaker at the focus. The reflected beam is uniform and passes to the back of the hall, where it is absorbed as completely as possible at the rear wall. The result is good speaking conditions with accommodation for an audience of 5000. The disadvantages are: (1) even with the large-scale reflector the area within which a speaker can stand is limited, and (2) all the incidental noise in the auditorium is focused on the speaker. If this type of design is to be effective it must, owing to diffraction effects, be designed on a generous scale, and it is applicable only in cases where all the speaking is done from one point. The problem presented by a council chamber or debating assembly can only be solved by a reflector equally effective for speakers in all parts of the hall, and this is best achieved by a low flat ceiling.

Concave surfaces always tend to give uneven distribution of sound, and hence if they are desired for artistic reasons they must be very carefully planned. The circular plan is never very good from the acoustic point of view, and the domed ceiling or barrel-vault ceiling must have a curvature suitably designed. If a domed ceiling has a radius of curvature nearly equal to its height at the centre, then sound from a source at floor level will be focused again on the floor level. If, on the other hand, the radius of curvature is twice the height, a fairly uniform distribution of sound at floor level will be obtained. Similar considerations will apply to the barrel-vault ceiling.

In all cases of reflection the difference in the time of arrival at the position of an auditor of the direct and reflected sounds is a very important consideration. Reverberation may be regarded as a continuous succession of echoes giving the sensation of an uninterrupted sound of diminishing intensity. A strong reflection occurring at a sufficiently long interval after the direct sound, however, gives the impression of a distinct echo and is very disturbing. To avoid this the time interval must not exceed about 1/15 sec., and therefore the path difference must not exceed about 80 ft. This means that reflections from the back wall should be avoided if the length of the hall is much in excess of 40 ft. A combination of curved surfaces and long path differences is most troublesome; the Albert Hall provides a good instance of these defects.

From this point of view one of the best examples of design is the Salle Pleyel in Paris, which is shown in section in fig. 19.18. The absorption at the back is made as complete as possible, and the whole design is intended to make the first reflections from the

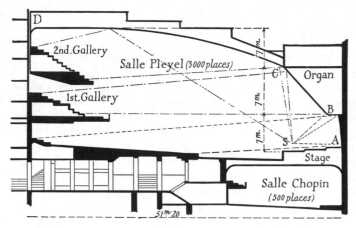

Fig. 19.18

boundaries effective over as large an area of the auditorium as possible. The excellence of the acoustic result is generally admitted.* A more recent example of this kind of design is the Music Hall of the Rockefeller Center, New York.

9. Protection against Noise.

The protection of buildings against noise is one of the most insistent problems of the architect. The use of new methods of construction and new building materials has intensified the problem and given rise to much disappointment and annoyance.

In the case of offices, committee rooms, halls, churches, &c., on noisy sites there is the difficulty due to the actual masking effect of air-borne noises transmitted by the windows. Fig. 19.19 gives the effect of various noise levels in reducing the percentage articulation and interfering with the reception of speech. In the case of dwelling-houses there is the annoyance caused by the transmission of air-borne noises from outside and also, particularly in flats, the transmission from floor to floor and from room to room. The Department of Industrial and Scientific Research has given a good deal of attention to the problem

* Andrade, *Nature*, Vol. 130, p. 332 (1932).

and has issued a publication containing general advice to architects and a valuable collection of statistics.*

Noise invades a room in three ways: (*a*) by percolation of airborne noise through interstices of the fabric or through openings; (*b*) by transmission due to diaphragm action of walls, floors, doors and windows; (*c*) by transmission due to structure-borne vibration, communicated to the parts of a building through the air or through the ground or by direct impact, e.g. a footstep.

With regard to (*a*), the amount of sound which will pass through a small crack or aperture is surprising. P. E. Sabine † quotes laboratory tests to show that a metal surface with the proper size and spacing

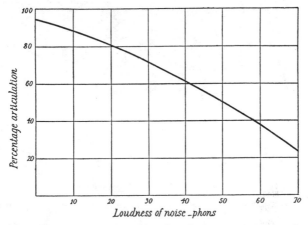

Fig. 19.19.—Curve showing the interfering effect of noise upon the hearing of speech

of holes in which the area of the perforations is only ⅛ of the total area can transmit 97 per cent of the sound falling on it and remain highly reflecting for light. This serves to emphasize the importance of tight-fitting windows and doors if designed as protection against noise. With regard to (*b*), it has been shown that massiveness is the important quality for a defensive wall or partition. Much experimental work has been done on the transmission of noise through partitions. P. E. Sabine has used a method depending on the measurement of the time of reverberation in two chambers separated by various test partitions. The theory of the method has been discussed by Buckingham.‡ Direct measurements of transmission have also been made at the National Physical Laboratory by Davis and Littler.§ These and later experiments are discussed by Constable and Aston ‖, who give results for

* *Building Research, Bulletin* No. 14 (1933).   † *Journ. Frankl. Inst.*, Vol. 217, p. 443 (1934).
‡ *Scientific Papers of the Bureau of Standards*, Vol. 20, p. 194 (1924–6).
§ *Phil. Mag.*, Vol. 7, p. 1050 (1929).   ‖ *Phil. Mag.*, Vol. 23, p. 161 (1937).

a great variety of materials. The measurements were made by using a loud-speaker as source in a highly absorbing chamber, and an exploring microphone in another highly absorbing chamber, the two chambers communicating through an aperture which could be closed by the partition under test. When the sound reduction in decibels is plotted against the logarithm of the mass of the partition per square foot the graph is an almost perfect straight line at low frequencies and only slightly curved at high frequencies. Fig. 19.20 shows the results for a selection of common materials. The insulation of a 4½-in. brick wall amounts to about 48 db. If the thickness of the wall is doubled its insulation is only increased to about 53 db. On the other

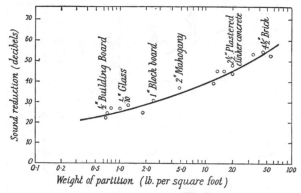

Fig. 19.20.—Relation between sound reduction in decibels and weight per square foot of single homogeneous partitions

Sound reduction averaged for frequencies 200, 300, 500, 700, 1000, 1600 and 2000 cycles per second

hand, two entirely separate 4½-in. brick walls would each give an insulation of 48 db. or about 96 db. in all. This suggests the use of non-homogeneous double or multiple partitions. The efficiency of these is very great if the components are entirely separate. If the air space between is bridged by numerous ties or filled with insulating material the coupling thus provided may cause the structure to vibrate as a whole, and as Constable has shown, this may for certain frequencies give even less insulation than either component singly.*

Windows are of course a source of special difficulty. When they are open for purposes of ventilation sound enters freely. If the window faces on to a noisy site it must be kept closed and the necessary ventilation must be provided otherwise. The following figures are given by McLachlan.†

* *Proc. Phys. Soc.*, Vol. 48, pp. 690, 914 (1936).
† *Noise* (Oxford University Press, 1935).

NOISE IN THIRD-FLOOR OFFICE IN FLEET STREET, LONDON

Source of Sound	Condition			
	Windows shut	3 Ventilators and 1 window open	All Ventilators and 5 windows open	Microphone outside window
	phons	*phons*	*phons*	*phons*
Medium traffic	60	64	69	75
Heavy traffic	65	73	76	80
Buses starting	69	—	—	—
Motor-horns	70	—	—	82

Double glazing adds greatly to the insulation efficiency, especially if there is a heavy mounting and a reasonable air space. The air, however, may act as a coupling between the two planes and for low frequencies there is a spacing which gives minimum insulation. The results for a particular case are shown graphically in fig. 19.21. The following figures for 21-oz. glass are from Constable and Aston (loc. cit.), the reduction being given in decibels.

Construction	Mass in lb./sq. ft.	Thickness in inches	Average sound reduction for frequencies			
			200 and 300	500, 700 and 1000	1000 and 2000	200, 300, 500, 700, 1000, 16,000 and 20,000
Single glazing	1·3	$\frac{3}{32}$	20	27	37	28
Double glazing at 8 in.	2·6	$8\frac{3}{16}$	40	52	66	53
7 in.		$7\frac{3}{16}$	36	47	62	48
6 in.		$6\frac{3}{16}$	36	50	67	51
5 in.		$5\frac{3}{16}$	35	49	64	49
3 in.		$3\frac{3}{16}$	28	52	64	49
2 in.		$2\frac{3}{16}$	23	49	64	46
1 in.		$1\frac{3}{16}$	30	42	65	42
$\frac{1}{2}$ in.		$\frac{11}{16}$	22	36	56	38
$\frac{1}{4}$ in.		$\frac{7}{16}$	23	32	52	35
$\frac{1}{8}$ in.		$\frac{5}{16}$	24	27	50	33

The protection of the various rooms in a house against noises originating in other rooms raises very much the same problems and requires very much the same treatment.* The most troublesome noises are structure-borne, i.e. carried from room to room through the material of the building. The conduction of sound is less efficient

* A discussion of the results of a long series of tests is given in *Building Research, Bulletin*, No. 14 (D. S. I. R., 1933).

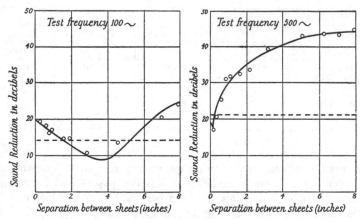

Fig. 19.21.—The influence of spacing of the components upon the noise insulating value of a double window of 21-oz. glass, showing a position of minimum insulation

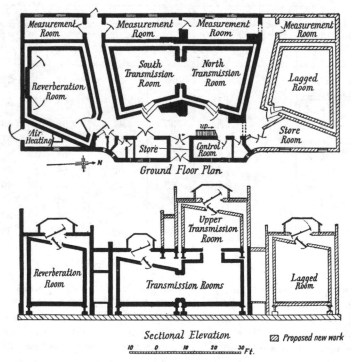

Fig. 19.22.—Sectional plans of acoustics laboratory, National Physical Laboratory

through a discontinuous medium such as a wall of bricks set in lime mortar than along a more homogeneous material like concrete or steel. Where steel-frame construction is used it is particularly important to reduce transmission by the use of anti-vibration mats under stanchions and the sound insulation of joints at bearings. Unbridged air cavities between rooms are the most effective, but completely unbridged cavities are only possible in the case of two separate structures, each on its own foundation. This is the method of construction used in acoustical testing laboratories; fig. 19.22 shows the sectional plans for the building at the National Physical Laboratory. Reverberation can be measured in one room, transmission through a partition in the pair of rooms in the centre, and transmission through various floor and ceiling constructions by means of the upper and lower transmission rooms.

BIBLIOGRAPHY

BAGENAL, H., and WOOD, A.—*Planning for Good Acoustics.* Methuen, 1931.
A full account of the subject of architectural acoustics mainly from the point of view of the architect.

BARTLETT, F. C.—*The Problem of Noise.* Cambridge University Press, 1934.
Treated from the point of view of the psychologist.

BEATTY, R. T.—*Hearing in Man and Animals.* Bell, 1932.
A very good account of the borderline between the physiological and the physical.

BERGMANN, L.—*Ultrasonics.* Bell, 1938.
A very complete account of the subject to the date of publication.

BRAGG, SIR WILLIAM—*The World of Sound.* Bell, 1920.
The Christmas Lectures given by Sir William Bragg in 1919—a fascinating popular account of the subject.

CRANDALL, A. B.—*Vibrating Systems and Sounds.* Van Nostrand Company, 1926.
An excellent treatment of vibrations by fairly advanced methods.

DAVIS, A. H.—*Modern Acoustics.* Bell, 1934.
A good treatment of modern practical developments.

FLETCHER, H.—*Speech and Hearing.* Van Nostrand Company, 1929.
An account of recent work done mainly at the Bell Telephone Company's Research Laboratories.

GREENLEES, A. E.—*Amplification and Distribution of Sound.* Chapman and Hall, 1938.
An elementary treatment of microphones, loud-speakers, amplifiers, &c.

HELMHOLTZ, H.—*Sensations of Tone.* Translated by A. J. Ellis Longmans & Company, 1895. Dover reprint.
The standard work on the foundations of musical acoustics. A mine of information on the subject.

LAMB, H.—*Dynamical Theory of Sound.* Arnold, 1910. Dover reprint.
A mathematical treatment of classical theory.

McLACHLAN, N. W.—*Noise.* Oxford University Press, 1935.
Treated from the point of view of the engineer.

MILLER, D. C.—*The Science of Musical Sounds.* Macmillan, 1916.
A popular account of Miller's pioneer work on the analysis of musical notes.

MILLER, D. C.—*Sound Waves, their Shape and Speed.* Macmillan Company, New York, 1938.
An account of Miller's later work on the analysis of musical notes and on the sound waves from gun-fire.

OLSON, H. F., and MASSA, F.—*Applied Acoustics.* Blakiston, 1934.
A very full treatment of electrical applications.

RAWDON-SMITH, A. F.—*Theories of Sensation.* Cambridge University Press, 1938.
A physiological account of sound perception.

RAYLEIGH, LORD—*Theory of Sound.* Macmillan, 1877. Dover reprint.
Since published in other editions. An advanced textbook covering the whole subject as then developed and a good deal of original work. Not easy to read but full of good material.

RICHARDSON, E. G.—*Acoustics of Orchestral Instruments.* Arnold, 1929.
A very readable account of the subject.

RICHARDSON, E. G.—*Sound.* Arnold, 1927.
An intermediate textbook covering most aspects of the subject.

SABINE, W. C.—*Collected Papers on Acoustics.* Harvard University Press, 1922.
Dover reprint.
The pioneer work on the subject described in popular terms.

WOOD, A.—*Sound Waves and their Uses.* Blackie, 1930.
The Christmas Lectures at the Royal Institution, 1929.

WOOD, A. B.—*Textbook of Sound.* Bell, 1930.
An advanced textbook with special emphasis on electroacoustics.

WOOD, R. W.—*Supersonics.* Brown University, 1939.
A popular account of the production and properties of ultrasonic waves.

RECENT LITERATURE

CHAP. Par.

I. 11. M. J. Pryor, *Amer. Journ. Phys.*, Vol. 13, p. 110 (1945).

16. E. N. da C. Andrade, *Proc. Phys. Soc.*, Vol. 53, p. 329 (1941); P. Savic, *Nature*, Vol. 147, p. 241 (1941).

III. 1. *The Times* (Correspondence), Feb. 3, 5 and 7 (1947).

8. A. T. Jones, *Journ. Amer. Soc. Acoust.*, Vol. 16, p. 254 (1944–5) and Vol. 17, p. 151 (1945–6).

12. J. Miles, *Ibid.*, Vol. 14, p. 183 (1942–3).

IV. 1. H. M. Browning, *Phil. Mag.*, Vol. 33, p. 551 (1942); H. Samulon, *Journ. Amer. Soc. Acoust.*, Vol. 19, p. 191 (1947).

4. G. D. West, *Proc. Phys. Soc.*, Vol. 46, p. 186 (1934).

V. 6. W. S. Tucker, *Phil. Mag.*, Vol. 36, p. 473 (1945).

7. R. J. Dwyer, *Journ. Chem. Phys.*, Vol. 7, p. 40 (1939); W. H. Pielemeier, *Ibid.*, Vol. 8, p. 106 (1939); E. G. Richardson, *Nature*, Vol. 143, p. 638 (1939); V. O. Knudsen and E. Fricke, *Journ. Amer. Soc. Acoust.*, Vol. 12, p. 255 (1940–1); D. Telfair and W. H. Pielemeier, *Rev. Sci. Inst.*, Vol. 13, p. 122 (1942); W. H. Pielemeier and N. H. Byers, *Journ. Amer. Soc. Acoust.*, Vol. 15, p. 17 (1943–4); W. H. Pielemeier, *Ibid.*, p. 22; H. C. Hardy, *Ibid.*, p. 91; E. S. Stewart, J. L. Stewart and J. C. Hubbard, *Phys. Rev.*, Vol. 68, p. 231 (1945); M. Mokhtar and E. G. Richardson, *Proc. Roy. Soc.*, Vol. 184, p. 117 (1945); W. H. Pielemeier, *Journ. Amer. Soc. Acoust.*, Vol. 17, p. 24 (1945–6); E. S. Stewart, *Phys. Rev.*, Vol. 69, p. 632 (1946).

8. R. Lucas, *Journ. de Phys.*, Vol. 8, p. 41 (1937); H. O. Kneser, *Ann. d. Physik.*, Vol. 32, p. 277 (1938); W. T. Richards, *Rev. Mod. Phys.*, Vol. 11, p. 36 (1939); L. Zachoval, *J. de Physique*, Vol. 10, p. 350 (1939); G. K. Hartmann and A. B. Focke, *Phys. Rev.*, Vol. 57, p. 221 (1940); E. G. Richardson, *Proc. Phys. Soc.*, Vol. 52, p. 480 (1940); R. T. Beyer and M. C. Smith, *Journ. Amer. Soc. Acoust.*, Vol. 18, p. 424 (1946); C. E. Teeter, Jnr., *Ibid.*, p. 488; F. H. Willis, *Ibid.*, Vol. 19, p. 242 (1947).

VI. 1. A. E. Bate, *Proc. Phys. Soc.*, Vol. 50, p. 293 (1938).

4. R. J. Urick and H. L. Saxton, *Journ. Amer. Soc. Acoust.*, Vol. 19, p. 8 (1947).

6. C. H. Mortimer and E. B. Worthington, *Nature*, Vol. 145, p. 212 (1940); J. H. Jupe, *Electronics*, Vol. 13, p. 54 (April, 1940).

VII. 1. H. Kruglak and C. C. Cruse, *Amer. Journ. Phys.*, Vol. 8, p. 260 (1940).

3. V. O. Knudsen, *Journ. Amer. Soc. Acoust.*, Vol. 18, p. 90 (1946); G. W. Gilman, H. B. Conhead and E. H. Willis, *Ibid.*, Vol. 18, p. 274 (1946).

5. H. Sieg, *Elektrische Nachrichten-Technik*, Vol. 17, p. 193 (1940); B. Gutenberg, *Journ. Amer. Soc. Acoust.*, Vol. 14, p. 151 (1942–3); P. Rothwell, *Ibid.*, Vol. 19, p. 205 (1947).

CHAP. Par.

VIII. 3. G. W. Stewart, *Ibid.*, Vol. 17, p. 107 (1945–6).

7. R. W. Young, *Ibid.*, Vol. 19, p. 1 (1947).

10. W. B. Hales, *Ibid.*, Vol. 16, p. 137 (1944–5); I. B. Cohen, *Ibid.*, Vol. 17, p. 228 (1945–6).

IX. 5. J. C. Hubbard, *Amer. Journ. Phys.*, Vol. 8, p. 207 (1940), and *J. Gen. Physiol.*, Vol. 26, p. 179 (1942); W. H. Pielemeier, *Journ. Amer. Soc. Acoust.*, Vol. 17, p. 337 (1945–6).

6. H. Freundlish, *Inst. Chem. Engrs. Trans.*, Vol. 15, p. 223 (1937); W. T. Richards, *Rev. Mod. Phys.*, Vol. 11, p. 36 (1939); P. F. Ernst, *J. Sci. Inst.*, Vol. 22, p. 238 (1945); F. A. Firestone, *Journ. Amer. Soc. Acoust.*, Vol. 17, p. 287 (1945–6).

X. 4. R. C. Colwell, A. W. Friend and D. A. McGraw, *Frank. Inst. J.*, Vol. 225, p. 579 (1938); Vol. 227, p. 251 (1939); Vol. 230, p. 749 (1940).

7. H. C. Hardy, D. Telfair and W. H. Pielemeier, *Journ. Amer. Soc. Acoust.*, Vol. 13, p. 226 (1941–2); R. C. Colwell and L. H. Gibson, *Ibid.*, Vol. 12, p. 436 (1940–1); T. H. Quigley, *Phys. Rev.*, Vol. 67, p. 298 (1945); J. L. Stewart, *Rev. Sci. Inst.*, Vol. 17, p. 59 (1946).

8. J. W. M. Du Mond, E. R. Cohen, W. K. H. Panofsky and E. Deeds, *Journ. Amer. Soc. Acoust.*, Vol. 18, p. 97 (1946).

9. A. E. Bate, *J. Sci. Inst.*, Vol. 17, p. 68 (1940).

10. M. Mokhtar, *Phil. Mag.*, Vol. 27, p. 195 (1939).

11. R. T. Lagemann and W. S. Dunbar, *J. Phys. Chem.*, Vol. 49, p. 428 (1945).

11. W. L. Woolf, *Journ. Amer. Soc. Acoust.*, Vol. 15, p. 83 (1943).

15. F. E. Fox and G. D. Rock, *Rev. Sci. Inst.*, Vol. 10, p. 345 (1939); G. W. Willard, *Journ. Amer. Soc. Acoust.*, Vol. 12, p. 438 (1940–1); B. K. Singh, *Nature*, Vol. 156, p. 569 (1945); P. L. F. Jones and A. J. Gale, *Ibid.*, Vol. 157, p. 341 (1946); S. Bhagavantam and B. R. Rao, *Ibid.*, Vol. 158, p. 484 (1946).

17. J. H. McMillen, *Journ. Amer. Soc. Acoust.*, Vol. 18, p. 190 (1946).

19. R. Parshad, *Nature*, Vol. 156, p. 637 (1945); G. H. S. V. Peasada Ras, *Ibid.*, Vol. 157, p. 590 (1946); F. A. Firestone and J. R. Frederick, *Journ. Amer. Soc. Acoust.*, Vol. 18, p. 200 (1946).

XI. 13. O. Devik and H. Dahl, *Ibid.*, Vol. 10, p. 50 (1938–9); A. C. Merrington and C. W. Oatley, *Proc. Roy. Soc.*, Vol. 171A, p. 505 (1939); H. H. Roseberry and W. Conley Smith, *Journ. Amer. Soc. Acoust.*, Vol. 16, p. 123 (1944–5).

14. C. H. W. Brookes-Smith and J. A. Colls, *J. Sci. Inst.*, Vol. 16, p. 361 (1939); F. Massa, *Journ. Amer. Soc. Acoust.*, Vol. 17, p. 29 (1945–6); A. L. Di Mattia and F. M. Wiener, *Ibid.*, Vol. 18, p. 341 (1946); T. H. Bonn, *Ibid.*, p. 496; F. Mason, *Electronics*, Vol. 19, p. 218 (May, 1946).

16. R. C. Jones, *Journ. Amer. Soc. Acoust.*, Vol. 18, p. 371 (1946).

XII. 1. S. S. Stevens and J. Volkmann, *Amer. J. Psychol.*, Vol. 53, p. 329 (1940); D. Lewis, M. Cowan and G. Fairbanks, *J. Exper. Psychol.*, Vol. 27, p. 23 (1940).

6. *Journ. Sci. Inst.*, Vol. 17, p. 72 (1940); R. P. McLoughlin, *Journ. Amer. Soc. Acoust.*, Vol. 17, p. 46 (1945–6).

10. L. Fleischmann, *Ibid.*, Vol. 15, p. 103 (1943); G. F. Herrenden-Harker, *Amer. Journ. Phys.*, Vol. 12, p. 175 (1944).

11. *Nature*, Vol. 149, p. 416 (1942); G. F. Herrenden-Harker, *Amer. J. Phys.*, Vol. 13, p. 351 (1945).

12. C. G. McIlwraith, *Rev. Sci. Inst.*, Vol. 12, p. 612 (1941).

XIII. 1. W. H. Lichte, *J. Exper. Psychol.*, Vol. 28, p. 455 (1941).

8. L. Y. Lacy, *Journ. Amer. Soc. Acoust.*, Vol. 18, p. 19 (1946).

10. D. Lewis and W. H. Lichte, *J. Exp. Psychol.*, Vol. 24, p. 254 (1939); F. A. Saunders, *Journ. Amer. Soc. Acoust.*, Vol. 16, p. 101 (1944–5) and Vol. 18, p. 395 (1946).

11. D. Lewis and C. Tuthill, *Ibid.*, Vol. 11, p. 451 (1939–40); E. G. Richardson, *Nature*, Vol. 145, p. 841 (1940); R. K. Potter, *Science*, Vol. 102, p. 463 (1945); J. C. Steinberg and N. R. French, *Journ. Amer. Soc. Acoust.*, Vol. 18, p. 4 (1946); R. R. Riesz and L. Schott, *Ibid.*, p. 50; H. Dudley and O. O. Gruenz, Jnr., *Ibid.*, p. 62; G. A. Kopp and H. C. Green, *Ibid.*, p. 74; J. P. Egan and F. M. Wiener, *Ibid.*, p. 435.

12. G. Fairbanks, *Ibid.*, Vol. 11, p. 457 (1940).

XIV. 7. N. Davy, J. H. Littlewood and M. McCaig, *Phil. Mag.*, Vol. 27, p. 133 (1939).

8. H. Backhaus and G. Weymann, *Akust. Z.*, Vol. 4, p. 302 (1939); F. A. Saunders, *Journ. Amer. Soc. Acoust.*, Vol. 17, p. 169 (1945–6).

XV. 2. J. M. A. Lenihan and E. G. Richardson, *Phil. Mag.*, Vol. 29, p. 409 (1940); A. T. Jones, *Journ. Amer. Soc. Acoust.*, Vol. 12, p. 387 (1940–1) and Vol. 14, p. 131 (1942–3).

XVI. 18. M. D. Waller, *Proc. Phys. Soc.*, Vol. 45, p. 101 (1933) and Vol. 46, p. 116 (1934); *Nature*, Vol. 135, p. 475 (1935); *Proc. Phys. Soc.*, Vol. 49, p. 522 (1937) and Vol. 50, p. 70 (1938) and Vol. 51, p. 831 (1939); *Nature*, Vol. 143, p. 27 (1939); *Proc. Phys. Soc.*, Vol. 52, p. 452 (1940); *Nature*, Vol. 148, p. 185 (1941); *Proc. Phys. Soc.*, Vol. 53, p. 35 (1941).

XVII. 2. S. S. Stevens, C. T. Morgan and J. Volkmann, *Amer. J. Psych.*, Vol. 54, p. 315 (1941); W. R. Garner and G. A. Miller, *Journ. Exp. Psychol.*, Vol. 34, p. 450 (1944); F. M. Wiener and D. A. Ross, *Journ. Amer. Soc. Acoust.*, Vol. 18, p. 401 (1946).

4. W. R. Thurlow, *Psychol. Bull.*, Vol. 39, p. 503 (1942).

5. Don Lewis, *Psych. Rev.*, Vol. 47, p. 169 (1940); C. R. Moe, *Journ. Amer. Soc. Acoust.*, Vol. 14, p. 159 (1942–3).

8. E. G. Wever, C. W. Bray and M. Lawrence, *Journ. Exper. Psychol.*, Vol. 27, pp. 217 and 469 (1940); E. Allen, *Nature*, Vol. 156, p. 84 (1945).

CHAP. Par.

XVII.   9.   D. Lewis and M. J. Larsen, *Journ. Exper. Psychol.*, Vol. 27, p. 601 (1940).

     10.   D. Silverman, *Electronics*, Vol. 12, p. 34 (Feb., 1939); A. J. King, R. W. Guelke, C. R. Maguire and R. A. Scott, *J. Inst. E.E.*, Vol. 882, p. 163 (1941); P. E. Sabine, *Journ. Amer. Soc. Acoust.*, Vol. 13, p. 210 (1941–2).

     12.   J. Lewis and M. J. Larsen, *J. Exper. Psych.*, Vol. 28, p. 163 (1941).

     13.   C. S. Hallpike, H. Hartridge and A. F. Rawdon-Smith, *Phys. Soc. Proc.* Vol. 49, p. 190 (1937); J. A. Reboul, *Journ. de Physique*, Vol. 9, p. 428 (1938); E. G. Wever, C. W. Bray and M. Lawrence, *Journ. Amer. Soc. Acoust.*, Vol. 12, p. 268 (1940); R. C. Jones, S. S. Stevens and M. H. Lurie, *Ibid.*, p. 281 ; C. S. Hallpike and P. Scott, *J. Physiol.*, Vol. 99, p. 76 (1940); Harvey Fletcher, *Rev. Mod. Phys.*, Vol. 12, p. 47 (1940); D. M. Speaker, *Electronics*, Vol. 14, p. 38 (Sept., 1941); W. R. Thurlow, *J. Exper. Psych.*, Vol. 32, p. 344 (1943); F. C. Ormerod, *J. Laryng.*, Vol. 58, p. 1 (1943); E. D. Adrian, *Ibid.*, p. 15; P. Kellaway, *Amer. J. Psychol.*, Vol. 58, p. 25 (1945).

     14.   T. S. Littler, *Nature*, Vol. 146, p. 217 (1940); E. D. D. Dickson, *J. Laryngol.*, Vol. 57, p. 8 (1942); J. E. McGibbon, *Ibid*, p. 14; H. A. Carter, *Journ. Amer. Soc. Acoust.*, Vol. 15, p. 87 (1943–4); H. L. Haines, *Ibid.*, Vol. 17, p. 136 (1954–6); J. D. Harris, *Ibid.*, p. 139; L. Ruedi and W. Furrer, *Ibid.*, Vol. 18, p. 409 (1946).

XVIII.   2.   H. G. Tasker, *J. Soc. Mot. Pict. Engrs.*, Vol. 39, p. 213 (1942); B. B. Bauer, *Journ. Amer. Soc. Acoust.*, Vol. 18, p. 387 (1946).

     3.   W. Harris, *Junior Inst. Engl. J.*, Vol. 48, p. 257 (1938); N. Levinson, *Electronics*, Vol. 14, p. 37 (Feb., 1941); E. W. Kellogg, *J. Soc. Mot. Pict. Engrs.*, Vol. 44, p. 151 (1945).

     14.   T. Lindenberg, Jnr., *Electronics*, Vol. 18, p. 108 (June 1945); B. B. Bauer, *Journ. Amer. Soc. Acoust.*, Vol. 16, p. 246 (1945); A. L. Williams, *J. Soc. Mot. Pict. Engrs.*, Vol. 33, p. 203 (1939).

     15.   J. Moir, *Wireless World*, Vol. 49, pp. 320 and 362 (1943).

     17.   F. Massa, *Proc. I.R.E.*, Vol. 26, p. 720 (1938); A. J. Sanial, *Electronics*, Vol. 12, p. 16 (Jan., 1939).

     18.   H. Fletcher, *Proc. I.R.E.*, Vol. 30, p. 266 (1942); G. M. Nixon, *Journ. Amer. Soc. Acoust.*, Vol. 17, p. 132 (1945–6).

XIX.   1.   P. M. Morse and R. H. Bolt, *Rev. Mod. Phys.*, Vol. 16, p. 69 (1944).

     2.   D. Y. Maa, *Journ. Amer. Soc. Acoust.*, Vol. 13, p. 170 (1941–2).

     3.   F. V. Hunt, L. L. Beranek and D. Y. Maa, *Ibid.*, Vol. 11, p. 80 (1939–40); R. B. Watson, *Ibid.*, Vol. 18, p. 119 (1946); D. Y. Maa, *Ibid.*, p. 134.

     4.   C. M. Harris, *Ibid.*, Vol. 17, p. 242 (1945–6); R. A. Scott, *Proc. Phys. Soc.*, Vol. 58, p. 358 (1946); H. Feshbach and C. M. Harris, *Journ. Amer. Soc. Acoust.*, Vol. 18, p. 472 (1946).

     6.   P. M. Morse, R. H. Bolt and R. L. Brown, *Ibid.*, Vol. 12, p. 217 (1940–1); P. E. Sabine, *Ibid.*, p. 317; A. Gemant, *J. Applied Physics*, Vol. 12, p. 725 (1941); L. L. Beranek, *Journ. Amer. Soc. Acoust.*, Vol. 13, p. 248 (1941–2); W. F. Meeker and F. H. Slaymarker, *Ibid.*, Vol. 16, p. 178 (1944–5); C. M. Harris, *Ibid.*, Vol. 17, p. 35 (1945–6); R. A. Scott, *Proc. Phys. Soc.*, Vol. 58, p. 253 (1946).

CHAP. PAR.

XIX. 7. P. C. Goldmark and S. Hendricks, *Journ. Soc. Mot. Pict. Engrs.*, Vol. 33, p. 635 (1939); M. Rettinger, *Ibid.*, p. 410; J. P. Maxfield and C. C. Potwin, *Journ. Amer. Soc. Acoust.*, Vol. 11, p. 390 (1939–40); V. O. Knudsen, *Ibid.*, p. 383; A. Goodman, *Journ. Soc. Mot. Pict. Engrs.*, Vol. 37, p. 510 (1941); M. Rettinger, *Ibid.*, Vol. 39, p. 186 (1942).

8. M. Rettinger, *Proc. I.R.E.*, Vol. 28, p. 296 (1940); C. P. Boner, *Journ. Amer. Soc. Acoust.*, Vol. 13, p. 244 (1941–2); E. J. Content and L. Green, Jnr., *Proc. I.R.E.*, Vol. 32, p. 72 (1944); H. A. Chinn and P. Eisenberg, *Ibid.*, Vol. 33, p. 571 (1945); J. P. Maxfield and W. J. Aldersheim, *Jour. Amer. Soc. Acoust.*, Vol. 19, p. 71 (1947).

9. J. E. R. Constable, *Proc. Phys. Soc.*, Vol. 50, p. 368 (1938); W. Allen, *J. Roy. Soc. Arts.*, Vol. 91, p. 135 (1943).

NAME INDEX

SUBJECT INDEX

CATALOGUE OF DOVER BOOKS

BOOKS EXPLAINING SCIENCE AND MATHEMATICS

General

WHAT IS SCIENCE?, Norman Campbell. This excellent introduction explains scientific method, role of mathematics, types of scientific laws. Contents: 2 aspects of science, science & nature, laws of science, discovery of laws, explanation of laws, measurement & numerical laws, applications of science. 192pp. 5⅜ x 8. S43 Paperbound **$1.25**

THE COMMON SENSE OF THE EXACT SCIENCES, W. K. Clifford. Introduction by James Newman, edited by Karl Pearson. For 70 years this has been a guide to classical scientific and mathematical thought. Explains with unusual clarity basic concepts, such as extension of meaning of symbols, characteristics of surface boundaries, properties of plane figures, vectors, Cartesian method of determining position, etc. Long preface by Bertrand Russell. Bibliography of Clifford. Corrected, 130 diagrams redrawn. 249pp. 5⅜ x 8.
T61 Paperbound **$1.60**

SCIENCE THEORY AND MAN, Erwin Schrödinger. This is a complete and unabridged reissue of SCIENCE AND THE HUMAN TEMPERAMENT plus an additional essay: "What is an Elementary Particle?" Nobel laureate Schrödinger discusses such topics as nature of scientific method, the nature of science, chance and determinism, science and society, conceptual models for physical entities, elementary particles and wave mechanics. Presentation is popular and may be followed by most people with little or no scientific training. "Fine practical preparation for a time when laws of nature, human institutions . . . are undergoing a critical examination without parallel," Waldemar Kaempffert, N. Y. TIMES. 192pp. 5⅜ x 8.
T428 Paperbound **$1.35**

FADS AND FALLACIES IN THE NAME OF SCIENCE, Martin Gardner. Examines various cults, quack systems, frauds, delusions which at various times have masqueraded as science. Accounts of hollow-earth fanatics like Symmes; Velikovsky and wandering planets; Hoerbiger; Bellamy and the theory of multiple moons; Charles Fort; dowsing, pseudoscientific methods for finding water, ores, oil. Sections on naturopathy, iridiagnosis, zone therapy, food fads, etc. Analytical accounts of Wilhelm Reich and orgone sex energy; L. Ron Hubbard and Dianetics; A. Korzybski and General Semantics; many others. Brought up to date to include Bridey Murphy, others. Not just a collection of anecdotes, but a fair, reasoned appraisal of eccentric theory. Formerly titled IN THE NAME OF SCIENCE. Preface. Index. x + 384pp. 5⅜ x 8. T394 Paperbound **$1.50**

A DOVER SCIENCE SAMPLER, edited by George Barkin. 64-page book, sturdily bound, containing excerpts from over 20 Dover books, explaining science. Edwin Hubble, George Sarton, Ernst Mach, A. d'Abro, Galileo, Newton, others, discussing island universes, scientific truth, biological phenomena, stability in bridges, etc. Copies limited; no more than 1 to a customer,
FREE

POPULAR SCIENTIFIC LECTURES, Hermann von Helmholtz. Helmholtz was a superb expositor as well as a scientist of genius in many areas. The seven essays in this volume are models of clarity, and even today they rank among the best general descriptions of their subjects ever written. "The Physiological Causes of Harmony in Music" was the first significant physiological explanation of musical consonance and dissonance. Two essays, "On the Interaction of Natural Forces" and "On the Conservation of Force," were of great importance in the history of science, for they firmly established the principle of the conservation of energy. Other lectures include "On the Relation of Optics to Painting," "On Recent Progress in the Theory of Vision," "On Goethe's Scientific Researches," and "On the Origin and Significance of Geometrical Axioms." Selected and edited with an introduction by Professor Morris Kline. xii + 286pp. 5⅜ x 8½. T799 Paperbound **$1.45**

BOOKS EXPLAINING SCIENCE AND MATHEMATICS

Physics

CONCERNING THE NATURE OF THINGS, Sir William Bragg. Christmas lectures delivered at the Royal Society by Nobel laureate. Why a spinning ball travels in a curved track; how uranium is transmuted to lead, etc. Partial contents: atoms, gases, liquids, crystals, metals, etc. No scientific background needed; wonderful for intelligent child. 32pp. of photos, 57 figures. xii + 232pp. 5⅜ x 8. T31 Paperbound **$1.50**

THE RESTLESS UNIVERSE, Max Born. New enlarged version of this remarkably readable account by a Nobel laureate. Moving from sub-atomic particles to universe, the author explains in very simple terms the latest theories of wave mechanics. Partial contents: air and its relatives, electrons & ions, waves & particles, electronic structure of the atom, nuclear physics. Nearly 1000 illustrations, including 7 animated sequences. 325pp. 6 x 9.
T412 Paperbound **$2.00**

FROM EUCLID TO EDDINGTON: A STUDY OF THE CONCEPTIONS OF THE EXTERNAL WORLD, Sir Edmund Whittaker. A foremost British scientist traces the development of theories of natural philosophy from the western rediscovery of Euclid to Eddington, Einstein, Dirac, etc. The inadequacy of classical physics is contrasted with present day attempts to understand the physical world through relativity, non-Euclidean geometry, space curvature, wave mechanics, etc. 5 major divisions of examination: Space; Time and Movement; the Concepts of Classical Physics; the Concepts of Quantum Mechanics; the Eddington Universe. 212pp. 5⅜ x 8.   T491 Paperbound **$1.35**

PHYSICS, THE PIONEER SCIENCE, L. W. Taylor. First thorough text to place all important physical phenomena in cultural-historical framework; remains best work of its kind. Exposition of physical laws, theories· developed chronologically, with great historical, illustrative experiments diagrammed, described, worked out mathematically. Excellent physics text for self-study as well as class work. Vol. 1: Heat, Sound: motion, acceleration, gravitation, conservation of energy, heat engines, rotation, heat, mechanical energy, etc. 211 illus. 407pp. 5⅜ x 8. Vol. 2: Light, Electricity: images, lenses, prisms, magnetism, Ohm's law, dynamos, telegraph, quantum theory, decline of mechanical view of nature, etc. Bibliography. 13 table appendix. Index. 551 illus. 2 color plates. 508pp. 5⅜ x 8.

Vol. 1 S565 Paperbound **$2.00**
Vol. 2 S566 Paperbound **$2.00**
The set **$4.00**

A SURVEY OF PHYSICAL THEORY, Max Planck. One of the greatest scientists of all time, creator of the quantum revolution in physics, writes in non-technical terms of his own discoveries and those of other outstanding creators of modern physics. Planck wrote this book when science had just crossed the threshold of the new physics, and he communicates the excitement felt then as he discusses electromagnetic theories, statistical methods, evolution of the concept of light, a step-by-step description of how he developed his own momentous theory, and many more of the basic ideas behind modern physics. Formerly "A Survey of Physics." Bibliography. Index. 128pp. 5⅜ x 8.   S650 Paperbound **$1.15**

THE ATOMIC NUCLEUS, M. Korsunsky. The only non-technical comprehensive account of the atomic nucleus in English. For college physics students, etc. Chapters cover: Radioactivity, the Nuclear Model of the Atom, the Mass of Atomic Nuclei, the Disintegration of Atomic Nuclei, the Discovery of the Positron, the Artificial Transformation of Atomic Nuclei, Artificial Radioactivity, Mesons, the Neutrino, the Structure of Atomic Nuclei and Forces Acting Between Nuclear Particles, Nuclear Fission, Chain Reaction, Peaceful Uses, Thermonuclear Reactions. Slightly abridged edition. Translated by G. Yankovsky. 65 figures. Appendix includes 45 photographic illustrations. 413 pp. 5⅜ x 8.   S1052 Paperbound **$2.00**

PRINCIPLES OF MECHANICS SIMPLY EXPLAINED, Morton Mott-Smith. Excellent, highly readable introduction to the theories and discoveries of classical physics. Ideal for the layman who desires a foundation which will enable him to understand and appreciate contemporary developments in the physical sciences. Discusses: Density, The Law of Gravitation, Mass and Weight, Action and Reaction, Kinetic and Potential Energy, The Law of Inertia, Effects of Acceleration, The Independence of Motions, Galileo and the New Science of Dynamics, Newton and the New Cosmos, The Conservation of Momentum, and other topics. Revised edition of "This Mechanical World." Illustrated by E. Kosa, Jr. Bibliography and Chronology. Index. xiv + 171pp. 5⅜ x 8½.   T1067 Paperbound **$1.00**

THE CONCEPT OF ENERGY SIMPLY EXPLAINED, Morton Mott-Smith. Elementary, non-technical exposition which traces the story of man's conquest of energy, with particular emphasis on the developments during the nineteenth century and the first three decades of our own century. Discusses man's earlier efforts to harness energy, more recent experiments and discoveries relating to the steam engine, the engine indicator, the motive power of heat, the principle of excluded perpetual motion, the bases of the conservation of energy, the concept of entropy, the internal combustion engine, mechanical refrigeration, and many other related topics. Also much biographical material. Index. Bibliography. 33 illustrations. ix + 215pp. 5⅜ x 8½.   T1071 Paperbound **$1.25**

HEAT AND ITS WORKINGS, Morton Mott-Smith. One of the best elementary introductions to the theory and attributes of heat, covering such matters as the laws governing the effect of heat on solids, liquids and gases, the methods by which heat is measured, the conversion of a substance from one form to another through heating and cooling, evaporation, the effects of pressure on boiling and freezing points, and the three ways in which heat is transmitted (conduction, convection, radiation). Also brief notes on major experiments and discoveries. Concise, but complete, it presents all the essential facts about the subject in readable style. Will give the layman and beginning student a first-rate background in this major topic in physics. Index. Bibliography. 50 illustrations. x + 165pp. 5⅜ x 8½. T978 Paperbound **$1.15**

THE STORY OF ATOMIC THEORY AND ATOMIC ENERGY, J. G. Feinberg. Wider range of facts on physical theory, cultural implications, than any other similar source. Completely non-technical. Begins with first atomic theory, 600 B.C., goes through A-bomb, developments to 1959. Avogadro, Rutherford, Bohr, Einstein, radioactive decay, binding energy, radiation danger, future benefits of nuclear power, dozens of other topics, told in lively, related, informal manner. Particular stress on European atomic research. "Deserves special mention . . . authoritative," Saturday Review. Formerly "The Atom Story." New chapter to 1959. Index. 34 illustrations. 251pp. 5⅜ x 8.   T625 Paperbound **$1.60**

THE STRANGE STORY OF THE QUANTUM, AN ACCOUNT FOR THE GENERAL READER OF THE GROWTH OF IDEAS UNDERLYING OUR PRESENT ATOMIC KNOWLEDGE, B. Hoffmann. Presents lucidly and expertly, with barest amount of mathematics, the problems and theories which led to modern quantum physics. Dr. Hoffmann begins with the closing years of the 19th century, when certain trifling discrepancies were noticed, and with illuminating analogies and examples takes you through the brilliant concepts of Planck, Einstein, Pauli, de Broglie, Bohr, Schroedinger, Heisenberg, Dirac, Sommerfeld, Feynman, etc. This edition includes a new, long postscript carrying the story through 1958. "Of the books attempting an account of the history and contents of our modern atomic physics which have come to my attention, this is the best," H. Margenau, Yale University, in "American Journal of Physics." 32 tables and line illustrations. Index. 275pp. 5⅜ x 8. T518 Paperbound **$1.50**

THE EVOLUTION OF SCIENTIFIC THOUGHT FROM NEWTON TO EINSTEIN, A. d'Abro. Einstein's special and general theories of relativity, with their historical implications, are analyzed in non-technical terms. Excellent accounts of the contributions of Newton, Riemann, Weyl, Planck, Eddington, Maxwell, Lorentz and others are treated in terms of space and time, equations of electromagnetics, finiteness of the universe, methodology of science. 21 diagrams. 482pp. 5⅜ x 8. T2 Paperound **$2.25**

THE RISE OF THE NEW PHYSICS, A. d'Abro. A half-million word exposition, formerly titled THE DECLINE OF MECHANISM, for readers not versed in higher mathematics. The only thorough explanation, in everyday language, of the central core of modern mathematical physical theory, treating both classical and modern theoretical physics, and presenting in terms almost anyone can understand the equivalent of 5 years of study of mathematical physics. Scientifically impeccable coverage of mathematical-physical thought from the Newtonian system up through the electronic theories of Dirac and Heisenberg and Fermi's statistics. Combines both history and exposition; provides a broad yet unified and detailed view, with constant comparison of classical and modern views on phenomena and theories. "A must for anyone doing serious study in the physical sciences," JOURNAL OF THE FRANKLIN INSTITUTE. "Extraordinary faculty . . . to explain ideas and theories of theoretical physics in the language of daily life," ISIS. First part of set covers philosophy of science, drawing upon the practice of Newton, Maxwell, Poincaré, Einstein, others, discussing modes of thought, experiment, interpretations of causality, etc. In the second part, 100 pages explain grammar and vocabulary of mathematics, with discussions of functions, groups, series, Fourier series, etc. The remainder is devoted to concrete, detailed coverage of both classical and quantum physics, explaining such topics as analytic mechanics, Hamilton's principle, wave theory of light, electromagnetic waves, groups of transformations, thermodynamics, phase rule, Brownian movement, kinetics, special relativity, Planck's original quantum theory, Bohr's atom, Zeeman effect, Broglie's wave mechanics, Heisenberg's uncertainty, Eigen-values, matrices, scores of other important topics. Discoveries and theories are covered for such men as Alembert, Born, Cantor, Debye, Euler, Foucault, Galois, Gauss, Hadamard, Kelvin, Kepler, Laplace, Maxwell, Pauli, Rayleigh, Volterra, Weyl, Young, more than 180 others. Indexed. 97 illustrations. ix + 982pp. 5⅜ x 8. T3 Volume 1, Paperbound **$2.25**
T4 Volume 2, Paperbound **$2.25**

SPINNING TOPS AND GYROSCOPIC MOTION, John Perry. Well-known classic of science still unsurpassed for lucid, accurate, delightful exposition. How quasi-rigidity is induced in flexible and fluid bodies by rapid motions; why gyrostat falls, top rises; nature and effect on climatic conditions of earth's precessional movement; effect of internal fluidity on rotating bodies, etc. Appendixes describe practical uses to which gyroscopes have been put in ships, compasses, monorail transportation. 62 figures. 128pp. 5⅜ x 8. T416 Paperbound **$1.00**

THE UNIVERSE OF LIGHT, Sir William Bragg. No scientific training needed to read Nobel Prize winner's expansion of his Royal Institute Christmas Lectures. Insight into nature of light, methods and philosophy of science. Explains lenses, reflection, color, resonance, polarization, x-rays, the spectrum, Newton's work with prisms, Huygens' with polarization, Crookes' with cathode ray, etc. Leads into clear statement of 2 major historical theories of light, corpuscle and wave. Dozens of experiments you can do. 199 illus., including 2 full-page color plates. 293pp. 5⅜ x 8. S538 Paperbound **$1.85**

THE STORY OF X-RAYS FROM RÖNTGEN TO ISOTOPES, A. R. Bleich. Non-technical history of x-rays, their scientific explanation, their applications in medicine, industry, research, and art, and their effect on the individual and his descendants. Includes amusing early reactions to Röntgen's discovery, cancer therapy, detections of art and stamp forgeries, potential risks to patient and operator, etc. Illustrations show x-rays of flower structure, the gall bladder, gears with hidden defects, etc. Original Dover publication. Glossary. Bibliography. Index. 55 photos and figures. xiv + 186pp. 5⅜ x 8. T662 Paperbound **$1.35**

ELECTRONS, ATOMS, METALS AND ALLOYS, Wm. Hume-Rothery. An introductory-level explanation of the application of the electronic theory to the structure and properties of metals and alloys, taking into account the new theoretical work done by mathematical physicists. Material presented in dialogue-form between an "Old Metallurgist" and a "Young Scientist." Their discussion falls into 4 main parts: the nature of an atom, the nature of a metal, the nature of an alloy, and the structure of the nucleus. They cover such topics as the hydrogen atom, electron waves, wave mechanics, Brillouin zones, co-valent bonds, radioactivity and natural disintegration, fundamental particles, structure and fission of the nucleus, etc. Revised, enlarged edition. 177 illustrations. Subject and name indexes. 407pp. 5⅜ x 8½. S1046 Paperbound **$2.25**

OUT OF THE SKY, H. H. Nininger. A non-technical but comprehensive introduction to "meteoritics", the young science concerned with all aspects of the arrival of matter from outer space. Written by one of the world's experts on meteorites, this work shows how, despite difficulties of observation and sparseness of data, a considerable body of knowledge has arisen. It defines meteors and meteorites; studies fireball clusters and processions, meteorite composition, size, distribution, showers, explosions, origins, craters, and much more. A true connecting link between astronomy and geology. More than 175 photos, 22 other illustrations. References. Bibliography of author's publications on meteorites. Index. viii + 336pp. 5⅜ x 8. T519 Paperbound **$1.85**

SATELLITES AND SCIENTIFIC RESEARCH, D. King-Hele. Non-technical account of the manmade satellites and the discoveries they have yielded up to the autumn of 1961. Brings together information hitherto published only in hard-to-get scientific journals. Includes the life history of a typical satellite, methods of tracking, new information on the shape of the earth, zones of radiation, etc. Over 60 diagrams and 6 photographs. Mathematical appendix. Bibliography of over 100 items. Index. xii + 180pp. 5⅜ x 8½. T703 Paperbound **$2.00**

BOOKS EXPLAINING SCIENCE AND MATHEMATICS

Mathematics

CHANCE, LUCK AND STATISTICS: THE SCIENCE OF CHANCE, Horace C. Levinson. Theory of probability and science of statistics in simple, non-technical language. Part I deals with theory of probability, covering odd superstitions in regard to "luck," the meaning of betting odds, the law of mathematical expectation, gambling, and applications in poker, roulette, lotteries, dice, bridge, and other games of chance. Part II discusses the misuse of statistics, the concept of statistical probabilities, normal and skew frequency distributions, and statistics applied to various fields—birth rates, stock speculation, insurance rates, advertising, etc. "Presented in an easy humorous style which I consider the best kind of expository writing," Prof. A. C. Cohen, Industry Quality Control. Enlarged revised edition. Formerly titled "The Science of Chance." Preface and two new appendices by the author. Index. xiv + 365pp. 5⅜ x 8. T1007 Paperbound **$1.85**

PROBABILITIES AND LIFE, Emile Borel. Translated by M. Baudin. Non-technical, highly readable introduction to the results of probability as applied to everyday situations. Partial contents: Fallacies About Probabilities Concerning Life After Death; Negligible Probabilities and the Probabilities of Everyday Life; Events of Small Probability; Application of Probabilities to Certain Problems of Heredity; Probabilities of Deaths, Diseases, and Accidents; On Poisson's Formula. Index. 3 Appendices of statistical studies and tables. vi + 87pp. 5⅜ x 8½. T121 Paperbound **$1.00**

GREAT IDEAS OF MODERN MATHEMATICS: THEIR NATURE AND USE, Jagjit Singh. Reader with only high school math will understand main mathematical ideas of modern physics, astronomy, genetics, psychology, evolution, etc., better than many who use them as tools, but comprehend little of their basic structure. Author uses his wide knowledge of non-mathematical fields in brilliant exposition of differential equations, matrices, group theory, logic, statistics, problems of mathematical foundations, imaginary numbers, vectors, etc. Original publication. 2 appendices. 2 indexes. 65 illustr. 322pp. 5⅜ x 8. S587 Paperbound **$1.75**

MATHEMATICS IN ACTION, O. G. Sutton. Everyone with a command of high school algebra will find this book one of the finest possible introductions to the application of mathematics to physical theory. Ballistics, numerical analysis, waves and wavelike phenomena, Fourier series, group concepts, fluid flow and aerodynamics, statistical measures, and meteorology are discussed with unusual clarity. Some calculus and differential equations theory is developed by the author for the reader's help in the more difficult sections. 88 figures. Index. viii + 236pp. 5⅜ x 8. T440 Clothbound **$3.50**

THE FOURTH DIMENSION SIMPLY EXPLAINED, edited by H. P. Manning. 22 essays, originally Scientific American contest entries, that use a minimum of mathematics to explain aspects of 4-dimensional geometry: analogues to 3-dimensional space, 4-dimensional absurdities and curiosities (such as removing the contents of an egg without puncturing its shell), possible measurements and forms, etc. Introduction by the editor. Only book of its sort on a truly elementary level, excellent introduction to advanced works. 82 figures. 251pp. 5⅜ x 8. T711 Paperbound **$1.35**

MATHEMATICS—INTERMEDIATE TO ADVANCED

General

INTRODUCTION TO APPLIED MATHEMATICS, Francis D. Murnaghan. A practical and thoroughly sound introduction to a number of advanced branches of higher mathematics. Among the selected topics covered in detail are: vector and matrix analysis, partial and differential equations, integral equations, calculus of variations, Laplace transform theory, the vector triple product, linear vector functions, quadratic and bilinear forms, Fourier series, spherical harmonics, Bessel functions, the Heaviside expansion formula, and many others. Extremely useful book for graduate students in physics, engineering, chemistry, and mathematics. Index. 111 study exercises with answers. 41 illustrations. ix + 389pp. 5⅜ x 8½.
S1042 Paperbound **$2.00**

OPERATIONAL METHODS IN APPLIED MATHEMATICS, H. S. Carslaw and J. C. Jaeger. Explanation of the application of the Laplace Transformation to differential equations, a simple and effective substitute for more difficult and obscure operational methods. Of great practical value to engineers and to all workers in applied mathematics. Chapters on: Ordinary Linear Differential Equations with Constant Coefficients;; Electric Circuit Theory; Dynamical Applications; The Inversion Theorem for the Laplace Transformation; Conduction of Heat; Vibrations of Continuous Mechanical Systems; Hydrodynamics; Impulsive Functions; Chains of Differential Equations; and other related matters. 3 appendices. 153 problems, many with answers. 22 figures. xvi + 359pp. 5⅜ x 8½.
S1011 Paperbound **$2.25**

APPLIED MATHEMATICS FOR RADIO AND COMMUNICATIONS ENGINEERS, C. E. Smith. No extraneous material here!—only the theories, equations, and operations essential and immediately useful for radio work. Can be used as refresher, as handbook of applications and tables, or as full home-study course. Ranges from simplest arithmetic through calculus, series, and wave forms, hyperbolic trigonometry, simultaneous equations in mesh circuits, etc. Supplies applications right along with each math topic discussed. 22 useful tables of functions, formulas, logs, etc. Index. 166 exercises, 140 examples, all with answers. 95 diagrams. Bibliography. x + 336pp. 5⅜ x 8.
S141 Paperbound **$1.75**

Algebra, group theory, determinants, sets, matrix theory

ALGEBRAS AND THEIR ARITHMETICS, L. E. Dickson. Provides the foundation and background necessary to any advanced undergraduate or graduate student studying abstract algebra. Begins with elementary introduction to linear transformations, matrices, field of complex numbers; proceeds to order, basal units, modulus, quaternions, etc.; develops calculus of linears sets, describes various examples of algebras including invariant, difference, nilpotent, semi-simple. "Makes the reader marvel at his genius for clear and profound analysis," Amer. Mathematical Monthly. Index. xii + 241pp. 5⅜ x 8.
S616 Paperbound **$1.50**

THE THEORY OF EQUATIONS WITH AN INTRODUCTION TO THE THEORY OF BINARY ALGEBRAIC FORMS, W. S. Burnside and A. W. Panton. Extremely thorough and concrete discussion of the theory of equations, with extensive detailed treatment of many topics curtailed in later texts. Covers theory of algebraic equations, properties of polynomials, symmetric functions, derived functions, Horner's process, complex numbers and the complex variable, determinants and methods of elimination, invariant theory (nearly 100 pages), transformations, introduction to Galois theory, Abelian equations, and much more. Invaluable supplementary work for modern students and teachers. 759 examples and exercises. Index in each volume. Two volume set. Total of xxiv + 604pp. 5⅜ x 8.
S714 Vol I Paperbound **$1.85**
S715 Vol II Paperbound **$1.85**
The set **$3.70**

COMPUTATIONAL METHODS OF LINEAR ALGEBRA, V. N. Faddeeva, translated by **C. D. Benster.** First English translation of a unique and valuable work, the only work in English presenting a systematic exposition of the most important methods of linear algebra—classical and contemporary. Shows in detail how to derive numerical solutions of problems in mathematical physics which are frequently connected with those of linear algebra. Theory as well as individual practice. Part I surveys the mathematical background that is indispensable to what follows. Parts II and III, the conclusion, set forth the most important methods of solution, for both exact and iterative groups. One of the most outstanding and valuable features of this work is the 23 tables, double and triple checked for accuracy. These tables will not be found elsewhere. Author's preface. Translator's note. New bibliography and index. x + 252pp. 5⅜ x 8.
S424 Paperbound **$1.95**

ALGEBRAIC EQUATIONS, E. Dehn. Careful and complete presentation of Galois' theory of algebraic equations; theories of Lagrange and Galois developed in logical rather than historical form, with a more thorough exposition than in most modern books. Many concrete applications and fully-worked-out examples. Discusses basic theory (very clear exposition of the symmetric group); isomorphic, transitive, and Abelian groups; applications of Lagrange's and Galois' theories; and much more. Newly revised by the author. Index. List of Theorems. xi + 208pp. 5⅜ x 8.
S697 Paperbound **$1.45**

Differential equations, ordinary and partial; integral equations

INTRODUCTION TO THE DIFFERENTIAL EQUATIONS OF PHYSICS, L. Hopf. Especially valuable to the engineer with no math beyond elementary calculus. Emphasizing intuitive rather than formal aspects of concepts, the author covers an extensive territory. Partial contents: Law of causality, energy theorem, damped oscillations, coupling by friction, cylindrical and spherical coordinates, heat source, etc. Index. 48 figures. 160pp. 5⅜ x 8.
S120 Paperbound **$1.25**

INTRODUCTION TO THE THEORY OF LINEAR DIFFERENTIAL EQUATIONS, E. G. Poole. Authoritative discussions of important topics, with methods of solution more detailed than usual, for students with background of elementary course in differential equations. Studies existence theorems, linearly independent solutions; equations with constant coefficients; with uniform analytic coefficients; regular singularities; the hypergeometric equation; conformal representation; etc. Exercises. Index. 210pp. 5⅜ x 8. S629 Paperbound **$1.65**

DIFFERENTIAL EQUATIONS FOR ENGINEERS, P. Franklin. Outgrowth of a course given 10 years at M. I. T. Makes most useful branch of pure math accessible for practical work. Theoretical basis of D.E.'s; solution of ordinary D.E.'s and partial derivatives arising from heat flow, steady-state temperature of a plate, wave equations; analytic functions; convergence of Fourier Series. 400 problems on electricity, vibratory systems, other topics. Formerly "Differential Equations for Electrical Engineers." Index 41 illus. 307pp. 5⅜ x 8.
S601 Paperbound **$1.65**

DIFFERENTIAL EQUATIONS, F. R. Moulton. A detailed, rigorous exposition of all the non-elementary processes of solving ordinary differential equations. Several chapters devoted to the treatment of practical problems, especially those of a physical nature, which are far more advanced than problems usually given as illustrations. Includes analytic differential equations; variations of a parameter; integrals of differential equations; analytic implicit functions; problems of elliptic motion; sine-amplitude functions; deviation of formal bodies; Cauchy-Lipschitz process; linear differential equations with periodic coefficients; differential equations in infinitely many variations; much more. Historical notes. 10 figures. 222 problems. Index. xv + 395pp. 5⅜ x 8. S451 Paperbound **$2.00**

DIFFERENTIAL AND INTEGRAL EQUATIONS OF MECHANICS AND PHYSICS (DIE DIFFERENTIAL-UND INTEGRALGLEICHUNGEN DER MECHANIK UND PHYSIK), edited by P. Frank and R. von Mises. Most comprehensive and authoritative work on the mathematics of mathematical physics available today in the United States: the standard, definitive reference for teachers, physicists, engineers, and mathematicians—now published (in the original German) at a relatively inexpensive price for the first time! Every chapter in this 2,000-page set is by an expert in his field: Carathéodory, Courant, Frank, Mises, and a dozen others. Vol I, on mathematics, gives concise but complete coverages of advanced calculus, differential equations, integral equations, and potential, and partial differential equations. Index. xxiii + 916pp. Vol. II (physics): classical mechanics, optics, continuous mechanics, heat conduction and diffusion, the stationary and quasi-stationary electromagnetic field, electromagnetic oscillations, and wave mechanics. Index. xxiv + 1106pp. Two volume set. Each volume available separately. 5⅝ x 8⅜.
S787 Vol I Clothbound **$7.50**
S788 Vol II Clothbound **$7.50**
The set **$15.00**

LECTURES ON CAUCHY'S PROBLEM, J. Hadamard. Based on lectures given at Columbia, Rome, this discusses work of Riemann, Kirchhoff, Volterra, and the author's own research on the hyperbolic case in linear partial differential equations. It extends spherical and cylindrical waves to apply to all (normal) hyperbolic equations. Partial contents: Cauchy's problem, fundamental formula, equations with odd number, with even number of independent variables; method of descent. 32 figures. Index. iii + 316pp. 5⅜ x 8.   S105 Paperbound **$1.75**

THEORY OF DIFFERENTIAL EQUATIONS, A. R. Forsyth. Out of print for over a decade, the complete 6 volumes (now bound as 3) of this monumental work represent the most comprehensive treatment of differential equations ever written. Historical presentation includes in 2500 pages every substantial development. Vol. 1, 2: EXACT EQUATIONS, PFAFF'S PROBLEM; ORDINARY EQUATIONS, NOT LINEAR: methods of Grassmann, Clebsch, Lie, Darboux; Cauchy's theorem; branch points; etc. Vol. 3, 4: ORDINARY EQUATIONS, NOT LINEAR; ORDINARY LINEAR EQUATIONS: Zeta Fuchsian functions, general theorems on algebraic integrals, Brun's theorem, equations with uniform periodic coffiecients, etc. Vol. 4, 5: PARTIAL DIFFERENTIAL EQUATIONS: 2 existence-theorems, equations of theoretical dynamics, Laplace transformations, general transformation of equations of the 2nd order, much more. Indexes. Total of 2766pp. 5⅜ x 8. S576-7-8 Clothbound: the set **$15.00**

PARTIAL DIFFERENTIAL EQUATIONS OF MATHEMATICAL PHYSICS, A. G. Webster. A keystone work in the library of every mature physicist, engineer, researcher. Valuable sections on elasticity, compression theory, potential theory, theory of sound, heat conduction, wave propagation, vibration theory. Contents include: deduction of differential equations, vibrations, normal functions, Fourier's series, Cauchy's method, boundary problems, method of Riemann-Volterra. Spherical, cylindrical, ellipsoidal harmonics, applications, etc. 97 figures. vii + 440pp. 5⅜ x 8. S263 Paperbound **$2.00**

ELEMENTARY CONCEPTS OF TOPOLOGY, P. Alexandroff. First English translation of the famous brief introduction to topology for the beginner or for the mathematician not undertaking extensive study. This unusually useful intuitive approach deals primarily with the concepts of complex, cycle, and homology, and is wholly consistent with current investigations. Ranges from basic concepts of set-theoretic topology to the concept of Betti groups. "Glowing example of harmony between intuition and thought," David Hilbert. Translated by A. E. Farley. Introduction by D. Hilbert. Index. 25 figures. 73pp. 5⅜ x 8.   S747 Paperbound $1.00

Number theory

INTRODUCTION TO THE THEORY OF NUMBERS, L. E. Dickson. Thorough, comprehensive approach with adequate coverage of classical literature, an introductory volume beginners can follow. Chapters on divisibility, congruences, quadratic residues & reciprocity, Diophantine equations, etc. Full treatment of binary quadratic forms without usual restriction to integral coefficients. Covers infinitude of primes, least residues, Fermat's theorem, Euler's phi function, Legendre's symbol, Gauss's lemma, automorphs, reduced forms, recent theorems of Thue & Siegel, many more. Much material not readily available elsewhere. 239 problems. Index. I figure. viii + 183pp. 5⅜ x 8.   S342 Paperbound $1.65

ELEMENTS OF NUMBER THEORY, I. M. Vinogradov. Detailed 1st course for persons without advanced mathematics; 95% of this book can be understood by readers who have gone no farther than high school algebra. Partial contents: divisibility theory, important number theoretical functions, congruences, primitive roots and indices, etc. Solutions to both problems and exercises. Tables of primes, indices, etc. Covers almost every essential formula in elementary number theory! Translated from Russian. 233 problems, 104 exercises. viii + 227pp. 5⅜ x 8.   S259 Paperbound $1.60

THEORY OF NUMBERS and DIOPHANTINE ANALYSIS, R. D. Carmichael. These two complete works in one volume form one of the most lucid introductions to number theory, requiring only a firm foundation in high school mathematics. "Theory of Numbers," partial contents: Eratosthenes' sieve, Euclid's fundamental theorem, G.C.F. and L.C.M. of two or more integers, linear congruences, etc "Diophantine Analysis": rational triangles, Pythagorean triangles, equations of third, fourth, higher degrees, method of functional equations, much more. "Theory of Numbers": 76 problems. Index. 94pp. "Diophantine Analysis": 222 problems. Index. 118pp. 5⅜ x 8.   S529 Paperbound $1.35

Numerical analysis, tables

MATHEMATICAL TABLES AND FORMULAS, Compiled by Robert D. Carmichael and Edwin R. Smith. Valuable collection for students, etc. Contains all tables necessary in college algebra and trigonometry, such as five-place common logarithms, logarithmic sines and tangents of small angles, logarithmic trigonometric functions, natural trigonometric functions, four-place antilogarithms, tables for changing from sexagesimal to circular and from circular to sexagesimal measure of angles, etc. Also many tables and formulas not ordinarily accessible, including powers, roots, and reciprocals, exponential and hyperbolic functions, ten-place logarithms of prime numbers, and formulas and theorems from analytical and elementary geometry and from calculus. Explanatory introduction. viii + 269pp. 5⅜ x 8½.
                     S111 Paperbound $1.00

MATHEMATICAL TABLES, H. B. Dwight. Unique for its coverage in one volume of almost every function of importance in applied mathematics, engineering, and the physical sciences. Three extremely fine tables of the three trig functions and their inverse functions to thousandths of radians; natural and common logarithms; squares, cubes; hyperbolic functions and the inverse hyperbolic functions; $(a^2 + b^2)$ exp. ½a; complete elliptic integrals of the 1st and 2nd kind; sine and cosine integrals; exponential integrals Ei(x) and Ei($-x$); binomial coefficients; factorials to 250; surface zonal harmonics and first derivatives; Bernoulli and Euler numbers and their logs to base of 10; Gamma function; normal probability integral; over 60 pages of Bessel functions; the Riemann Zeta function. Each table with formulae generally used, sources of more extensive tables, interpolation data, etc. Over half have columns of differences, to facilitate interpolation. Introduction. Index. viii + 231pp. 5⅜ x 8.
                     S445 Paperbound $2.00

TABLES OF FUNCTIONS WITH FORMULAE AND CURVES, E. Jahnke & F. Emde. The world's most comprehensive 1-volume English-text collection of tables, formulae, curves of transcendent functions. 4th corrected edition, new 76-page section giving tables, formulae for elementary functions—not in other English editions. Partial contents: sine, cosine, logarithmic integral; factorial function; error integral; theta functions; elliptic integrals, functions; Legendre, Bessel, Riemann, Mathieu, hypergeometric functions, etc. Supplementary books. Bibliography. Indexed. "Out of the way functions for which we know no other source," SCIENTIFIC COMPUTING SERVICE, Ltd. 212 figures. 400pp. 5⅜ x 8.   S133 Paperbound $2.00

CHEMISTRY AND PHYSICAL CHEMISTRY

ORGANIC CHEMISTRY, F. C. Whitmore. The entire subject of organic chemistry for the practicing chemist and the advanced student. Storehouse of facts, theories, processes found elsewhere only in specialized journals. Covers aliphatic compounds (500 pages on the properties and synthetic preparation of hydrocarbons, halides, proteins, ketones, etc.), alicyclic compounds, aromatic compounds, heterocyclic compounds, organophosphorus and organometallic compounds. Methods of synthetic preparation analyzed critically throughout. Includes much of biochemical interest. "The scope of this volume is astonishing," INDUSTRIAL AND ENGINEERING CHEMISTRY. 12,000-reference index. 2387-item bibliography. Total of x + 1005pp. 5⅜ x 8. Two volume set.

S700 Vol I Paperbound **$2.25**
S701 Vol II Paperbound **$2.25**
The set **$4.50**

THE MODERN THEORY OF MOLECULAR STRUCTURE, Bernard Pullman. A reasonably popular account of recent developments in atomic and molecular theory. Contents: The Wave Function and Wave Equations (history and bases of present theories of molecular structure); The Electronic Structure of Atoms (Description and classification of atomic wave functions, etc.); Diatomic Molecules; Non-Conjugated Polyatomic Molecules; Conjugated Polyatomic Molecules; The Structure of Complexes. Minimum of mathematical background needed. New translation by David Antin of "La Structure Moleculaire." Index. Bibliography. vii + 87pp. 5⅜ x 8½.
S987 Paperbound **$1.00**

CATALYSIS AND CATALYSTS, Marcel Prettre, Director, Research Institute on Catalysis. This brief book, translated into English for the first time, is the finest summary of the principal modern concepts, methods, and results of catalysis. Ideal introduction for beginning chemistry and physics students. Chapters: Basic Definitions of Catalysis (true catalysis and generalization of the concept of catalysis); The Scientific Bases of Catalysis (Catalysis and chemical thermodynamics, catalysis and chemical kinetics); Homogeneous Catalysis (acid-base catalysis, etc.); Chain Reactions; Contact Masses; Heterogeneous Catalysis (Mechanisms of contact catalyses, etc.); and Industrial Applications (acids and fertilizers, petroleum and petroleum chemistry, rubber, plastics, synthetic resins, and fibers). Translated by David Antin. Index. vi + 88pp. 5⅜ x 8½.
S998 Paperbound **$1.00**

POLAR MOLECULES, Pieter Debye. This work by Nobel laureate Debye offers a complete guide to fundamental electrostatic field relations, polarizability, molecular structure. Partial contents: electric intensity, displacement and force, polarization by orientation, molar polarization and molar refraction, halogen-hydrides, polar liquids, ionic saturation, dielectric constant, etc. Special chapter considers quantum theory. Indexed. 172pp. 5⅜ x 8.
S64 Paperbound **$1.65**

THE ELECTRONIC THEORY OF ACIDS AND BASES, W. F. Luder and Saverio Zuffanti. The first full systematic presentation of the electronic theory of acids and bases—treating the theory and its ramifications in an uncomplicated manner. Chapters: Historical Background; Atomic Orbitals and Valence; The Electronic Theory of Acids and Bases; Electrophilic and Electrodotic Reagents; Acidic and Basic Radicals; Neutralization; Titrations with Indicators; Displacement; Catalysis; Acid Catalysis; Base Catalysis; Alkoxides and Catalysts; Conclusion. Required reading for all chemists. Second revised (1961) eidtion, with additional examples and references. 3 figures. 9 tables. Index. Bibliography xii + 165pp. 5⅜ x 8.
S201 Paperbound **$1.50**

KINETIC THEORY OF LIQUIDS, J. Frenkel. Regarding the kinetic theory of liquids as a generalization and extension of the theory of solid bodies, this volume covers all types of arrangements of solids, thermal displacements of atoms, interstitial atoms and ions, orientational and rotational motion of molecules, and transition between states of matter. Mathematical theory is developed close to the physical subject matter. 216 bibliographical footnotes. 55 figures. xi + 485pp. 5⅜ x 8.
S95 Paperbound **$2.55**

THE PRINCIPLES OF ELECTROCHEMISTRY, D. A. MacInnes. Basic equations for almost every subfield of electrochemistry from first principles, referring at all times to the soundest and most recent theories and results; unusually useful as text or as reference. Covers coulometers and Faraday's Law, electrolytic conductance, the Debye-Hueckel method for the theoretical calculation of activity coefficients, conductance cells, standard electrode potentials, thermodynamic ionization constants, pH, potentiometric titrations, irreversible phenomena, Planck's equation, and much more. "Excellent treatise," AMERICAN CHEMICAL SOCIETY JOURNAL. "Highly recommended," CHEMICAL AND METALLURGICAL ENGINEERING. 2 Indices. Appendix. 585-item bibliography. 137 figures. 94 tables. ii + 478pp. 5⅜ x 8⅜.
S52 Paperbound **$2.45**

THE PHASE RULE AND ITS APPLICATION, Alexander Findlay. Covering chemical phenomena of 1, 2, 3, 4, and multiple component systems, this "standard work on the subject" (NATURE, London), has been completely revised and brought up to date by A. N. Campbell and N. O. Smith. Brand new material has been added on such matters as binary, tertiary liquid equilibria, solid solutions in ternary systems, quinary systems of salts and water. Completely revised to triangular coordinates in ternary systems, clarified graphic representation, solid models, etc. 9th revised edition. Author, subject indexes. 236 figures. 505 footnotes, mostly bibliographic. xii + 494pp. 5⅜ x 8.
S91 Paperbound **$2.50**

PHYSICS

General physics

FOUNDATIONS OF PHYSICS, R. B. Lindsay & H. Margenau. Excellent bridge between semi-popular works & technical treatises. A discussion ot methods of physical description, construction of theory; valuable tor physicist with elementary calculus who is interested in ideas that give meaning to data, tools of modern physics. Contents include symbolism, mathematical equations; space & time foundations of mechanics; probability; physics & continua; electron theory; special & general relativity; quantum mechanics; causality. "Thorough and yet not overdetailed. Unreservedly recommended," NATURE (London). Unabridged, corrected edition. List of recommended readings. 35 illustrations. xi + 537pp. 5⅜ x 8.
S377 Paperbound **$2.75**

FUNDAMENTAL FORMULAS OF PHYSICS, ed. by D. H. Menzel. Highly useful, fully inexpensive reference and study text, ranging trom simple to highly sophisticated operations. Mathematics integrated into text—each cnapter stands as short textbook ot field represented. Vol. 1: Statistics, Physical Constants, Special Theory of Relativity, Hydrodynamics, Aerodynamics, Boundary Value Problems in Math. Physics; Viscosity, Electromagnetic Theory, etc. Vol. 2: Sound, Acoustics, Geometrical Optics, Electron Optics, High-Energy Phenomena, Magnetism, Biophysics, much more. Index. Total of 800pp. 5⅜ x 8. Vol. 1 S595 Paperbound **$2.00**
Vol. 2 S596 Paperbound **$2.00**

MATHEMATICAL PHYSICS, D. H. Menzel. Thorough one-volume treatment of the mathematical techniques vital for classic mechanics, electromagnetic theory, quantum theory, and relativity. Written by the Harvard Protessor of Astrophysics for junior, senior, and graduate courses, it gives clear explanations of all those aspects of function theory, vectors, matrices, dyadics, tensors, partial differential equations, etc., necessary tor the understanding of the various physical theories. Electron theory, relativity, and other topics seldom presented appear here in considerable detail. Scores of definitions, conversion factors, dimensional constants, etc. "More detailed than normal for an advanced text . . . excellent set of sections on Dyadics, Matrices, and Tensors," JOURNAL OF THE FRANKLIN INSTITUTE. Index. 193 problems, with answers. x + 412pp. 5⅜ x 8. S56 Paperbound **$2.00**

THE SCIENTIFIC PAPERS OF J. WILLARD GIBBS. All the published papers of America's outstanding theoretical scientist (except for "Statistical Mechanics" and "Vector Analysis"). Vol I (thermodynamics) contains one of the most brilliant of all 19th-century scientific papers—the 300-page "On the Equilibrium of Heterogeneous Substances," which tounded the science of physical chemistry, and clearly stated a number of highly important natural laws for the first time; 8 other papers complete the first volume. Vol II includes 2 papers on dynamics, 8 on vector analysis and multiple algebra, 5 on the electromagnetic theory of light, and 6 miscellaneous papers. Biographical sketch by H. A. Bumstead. Total of xxxvi + 718pp. 5⅝ x 8⅜.
S721 Vol I Paperbound **$2.50**
S722 Vol II Paperbound **$2.00**
The set **$4.50**

BASIC THEORIES OF PHYSICS, Peter Gabriel Bergmann. Two-volume set which presents a critical examination of important topics in the major subdivisions of classical and modern physics. The first volume is concerned with classical mechanics and electrodynamics: mechanics of mass points, analytical mechanics, matter in bulk, electrostatics and magnetostatics, electromagnetic interaction, the field waves, special relativity, and waves. The second volume (Heat and Quanta) contains discussions of the kinetic hypothesis, physics and statistics, stationary ensembles, laws of thermodynamics, early quantum theories, atomic spectra, probability waves, quantization in wave mechanics, approximation methods, and abstract quantum theory. A valuable supplement to any thorough course or text.
Heat and Quanta: Index. 8 figures. x + 300pp. 5⅜ x 8½. S968 Paperbound **$2.00**
Mechanics and Electrodynamics: Index. 14 figures. vii + 280pp. 5⅜ x 8½.
S969 Paperbound **$1.75**

THEORETICAL PHYSICS, A. S. Kompaneyets. One of the very few thorough studies of the subject in this price range. Provides advanced students with a comprehensive theoretical background. Especially strong on recent experimentation and developments in quantum theory. Contents: Mechanics (Generalized Coordinates, Lagrange's Equation, Collision of Particles, etc.), Electrodynamics (Vector Analysis, Maxwell's equations, Transmission of Signals, Theory of Relativity, etc.), Quantum Mechanics (the Inadequacy of Classical Mechanics, the Wave Equation, Motion in a Central Field, Quantum Theory of Radiation, Quantum Theories of Dispersion and Scattering, etc.), and Statistical Physics (Equilibrium Distribution of Molecules in an Ideal Gas, Boltzmann statistics, Bose and Fermi Distribution, Thermodynamic Quantities, etc.). Revised to 1961. Translated by George Yankovsky, authorized by Kompaneyets. 137 exercises. 56 figures. 529pp. 5⅜ x 8½. S972 Paperbound **$2.50**

ANALYTICAL AND CANONICAL FORMALISM IN PHYSICS, André Mercier. A survey, in one volume, of the variational principles (the key principles—in mathematical form—from which the basic laws of any one branch of physics can be derived) of the several branches of physical theory, together with an examination of the relationships among them. Contents: the Lagrangian Formalism, Lagrangian Densities, Canonical Formalism, Canonical Form of Electrodynamics, Hamiltonian Densities, Transformations, and Canonical Form with Vanishing Jacobian Determinant. Numerous examples and exercises. For advanced students, teachers, etc. 6 figures. Index. viii + 222pp. 5⅜ x 8½. S1077 Paperbound **$1.75**

MATHEMATICAL PUZZLES AND RECREATIONS

AMUSEMENTS IN MATHEMATICS, Henry Ernest Dudeney. The foremost British originator of mathematical puzzles is always intriguing, witty, and paradoxical in this classic, one of the largest collections of mathematical amusements. More than 430 puzzles, problems, and paradoxes. Mazes and games, problems on number manipulation, unicursal and other route problems, puzzles on measuring, weighing, packing, age, kinship, chessboards, joining, crossing river, plane figure dissection, and many others. Solutions. More than 450 illustrations. vii + 258pp. 5⅜ x 8.   T473 Paperbound **$1.25**

SYMBOLIC LOGIC and THE GAME OF LOGIC, Lewis Carroll. "Symbolic Logic" is not concerned with modern symbolic logic, but is instead a collection of over 380 problems posed with charm and imagination, using the syllogism, and a fascinating diagrammatic method of drawing conclusions. In "The Game of Logic," Carroll's whimsical imagination devises a logical game played with 2 diagrams and counters (included) to manipulate hundreds of tricky syllogisms. The final section, "Hit or Miss" is a lagniappe of 101 additional puzzles in the delightful Carroll manner. Until this reprint edition, both of these books were rarities costing up to $15 each. Symbolic Logic: Index, xxxi + 199pp. The Game of Logic: 96pp. Two vols. bound as one. 5⅜ x 8.   T492 Paperbound **$1.50**

MAZES AND LABYRINTHS: A BOOK OF PUZZLES, W. Shepherd. Mazes, formerly associated with mystery and ritual, are still among the most intriguing of intellectual puzzles. This is a novel and different collection of 50 amusements that embody the principle of the maze: mazes in the classical tradition; 3-dimensional, ribbon, and Möbius-strip mazes; hidden messages; spatial arrangements; etc.—almost all built on amusing story situations. 84 illustrations. Essay on maze psychology. Solutions. xv + 122pp. 5⅜ x 8.   T731 Paperbound **$1.00**

MATHEMATICAL RECREATIONS, M. Kraitchik. Some 250 puzzles, problems, demonstrations of recreational mathematics for beginners & advanced mathematicians. Unusual historical problems from Greek, Medieval, Arabic, Hindu sources: modern problems based on "mathematics without numbers," geometry, topology, arithmetic, etc. Pastimes derived from figurative numbers, Mersenne numbers, Fermat numbers; fairy chess, latruncles, reversi, many topics. Full solutions. Excellent for insights into special fields of math. 181 illustrations. 330pp. 5⅜ x 8.   T163 Paperbound **$1.75**

MATHEMATICAL PUZZLES OF SAM LOYD, Vol. I, selected and edited by M. Gardner. Puzzles by the greatest puzzle creator and innovator. Selected from his famous "Cyclopedia of Puzzles," they retain the unique style and historical flavor of the originals. There are posers based on arithmetic, algebra, probability, game theory, route tracing, topology, counter, sliding block, operations research, geometrical dissection. Includes his famous "14-15" puzzle which was a national craze, and his "Horse of a Different Color" which sold millions of copies. 117 of his most ingenious puzzles in all, 120 line drawings and diagrams. Solutions. Selected references. xx + 167pp. 5⅜ x 8.   T498 Paperbound **$1.00**

MY BEST PUZZLES IN MATHEMATICS, Hubert Phillips ("Caliban"). Caliban is generally considered the best of the modern problemists. Here are 100 of his best and wittiest puzzles, selected by the author himself from such publications as the London Daily Telegraph, and each puzzle is guaranteed to put even the sharpest puzzle detective through his paces. Perfect for the development of clear thinking and a logical mind. Complete solutions are provided for every puzzle. x + 107pp. 5⅜ x 8½.   T91 Paperbound **$1.00**

MY BEST PUZZLES IN LOGIC AND REASONING, H. Phillips ("Caliban"). 100 choice, hitherto unavailable puzzles by England's best-known problemist. No special knowledge needed to solve these logical or inferential problems, just an unclouded mind, nerves of steel, and fast reflexes. Data presented are both necessary and just sufficient to allow one unambiguous answer. More than 30 different types of puzzles, all ingenious and varied, many one of a kind, that will challenge the expert, please the beginner. Original publication. 100 puzzles, full solutions. x + 107pp. 5⅜ x 8½.   T119 Paperbound **$1.00**

MATHEMATICAL PUZZLES FOR BEGINNERS AND ENTHUSIASTS, G. Mott-Smith. 188 mathematical puzzles to test mental agility. Inference, interpretation, algebra, dissection of plane figures, geometry, properties of numbers, decimation, permutations, probability, all enter these delightful problems. Puzzles like the Odic Force, How to Draw an Ellipse, Spider's Cousin, more than 180 others. Detailed solutions. Appendix with square roots, triangular numbers, primes, etc. 135 illustrations. 2nd revised edition. 248pp. 5⅜ x 8.   T198 Paperbound **$1.00**

MATHEMATICS, MAGIC AND MYSTERY, Martin Gardner. Card tricks, feats of mental mathematics, stage mind-reading, other "magic" explained as applications of probability, sets, theory of numbers, topology, various branches of mathematics. Creative examination of laws and their applications with scores of new tricks and insights. 115 sections discuss tricks wtih cards, dice, coins; geometrical vanishing tricks, dozens of others. No sleight of hand needed; mathematics guarantees success. 115 illustrations. xii + 174pp. 5⅜ x 8.
T335 Paperbound **$1.00**

CATALOGUE OF DOVER BOOKS

RECREATIONS IN THE THEORY OF NUMBERS: THE QUEEN OF MATHEMATICS ENTERTAINS, Albert H. Beiler. The theory of numbers is often referred to as the "Queen of Mathematics." In this book Mr. Beiler has compiled the first English volume to deal exclusively with the recreational aspects of number theory, an inherently recreational branch of mathematics. The author's clear style makes for enjoyable reading as he deals with such topics as: perfect numbers, amicable numbers, Fermat's theorem, Wilson's theorem, interesting properties of digits, methods of factoring, primitive roots, Euler's function, polygonal and figurate numbers, Mersenne numbers, congruence, repeating decimals, etc. Countless puzzle problems, with full answers and explanations. For mathematicians and mathematically-inclined laymen, etc. New publication. 28 figures. 9 illustrations. 103 tables. Bibliography at chapter ends. vi + 247pp. 5⅜ x 8½. T1096 Paperbound **$1.85**

PAPER FOLDING FOR BEGINNERS, W. D. Murray and F. J. Rigney. A delightful introduction to the varied and entertaining Japanese art of origami (paper folding), with a full crystal-clear text that anticipates every difficulty; over 275 clearly labeled diagrams of all important stages in creation. You get results at each stage, since complex figures are logically developed from simpler ones. 43 different pieces are explained: place mats, drinking cups, bonbon boxes, sailboats, frogs, roosters, etc. 6 photographic plates. 279 diagrams. 95pp. 5⅜ x 8⅜. T713 Paperbound **$1.00**

1800 RIDDLES, ENIGMAS AND CONUNDRUMS, Darwin A. Hindman. Entertaining collection ranging from hilarious gags to outrageous puns to sheer nonsense—a welcome respite from sophisticated humor. Children, toastmasters, and practically anyone with a funny bone will find these zany riddles tickling and eminently repeatable. Sample: "Why does Santa Claus always go down the chimney?" "Because it soots him." Some old, some new—covering a wide variety of subjects. New publication. iii + 154pp. 5⅜ x 8½. T1059 Paperbound **$1.00**

EASY-TO-DO ENTERTAINMENTS AND DIVERSIONS WITH CARDS, STRING, COINS, PAPER AND MATCHES, R. M. Abraham. Over 300 entertaining games, tricks, puzzles, and pastimes for children and adults. Invaluable to anyone in charge of groups of youngsters, for party givers, etc. Contains sections on card tricks and games, making things by paperfolding—toys, decorations, and the like; tricks with coins, matches, and pieces of string; descriptions of games; toys that can be made from common household objects; mathematical recreations; word games; and 50 miscellaneous entertainments. Formerly "Winter Nights Entertainments." Introduction by Lord Baden Powell. 329 illustrations. v + 186pp. 5⅜ x 8. T921 Paperbound **$1.00**

DIVERSIONS AND PASTIMES WITH CARDS, STRING, PAPER AND MATCHES, R. M. Abraham. Another collection of amusements and diversion for game and puzzle fans of all ages. Many new paperfolding ideas and tricks, an extensive section on amusements with knots and splices, two chapters of easy and not-so-easy problems, coin and match tricks, and lots of other parlor pastimes from the agile mind of the late British problemist and gamester. Corrected and revised version. Illustrations. 160pp. 5⅜ x 8½. T1127 Paperbound **$1.00**

STRING FIGURES AND HOW TO MAKE THEM: A STUDY OF CAT'S-CRADLE IN MANY LANDS, Caroline Furness Jayne. In a simple and easy-to-follow manner, this book describes how to make 107 different string figures. Not only is looping and crossing string between the fingers a common youthful diversion, but it is an ancient form of amusement practiced in all parts of the globe, especially popular among primitive tribes. These games are fun for all ages and offer an excellent means for developing manual dexterity and coordination. Much insight also for the anthropological observer on games and diversions in many different cultures. Index. Bibliography. Introduction by A. C. Haddon, Cambridge University. 17 full-page plates. 950 illustrations. xxiii + 407pp. 5⅜ x 8½. T152 Paperbound **$2.00**

CRYPTANALYSIS, Helen F. Gaines. (Formerly ELEMENTARY CRYPTANALYSIS.) A standard elementary and intermediate text for serious students. It does not confine itself to old material, but contains much that is not generally known, except to experts. Concealment, Transposition, Substitution ciphers; Vigenere, Kasiski, Playfair, multafid, dozens of other techniques. Appendix with sequence charts, letter frequencies in English, 5 other languages, English word frequencies. Bibliography. 167 codes. New to this edition: solution to codes. vi + 230pp. 5⅜ x 8. T97 Paperbound **$2.00**

MAGIC SQUARES AND CUBES, W. S. Andrews. Only book-length treatment in English, a thorough non-technical description and analysis. Here are nasik, overlapping, pandiagonal, serrated squares; magic circles, cubes, spheres, rhombuses. Try your hand at 4-dimensional magical figures! Much unusual folklore and tradition included. High school algebra is sufficient. 754 diagrams and illustrations. viii + 419pp. 5⅜ x 8. T658 Paperbound **$1.85**

CALIBAN'S PROBLEM BOOK: MATHEMATICAL, INFERENTIAL, AND CRYPTOGRAPHIC PUZZLES, H. Phillips ("Caliban"), S. T. Shovelton, G. S. Marshall. 105 ingenious problems by the greatest living creator of puzzles based on logic and inference. Rigorous, modern, piquant, and reflecting their author's unusual personality, these intermediate and advanced puzzles all involve the ability to reason clearly through complex situations; some call for mathematical knowledge, ranging from algebra to number theory. Solutions. xi + 180pp. 5⅜ x 8. T736 Paperbound **$1.25**

FICTION

THE LAND THAT TIME FORGOT and THE MOON MAID, Edgar Rice Burroughs. In the opinion of many, Burroughs' best work. The first concerns a strange island where evolution is individual rather than phylogenetic. Speechless anthropoids develop into intelligent human beings within a single generation. The second projects the reader far into the future and describes the first voyage to the Moon (in the year 2025), the conquest of the Earth by the Moon, and years of violence and adventure as the enslaved Earthmen try to regain possession of their planet. "An imaginative tour de force that keeps the reader keyed up and expectant," NEW YORK TIMES. Complete, unabridged text of the original two novels (three parts in each). 5 illustrations by J. Allen St. John. vi + 552pp. 5⅜ x 8½.
T1020 Clothbound **$3.75**
T358 Paperbound **$2.00**

AT THE EARTH'S CORE, PELLUCIDAR, TANAR OF PELLUCIDAR: THREE SCIENCE FICTION NOVELS BY EDGAR RICE BURROUGHS. Complete, unabridged texts of the first three Pellucidar novels. Tales of derring-do by the famous master of science fiction. The locale for these three related stories is the inner surface of the hollow Earth where we discover the world of Pellucidar, complete with all types of bizarre, menacing creatures, strange peoples, and alluring maidens—guaranteed to delight all Burroughs fans and a wide circle of adventure lovers. Illustrated by J. Allen St. John and P. F. Berdanier. vi + 433pp. 5⅜ x 8½.
T1051 Paperbound **$2.00**

THE PIRATES OF VENUS and LOST ON VENUS: TWO VENUS NOVELS BY EDGAR RICE BURROUGHS. Two related novels, complete and unabridged. Exciting adventure on the planet Venus with Earthman Carson Napier broken-field running through one dangerous episode after another. All lovers of swashbuckling science fiction will enjoy these two stories set in a world of fascinating societies, fierce beasts, 5000-ft. trees, lush vegetation, and wide seas. Illustrations by Fortunino Matania. Total of vi + 340pp. 5⅜ x 8½. T1053 Paperbound **$1.75**

A PRINCESS OF MARS and A FIGHTING MAN OF MARS: TWO MARTIAN NOVELS BY EDGAR RICE BURROUGHS. "Princess of Mars" is the very first of the great Martian novels written by Burroughs, and it is probably the best of them all; it set the pattern for all of his later fantasy novels and contains a thrilling cast of strange peoples and creatures and the formula of Olympian heroism amidst ever-fluctuating fortunes which Burroughs carries off so successfully. "Fighting Man" returns to the same scenes and cities—many years later. A mad scientist, a degenerate dictator, and an indomitable defender of the right clash—with the fate of the Red Planet at stake! Complete, unabridged reprinting of original editions. Illustrations by F. E. Schoonover and Hugh Hutton. v + 356pp. 5⅜ x 8½.
T1140 Paperbound **$1.75**

THREE MARTIAN NOVELS, Edgar Rice Burroughs. Contains: Thuvia, Maid of Mars; The Chessmen of Mars; and The Master Mind of Mars. High adventure set in an imaginative and intricate conception of the Red Planet. Mars is peopled with an intelligent, heroic human race which lives in densely populated cities and with fierce barbarians who inhabit dead sea bottoms. Other exciting creatures abound amidst an inventive framework of Martian history and geography. Complete unabridged reprintings of the first edition. 16 illustrations by J. Allen St. John. vi + 499pp. 5⅜ x 8½. T39 Paperbound **$1.85**

THREE PROPHETIC NOVELS BY H. G. WELLS, edited by E. F. Bleiler. Complete texts of "When the Sleeper Wakes" (1st book printing in 50 years), "A Story of the Days to Come," "The Time Machine" (1st complete printing in book form). Exciting adventures in the future are as enjoyable today as 50 years ago when first printed. Predict TV, movies, intercontinental airplanes, prefabricated houses, air-conditioned cities, etc. First important author to foresee problems of mind control, technological dictatorships. "Absolute best of imaginative fiction," N. Y. Times. Introduction. 335pp. 5⅜ x 8. T605 Paperbound **$1.50**

28 SCIENCE FICTION STORIES OF H. G. WELLS. Two full unabridged novels, MEN LIKE GODS and STAR BEGOTTEN, plus 26 short stories by the master science-fiction writer of all time. Stories of space, time, invention, exploration, future adventure—an indispensable part of the library of everyone interested in science and adventure. PARTIAL CONTENTS: Men Like Gods, The Country of the Blind, In the Abyss, The Crystal Egg, The Man Who Could Work Miracles, A Story of the Days to Come, The Valley of Spiders, and 21 more! 928pp. 5⅜ x 8.
T265 Clothbound **$4.50**

THE WAR IN THE AIR, IN THE DAYS OF THE COMET, THE FOOD OF THE GODS: THREE SCIENCE FICTION NOVELS BY H. G. WELLS. Three exciting Wells offerings bearing on vital social and philosophical issues of his and our own day. Here are tales of air power, strategic bombing, East vs. West, the potential miracles of science, the potential disasters from outer space, the relationship between scientific advancement and moral progress, etc. First reprinting of "War in the Air" in almost 50 years. An excellent sampling of Wells at his storytelling best. Complete, unabridged reprintings. 16 illustrations. 645pp. 5⅜ x 8½.
T1135 Paperbound **$2.00**

SEVEN SCIENCE FICTION NOVELS, H. G. Wells. Full unabridged texts of 7 science-fiction novels of the master. Ranging from biology, physics, chemistry, astronomy to sociology and other studies, Mr. Wells extrapolates whole worlds of strange and intriguing character. "One will have to go far to match this for entertainment, excitement, and sheer pleasure . . . ," NEW YORK TIMES. Contents: The Time Machine, The Island of Dr. Moreau, First Men in the Moon, The Invisible Man, The War of the Worlds, The Food of the Gods, In the Days of the Comet. 1015pp. 5⅜ x 8. T264 Clothbound **$4.50**

BEST GHOST STORIES OF J. S. LE FANU, Selected and introduced by E. F. Bleiler. LeFanu is deemed the greatest name in Victorian supernatural fiction. Here are 16 of his best horror stories, including 2 nouvelles: "Carmilla," a classic vampire tale couched in a perverse eroticism, and "The Haunted Baronet." Also: "Sir Toby's Will," "Green Tea," "Schalken the Painter," "Ultor de Lacy," "The Familiar," etc. The first American publication of about half of this material: a long-overdue opportunity to get a choice sampling of LeFanu's work. New selection (1964). 8 illustrations. 5⅜ x 8⅜. T415 Paperbound **$1.85**

THE WONDERFUL WIZARD OF OZ, L. F. Baum. Only edition in print with all the original W. W. Denslow illustrations in full color—as much a part of "The Wizard" as Tenniel's drawings are for "Alice in Wonderland." "The Wizard" is still America's best-loved fairy tale, in which, as the author expresses it, "The wonderment and joy are retained and the heartaches and nightmares left out." Now today's young readers can enjoy every word and wonderful picture of the original book. New introduction by Martin Gardner. A Baum bibliography. 23 full-page color plates. viii + 268pp. 5⅜ x 8. T691 Paperbound **$1.50**

GHOST AND HORROR STORIES OF AMBROSE BIERCE, Selected and introduced by E. F. Bleiler. 24 morbid, eerie tales—the cream of Bierce's fiction output. Contains such memorable pieces as "The Moonlit Road," "The Damned Thing," "An Inhabitant of Carcosa," "The Eyes of the Panther," "The Famous Gilson Bequest," "The Middle Toe of the Right Foot," and other chilling stories, plus the essay, "Visions of the Night" in which Bierce gives us a kind of rationale for his aesthetic of horror. New collection (1964). xxii + 199pp. 5⅜ x 8⅜. T767 Paperbound **$1.00**

HUMOR

MR. DOOLEY ON IVRYTHING AND IVRYBODY, Finley Peter Dunne. Since the time of his appearance in 1893, "Mr. Dooley," the fictitious Chicago bartender, has been recognized as America's most humorous social and political commentator. Collected in this volume are 102 of the best Dooley pieces—all written around the turn of the century, the height of his popularity. Mr. Dooley's Irish brogue is employed wittily and penetratingly on subjects which are just as fresh and relevant today as they were then: corruption and hypocrisy of politicans, war preparations and chauvinism, automation, Latin American affairs, superbombs, etc. Other articles range from Rudyard Kipling to football. Selected with an introduction by Robert Hutchinson. xii + 244pp. 5⅜ x 8½. T626 Paperbound **$1.00**

RUTHLESS RHYMES FOR HEARTLESS HOMES and MORE RUTHLESS RHYMES FOR HEARTLESS HOMES, Harry Graham ("Col. D. Streamer"). A collection of Little Willy and 48 other poetic "disasters." Graham's funniest and most disrespectful verse, accompanied by original illustrations. Nonsensical, wry humor which employs stern parents, careless nurses, uninhibited children, practical jokers, single-minded golfers, Scottish lairds, etc. in the leading roles. A precursor of the "sick joke" school of today. This volume contains, bound together for the first time, two of the most perennially popular books of humor in England and America. Index. vi + 69pp. 5⅜ x 8. T930 Paperbound **75¢**

A WHIMSEY ANTHOLOGY, Collected by Carolyn Wells. 250 of the most amusing rhymes ever written. Acrostics, anagrams, palindromes, alphabetical jingles, tongue twisters, echo verses, alliterative verses, riddles, mnemonic rhymes, interior rhymes, over 40 limericks, etc. by Lewis Carroll, Edward Lear, Joseph Addison, W. S. Gilbert, Christina Rossetti, Chas. Lamb, James Boswell, Hood, Dickens, Swinburne, Leigh Hunt, Harry Graham, Poe, Eugene Field, and many others. xiv + 221pp. 5⅜ x 8½. T195 Paperbound **$1.25**

MY PIOUS FRIENDS AND DRUNKEN COMPANIONS and MORE PIOUS FRIENDS AND DRUNKEN COMPANIONS, Songs and ballads of Conviviality Collected by Frank Shay. Magnificently illuminated by John Held, Jr. 132 ballads, blues, vaudeville numbers, drinking songs, cowboy songs, sea chanties, comedy songs, etc. of the Naughty Nineties and early 20th century. Over a third are reprinted with music. Many perennial favorites such as: The Band Played On, Frankie and Johnnie, The Old Grey Mare, The Face on the Bar-room Floor, etc. Many others unlocatable elsewhere: The Dog-Catcher's Child, The Cannibal Maiden, Don't Go in the Lion's Cage Tonight, Mother, etc. Complete verses and introductions to songs. Unabridged republication of first editions, 2 Indexes (song titles and first lines and choruses). Introduction by Frank Shay. 2 volumes bounds as 1. Total of xvi + 235pp. 5⅜ x 8½. T946 Paperbound **$1.25**

MAX AND MORITZ, Wilhelm Busch. Edited and annotated by H. Arthur Klein. Translated by H. Arthur Klein, M. C. Klein, and others. The mischievous high jinks of Max and Moritz, Peter and Paul, Ker and Plunk, etc. are delightfully captured in sketch and rhyme. (Companion volume to "Hypocritical Helena.") In addition to the title piece, it contians: Ker and Plunk; Two Dogs and Two Boys; The Egghead and the Two Cut-ups of Corinth; Deceitful Henry; The Boys and the Pipe; Cat and Mouse; and others. (Original German text with accompanying English translations.) Afterword by H. A. Klein. vi + 216pp. 5⅜ x 8½.
T181 Paperbound **$1.15**

THROUGH THE ALIMENTARY CANAL WITH GUN AND CAMERA: A FASCINATING TRIP TO THE INTERIOR, Personally Conducted by George S. Chappell. In mock-travelogue style, the amusing account of an imaginative journey down the alimentary canal. The "explorers" enter the esophagus, round the Adam's Apple, narrowly escape from a fierce Amoeba, struggle through the impenetrable Nerve Forests of the Lumbar Region, etc. Illustrated by the famous cartoonist, Otto Soglow, the book is as much a brilliant satire of academic pomposity and professional travel literature as it is a clever use of the facts of physiology for supremely comic purposes. Preface by Robert Benchley. Author's Foreword. 1 Photograph. 17 illustrations by O. Soglow. xii + 114pp. 5⅜ x 8½.
T376 Paperbound **$1.00**

THE BAD CHILD'S BOOK OF BEASTS, MORE BEASTS FOR WORSE CHILDREN, and A MORAL ALPHABET, H. Belloc. Hardly an anthology of humorous verse has appeared in the last 50 years without at least a couple of these famous nonsense verses. But one must see the entire volumes—with all the delightful original illustrations by Sir Basil Blackwood—to appreciate fully Belloc's charming and witty verses that play so subacidly on the platitudes of life and morals that beset his day—and ours. A great humor classic. Three books in one. Total of 157pp. 5⅜ x 8.
T749 Paperbound **$1.00**

THE DEVIL'S DICTIONARY, Ambrose Bierce. Sardonic and irreverent barbs puncturing the pomposities and absurdities of American politics, business, religion, literature, and arts, by the country's greatest satirist in the classic tradition. Epigrammatic as Shaw, piercing as Swift, American as Mark Twain, Will Rogers, and Fred Allen. Bierce will always remain the favorite of a small coterie of enthusiasts, and of writers and speakers whom he supplies with "some of the most gorgeous witticisms of the English language." (H. L. Mencken) Over 1000 entries in alphabetical order. 144pp. 5⅜ x 8.
T487 Paperbound **$1.00**

THE COMPLETE NONSENSE OF EDWARD LEAR. This is the only complete edition of this master of gentle madness available at a popular price. A BOOK OF NONSENSE, NONSENSE SONGS, MORE NONSENSE SONGS AND STORIES in their entirety with all the old favorites that have delighted children and adults for years. The Dong With A Luminous Nose, The Jumblies, The Owl and the Pussycat, and hundreds of other bits of wonderful nonsense. 214 limericks, 3 sets of Nonsense Botany, 5 Nonsense Alphabets. 546 drawings by Lear himself, and much more. 320pp. 5⅜ x 8.
T167 Paperbound **$1.00**

SINGULAR TRAVELS, CAMPAIGNS, AND ADVENTURES OF BARON MUNCHAUSEN, R. E. Raspe, with 90 illustrations by Gustave Doré. The first edition in over 150 years to reestablish the deeds of the Prince of Liars exactly as Raspe first recorded them in 1785—the genuine Baron Munchausen, one of the most popular personalities in English literature. Included also are the best of the many sequels, written by other hands. Introduction on Raspe by J. Carswell. Bibliography of early editions. xliv + 192pp. 5⅜ x 8. T698 Paperbound **$1.00**

HOW TO TELL THE BIRDS FROM THE FLOWERS, R. W. Wood. How not to confuse a carrot with a parrot, a grape with an ape, a puffin with nuffin. Delightful drawings, clever puns, absurd little poems point out farfetched resemblances in nature. The author was a leading physicist. Introduction by Margaret Wood White. 106 illus. 60pp. 5⅜ x 8.
T523 Paperbound **75¢**

JOE MILLER'S JESTS OR, THE WITS VADE-MECUM. The original Joe Miller jest book. Gives a keen and pungent impression of life in 18th-century England. Many are somewhat on the bawdy side and they are still capable of provoking amusement and good fun. This volume is a facsimile of the original "Joe Miller" first published in 1739. It remains the most popular and influential humor book of all time. New introduction by Robert Hutchinson. xxi + 70pp. 5⅜ x 8½.
T423 Paperbound **$1.00**

Prices subject to change without notice.

Dover publishes books on art, music, philosophy, literature, languages, history, social sciences, psychology, handcrafts, orientalia, puzzles and entertainments, chess, pets and gardens, books explaining science, intermediate and higher mathematics, mathematical physics, engineering, biological sciences, earth sciences, classics of science, etc. Write to:

Dept. catrr.
Dover Publications, Inc.
180 Varick Street, N.Y. 14, N.Y.